Lift Up Your Hearts

Psalms, Hymns, and Spiritual Songs

Lift Up Your Hearts
Psalms, Hymns, and Spiritual Songs

FAITH
ALIVE.
Christian Resources

Grand Rapids, Michigan

Lift Up Your Hearts: Psalms, Hymns, and Spiritual Songs

© 2013, Faith Alive Christian Resources, 2850 Kalamazoo Ave. SE, Grand Rapids, Michigan 49560. All rights reserved. Printed in the United States of America. This book and any copyrighted portions of it may not be reproduced in any manner whatsoever without written permission from Faith Alive Christian Resources or the specified copyright holders unless noted.

Please address questions about use of copyrighted materials to Permissions, Faith Alive Christian Resources, 2850 Kalamazoo Ave. SE, Grand Rapids, MI 49560; phone: 800-333-8300; fax: 616-224-0834; email: permissions@faithaliveresources.org.

The publisher gratefully acknowledges permission to reproduce the words and music granted by publishers, organizations, and individuals listed as copyright holders with each song. A complete list of contact information for all copyright holders can be found online at www.liftupyourheartshymnal.org. Addresses and contact information for many of the copyright holders can also be found in the copyright holder index near the end of this volume. Every effort has been made to trace the owner or holder of each copyright. If any rights have been inadvertently infringed upon, the publisher asks that the omission be excused and agrees to make the necessary corrections in subsequent printings.

For the use of numerous Scripture and other texts printed in this book the publisher gratefully acknowledges permissions granted by copyright holders as referenced in Acknowledgments, which hereby becomes an extension of this copyright page.

ISBN 978-1-59255-559-8 (regular binding); ISBN 978-1-59255-793-6 (spiral binding);
ISBN 978-1-59255-781-3 (digital music and words for printing);
ISBN 978-1-59255-782-0 (music and words for reading);
ISBN 978-1-59255-779-0 (music and words for projection);
ISBN 978-1-59255-780-6 (words only for print or projection)

10 9 8 7 6 5 4 3 2 1

Contents

Preface

One of the great gifts of life in Jesus Christ is the gift and privilege of worship—to draw near to God to receive God's Word; to respond in thanksgiving and praise, lament, and confession; to receive the signs and seals of God's love in baptism and the Lord's Supper; to testify to God's faithfulness; to contemplate God's promises; to dedicate our lives to God's service. All of it—whether in public worship, or in the echoes of public worship that resound through other aspects of church life and personal devotion—becomes a gift through the work of the Holy Spirit who unites us with our ascended Lord and helps us to taste and see that God is good. What a gift it is to lift up our hearts to God!

Further, what a gift it is to participate in all of this *together*—with the other voices in our worshiping communities and with all members of Christ's body throughout time and space. This book is designed to strengthen singing together in all sorts of worshiping communities, small and large, new and old, and to make possible the sharing of gifts within the worldwide body of Christ with resources drawn from a stunningly diverse range of cultures, languages, and musical genres.

In a diverse world it is a testimony to our unity in Christ that two denominations, the Christian Reformed Church in North America and the Reformed Church in America, have joined together to produce this volume of songs endorsed by each denomination—a book available for use both within and beyond the two thousand worshiping communities that make up these two bodies.

One of the privileges of living in today's world is the opportunity to learn from and explore a wide variety of the songs of God's people from many musical cultures across time and space. Our churches resound with a broad spectrum of music, from majestic hymns to rhythmic gospel songs, from rock tempo praise songs to the contemplative strains of a Taizé refrain. With such a rich abundance of songs, musical styles, and even varying versions of the same text, it seems wise, then, to appoint a curator to assemble a core collection of biblically faithful, theologically sound, and congregationally accessible music for worship. The thirteen-member editorial team took on the task of curator, and along with an eighty-member advisory committee and other experts, they searched out heart songs of the church, explored thousands of texts, and evaluated new melodies and harmonies. The volume you hold in your hands is the result— a core collection that is biblical, Reformed, balanced, and accessible.

While the message of the gospel doesn't change, the context in which we worship does. We see the great wisdom and depth of texts that have stood the test of time and desire to hold on to the gifts of previous generations while wanting to give voice to our prayers, praises, and laments particular to this generation. In *Lift Up Your Hearts* you'll find not only treasured hymns but also new hymns, contemporary songs, and songs from the global church.

God's people have learned many times throughout history how important it is that we tell the whole story of God—from creation to re-creation. We need to remember; and as we remember, we teach our children the story of God's work in this world, God's work in our families and relationships, and God's work through us to the world. It is this story that forms the outline for the first half of *Lift Up Your Hearts*. Beginning with creation and our fall into sin, through the Old Testament narratives and the hope of Advent, to the birth, life, death, and resurrection of Christ, and onward to the gift of the Holy Spirit of Pentecost and the promise of the new creation, we find our story woven into the fabric, creating a beautiful testimony to the grace of God in our own lives. Here we also find prayers and prayer outlines that name many of our praises and laments asking God to continue to be a part of our story in mighty and even miraculous ways.

Lift Up Your Hearts also supports the full range of actions in worship. The second half of this hymnal follows a basic order of worship, from the Call to Worship to the Benediction. It includes many prayers and other short litanies but also larger liturgies for baptism and the Lord's Supper, creeds, and a call to live out our baptismal calling to be the missional church.

Lift Up Your Hearts celebrates the long history of Christian psalm singing. Included are all 150 psalms—both beloved familiar settings and new settings, each helping us to enter into the psalm in a way that fits its function as a prayer, exhortation, or prophetic announcement. Some psalm settings are very close in form, content, and imagery to the corresponding biblical psalms, while others exercise greater interpretive freedom. Some portions of the psalms are heartily sung, while others may call for reading with a sung refrain or even changing the emotive energy of a single stanza to better convey the message of the psalm and in doing so, covering the full range of human emotion.

Lift Up Your Hearts is designed to serve people in many roles:

- It is first of all designed for group singing—in *congregations, small groups, church education classes, schools, camps,* and more.

- It is also designed to be a comprehensive resource for *pastors* and *worship planners* with extensive indexes for looking up titles, Scriptures, subjects, tunes, and meters to help the planning process.

- It can serve as an essential resource for both *praise teams* and *choirs*, with harmonies, descants, canons, and other musical resources. Praise teams will appreciate the many contemporary songs and the traditional hymnal repertoire that can easily be adapted for their use.

- *Choral conductors* will find ample four-part hymn arrangements for their *adult choir*, songs fitting for the *children's choir*, and a good number of canons.

Lift Up Your Hearts is more than a hymnal for corporate worship.

- There are additional *services for morning, evening, and night prayer* useful for *small groups* and the *opening of meetings*.

- *Pastoral care* resources are included that can be used for events in the life of the church; this hymnal is also a useful resource for hospital and home visits.

- For *personal and family devotions,* the songs, prayers, and Scriptures can be sung, played, or read.

- *Accessible accompaniments* throughout the book, including some intentionally simplified accompaniments, encourage younger musicians to grow and develop into the next generation of church musicians.

- The contents can also be used as part of a *curriculum for teaching* both new and lifelong Christians the overarching story of God's love.

With such a feast set before us, where do we even begin? The best feast is one that is savored, where time is taken to taste and relish the delights of a familiar dish, a favorite food presented in a different way, or the discovery of a new favorite. So it is with this collection. With over 850 songs to choose from, begin with a hundred songs that your church already knows well and another hundred that are familiar. From there, build your repertoire slowly, exploring different genres and learning texts that are particularly suited for your congregation's context. Savor the old and new. When introducing a new song, have it played one Sunday by an instrumentalist as part of a prelude, offertory, postlude, or time of reflection; then on the following week have it sung by a soloist or small ensemble; later include the congregation, singing it for a number of services until you can add it to the list of songs your church is familiar with. Be creative; search for other ways and opportunities for your congregation to learn the songs. And, most important, don't forget the children and youth.

Have them share with the congregation their heart songs—you may be surprised to learn what they are.

Our prayer is that this musical feast is deep enough to give voice to our praises and laments, contain both our sung prayers and God's words to us, and play a significant role in the faith formation of Christians old and young alike. May God take the work of our hands and the songs of our hearts, and use them for his glory.

Editors
Joyce Borger—Senior Editor
Martin Tel—Editor for Psalms
John D. Witvliet—Editor for Liturgical Resources

Assistants to the Editors
Diane Dykgraaf
Rebecca Hoeksema

Editorial Committee Members
Carol Bechtel
Claudia Godoy-Cortés
Christopher J. Kingdom-Grier
Brenda Kuyper
Joel Navarro
Gordon Pols
Tim TenClay
Paul Thé
Annetta VanderLugt
Leonard Vander Zee

We are grateful for the work of the advisory committee who helped us discern the heart songs of the church and provided helpful advice and feedback throughout the development of this hymnal.

Michael Alonzo, Apple Valley, Calif.
James Audlin, Kingston, N.Y.
Julia Bailey, Anaheim, Calif.
Judith A. Baker, Jenison, Mich.
Elisabeth Bakker, Fairport, N.Y.
David Banga, Granger, Ind.
Sharon Bleeker, Raymond, Minn.
Andrew Bouma, Woodstock, Ont.
Ryan Braam, Welland, Ont.
James Brumm, Rensselaer, N.Y.
Marie Sutton Burnham, Newark, N.Y.
Sharon Buwalda, Corsica, S.D.
Meeke Claus, Woodstock, Ont.
Vicki Cok, Waterloo, Ont.
Janet Danielson, Burnaby, B.C.
Michelle DePooter, Montreal , Que.
Dale Dickau, Red Deer, Alta.
Karl Digerness, San Francisco, Calif.
Ruth Dilley, Whitehouse Station, N.J.
Judy Doot, Villa Park, Ill.
Ben Dykhouse, Chino, Calif.
Jill Friend, Boone, Iowa
Curt Gesch, Telkwa, B.C.
Brittany Groen, Burnaby, B.C.
Elizabeth Hance, North Brunswick, N.J.
Paul Hansen, Hull, Iowa
Stephen Hasper, Hudsonville, Mich.
Judy Heethuis, McBain, Mich.
Judy Hilbelink, Orange City, Iowa
Lyn Howerzyl, Sully, Iowa
James Huang, Forest Hills, N.Y.
Glenda Hull, Edmonton, Alta.
Laurie Jabaay, South Holland, Ill.
Jeanie Kammeraad, Grand Rapids , Mich.
Joy Koning, Kalamazoo, Mich.
Ann Koops Hays, Milltown, N.J.
Jean Kramer, Drayton, Ont.
David Landegent, Holland, Mich.
Randal Lubbers, Lake Crystal, Minn.
Thomas McCrossan, Schenectady, N.Y.
Chad Meeuwse, Modesto, Calif.
Tom Merchant, Fulton, Ill.

Brenda Molendyk, Zeeland, Mich.
Mark Nandor, Columbus, Ohio
Robert Oehme, Ellenville, N.Y.
Dewi Pangaribuan, East Windsor, N.J.
Chandra Pasma, Ottawa, Ont.
Tom Peterson, Ada, Mich.
Flo Powell, Bushkill, Pa.
Ronald Redder, Ada, Mich.
Stephanie Scholman, Burlington, Ont.
Deborah Swanson, Grand Rapids, Mich.
Glenn Tiedemann, Wharton, N.J.
Rachel Rensink-Hoff, St. Catharines, Ont.
Katie Roelofs, Linthicum Heights, Md.
Marcia Schulz, Kanawha, Iowa
Michelle Scripps, Sioux Center, Iowa
Rod Snaterse, Edmonton, Alta.
Kevin Soodsma, Grand Rapids, Mich.
Ivan Stefanov, North Hampton, N.H.
Heather Sukkau, Langley, B.C.
Stephen Terpstra, Hamilton, Ont.
Peter Tigchelaar, Dundas, Ont.
Carl Tuyl, Toronto, Ont. (*in memoriam*)
Trudy Van Beekum, Wycoff, N.J.
Rika van den Heever, Edmonton, Alta.
Susan Van Kley, Crete, Ill.
Richard Van Oss, Zeeland, Mich.
Willie Van Schepen, Lynden, Wash.
James Van Zetten, Chicago, Ill.
Karen Vanden Akker, Leota, Minn.
Cynthia Vandenburgh, Conklin, Mich.
Jana Vanderlaan, Grand Rapids , Mich.
Audrey VanderSchans, Abbotsford, B.C.
Rick Vanderwal, DeMotte, Ind.
Joe Veltman, New Berlin, Wis.
Kyle Vohlken, Holland, Mich.
Carol Vroom, Orland Park, Ill.
Kenneth Walsh, Kingston, N.Y.
Jacob Weeda, St. Martin, Mich.
Lynda Westervelt, Picton, Ont.
Todd Zuidema, Hull, Iowa
Janice Zuidema, Spring Lake, Mich.

About the music

Simplified arrangements: We have attempted to preserve the integrity of the music while maintaining a style consistent with a hymnal. Music was also simplified in cases where it became necessary for purposes of accessibility to the church musician and singer, and also to fit on a limited number of pages while still providing enough of an accompaniment to support congregational singing.

Chords: Basic chords are provided for every song for guitarists and pianists who read or improvise from the chordal structure. Guitarists may need to ignore some of the information provided for the keyboardist (i.e., the indication of bass notes and sevenths and ninths). More accomplished guitarists or keyboardists may also desire to fill in more of the chordal structure. Again, what is provided is the basic resource. A capo chart to assist guitarists with some of the more difficult keys is available at www.LiftUpYourHeartsHymnal.org.

Musical terms/abbreviations:

(⌒)—optional fermatas are used where there are a variety of acceptable performance practices.

(#)—You may find a sharp in parentheses at the end of a piece. The sharp is meant to be played on the last stanza changing the chord from minor to major (known as a Picardy Third).

st.—stanza, used in reference to song texts

tr.—translated

vv.—verses, used in reference to Scripture

Other versions available

- In addition to this pew version of the hymnal, the following versions are available electronically.
  (Note: Additional copyright permission or licensing is necessary for reprinting and projection when using these resources.)
- Music and Words for Projection
- Words Only for Print and Projection
- Music and Words for Printing
- Music and Words for Reading Only

An accompaniment edition is being planned to provide fuller and more complex accompaniments for many songs, alternate arrangements for often-used tunes, and additional arrangements for piano or organ accompaniment.

Additional free online resources including indexes and a growing number of background notes, audio files, and more are all available at *www.LiftUpYourHearts Hymnal.org.*

The Story of Creation and Redemption

All People That on Earth Do Dwell

1

PSALM 100

1 All peo-ple that on earth do dwell, sing to the Lord with cheer-ful voice.
2 Know that the LORD is God in-deed; he formed us all with-out our aid.
3 O en-ter then his gates with joy, with-in his courts his praise pro-claim.
4 Be-cause the LORD our God is good, his mer-cy is for-ev-er sure.

Serve him with joy, his prais-es tell, come now be-fore him and re-joice!
We are the flock he comes to feed, the sheep who by his hand were made.
Let thank-ful songs your tongues em-ploy, O bless and mag-ni-fy his name.
His faith-ful-ness at all times stood and shall from age to age en-dure.

French

1 Vous, qui sur la terre habitez,
   chantez à pleine voix, chantez,
   réjouissezvous au Seigneur,
   égayezvous à son honneur.

2 Lui seul est notre souverain,
   c'est lui qui nous fit de sa main:
   nous le peuple qu'il mènera,
   le troupeau qu'il rassemblera.

3 Présentez-vous tous devant lui,
   dans sa maison dès aujourd'hui;
   célébrez son nom glorieux,
   exaltez-le jusques aux cieux.

4 Pour toi, Seigneur, que notre amour
   se renouvelle chaque jour:
   ta bonté, ta fidélité,
   demeurent pour l'éternité.

Dutch

1 Juicht Gode toe, bazuint en zingt,
   Treedt nader tot gij Hem omringt,
   gij aard' alom, zijn rijksdomein,
   zult voor den HEER dienstvaardig zijn.

2 Roept uit met blijdschap: "God is Hij.
   Hij schiep ons, Hem behoren wij,
   zijn volk, de schapen die Hij hoedt
   en als beminden weidt en voedt."

3 Treedt statig binnen door de poort.
   Hier staat zijn troon, hier woont zijn Woord.
   Heft hier voor God uw lofzang aan:
   Gebenedijd zijn grote naam.

4 Want God is overstelpend goed,
   die ons in vrede wonen doet.
   Zijn goedheid is als morgendauw:
   elk nieuw geslacht ervaart zijn trouw.

Additional languages on following pages
For an alternate arrangement see 843, 924

(continues)

Hungarian

1 E földön ti minden népek,
   az Istennek örvendjetek,
   előtte szép énekekkel
   szolgáljátok őt víg szívvel!

2 Tudjátok, hogy ez az Isten,
   ki minket teremtett bölcsen,
   és mi vagyunk ő népei
   és ő nyájának juhai.

3 Ő kapuin menjetek be,
   hálát advján szívetekbe'!
   jer, menjünk be tornácába,
   néki nagy hálákat adva!

4 Mert nagy az ő kegyessége,
   és megmarad mindörökre,
   és ő hűsége mindenha
   megáll és el nem fogy soha.

German

1 Nun jauchzt dem Herren, alle Welt!
   Kommt her, zu seinem Dienst euch stellt,
   kommt mit Frohlocken, säumet nicht,
   kommt vor sein heilig Angesicht.

2 Erkennt, dass Gott ist unser Herr,
   der uns erschaffen ihm zur Ehr.
   Als guter Hirt ist er bereit,
   zu führen uns auf seine Weid.

3 Die ihr nun wollet bei ihm sein,
   kommt, geht zu seinen Toren ein
   mit Loben durch der Psalmen Klang,
   zu seinem Hause mit Gesang.

4 Er ist voll Güt und Freundlichkeit,
   voll Lieb und Treu zu jeder Zeit.
   Sein Gnad währt immer dort und hier
   und seine Wahrheit für und für.

Indonesian

1 Hai bumi, bergembiralah
   dan pada TUHAN menyembah!
   Mari menghadap Yang Kudus;
   bersukacitalah terus!

2 Akuilah dengan teguh:
   TUHANlah saja Allahmu!
   Pencipta kita Dialah;
   kita kawanan dombaNya.

3 Masukilah gapuraNya,
   bawa syukurmu naik serta:
   nyanyikan sukacitamu
   di pelataran Bait Kudus!

4 Abadi TUHAN mahabaik,
   kasih setiaNya ajaib
   dan perjanjianNya teguh
   turun temurun bagimu!

Spanish

1 Oh pueblos todos alabad
   en alta voz a Dios cantad,
   regocijaos en su honor
   servid alegres al Señor.

2 El soberano Creador
   de nuestra vida es el autor;
   el pueblo suyo somos ya,
   rebaño que Él pastoreará.

3 A su santuario pues entrad,
   y vuestras vidas ofrendad;
   al nombre augusto dad loor,
   que al mundo llena de esplendor.

4 Incomparable es su bondad,
   y para siempre su verdad;
   de bienes colma nuestro ser
   su gracia no ha de fenecer.

Words: English William Kethe, 1561, alt., P.D.; French tr. Roger Chapal 1970, after Théodore de Bèze, 1562,
© Fédération Musique et Chant de la Réforme, c/o Editions Olivétan; Chinese tr. Timothy Ting Fang Lew,
rev. Ernest Yang © Chinese Christian Literature Council Ltd.; Dutch tr. Willem Barnard, 1967, © *Interker-kelijke Stichting voor het Kerklied*, Leidschendam; German tr. after Cornelius Becker; Hungarian tr. Albert
Szenczi Molnár, 1607; Indonesian tr. H.A. Pandopo © 1989 Yamuger, Indonesian Institute for Sacred Music;
Japanese tr. from *The 150 Genevan Psalm Songs in Japanese* (The General Assembly of Reformed Church in
Japan Publishing Committee, 2006); Korean tr. The United Methodist Korean Hymnal Committee © 2001
The United Methodist Publishing House, admin. The Copyright Company; Spanish tr. Federico J. Pagura,
1960, © Federico J. Pagura; Swahili tr. *Nyimbo Standard*
Music (GENEVAN 134/OLD HUNDREDTH 8.8.8.8): Louis Bourgeois, 1551, P.D.

Swahili

1 Enyi mkaao nchi, mwimbieni Mungu sana,
  msifuni kwa sauti kuu, mbele zake mwakutana.

2 Mungu mwamjua, kwani aliyetuumba ndiye,
  atuchunga malishani, na tu kundi lake Yeye.

3 Haya! malangoni mwake, hata nyuani, imbeni;
  mulikuze Jina lake, Jina la Bwana si duni.

4 Kwani, Jehova ni mwema ana rehema milele;
  kweli yake yasimama leo na kesho vivile.

Arabic

١ يـا ارض غـني بالسـرور لربنـا السـامي العظيـم
  هيا اعبدوا الـرب الغفـور بالابتهـاج المسـتديم

٢ هو الـذي صـنعنا ونحن شـعب مقتنـاه
  نحن لمن احينـا قطيعـه الـذي افتـداه

٣ هيا اقصـدوا اعتابـه وبـاركوه حامدين
  ثـم ادخلـوا ابوابـه ديـاره مسـبحين

٤ فصـالح هو الالـه رحمتـه الـي الابـد
  لكـل ادوار الحيـاه امانة الـرب الصـمد

Chinese	*Japanese*	*Korean*
1 普天之下萬族萬邦， 皆當向主歡呼頌揚， 樂意事奉，虔誠頌讚， 主前崇拜，高聲歌唱。	1 地はみな声あげ 主をたたえまつれ。 歌いつつ来たり 喜び仕えよ。	1 온 땅의 모든 사람들 흥겨운 소리 높여서 기쁘게 주를 섬기며 주 앞에 나와 찬양해
2 當知主是獨一真神， 不藉人力創造萬人， 賜人身心，賜人糧食， 招集萬民進祂羊群。	2 われら造りたもう 主こそ神と知れ。 われらはその民 その牧の羊。	2 우리를 친히 만드신 주 하나님을 경배해 우리는 모두 주의 것 그 기르시는 양일세
3 大家踴躍踏進主門， 歡欣快樂入主院庭， 同心一意感謝真神， 高歌頌揚讚美主名。	3 歌もてほめつつ 大前に進め。 主の宮に入りて 御名を賛美せよ。	3 찬송함으로 그 문에 기뻐함으로 그 전에 주 이름 찬양하면서 온전한 경배 드리세
4 我主、我神、祂本善良， 我主憐憫、慈愛永存， 我主真理亙古不變， 我主恩德萬世永恆。	4 主は恵み深く 憐れみは尽きず、 変わらぬまことは よろず代におよぶ。	4 선하신 우리 하나님 그 자비 영원하시고 그 진리 변치 않으며 영원히 함께 하시리

O Worship the King

PSALM 104

1 O wor-ship the King all - glo - rious a - bove, O grate - ful - ly
2 O tell of his might and sing of his grace, whose robe is the
3 Your boun - ti - ful care, what tongue can re - cite? It breathes in the

sing his power and his love: our shield and de - fend - er, the
light, whose can - o - py space. His char - iots of wrath the deep
air, it shines in the light; it streams from the hills, it de -

An - cient of Days, pa - vil-ioned in splen-dor and gird - ed with praise.
thun - der-clouds form, and dark is his path on the wings of the storm.
scends to the plain, and sweet-ly dis-tills in the dew and the rain.

4 Frail children of dust, and feeble as frail,
in you do we trust, nor find you to fail.
Your mercies, how tender, how firm to the end,
our Maker, Defender, Redeemer, and Friend!

5 O measureless Might, unchangeable Love,
whom angels delight to worship above!
Your ransomed creation, with glory ablaze,
in true adoration shall sing to your praise!

For another setting of Ps. 104 see 11

Words: Robert Grant, 1833, alt, P.D.
Music (LYONS 10.10.11.11): W. Gardiner's *Sacred Melodies*, 1815; attr. Johann Michael Haydn, P.D.

The Heavens Declare Your Glory

PSALM 19

1 The heavens de-clare your glo-ry, the fir-ma-ment your power;
2 The sun with roy-al splen-dor goes forth to chant your praise,
3 All heaven on high re-joic-es to do its Mak-er's will;

day un-to day the sto-ry re-peats from hour to hour.
and moon-beams soft and ten-der their gen-tler an-them raise.
the stars with sol-emn voic-es re-sound your prais-es still.

Night un-to night re-ply-ing, pro-claims in ev-ery land,
O'er ev-ery tribe and na-tion the mu-sic is out-poured,
So let my whole be-hav-ior, each thought, each deed I do,

O LORD, with voice un-dy-ing, the won-ders of your hand.
the song of all cre-a-tion to you, cre-a-tion's Lord.
be, LORD, my strength, my Sav-ior, a cease-less song to you.

For another setting of Ps. 19 see 719

Words: Thomas R. Birks, 1874, alt., P.D.
Music (FAITHFUL 7.6.7.6 D): Johann S. Bach (1685-1750); adapt. from *My Heart Ever Faithful*, Cantata 68, P.D.

4 God of Wonders

Words and Music (GOD OF WONDERS): Marc Byrd, Steve Hindalong; arr. Albert Chung © 2000 New Spring
Publishing (ASCAP)/Never Say Never Songs (ASCAP), admin. New Spring Publishing/Storm Boy Music
(BMI)/Meaux Mercy (BMI), admin. EMI CMG Publishing

(continues)

Hal - le - lu - jah! to the Lord of heav-en and earth.

God of won - ders, be-yond our gal - ax -

y, you are ho - ly, ho - ly.

Pre - cious Lord, re-veal your heart to me, Fa-ther ho - ly,

ho - ly; the u - ni-verse de-clares your maj - es -

5 Let All Things Now Living

Words: Katherine K. Davis, 1939, P.D.
Music (ASH GROVE 6.6.11.6.6.11 D): Welsh; desc. Katherine K. Davis © 1939, 1966 E.C. Schirmer Music Co.

6 Praise the Lord, Sing Hallelujah

PSALM 148

1 Praise the LORD, sing hal - le - lu - jah, from the heav-ens praise his
2 Let them praise the LORD their Mak - er: they were made at his com-
3 All you fruit-ful trees and ce - dars, ev - ery hill and moun-tain

name; praise the LORD, our great Cre - a - tor; all his an - gels,
mand. God es - tab - lished them for - ev - er; his de - cree shall
high, creep-ing things and beasts and cat - tle, birds that in the

praise pro - claim. All his hosts, to - geth - er praise him, sun and
ev - er stand. Let the earth sing hal - le - lu - jah: rag - ing
heav - ens fly, kings of earth and all you peo - ple, princ - es

moon and stars on high; praise the LORD, O heavens of
seas, you mon - sters all, fire and hail and snow and
great, earth's judg - es all; praise his name, young men and

For other settings of Ps. 148 see 550, 555

Words: *Bible Songs Hymnal*, 1927, alt., P.D.
Music (PRAISE JEHOVAH 8.7.8.7 with refrain): William J. Kirkpatrick (1838-1921), P.D.

7 Sing Praise to the Lord, You People of Grace

PSALM 150

1 Sing praise to the Lord, you peo-ple of grace; fill
heaven with the songs that sound from this place; since you are God's
ser-vants and meet in his name, his won-ders de-
clare and his glo-ry pro-claim.

2 His great-ness ex-ceeds what words can ex-plain, and
his is the power no force can re-strain; with fan-fares of
horns and cre-scend-os of strings raise an-thems to
ho-nor the King of all kings.

3 Where mu-sic is made, let rhy-thms a-bound: let
cym-bals and drums add weight to the sound; with dance that is
grace-ful and words that are clear, bring joy to the
God you a-dore and re-vere.

4 Yield all that you are to wor-ship the Lord— see
life as a psalm, each mo-ment a chord; let har-mo-nies
flour-ish and mel-o-dies soar— let all that has
breath praise the Lord ev-er-more.

For other settings of Ps. 150 see 563, 952

Words: Martin Leckebusch © 2006 Kevin Mayhew Ltd.
Music (CHU LEUNG 10.10.11.11): Swee Hong Lim, Singapore © 2000 and arr. © 2010 Swee Hong Lim, admin.
General Board of Global Ministries t/a GBGMusik

Refrain B♭maj7 C9 Am7 Dm E♭
Two part

Hal - le! Hal - le - lu - jah! Hal - le! Hal - le!

Gm11 C B♭maj7 C9

Hal - le - lu - jah! Hal - le! Hal - le - lu -

Am7 Dm E♭ C7 F B♭/C F

jah! Hal - le! Hal - le! Hal - le - lu - jah!

Affirmation: How We Know God 8

We know God by two means:

**First, by the creation, preservation,
and government of the universe,
since that universe is before our eyes
like a beautiful book
in which all creatures,
great and small,
are as letters
to make us ponder
the invisible things of God:
God's eternal power and divinity.**

All these things are enough
to convict humans
and to leave them without excuse.

**Second, God makes himself known
to us more clearly
by his holy and divine Word,
as much as we need in this life,
for God's glory
and for our salvation.**

Text: Belgic Confession, Article 2

9   The Mighty God with Power Speaks

PSALM 50

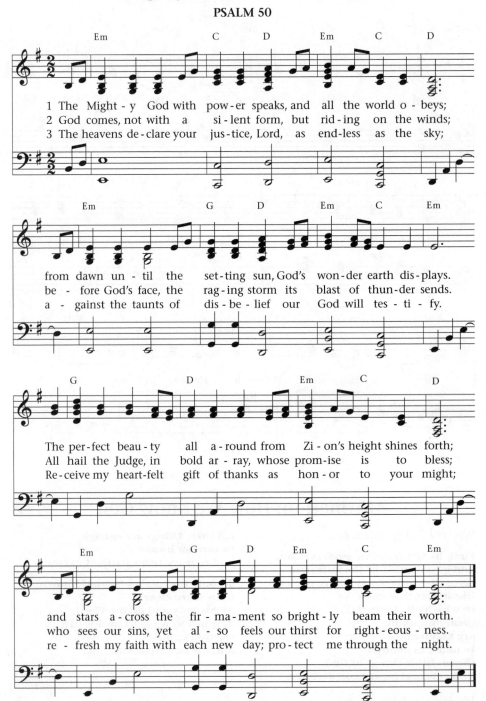

1 The Might - y God with pow - er speaks, and all the world o - beys;
2 God comes, not with a si - lent form, but rid - ing on the winds;
3 The heavens de - clare your jus - tice, Lord, as end - less as the sky;

from dawn un - til the set - ting sun, God's won - der earth dis - plays.
be - fore God's face, the rag - ing storm its blast of thun - der sends.
a - gainst the taunts of dis - be - lief our God will tes - ti - fy.

The per - fect beau - ty all a - round from Zi - on's height shines forth;
All hail the Judge, in bold ar - ray, whose prom - ise is to bless;
Re - ceive my heart - felt gift of thanks as hon - or to your might;

and stars a - cross the fir - ma - ment so bright - ly beam their worth.
who sees our sins, yet al - so feels our thirst for right - eous - ness.
re - fresh my faith with each new day; pro - tect me through the night.

For another setting of Ps. 50 see 379

Words: Michael Morgan © 1999, 2011 Michael Morgan, admin. Faith Alive Christian Resources
Music (STAR OF COUNTY DOWN 8.6.8.6 D): Irish traditional; arr. Rory Cooney (b. 1952)
© 1990 GIA Publications, Inc.

We Sing the Mighty Power of God

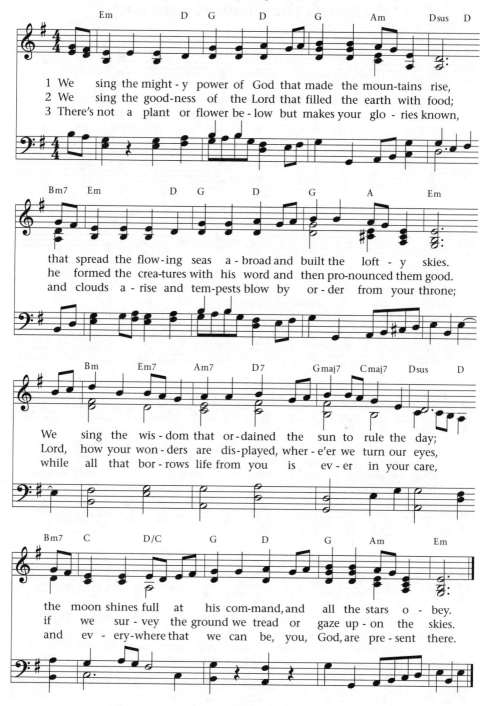

1 We sing the might-y power of God that made the moun-tains rise,
2 We sing the good-ness of the Lord that filled the earth with food;
3 There's not a plant or flower be-low but makes your glo-ries known,

that spread the flow-ing seas a-broad and built the loft-y skies.
he formed the crea-tures with his word and then pro-nounced them good.
and clouds a-rise and tem-pests blow by or-der from your throne;

We sing the wis-dom that or-dained the sun to rule the day;
Lord, how your won-ders are dis-played, wher-e'er we turn our eyes,
while all that bor-rows life from you is ev-er in your care,

the moon shines full at his com-mand, and all the stars o-bey.
if we sur-vey the ground we tread or gaze up-on the skies.
and ev-ery-where that we can be, you, God, are pre-sent there.

For an alternate arrangement see 162

Words: Isaac Watts, 1715, alt. P.D.
Music (KINGSFOLD 8.6.8.6 D): traditional English; arr. Alfred V. Fedak © 2012 Faith Alive Christian Resources

11 We Worship You, Whose Splendor Dwarfs the Cosmos PSALM 104

1 We wor-ship you, whose splen-dor dwarfs the cos-mos,
2 You made the earth, de-ter-min-ing its or-bit:
3 The wa-ters flow, till plain and pas-ture flour-ish;
4 You formed the moon to mark the pass-ing sea-sons;

whose ver-y clothes are robes of daz-zling light;
prim-e-val cha-os fled at your com-mand.
the for-est thrives— there birds may free-ly nest;
you gave the sun, whose ra-diance lights the day;

on wind and cloud you ride a-cross the heav-ens;
You send the streams from moun-tain peak to val-ley,
the thirst-y crea-tures drink and find re-fresh-ment;
as each new morn-ing calls us to your ser-vice,

your word bids fi-ery an-gels soar in flight. *To Stanza 2*
and yet pre-vent them flood-ing all the land. *To Refrain*
and hu-man hearts with wine and grain are blessed. *To Stanza 4*
the wild-life of the night-time steals a-way. *To Refrain*

For another setting of Ps. 104 see 2

Words: Martin Leckebusch © 2006 Kevin Mayhew Ltd.
Music (TIDINGS 11.10.11.10 refrain 9.11): James Walch, 1875, P.D.

Lord God, our voic-es glad-ly we raise,

join - ing cre - a - tion's un-end-ing hymn of praise.

5 Unnumbered marvels emphasize
  your wisdom:
who knows what mysteries lie
  beneath the sea?
Yet every mouth relies on your provision:
without your care, how brief
  our lives would be. *To Stanza 6*

6 May you rejoice in all you have created,
  though just your glance could set
  the earth ablaze;
may we direct our lives to bring
  you pleasure,
and praise you with the song
  of all our days. *To Refrain*

O Lord, Our Lord 12
PSALM 8:1

O Lord, our Lord, how ex - cel-lent is thy name.

O Lord, our Lord, how ex - cel-lent is thy name.

Words: Psalm 8:1
Music (HOW EXCELLENT 11.11): Richard Smallwood (b. 1948); arr. Stephen Key © 2000 GIA Publications, Inc.

13 Have Mercy on Us, God Most High

1 Have mer-cy on us, God Most High, who lift our hearts to thee;
2 How won-der-ful cre-a-tion is, the work which thou did bless;

have mer-cy now, most mer-ci-ful, most ho-ly Trin-i-ty.
and, O what then must thou be like, e-ter-nal love-li-ness!

When heaven and earth were yet un-made, when time was yet un-known,
Most an-cient of all mys-ter-ies! Low at thy throne we lie:

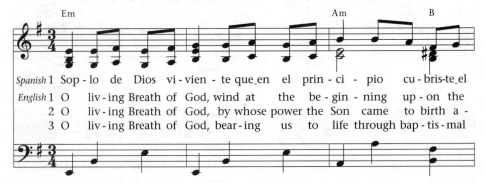

thou in thy bliss and maj-es-ty did live and love a-lone.
have mer-cy now, most mer-ci-ful, most ho-ly Trin-i-ty.

For music see 10, 162

Words: Frederick William Faber (1814-1863), P.D.
Music (KINGSFOLD 8.6.8.6 D): traditional English, P.D.

14 Soplo de Dios/O Living Breath

Spanish 1 Sop-lo de Dios vi-vien-te que_en el prin-ci-pio cu-bris-te_el

English 1 O liv-ing Breath of God, wind at the be-gin-ning up-on the
2 O liv-ing Breath of God, by whose power the Son came to birth a-
3 O liv-ing Breath of God, bear-ing us to life through bap-tis-mal

Words: Osvaldo Catena (1920-1986); tr. Gerhard M. Cartford (b. 1923) © 1998 Augsburg Fortress
Music (VARVINDAR FRISKA 8.9.8.8 refrain 7.7.6.4.6): Swedish folk tune; arr. *Evangelical Lutheran Worship*
© 2006 Augsburg Fortress

a - gua, Sop - lo de Dios vi - vien - te que fe - cun -
wa - ters; O liv - ing Breath of God, bear - ing the cre -
mong us; O liv - ing Breath of God, who to the cre -
wa - ters; O liv - ing Breath of God, sigh - ing with cre -

da - ste la cre - a - ción: Ven hoy a nues - tras
a - tion to won - drous birth: Come now, and fill our
a - tion gives life a - new:
a - tion for free - dom's birth:

al - mas, in - fún - de - nos tus do - nes;
spir - its; pour out your gifts a - bun - dant.

So - plo de Dios vi - vien - te, O San - to Es - pí - ri - tu del Se - ñor.
O liv - ing Breath of God, Ho - ly Spir - it, breathe in us as we pray.

Spanish

2 Soplo de Dios viviente por quien el Hijo se hizo hombre,
Soplo de Dios viviente que renovaste la creación: *Refrain*

3 Soplo de Dios viviente por quien nacemos en el bautismo,
Soplo de Dios viviente que consagraste la creación: *Refrain*

15

The First Place

COLOSSIANS 1:15-20

1 Je - sus, the per-fect pic-ture of the un-seen God. Ma - ker
2 Vic - tor, o - ver sin and death you tri - umphed. First-born,

of things we can-not com-pre-hend. Wis - dom, the earth dis-
you've shown us life be-yond the grave. Bride-groom, we long for

plays your strength and beau - ty. Sov - ereign, yes, ev - ery
you in ex - pec - ta - tion. Je - sus, your church re -

throne knows you are God.
joic - es to pro - claim.

Ev-ery inch of this un - i-verse be-

longs to you, O Christ. For through you and for you it was made.

Your cre - a - tion en - dures by the or - der of your hand. So

you must have in all things the first place.

Jesus: Image of the Invisible God   16
COLOSSIANS 1:12-18

Give thanks to the Father,
who has enabled you to share in
the inheritance of the saints in the light.

**He has rescued us from
the power of darkness
and transferred us into
the kingdom of his beloved Son,
in whom we have redemption,
the forgiveness of sins.**

He is the image of the invisible God,
the firstborn of all creation;
for in him all things
in heaven and on earth were created,

things visible and invisible,
whether thrones or dominions
or rulers or powers
**—all things have been created
through him and for him.**

He himself is before all things,
and in him all things hold together.
He is the head of the body,
the church;
he is the beginning,
**the firstborn from the dead,
so that he might come to have
first place in everything.**

Text: Colossians 1:12-18, NRSV

17 Beautiful Savior

1 Beau - ti - ful Sav - ior! King of cre - a - tion! Son of
2 Fair are the mead - ows, fair are the wood - lands, robed in
3 Fair is the sun - shine, fair is the moon - light, bright the
4 Beau - ti - ful Sav - ior! Lord of the na - tions! Son of

God and Son of Man! Tru - ly I'd love thee,
flowers of bloom - ing spring; Je - sus is fair - er,
spar - kling stars on high; Je - sus shines bright - er,
God and Son of Man! Glo - ry and hon - or,

tru - ly I'd serve thee, Light of my soul, my joy, my crown.
Je - sus is pur - er; he makes our sor - rowing spir - it sing.
Je - sus shines pur - er than all the an - gels in the sky.
praise, ad - o - ra - tion, now and for - ev - er - more be thine!

*Optional descant for final time

Words: *Gesangbuch, Münster,* 1677; tr. Joseph A. Seiss, 1873, P.D.
Music (ST. ELIZABETH 5.5.7.5.5.8): *Schleissche Volkslieder,* 1842, P.D.

Touch the Earth Lightly

18

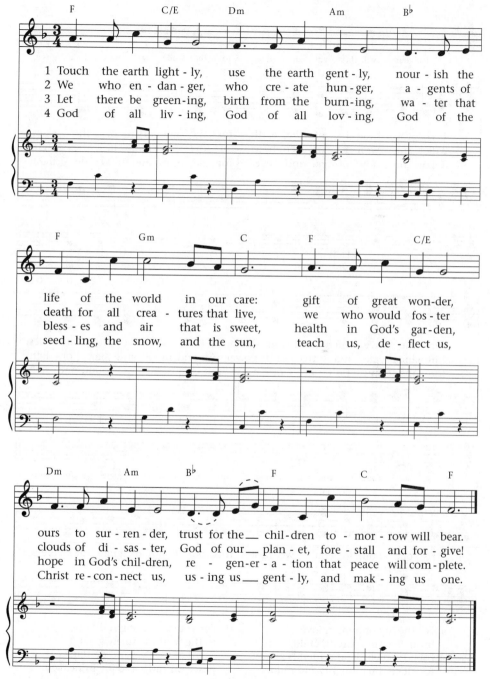

1 Touch the earth light - ly, use the earth gent - ly, nour - ish the
2 We who en - dan - ger, who cre - ate hun - ger, a - gents of
3 Let there be green-ing, birth from the burn-ing, wa - ter that
4 God of all liv - ing, God of all lov - ing, God of the

life of the world in our care: gift of great won-der,
death for all crea - tures that live, we who would fos - ter
bless - es and air that is sweet, health in God's gar-den,
seed - ling, the snow, and the sun, teach us, de - flect us,

ours to sur - ren - der, trust for the __ chil-dren to - mor - row will bear.
clouds of di - sas - ter, God of our __ plan - et, fore - stall and for - give!
hope in God's chil-dren, re - gen-er-a - tion that peace will com-plete.
Christ re - con - nect us, us - ing us __ gent - ly, and mak - ing us one.

Words: Shirley Erena Murray © 1992 Hope Publishing Company
Music (AI HU 10.10.10.10): Swee Hong Lim © 2005 Hope Publishing Company

19　　For the Beauty of the Earth

4 For the joy of human love,
　brother, sister, parent, child,
　friends on earth, and friends above,
　for all gentle thoughts and mild,
　Refrain

5 For yourself, best gift divine,
　to the world so freely given,
　agent of God's grand design:
　peace on earth and joy in heaven.
　Refrain

Words: Folliott S. Pierpont, 1864, alt., P.D.
Music (DIX 7.7.7.7.7.7): Conrad Kocher, 1838; adapt. William H. Monk, 1861, P.D.; desc. Sydney H.
Nicholson, 1944, © The Royal School of Church Music

All Things Bright and Beautiful

20

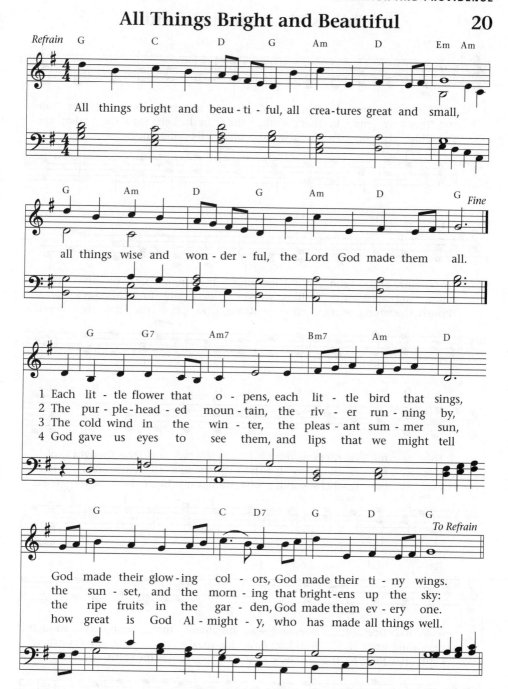

Refrain

All things bright and beau-ti-ful, all crea-tures great and small,
all things wise and won-der-ful, the Lord God made them all.

1 Each lit - tle flower that o - pens, each lit - tle bird that sings,
2 The pur - ple - head - ed moun - tain, the riv - er run - ning by,
3 The cold wind in the win - ter, the pleas - ant sum - mer sun,
4 God gave us eyes to see them, and lips that we might tell

God made their glow - ing col - ors, God made their ti - ny wings.
the sun - set, and the morn - ing that bright-ens up the sky:
the ripe fruits in the gar - den, God made them ev - ery one.
how great is God Al - might - y, who has made all things well.

Words: Cecil F. Alexander, 1848, P.D.
Music (ROYAL OAK 7.6.7.6 with refrain 7.6.7.6): melody English traditional, *The Dancing Master*, 1686; harm.
John Worst, 1974, alt. © 1987 Faith Alive Christian Resources

21 This Is My Father's World

1 This is my Fa-ther's world, and to my lis-tening ears all
2 This is my Fa-ther's world; the birds their car - ols raise; the
3 This is my Fa-ther's world; oh, let me not for - get that,

na - ture sings, and round me rings the mu - sic of the spheres.
morn - ing light, the lil - y white, de - clare their Ma-ker's praise.
though the wrong seems oft so strong, God is the Rul - er yet.

This is my Fa-ther's world; I rest me in the thought of
This is my Fa-ther's world; he shines in all that's fair. In the
This is my Fa-ther's world; why should my heart be sad? The

rocks and trees, of skies and seas; his hand the won-ders wrought.
rus - tling grass I hear him pass; he speaks to me ev-ery-where.
Lord is King, let the heav-ens ring! God reigns; let the earth be glad.

Words: Maltbie D. Babcock (1858-1901), P.D.
Music (TERRA BEATA 6.6.8.6 D): English; adapt. Franklin L. Sheppard (1852-1930), P.D.

Rejoice, You Righteous, in the Lord

PSALM 33

1 Re - joice, you right-eous, in the Lord, in song your voic - es raise;
2 Let ev - ery na - tion, ev - ery land u - nite with one ac - cord,
3 Be - hold, God's ev - er - watch-ful eye sees through our dark de - spair;

a - wake the psal - ter - y and harp, lift up God's name in praise!
and hum - bly lay their heart-felt prayers in awe be - fore the Lord.
the arms of grace en - cir - cle us with strong, yet ten - der care;

For by God's word the heavens were hung; God laid the sea and land,
How hap - py are God's faith - ful ones, how blest God's cho-sen heirs,
the hope of all the a - ges past, that sets at peace our fears,

and all that fills the fir - ma - ment were made at God's com-mand.
for sure - ly an in - her - i - tance of glo - ry shall be theirs!
God's mer - cy and God's stead-fast love shall fol - low all our years.

For an alternate arrangement see 679; for music in a higher key see 726

Words: Michael Morgan © 1999, 2011 Michael Morgan, admin. Faith Alive Christian Resources
Music (ELLACOMBE 8.6.8.6 D): *Gesangbuch der Herzogl,* Hofkapelle, Würtemberg, 1784, P.D.

23 Children of the Heavenly Father

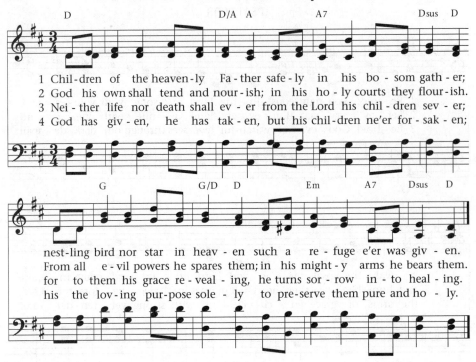

1 Chil-dren of the heaven-ly Fa-ther safe-ly in his bo-som gath-er;
2 God his own shall tend and nour-ish; in his ho-ly courts they flour-ish.
3 Nei-ther life nor death shall ev-er from the Lord his chil-dren sev-er;
4 God has giv-en, he has tak-en, but his chil-dren ne'er for-sak-en;

nest-ling bird nor star in heav-en such a re-fuge e'er was giv-en.
From all e-vil powers he spares them; in his might-y arms he bears them.
for to them his grace re-veal-ing, he turns sor-row in-to heal-ing.
his the lov-ing pur-pose sole-ly to pre-serve them pure and ho-ly.

Words: Carolina Sandell Berg (1832-1903); tr. Ernst W. Olson (1870-1958) © 1925 Board of Publication
    Lutheran Church in America, ren. 1963, admin. Augsburg Fortress
Music (TRYGGARE KAN INGEN VARA 8.8.8.8): Swedish folk tune, P.D.

24 Affirmation: God as Creator and Provider

What do you believe when you say,
"I believe in God, the Father almighty,
creator of heaven and earth"?

**That the eternal Father of our Lord Jesus Christ,
who out of nothing created heaven and earth
and everything in them,
who still upholds and rules them
by his eternal counsel and providence,
is my God and Father because of Christ the Son.
I trust God so much that I do not doubt
he will provide whatever I need
for body and soul, and will turn to my good
whatever adversity he sends upon me in this sad world.
God is able to do this because he is almighty God
and desires to do this because he is a faithful Father.**

(continues)

What do you understand by the providence of God?

**The almighty and ever present power of God
by which God upholds, as with his hand,
heaven and earth and all creatures,
and so rules them that leaf and blade, rain and drought,
fruitful and lean years, food and drink,
health and sickness, prosperity and poverty—
all things, in fact,
come to us not by chance but by his fatherly hand.**

Text: Heidelberg Catechism Q&A 26, 27

God Moves in a Mysterious Way 25

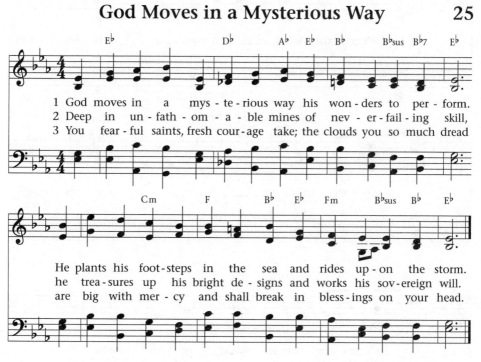

1 God moves in a mys-te-rious way his won-ders to per-form.
2 Deep in un-fath-om-a-ble mines of nev-er-fail-ing skill,
3 You fear-ful saints, fresh cour-age take; the clouds you so much dread

He plants his foot-steps in the sea and rides up-on the storm.
he trea-sures up his bright de-signs and works his sov-ereign will.
are big with mer-cy and shall break in bless-ings on your head.

4 His purposes will ripen fast,
  unfolding every hour.
  The bud may have a bitter taste,
  but sweet will be the flower.

5 Blind unbelief is sure to err
  and scan his work in vain.
  God is his own interpreter,
  and he will make it plain.

Words: William Cowper, 1774, P.D.
Music (DUNDEE 8.6.8.6): *Scottish Psalter,* 1615; harm. Thomas Ravenscroft (1592-1635), alt., P.D.

26   He's Got the Whole World in His Hands

2 He's got the wind and the rain. . .   4 He's got you and me, brother,. . .
3 He's got the little tiny baby. . .   5 He's got you and me, sister,. . .

6 He's got everybody here. . .

Words: traditional
Music (WHOLE WORLD irregular): African American spiritual; arr. Hezekiah Brinson Jr (b. 1958) © 1990

Many and Great

1 Man - y and great, O God, are your works,
2 Grant us com - mu - nion with you, our God,

Mak - er of earth and sky. Your hands have
though you tran - scend the stars. Come close to

set the heav - ens with stars; your fin - gers spread the
us and stay by our side: with you are found the

moun - tains and plains. You mere - ly spoke and
true gifts that last. Bless us with life that

wa - ters were formed; deep seas o - bey your voice.
nev - er shall end, e - ter - nal life with you.

Words: Joseph R. Renville (1779-1846); tr. Philip Frazier (1892-1964), P.D.
Music (LACQUIPARLE 9.6.9.9.9.6): traditional Dakota; arr. Lara Baatenburg, 2009, © 2012 Faith Alive
Christian Resources

28 God Marked a Line and Told the Sea

1 God marked a line and told the sea its surg - ing
2 God set one lim - it in the glade where tempt - ing,
3 The line, the lim - it, and the law are pat - terns

tides and waves were free to trav - el up the
fruit - ed branch - es swayed, and that first lim - it
meant to help us draw a bound be - tween what

slop - ing strand but not to o - ver - take the land.
stands be - hind the lim - its that the law de - fined.
life re - quires and all the things our heart de - sires.

4 But, discontent with finite powers,
we reach to take what is not ours
and then defend our claim by force
and swerve from life's intended course.

5 We are not free when we're confined
to every wish that sweeps the mind,
but free when freely we accept
the sacred bounds that must be kept.

Words: Thomas H. Troeger © Oxford University Press, Inc., 1994, assigned to Oxford University Press 2010,
reproduced by permission
Music (DEO GRACIAS 8.8.8.8): English, 15th c.; harm. Carl Schalk, 1969, © 1969 Concordia Publishing House

How Sweet Was the Garden, Fertile and Fair   29

1 How sweet was the gar - den, fer - tile and fair, the
2 We free - ly could eat from all but one tree (for -
3 From dark, bit - ter fruit came forth a bright seed, for

first and best home God gave to our care, a
bid - den, per - haps, lest gods we might be?), but
God did not turn from us in our need; the

par - a - dise lav - ished on crea - tures of clay; yet
tast - ing we grew not di - vine af - ter all: the
love that first formed us em - brac - es us still and

we were not will - ing to fol - low God's way.
fruit in our mouth turned from nec - tar to gall.
woos us from wan - dering to fol - low God's will.

Words: Carl P. Daw Jr (b. 1944) © 1996 Hope Publishing Company
Music (LONG ISLAND SOUND 10.10.11.11): Rusty Edwards © 1992 Hope Publishing Company

30 God, Let Me Like a Spreading Tree

PSALM 52

1 God, let me like a spread-ing tree, grow as I trust
2 You cun-ning liar, why pub - li - cize your e - vil need
3 May God rise up to pull you down, up-root and sweep
4 God, let me like a spread-ing tree, grow as I trust

in your sure love. Where loy - al ser - vants of - fer praise
to harm the good? Your slan - derous tongue is ra - zor - sharp,
you far a - way. Then may the just look on a - ghast
in your sure love. Where loy - al ser - vants of - fer praise

with - in your house, I'll add my voice to glo - ri - fy your ho - ly name.
honed to ful - fill ma - li-cious plans; you love the lie and hate the truth.
and mock the one who val-ued wealth, who trust-ed rich-es more than God.
with - in your house, I'll add my voice to glo - ri - fy your ho - ly name.

Sing slowly, softly; with a sense of weariness. Stanzas 2 and 3 may be sung by a solo voice.

For another setting of Ps. 52 see 31

Words: Doug Gay, rev. John L. Bell (b. 1949) © 2011 Wild Goose Resource Group, Iona Community, Scotland, GIA Publications, Inc., exclusive North American agent
Music (BACA 8.8.8.8.8.8): William R. Bradbury (1816-1868); harm. John L. Bell (b. 1949) © 2011 Wild Goose Resource Group, Iona Community, Scotland, GIA Publications, Inc., exclusive North American agent

Prayers of the Oppressed and Oppressor   31

These prayers may be prayed with the reading or singing of Psalm 52 or Psalm 75 or other psalms of imprecation. The prayer on the left assumes the voice of the psalmist in praying for judgment against those who hurt or oppress. The prayer on the right assumes the voice of a person who may be the oppressor, the one that the psalmist is praying against.

A. PRAYER OF THOSE WHO HAVE BEEN WRONGED

Holy God, hear my prayer.

Witness my heartache and defend me,
for I have walked in your way.

Bring to justice
   those whose words have hurt me,
   those whose lies have broken my trust,
   and those who seek after their own
      abundance and well-being
      at the cost of others.

In your mercy, uproot all evil,
that righteousness may prevail.

Amid the faithful
I will proclaim your name.

Amen.

B. PRAYER OF THOSE WHO HAVE WRONGED

Gracious God, hear my prayer.

Search my heart and humble me,
and if I have strayed from your way, correct me.

Be merciful and help me see
   if my words have been hurtful,
   if I have pursued lies over truth,
   or if I have used my power and
      influence to gain more for myself
      at the cost of others.

If you were to mark our sins, Lord,
who could stand?

Forgive me,
and root me in your steadfast love.

Amen.

For another setting of Ps. 52 see 30; for Ps. 75 see 32
Text: Melissa Haupt, 2012, © Creative Commons Attribution-NonCommercial-ShareAlike

O God, Your Deeds Are Unsurpassed   32

PSALM 75

1 O God, your deeds are unsurpassed;
  no richer grace can earth impart.
  Your Name is near; you hold us fast.
  Your love enfolds each yearning heart,
  your love enfolds each yearning heart.

2 Remove our pride lest we must taste
  the judgment cup of bitter gall.
  Let not our bold ambitions take
  the praise from you, who gives us all,
  the praise from you, who gives us all.

3 Help us to know humility,
  to follow you in all your ways.
  From self-conceit, Lord, set us free
  to know ourselves and sing your praise,
  to know ourselves and sing your praise.

For music see 30
For another setting of Ps. 75 see 31
Words: Michael Morgan © 2011 Michael Morgan, admin. Faith Alive Christian Resources

33 All Have Sinned

PSALM 14 AND 53

1 Hear the fool say-ing loud and long, there's no God; we're
2 God looks down from his throne on high, search-ing for a
3 E - vil ones who at - tack the poor, steal their bread, then

all a - lone. Poi - son words that pol - lute the air,
heart that's wise, an - y - one who will seek his face,
rage for more; but the Lord will de - fend his own.

Refrain

spread - ing ev - ery - where.
leave their wick - ed ways. All have sinned, all have
Ev - ery - one will know.

turned a - side, and there's no one right - eous. But re - demp - tion will

one day come from Zi - on, so re - joice!

Words: Bev Herrema © 2011 Pilot Point Music, admin. Music Services
Music (BLAKE 8.7.8.5 refrain 3.5.6.11.3): Bev Herrema © 2011 Pilot Point Music, admin. Music Services

What Adam's Disobedience Cost

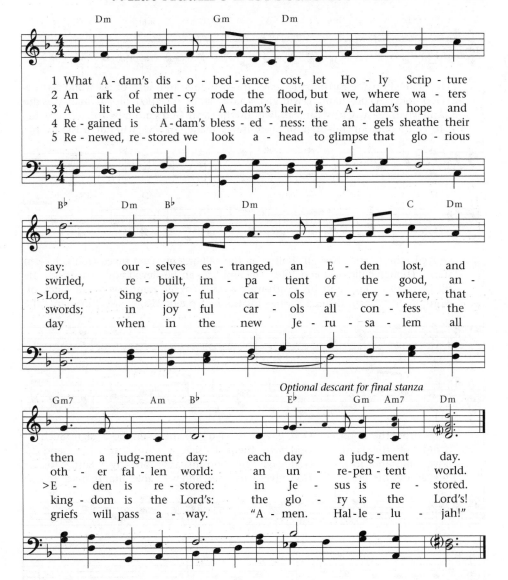

1 What Adam's disobedience cost, let Holy Scripture say:
2 An ark of mercy rode the flood, but we, where waters
3 A little child is Adam's heir, is Adam's hope and
4 Regained is Adam's blessedness: the angels sheathe their
5 Renewed, restored we look ahead to glimpse that glorious

say: ourselves estranged, an Eden lost, and
swirled, rebuilt, impatient of the good, an-
>Lord, Sing joyful carols everywhere, that
swords; in joyful carols all confess the
day when in the new Jerusalem all

Optional descant for final stanza

then a judgment day: each day a judgment day.
other fallen world: an unrepentent world.
>Eden is restored: in Jesus is restored.
kingdom is the Lord's: the glory is the Lord's!
griefs will pass away. "Amen. Hallelujah!"

Optional prayer (1 Cor. 15:22)

God of our salvation,
we grieve for all of the pain and despair
that cascades down from
one generation to the next
because of human pride and arrogance.

Yet we marvel at the mystery of your promise
that Adam's heir would become

Adam's Savior and Lord.
We rejoice in hope that even though
in Adam all die,
so in Christ all will be made alive.

**Send your Comforter, we pray,
to strengthen us in this hope
through Jesus our Lord. Amen.**

For an alternate arrangement see 218

35   You Are Our God; We Are Your People

1 It rained on the earth for-ty days, for-ty nights, and all of the world was de-
2 God told A-bra-ham, "I will give you a land, a peo-ple as man-y as the
3 And when Je-sus Christ came to live on the earth, God's prom-ise to us was ful-
4 To us and our chil-dren the prom-ise is made, if we will but trust in his

stroyed. The ark No-ah built at the call-ing of God saved God's cho-sen
stars." Though child-less and old, he and Sar-ah be-lieved and trust-ed the
filled. His life and his death were a new cov-e-nant, as-sur-ance of
word. In bap-tism__ join-ing the peo-ple of God, we live in the

ones from the flood. God gave to No-ah the rain-bow sign:"Such a
word of the Lord. God gave them I-saac, a son, at last, and__
love full and free. God gave his Son, his__ on-ly Son; to__
power of his grace. God gives us life, and we give him thanks:"To__

flood I will not send a-gain— I am your God; you are my peo-ple."
this is the cov-e-nant he made: "I am your God; you are my peo-ple."
all who re-ceive him he says: "I am your God; you are my peo-ple."
you be our praise ev-er-more! You are our God; we are your peo-ple."

Words and Music (JANNA irregular): David A. Hoekema, 1978, © 1985 Faith Alive Christian Resources

Litany of Praise: Our Covenanting God 36

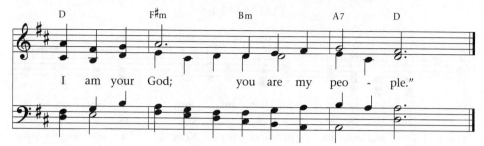

I am your God; you are my peo - ple."

Sung or Spoken Refrain:
I am your God; you are my people.

We bless and thank you, Lord our God,
for the promise you spoke to Noah:
"I establish my covenant with you:
Never again will all life
be destroyed by the waters
of a flood." *(Gen. 9:11)*
With joy,
your people heard the sure promise:

Refrain

For the promise you spoke
to Abraham and Sarah:
"I will establish my covenant
as an everlasting covenant
between me and you
and your descendants after you
for the generations to come,
to be your God and the God
of your descendants after you." *(Gen. 17:7)*
With joy,
your people heard the sure promise:

Refrain

For the promise you spoke to Moses, Miriam,
and the people of Israel:
"If you obey me fully
and keep my covenant,
then you will be
my treasured possession.
You will be for me a kingdom of priests
and a holy nation." *(Ex. 19:5-6)*
With joy,
your people heard the sure promise:

Refrain

For the promise you spoke to David:
"I will raise up your offspring
to succeed you,
your own flesh and blood,
and I will establish the throne
of his kingdom forever." *(2 Sam. 7:12-13)*
With joy,
your people heard the sure promise:

Refrain

For the promise
you spoke through Jeremiah:
"This is the covenant I will make
with the people of Israel:
I will put my law in their minds
and write it on their hearts.
I will be their God,
and they will be my people." *(Jer. 31:33)*
With joy,
your people heard the sure promise:

Refrain

For the promise you spoke through Jesus:
"This is my blood
of the new covenant,
which is poured out for many
for the forgiveness of sins."
(Matt. 26:28/Luke 22:20)
With joy,
your people heard the sure promise:

Refrain

Heirs of the promise, called by your Spirit,
we hear again these gracious promises.
With joy and trust we declare:
You are our God; we are your people.

Other biblical references to God's covenanting love can be added as appropriate to a given service.
Words and Music (JANNA fragment): David A. Hoekema, 1978, © 1985 Faith Alive Christian Resources

37 Te exaltaré/I Will Exalt

PSALM 145:1-5

Spanish
1 Te_e - xal - ta - ré, mi Dios, mi__ Rey, y ben - de - ci -
2 Ge - ne - ra - ción a ge - ne - ra - ción ce - le - bra -

English
1 I will ex - alt my God, my__ King; I will praise your
2 Each gen - er - a - tion to the__ next will pro - claim your

ré tu nom - bre. E - ter - na - men - te_y
rá tus o - bras y_a - nun - cia - rá tus
name for - ev - er. I will ex - alt your
works of splen - dor, and cel - e - brate your

pa - ra__ siem - pre, ca - da dí - a te ben - de - ci - ré.
po - de - ro - sos he - chos; ca - da dí - a te ben - de - ci - ré.
name__ for - ev - er; ev - ery day I'll praise your ho - ly name.
might - y deeds.__ Ev - ery day I'll praise your ho - ly name.

Refrain

Y a - la - ba - ré tu nom - bre e - ter - na -
I will praise your name for - ev - er; I will ex -

For other settings of Ps. 145 see 561, 562

Words: Casiodoro Cárdenas, 1979; tr. composite; st. 2 tr. Mary Louise Bringle, 2011
Music (ECUADOR irregular): Casiodoro Cárdenas, 1979; arr. Raquel Mora Martínez, 1979, © Raquel Mora Martinez

men - te y   pa - ra   siem - pre. Gran - de   es   Je - ho - vá   y
alt   your   name for - ev - er.   LORD our   God,   you are   great   and

dig - no   de su - pre - ma   a - la - ban   -   za;   y   su gran-
wor - thy   of the high - est   praise and   hon   -   or,   for   your___

de - za es in - es - cru - ta - ble;   ca - da   dí - a   te   ben - de - ci - ré.
great - ness is   far be - yond us;   ev - ery   day   I'll praise your   ho - ly   name.

Optional ending with descant

ca - da   dí - a   te   ben - de - ci - ré.
ev - ery   day   I'll   praise   your   ho - ly   name.

38 In a Deep, Unbounded Darkness

1 In a deep, un-bound-ed dark-ness long be-fore the first light shone,
2 Though our world is ev-er-chang-ing, you are con-stant, firm, and sure,
3 Joy trans-forms our lips to boast-ing on - ly in your match-less grace,
4 God of Ha - gar, God of Sa - rah, God of no - mad A - bra - ham;

you, O God, be - yond all mer - it, worked a won - der
faith - ful to your cov - enant prom - ise. Trust - ing you, we
send - ing Christ to dwell a - mong us, Word made flesh, in
God of Mir - iam, God of Mo - ses, Fier - y Pil - lar,

faith makes known: in your mer - cy, in your mer - cy, you em-
live, se - cure: sing - ing prais - es, sing - ing prais - es, long as
time and space: Friend and Sav - ior, Friend and Sav - ior, in whose
great I AM: lead us home-ward, lead us home - ward, to the

braced us as your own ev-er-more and ev-er-more.
heart and breath en - dure, ev-er-more and ev-er-more.
life we glimpse your face ev-er-more and ev-er-more.
love - feast of the Lamb ev-er-more and ev-er-more. A - men.

For an alternate arrangement see 54, 78

Words: based on anonymous Chinese poem, Mary Louise Bringle © 2012 GIA Publications, Inc.
Music (DIVINUM MYSTERIUM 8.7.8.7.8.7.7): Plainsong mode V, 13th c., P.D.

The God of Abraham Praise

1 The God of A-braham praise, who reigns en-throned a - bove,
2 He by his name has sworn, on this we shall de - pend,
3 The good-ly land I see, with peace and plen - ty blest,
4 There rules the Lord our King, the Lord our Right-eous - ness,
5 Tri - um-phant hosts on high give thanks to God and sing,

the An - cient of e - ter - nal days, the God of love!
and as on ea - gles' wings up-borne to heaven as - cend.
> a land of sa - cred lib - er - ty and end - less rest.
vic - to - rious o - ver death and sin, the Prince of Peace.
and "Ho - ly, ho - ly, ho - ly" cry, "Al - might - y King!"

The Lord, the great I AM, by earth and heaven con - fessed—
There we shall see his face; his power we shall a - dore
> There milk and hon - ey flow, and oil and wine a - bound;
On Zi - on's sa - cred height his king - dom he main-tains,
Hail, A-braham's God and ours! One might - y hymn we raise.

we bow be - fore his ho - ly name for - ev - er blest.
and sing the won - ders of his grace for - ev - er - more.
> the tree of life for - ev - er grows with mer - cy crowned.
and glo - rious with his saints in light for - ev - er reigns.
All power and maj - es - ty be yours and end - less praise!

Words: Thomas Olivers, ca. 1770, alt.; based on a Hebrew doxology, P.D.
Music (LEONI 6.6.8.4 D): Hebrew; adapt. Meyer Lyon, ca. 1770, P.D.

40 # I Will Be Your God

1 To A-bra-ham and Sa-rah the call of God was clear:
2 From A-bra-ham and Sa-rah a-rose a pil-grim race,
3 We of the gen-er-a-tion on whom God's hand is laid

"Go forth, and I will show you a coun-try rich and fair.
de-pen-dent for their jour-ney on God's a-bun-dant grace;
can jour-ney to the fu-ture se-cure and un-a-fraid,

You need not fear the jour - ney, for I have pledged my word
and in their heart was writ - ten by God this sav-ing word,
re - joic-ing in God's good - ness and trust-ing in his word,

that you shall be my peo - ple and I will be your God."
"That you shall be my peo - ple and I will be your God."
"That you shall be my peo - ple and I will be your God."

Words: Judith A. Fetter, 1984, (Gen. 12:1-3) © 1984 Judith A. Fetter
Music (NYLAND 7.6.7.6 D): Finnish; harm. David Evans (1874-1948) from the *Revised Church Hymnary*, 1927,
reproduced by permission of Oxford University Press

When Israel Fled from Egypt Land

PSALM 114

1 When Israel fled from Egypt land, from
2 The sea rolled back to form dry land, the
3 What made you part, O might-y sea? Why,
4 Now trem-ble, earth, the Lord is near; bow

for-eign tongue and cru-el hand, the LORD took Ju-dah
Jor-dan fled at God's com-mand. The moun-tains shook and
Jor-dan, did you turn to flee? Why, moun-tains, shake, why
down and see your God ap-pear. His might makes springs to

for his home and Is-rael for his ver-y own.
skipped like rams; the hills leapt up like lit-tle lambs.
skip like rams? And hills, why leap like lit-tle lambs?
gush and glow; from flint the cool-ing wa-ters flow.

Optional prayer of baptismal renewal

Redeeming God,
just as you saved your people through the parting of the sea
so you have saved us through Jesus.
We praise you for this astonishing grace:
    through Jesus, **we have died to sin;**
    with Jesus, **we were buried through baptism into death;**
    with Jesus, **we are raised to a new life.**
By your Spirit, help us offer ourselves to you,
as those who have been brought from death to life,
and may we serve you as instruments of righteousness. Amen.

Words: Henrietta Ten Harmsel, 1985, alt. © 1987 Faith Alive Christian Resources
Music (ANDRE 8.8.8.8): William B. Bradbury (1816-1868); alt., P.D.

42   When Israel Was in Egypt's Land

1 When Is - rael was in E - gypt's land,
2 The Lord told Mo - ses what to do, let my peo - ple go,
3 As Is - rael stood by the wa - ter - side,

op-pressed so hard they could not stand,
to lead the He - brew chil - dren through, let my peo - ple go.
at God's com - mand it did di - vide,

Refrain

Go down, *Go down,* Mo - ses, *Mo - ses,* way down in E - gypt's land,

tell old Pha - raoh: let my peo - ple go.

4 When they had reached the other shore,
let my people go,
they let the song of triumph soar,
let my people go. *Refrain*

5 Lord, help us all from bondage flee,
let my people go,
and let us all in Christ be free,
let my people go. *Refrain*

Words and Music (GO DOWN MOSES irregular): African American spiritual; harm. John W. Work (1871-1925), P.D.

Guide Me, O My Great Redeemer

43

1 Guide me, O my great Re - deem - er, pil - grim through this
2 O - pen now the crys - tal foun - tain, where the heal - ing
3 When I tread the verge of Jor - dan, bid my anx - ious

bar - ren land; I am weak, but you are might - y; hold me with your
wa - ters flow. Let the fire and cloud - y pil - lar lead me all my
fears sub - side. Death of death, and hell's de - struc - tion, land me safe on

power - ful hand. Bread of heav - en, bread of heav - en, feed me
jour - ney through. Strong De - liv - erer, strong De - liv - erer, ev - er
Ca - naan's side. Songs of prais - es, songs of prais - es I will

now and ev - er - more, feed me now and ev - er - more.
be my strength and shield, ev - er be my strength and shield.
ev - er sing to you, I will ev - er sing to you.

For an alternate arrangement see 926

Words: William Williams, 1745; st. 1 tr. Peter Williams, 1771, alt; st. 2-3 tr. William Williams, 1772, alt., P.D.
Music (CWM RHONDDA 8.7.8.7.8.7.7): John Hughes, 1907, P.D.

44 Lift Every Voice and Sing

1 Lift ev-ery voice and sing till earth and heav-en ring,
2 Ston-y the road we trod, bit-ter the chast-ening rod,
3 God of our wea-ry years, God of our si-lent tears,

ring with the har-mon-ies of lib-er-ty;
felt in the days when hope un-born had died;
thou who hast brought us thus far on the way;

let our re-joic-ing rise, high as the lis-tening skies,
yet with a stead-y beat, have not our wea-ry feet
thou who hast, by thy might, led us in-to the light,

let it re-sound loud as the roll-ing sea.
come to the place for which our peo-ple sighed?
keep us for-ev-er in the path, we pray.

Words: James W. Johnson (1871-1938), P.D.
Music (ANTHEM 6.6.10.6.6.10.14.14.6.6.10): J. Rosamund Johnson (1873-1954), P.D.

Em D

Sing a song full of the faith that the dark past has taught us,
We have come o - ver a way that with tears has been wa - tered;
Lest our feet stray from the plac - es, our God, where we met thee,

G Cm G

sing a song full of the hope that the pres - ent has brought
we have come, tread - ing our path through the blood of the slaugh -
lest, our hearts drunk with the wine of the world, we for - get

D7 G B7 E Am B7

us; fac - ing the ris - ing sun of our new day be -
tered, out from the gloom - y past, till now we stand at
thee; shad - owed be - neath thy hand, may we for - ev - er

C C#°7 G/D D7 G

gun, let us march on till vic - to - ry is won.
last where the white gleam of our bright star is cast.
stand, true to our God, true to our na - tive land.

45 Let David Be Remembered

PSALM 132

1 When Da-vid had a long-ing to build the Lord a house,
  he voiced his heart's in-ten-tion by means of sol-emn vows.
  His peo-ple caught the vi-sion: to build a sa-cred place
  where ho-ly joy and wor-ship would please the God of grace.

2 The Lord then vowed to Da-vid: his house would sure-ly last
  if on-ly his suc-ces-sors held God's com-mand-ments fast;
  God longed to set a-mong them a throne for heav-en's King;
  what joy and what a-bun-dance his pres-ence there would bring!

Words: Martin Leckebusch © 2003 Kevin Mayhew Ltd.
Music (THAXTED 7.6.7.6 triple): Gustav Holst (1874-1934), 1921, P.D.

Let Da - vid be re - mem - bered, your faith - ful ser - vant, Lord:
Let Da - vid's Lamp be light - ed, your cho - sen Ser - vant, Lord:

the depth of his de - vo - tion, the hard - ships he en - dured.
his king - dom be es - tab - lished, his tri - umph be as - sured.

Optional prayer for Christmas or Pentecost

God of grace and glory,
how we marvel at your ways:

For the Son of David, Son of Mary, Son of God,
**who came to dwell among us,
full of grace and truth.**

For the gift of your Spirit,
**who comes to dwell within us,
making us your temple.**

May the ancient prayer be fulfilled in us:
"Let your priests be clothed with righteousness,
and let your faithful shout for joy."

By the power of your Spirit:
**may we, your royal priesthood,
be clothed with righteousness.
may we, your royal priesthood,
shout for joy.**

**In the name of Jesus, Son of David,
we pray. Amen.**

46 How Lovely, Lord, How Lovely

PSALM 84

1 How love-ly, Lord, how love-ly is your a-bid-ing place;
2 In your blest courts to wor-ship, O God, a sin-gle day
3 A sun and shield for-ev-er are you, O Lord Most High;

my soul is long-ing, faint-ing, to feast up-on your grace.
is bet-ter than a thou-sand if I from you should stray.
you show-er us with bless-ings; no good will you de-ny.

The spar-row finds a shel-ter, a place to build her nest,
I'd rath-er keep the en-trance and claim you as my Lord
The saints, your grace re-ceiv-ing, from strength to strength shall go,

and so your tem-ple calls us with-in its walls to rest.
than rev-el in the rich-es the ways of sin af-ford.
and from their life shall riv-ers of bless-ing o-ver-flow.

For other settings of Ps. 84 see 506, 507

Words: Arlo Duba © 1986 Hope Publishing Company
Music (MERLE'S TUNE 7.6.7.6 D): Hal H. Hopson © 1983 Hope Publishing Company

O God, We Have Heard

47

PSALM 44

1 O God, we have heard what our par - ents have told,

Additional verses of Ps.44 may be read here recalling victories (vv.5-8) and lamenting defeats (vv.9-16).

2 If we had for - got - ten the name of our God
3 Yet all the day long for your sake we're con - sumed,
4 O why are you hid - ing the light of your face,

what won - ders you did in the great days of old.
or wor - shiped an i - dol with hands spread a - broad
de - feat - ed, de - rid - ed, to death we are doomed.
for - get - ting our bur - den, our grief and dis - grace?

O Lord, you a - lone are our God and our King!
would not the Al - might - y un - cov - er this sin?
Then why do you tar - ry? O God, now a - wake!
Our souls are bowed down and we cling to the dust;

Re - call - ing those vic - tories your prais - es we sing.
For God knows our hearts and the se - crets with - in.
Re - mem - ber your peo - ple; a - rise for our sake.
rise help, and re - deem us, your mer - cy we trust.*

*Optional ending: repeat stanza 1

Words: st. 1 Bert Polman, alt. © 1987 Faith Alive Christian Resources; st. 2-4 *Psalter*, 1912, alt., P.D.
Music (FOUNDATION 11.11.11.11): J. Funk's *A Compilation of Genuine Church Music*, 1832, P.D.;
harm. Dale Grotenhuis (1931-2012), 1985, © 1987 Faith Alive Christian Resources

48   It Is Good to Give Thanks to You, Lord

PSALM 106

1 It is good to give thanks to you, Lord, to re-
2 Our sin is the sin of our fore-bears: we have
3 Our an-ces-tors scorned all your won-ders, at the
4 Though time af-ter time you would save them, they in
5 O God, save us now in your mer-cy; bring us
6 Now blest be the Lord, God of Is-rael. Blest be

mem-ber all you have done; then you will re-mem-ber our
wronged you and have done e-vil, like those who once lived un-der
Red Sea ques-tioned their God; they fell from their faith in the
mal-ice dared to de-fy you; des-pite this, you came to their
back from all that of-fends you. Lord, look not a-lone at our
God both now and for-ev-er. Let na-tions and peo-ple cry,

prais-es when you look on your peo-ple with love.
bond-age, paid no heed un-to all you had done.
des-ert; there they put you, O Lord, to the test.
res-cue when you heard all their cries of dis-tress.
e-vil, but re-mem-ber com-pas-sion and love.
A-men! Praise the Lord, hal-le-lu-jah, A-men!

Words: John L. Bell (b. 1949) © 1988 Wild Goose Resource Group, Iona Community, Scotland, GIA Publications, Inc., exclusive North American agent
Music (NEW 106TH 9.9.9.9 refrain 6.8.6.7): John L. Bell (b. 1949) © 1988, arr. Marcus Hong © 2011 Wild Goose Resource Group, Iona Community, Scotland, admin. GIA Publications, Inc., exclusive North American agent

Refrain Dm | B♭maj7 | C Am7 | Dm Gm7 | Am A7

Oh, give thanks to the Lord, for God's love en-dures for - ev - er;

Dm | B♭maj7 | C Am7 | Gm7 Am7 | D

oh, give thanks to the Lord, for the Lord a - lone is good.

A Prayer of Confession and Assurance   49

Sing st. 1 of 48 or read Psalm 106:1-5

Gracious God
we thank and praise you
**for you are good
and your love endures forever.**

Despite your goodness,
both we and our ancestors have sinned.
**We don't act justly
or always do what is right.**

Sing st. 2-5 or read Psalm 106:6-47

The LORD is compassionate and gracious,
slow to anger, abounding in love.

He will not always accuse,
nor will he harbor his anger forever;
he does not treat us as our sins deserve
or repay us according to our iniquities.

For as high as the heavens are above the earth,
so great is his love for those who fear him;
as far as the east is from the west,
**so far has he removed
our transgressions from us.** *(Ps. 103:8-12)*

Sing st. 6 with refrain or read Psalm 106:48

Praise be to the LORD, the God of Israel,
from everlasting to everlasting.
Let all the people say,
"Amen!" Praise the LORD.

50 Those Who Place on God Reliance

PSALM 125

1 Those who place on God re - li-ance in de-spair shall not be moved.
2 Ev - er - last-ing is Mount Zi - on, from cre - a - tion's dawn till night;
3 God's good bless-ings shall be giv - en to all those who do God's will.
4 Those who work a - gainst God's heal-ing have their ill with ill re - paid.

As the moun-tains hug the val - ley, so em-braced are God's be - loved.
so e - ter - nal is God's prom - ise to all those who live a - right.
Just re - wards shall be their for - tune; God is with us, with us still.
All the faith - ful of the king-dom find their full re - demp-tion made.

Words: Michael Morgan © 1999, 2011 Michael Morgan, admin. Faith Alive Christian Resources
Music (HATIKVAH 8.7.8.7): traditional Hebrew melody; arr. Hal H. Hopson © 2008 Birnamwood Publications,
a division of MorningStar Music Publishers

51 When the Lord Restored Our Blessing

PSALM 126

1 When the Lord restored our blessing,
all delights were like a dream;
in defeat, a shout of victory;
in the sand, a flowing stream.

2 Mouths that once were parched
with anguish
now with shouts of joy are filled;
laughter now displaces sadness
for the goodness God has willed.

3 Bring us back to former glory,
lost through years of exile's pain;
generations long forgotten
seek God's favor to regain.

4 Those who plant their seeds
with grieving,
wetting soil with falling tears,
shall rejoice in time of harvest,
reaping hope for all their years.

For music see 50

For another setting of Ps. 126 see 55

Words: Michael Morgan © 1999, 2011 Michael Morgan, admin. Faith Alive Christian Resources

We Give Thanks unto You

PSALM 136

1 We give thanks un-to you, O God of might,
2 In your wis-dom and love you shaped the skies,
3 You have filled all the skies with glo-ry and light,
4 From of old you have led your peo-ple in faith, for your

love is nev-er end-ing;
we give thanks un-to you, the
you spread out the earth up-
the sun for the day and
you have shown your com-pas-sion,

God of gods,
on the sea,
moon for night, for your love is nev-er end-ing.
strength, and love,

5 *You delivered the ones who
    called_ unto you,*
for your love is never ending;
*from_ bondage to freedom,
    you brought them forth,*
for your love is never ending.

6 *You have opened the sea and
    brought your people through,*
for your love is never ending;
*brought them into a land that_
    flows with life,*
for your love is never ending.

7 *You remember your promise
    age_ to_ age,*
for your love is never ending;
*you show mercy on those
    of_ low degree,*
for your love is never ending.

8 *You give food and_ life to
    all_ living things,*
for your love is never ending;
*we give thanks unto you,
    the_ God of all,*
for your love is never ending.

Words and Music (BERAKAH irregular): Marty Haugen (b. 1950) © 1987 GIA Publications, Inc.

53 Song of the Prophets

Ancient Prophets 1 In a - ges past the might - y Lord by proph-ets spoke the

Sing one or more appropriate stanzas and conclude with the final stanza.

Final 18 Yet still in pres - ent, trou-bled days we seek to hear God's

Word, and from their lips God's great de - sign through -
voice, and in the face of our dis - tress, find

out the earth was heard. In rev - e - la - tion, par - a - ble,
rea - son to re - joice. Grant us the wis-dom to dis - cern

bold fan - ta - sy, and dream, they e - choed God's e -
through faith who we should be— a fall - en race, re -

Alternate tune: KINGSFOLD see 10, 162

Words: Michael Morgan © Faith Alive Christian Resources
Music (STAR OF COUNTY DOWN 8.6.8.6 D): Irish traditional; arr. Rory Cooney (b. 1952) © 1990
   GIA Publications, Inc.

ter - nal vow to ran - som and re - deem.
stored through grace, a cap - tive world set free.

Isaiah

2 A voice cries in the wilderness: "Prepare a desert way,
   where God may pass, bring righteousness, and rule without delay."
   The weak who wait upon the Lord with eagles' strength shall rise,
   imagined blessings of the past now real before their eyes.

Jeremiah

3 The lamentations of our lives, our sadness, and our fear
   God's faithfulness transforms to joy if we but persevere.
   The bowl the potter shaped from clay, now marred and disarrayed,
   shall be in course of time and space by God's hand be remade.

Ezekiel

4 The faithful bound in tyrants' chains shall find their hopes fulfilled,
   and stony hearts become true flesh as God's love is revealed.
   Dry bones will dance and whirlwinds sing when joy supplants despair,
   and every corner of the earth proclaim, the Lord is there!

Daniel

5 Blest be God's name from age to age, who strength and wisdom brings;
   who makes the roaring lions submit, and silent tongues to sing.
   Life's deep and hidden mysteries no more confound our will,
   for God will keep the covenant to love and lead us still.

Hosea

6 Come, let all flesh return to God, who breaks, then binds as one;
   who makes death-shadows disappear with resurrection sun.
   Return, O children, to the Lord, and blossom like the vine;
   God will set right each dreadful wrong, and life by grace refine.

Joel

7 Now sanctify a fast, O God, among your gathered host;
   cry out for joy to those who mourn; bring down the ones who boast.
   Come quickly, Lord, and make our hearts a worthy dwelling place,
   where conflict finds an ordered peace, and vengeance bends to grace.

Amos

8 The Lord in holiness has sworn the time shall surely come
   when evil foes are cast aside, the righteous gathered home.
   With humble hearts the faithful take their place among the least,
   and those who dine with servants greet the Giver of the feast!

(continues)

Obadiah

9 The day of wrath is close at hand, when God will draw the line
   between the good and wicked lot, the vinegar and wine.
   Their destiny lies at the end of chosen paths they trod:
   the sinners lost in dark dismay, the saints at home with God.

Jonah

10 Alone, I called in my distress, "Good Lord, deliver me!"
    And from the dreadful threat of death, God's mercy set me free.
    How can I then but offer up my life for all my days,
    or cease to lift my voice to God in songs of grateful praise?

Micah

11 With what shall I before the Lord come bearing as my due?
    God's blessings are a boundless store, my offerings but a few.
    Yet God does not unmeasured gifts of wealth require of me,
    but acts of justice, kindly love, and true humility.

Nahum

12 God's anger, slow and ever sure, will bring injustice down;
    the hateful find themselves by love encompassed all around.
    Prepare yourselves to be accused, to bear the chastening rod,
    for judgment and redemption meet before the throne of God.

Habakkuk

13 O Lord, how long will you not hear your servant's earnest plea?
    How many chains must I endure before you set me free?
    I cry, and still you turn away, my tears an empty wave;
    yet I will keep my vow to praise, and you your vow to save.

Zephaniah

14 The judgment day is drawing near, a day of wrath and gloom,
    when brooding clouds obscure the sun, and life becomes a tomb.
    The wicked shall be met with scorn, defeated by God's might;
    the Lord above the just will smile and sing with pure delight!

Haggai

15 Go to the hills, bring wood and stone to build a sacred place,
    where faithful in the Lord may kneel and meet God face to face.
    The firm foundation in God's law lets justice shine alone,
    its walls adorned with charity, and truth its cornerstone.

Zechariah

16 "Be strong!" God's forceful voice commands. "Your strength will set you free!
    Advance through faith against the foe; I'll bring you home to me.
    Rejoice as slaves who went before did shout in days of old:
    a humble king upon a colt will lead you to the fold."

Malachi

17 The Son of Righteousness will rise with healing in his wings,
    and every child will know the peace his sure redemption brings.
    His judgment, like refiner's fire, shall purify the soul,
    and outcasts find their broken hopes and shattered lives made whole.

Wisdom Calls

1 At the cross-roads of de - ci - sion Wis - dom calls to all and each:
2 On the ash heap of di - sas - ter "Where is God?" we cry and weep.
3 On a cross and in a man - ger God's com - pas - sion is made plain.

"Come, my chil - dren, learn and lis - ten— heed the ways I
Friends are false and faith un - cer - tain; Wis - dom seems be -
"Word made flesh" is God a - mong us; "He is risen" brings

seek to teach." Con - scious thoughts or in - tu - i - tion
yond our reach. Still she whis - pers from the whirl - wind
hope for pain. "Come, you wear - y," pleads the Sav - ior;

frame her words of grace and peace: "Choose the path - way of the Lord."
of our pain and of our grief: "Trust the good - ness of the Lord."
Wis - dom calls to us a - gain: "Cast your bur - dens on the Lord."

For an alternate arrangement see 38, 78

Words: Carol Bechtel © 2012 Carol Bechtel, admin. Faith Alive Christian Resources
Music (DIVINUM MYSTERIUM 8.7.8.7.8.7.7): Plainsong mode V, 13th c.; arr. Paul G. Bunjes © 1982
Concordia Publishing House

55 When God First Brought Us Back

PSALM 126

1 When God first brought us back from ex - ile, we were as dazed
2 Once more, O Lord, re - store your peo - ple; come with your sav -

as those who dream. Then were our mouths brim-ming with laugh-ter;
ing help a - gain, as to the brook - beds in the des - ert

joy from our lips gushed like a stream. The god - less cried in en - vious
you bring the sweet, re - viv-ing rain. Let those who sow with tears and

won - der, "Look what the Lord has done for them!" In - deed our
sigh - ing sing as they reap and joy pro - claim: may those who

God has great-ly blessed us; re-joice and sing, Je - ru - sa - lem!
weep when seed is scat - tered gath - er their sheaves and praise your name.

For another setting of Ps. 126 see 51

Words: Carl P. Daw Jr © 1996 Hope Publishing Company
Music (WAYFARING STRANGER 9.8.9.8 D): traditional American; arr. Horace Clarence Boyer (1935-2009)
© 1992 Horace Clarence Boyer

The season of Advent focuses our attention on both the first and second coming of Jesus Christ. Advent songs in this section identify with the people of Israel as they waited for the coming Messiah. For additional Advent songs focusing on the second coming of Jesus, see 470-482.

Come, Thou Long-Expected Jesus   56

Alternate tune: HYFRYDOL *see 351, 831*

Words: Charles Wesley (1744), P.D.
Music (STUTTGART 8.7.8.7): Christian F. Witt's *Psalmodia Sacra,* 1715; adapt. Henry J. Gauntlett, 1861; desc. John W. Wilson © 1983 Hope Publishing Company

57 Toda la tierra/All Earth Is Waiting

Spanish 1 To-da la tie-rra es-pe-ra_al Sal-va-dor: vie-ne_atra-er a los hom-bres la ver-dad, a sem-brar por el mun-do se-mi-lias de_a-mor. A to-dos los po-breas su bra-zo sal-va-rá. lle-nen de su luz!

English 1 All earth is wait-ing to see the Prom-ised One, and o-pen fur-rows a-wait the seed of God. All the world, bound and strug-gling, seeks true lib-er-ty; it cries out for jus-tice and search-es for the truth. brings us lib-er-ty.

Words: Alberto Taulé (b. 1932); tr. Madeleine Forell Marshall (b. 1946) © 1972, 1993 and tr. 1995 *Centro de Pastoral Litúrgica,* admin. OCP Publications

Music (TODA LA TIERRA irregular): Alberto Taulé; arr. © 1993, 2006 *Centro de Pastoral Litúrgica,* admin. OCP Publications

Spanish

2 Dice el profeta al pueblo de Israel:
   "Pronto la luz del Mesías brillará.
   Dios se acerca a nosotros:
      su nombre, Emanuel."
   ¡Germine la tierra amor y libertad!

3 De nuestra carne se quiso revestir,
      pobre y sencillo,
      de humilde corazón.
   Nacerá como entonces,
      vendrá a compartir
   la suerte del hombre,
      su angustia y su dolor.

4 Él viene siempre.
      Vivimos de esperar
   todos los días la vuelta de Jesús.
   ¡Contemplad su mirada,
      su voz escuchad,
   dejad que las sombras
      se llenen de su luz!

English

2 Thus says the prophet to those of Israel:
   "A virgin mother will bear Emmanuel,"
   one whose name is "God-with-us"
      our Savior shall be;
   with him hope will blossom
      once more within our hearts.

3 Mountains and valleys
      will have to be made plain;
   open new highways,
      new highways for the Lord.
   He is now coming closer, so come all and see,
   and open the doorways
      as wide as wide can be.

4 In lowly stable the Promised One appeared;
   yet feel his presence
      throughout the earth today,
   for he lives in all Christians
      and is with us now;
   again, with his coming he brings us liberty.

Prepare the Way 58

ISAIAH 40:3; 52:10

May be sung in canon

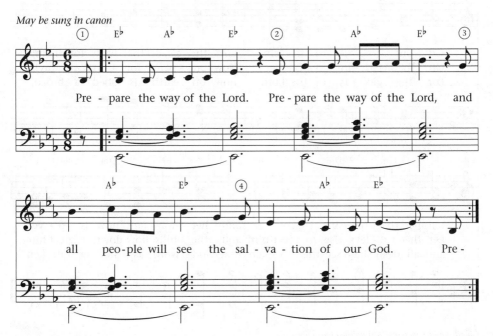

Pre - pare the way of the Lord. Pre - pare the way of the Lord, and

all peo-ple will see the sal - va - tion of our God. Pre -

Words: Isaiah 40:3, 52:10
Music (PREPARE THE WAY): Jacques Berthier (1923-1994) © 1984 Les Presses de Taizé, admin. GIA
Publications, Inc.

59 Comfort, Comfort Now My People

ISAIAH 40:1-5

1 Com-fort, com-fort now my peo-ple; speak of peace: so says our God.
2 For the her-ald's voice is cry-ing in the des-ert far and near,
3 Then make straight what long was crook-ed; make the rough-er plac-es plain.

Com-fort those who sit in dark-ness, mourn-ing un-der sor-row's load.
call-ing all to true re-pen-tance, since the king-dom now is here.
Let your hearts be true and hum-ble, as be-fits his ho-ly reign.

Cry out to Je-ru-sa-lem of the peace that waits for them;
Oh, that warn-ing cry o-bey! Now pre-pare for God a way!
For the glo-ry of the Lord now on earth is shed a-broad,

tell her that her sins I cov-er and her war-fare now is o-ver.
Let the val-leys rise to meet him and the hills bow down to greet him.
and all flesh shall see the to-ken that God's word is nev-er bro-ken.

Chord symbols represent a simplified harmony.

Words: Isaiah 40:1-5; vers. Johannes G. Olearius, 1671; tr. Catherine Winkworth, 1863, alt., P.D.
Music (FREU DICH SEHR/GENEVAN 42 | 8.7.8.7.7.7.8.8): Louis Bourgeois (ca. 1510-1561), 1551; harm. Johann
  Crüger (1598-1662), 1658, P.D.

Hark, the Glad Sound! The Savior Comes 60

Descant

4 Our glad ho - san - nas, Prince of Peace, your wel - come

1 Hark, the glad sound! The Sav - ior comes, the Sav - ior
2 He comes the pris - oners to re - lease, in Sa - tan's
3 He comes the bro - ken heart to bind, the wound - ed
4 Our glad ho - san - nas, Prince of Peace, your wel - come

shall pro - claim, and heaven's e - ter - nal

prom - ised long! Let ev - ery heart pre -
bond - age held; the gates of brass be -
soul to cure, and with the trea - sures
shall pro - claim, and heaven's e - ter - nal

arch - es ring with your be - lov - ed name.

pare a throne, and ev - ery voice a song.
fore him burst, the i - ron fet - ters yield.
of his grace to en - rich the hum - bled poor.
arch - es ring with your be - lov - ed name.

Words: Philip Doddridge (1735); based on Isaiah 61:1-2, P.D.
Music (RICHMOND 8.6.8.6): Thomas Haweis (1792); adapt. Samuel Webbe (1808); descant Craig S. Lang
(1891-1971) used by permission of Novello and Company, Ltd, admin. G. Schirmer, Inc.

61 O Come, O Come, Emmanuel

1 O come, O come, Em-man-u-el, and ran-som cap-tive
2 O come, O Wis-dom from on high, who or-dered all things
3 O come, O come, great Lord of might, who to thy tribes on
4 O come, thou branch of Jes-se's stem, un-to thine own and

Is - ra - el that mourns in lone - ly ex - ile here
might - i - ly; to us the path of knowl - edge show
Si - nai's height in an - cient times did give the law
res - cue them! From depths of hell your peo - ple save,

un - til the Son of God ap - pear.
and teach us in its ways to go. Re - joice! Re - joice! Em-
in cloud and maj - es - ty and awe.
and give them vic - tory o'er the grave.

man - u - el shall come to thee, O Is - ra - el.

(continues)

Words: *Psalteriolum Cantionum Catholicarum*, Köln, 1710; tr. Composite, P.D.
Music (VENI EMMANUEL 8.8.8.8 refrain 8.8): French processional, 15th c., P.D.; arr. *Evangelical Lutheran Worship* © 2006 Augsburg Fortress

5 O come, O Key of David, come
   and open wide our heavenly home.
   Make safe the way that leads on high,
   and close the path to misery.
   Refrain

6 O come, O Bright and Morning Star,
   and bring us comfort from afar!
   Disperse the gloomy clouds of night
   and death's dark shadows put to flight.
   Refrain

7 O come, desire of nations, bind
   all peoples in one heart and mind.
   Bid all our sad divisions cease,
   and be thyself our King of peace.
   Refrain

An Advent Lament   62

To use with "O Come, O Come Emmanuel": sing st. 1 and then read Psalm 74:1-11; sing st. 2 and then read vv. 12-17; sing st. 4 and then read vv. 18-23; and then sing st. 6 and the refrain. You may close with the following prayer or use this on its own.

Lord, remember us.
Have regard for your covenant.
We need your redemption.

Where hands have
   brought about destruction, desolation, and desecration,
where words have
   condemned, betrayed, and deceived,
where silence has
   concealed, isolated, and ignored—

O come, Emmanuel.

Shine light in the dark places,
speak peace in the lands haunted by violence,
and ransom your people.

**As we remember
your steadfast love and faithfulness,
we wait expectantly;
we rejoice in your coming.
Amen.**

63 My Soul in Stillness Waits

Words and Music (STILLNESS 10.7.11.10.11): Marty Haugen (b. 1950), based on Psalm 62:5 and "O" Antiphons
© 1982 GIA Publications, Inc.

O Shepherd, Hear and Lead Your Flock   64

PSALM 80

1 O Shep-herd, hear and lead your flock, as lambs we crave your care;
2 Our self-ish prayers de-serve God's wrath, our pride, a sud-den burst;
3 God's lin-eage, like a vine, once spread and flour-ished in the land;

what strength on earth ap-proach-es yours, what mer-cies can com-pare?
we have but stones to serve as bread, and tears to quell our thirst.
but now the vine-yard fails, the fruit lies with-ered in the sand.

Re-store, O God, your fav-or, the ra-diance of your face
Re-store, O God Al-might-y, the ra-diance of your face
Re-store, LORD God Al-might-y, the ra-diance of your face

to light-en and re-veal the gift of your re-deem-ing grace.
to light-en and re-veal the gift of your re-deem-ing grace.
to light-en and re-veal the gift of your re-deem-ing grace.

Chord symbols represent a simplified harmony.

65   Lord, You Have Lavished on Your Land

PSALM 85

Words: Marie J. Post, 1985, © 1987 Faith Alive Christian Resources
Music (MELITA 8.8.8.8.8.8): John B. Bykes (1823-1876), 1861, P.D.

With Joy I Heard My Friends Exclaim   66

PSALM 122

1 With joy I heard my friends ex-claim: "Come, let us in God's
2 How beau-ti-ful does Zi-on stand, a cit-y built com-
3 They come to learn the will of God, to pay their vows, God's

tem-ple meet." With-in your gates, O Zi-on blest, shall ev-er
pact and fair; the peo-ple of the Lord u-nite with joy and
grace to own, for there is judg-ment's roy-al seat, Mes-si-ah's

stand our will-ing feet.
praise to wor-ship there.   *Refrain* Come, let us go to the house of the Lord.
sure and last-ing throne.

Zi-on, sing; sing out your peace and joy.

4 For Zion's peace let prayers be made;
   may all that love you prosper well!
   Within your walls let peace abide,
   and gladness with your children dwell.
   Refrain

5 For love of friends and kindred dear,
   my heart's desire is Zion's peace,
   and for the house of God, the Lord,
   my loving care shall never cease.
   Refrain

For other settings of Ps. 122 see 508, 514

Words: *Psalter*, 1912, alt.; ref. Hal H. Hopson © 2008 Birnamwood Publications, a division of MorningStar
   Music Publishers, Inc.
Music (SUSSEX CAROL 8.8.8.8 refrain 10.9): English carol; arr. Ralph Vaughan Williams (1872-1958), P.D.

67 Blessed Be the God of Israel

LUKE 1:68-79

1 Blessed be the God of Is - ra - el, who comes to set us free
2 With prom-ised mer - cy will God still the cov - e - nant re - call,
3 My child, as proph-et of the Lord, you will pre-pare the way,

and rais - es up new hope for us: a Branch from Da - vid's tree.
the oath once sworn to A - bra - ham, from foes to save us all,
to tell God's peo - ple they are saved from sin's e - ter - nal sway.

So have the proph - ets long de-clared that with a might-y arm
that we might wor-ship with-out fear and of - fer lives of praise,
Then shall God's mer - cy from on high shine forth and nev - er cease

God would turn back our en - e - mies and all who wish us harm.
in ho - li - ness and right-eous - ness to serve God all our days.
to drive a - way the gloom of death and lead us in - to peace.

Chord symbols represent a simplified harmony.

Words: Carl P. Daw Jr (b. 1944) © 1989 Hope Publishing Company
Music: (FOREST GREEN 8.6.8.6 D): English folk tune; adapt. and harm. Ralph Vaughan Williams (1872-1958),
1906, P.D.

Told of God's Favor

1 Told of God's fav - or, told of God's pur-pose, Ma - ry said,
2 Yes to con - ceiv-ing, yes to the bo - dy chang-ing and
3 Yes to the wait-ing, yes to the la - bor, yes to the

"Tell me, how can this be?" Told of the Spir - it,
grow - ing, yes to the flesh— yes to the new life
hurt - ing, yes to the birth— yes to the ba - by,

told of the pow - er, told of the prom - ise, Ma - ry said yes.
kick-ing with - in her, yes to the plea - sure, yes to the pain.
yes to the fu - ture, yes to the ho - ly, yes to the world.

4 Told of Christ Jesus, told of the Spirit,
   can we say yes as Mary said yes?
   Yes for our bodies, yes for our spirits,
   yes for the future, yes for right now.

5 Praise to the Spirit, praise to the Most High
   sending the word that Mary was told.
   Praise to Christ Jesus, who was made welcome
   into our world when Mary said yes.

Words: Richard Leach, 1992, © 1994 Selah Publishing Company, Inc.
Music (BORDY 10.9.10.9): Russell Schulz-Widmar © 1994 Selah Publishing Company, Inc.

69 My Soul Cries Out with a Joyful Shout

LUKE 1:46-55

1 My_____ soul cries out with a joy-ful shout that the God of my
2 Though__ I am small, my__ God, my all, you__ work great__
3 From the halls of power to the for-tress tower, not a stone will be
4 Though the na-tions rage from age to age, we re-mem-ber who

heart is great, and my spir-it__ sings of the won-drous__
things in me, and your mer-cy will last from the depths of the
left on stone. Let the king be-ware for your jus-tice__
holds us fast: God's__ mer-cy__ must de-liv-er__

things that you bring to the ones who wait. You fixed your
past to the end of the age to be. Your ver-y
tears ev-ery ty-rant__ from his throne. The hun-gry
us from the con-quer-or's crush-ing grasp. This sav-ing

sight on your ser-vant's plight, and my weak-ness you
name puts the proud to shame, and to those who would
poor shall__ weep no more for the food they can
word that our fore-bears heard is the prom-ise which

Words: Rory Cooney (b. 1952), based on the *Magnificat*, © 1990 GIA Publications, Inc.
Music (STAR OF COUNTY DOWN 8.6.8.6 D refrain 9.8.10.8): Irish traditional; arr. Rory Cooney © 1990 GIA
  Publications, Inc.

70 On Jordan's Bank the Baptist's Cry

1 On Jor - dan's bank the Bap - tist's cry an - nounc - es
2 Then cleansed be ev - ery life from sin: make straight the
3 We hail you as our Sav - ior, Lord, our re - fuge

that the Lord is nigh. A - wake and hark - en,
way for God with - in, and let us all our
and our great re - ward. With - out your grace we

for he brings glad tid - ings of the King of kings!
hearts pre - pare for Christ to come and en - ter there.
waste a - way like flowers that with - er and de - cay.

4 Stretch forth your hand, our health restore,
and make us rise to fall no more.
O let your face upon us shine
and fill the world with love divine.

5 All praise to you, eternal Son,
whose advent has our freedom won,
whom with the Father we adore,
and Holy Spirit, evermore

For an alternate arrangement see 900

Words: Charles Coffin, 1736; tr. composite, P.D.
Music (PUER NOBIS 8.8.8.8): *Trier manuscript,* 15th c.; adapt. Michael Praetorius, 1609; harm. George Ratcliffe Woodward, 1910, P.D.

Creator of the Stars of Night

1 Cre - a - tor of the stars of night, your peo - ple's ev - er-
2 When this old world drew on toward night, you came—but not in
3 At your great name, O Je - sus, now all knees must bend, all

last - ing light, O Christ, re - deem - er of us all,
splen - dor bright, not as a mon - arch, but the child
hearts must bow: all things on earth with one ac - cord,

we pray you hear us when we call.
of Mar - y, bless - ed moth - er mild.
like those in heaven, shall call you Lord. *(A - men.)*

4 Come in your holy might, we pray;
   redeem us for eternal day;
   defend us while we dwell below
   from all assaults of our dread foe.

5 To God the Father, God the Son,
   and God the Spirit, Three in One,
   praise, honor, might, and glory be
   from age to age eternally. Amen.

Optional prayer

Creator God,
as we gaze into the heavens
in the quietness and mystery of the night,
we marvel at the splendor
of all that you have made.
We are humbly grateful
for the ways you have gifted us
to discover the wonders of the heavens,
so far beyond all that we might have imagined.

Then, when we discover that the one
through whom you made all of this
comes among us to heal and save us,
our hearts overflow
with astonishment and wonder.
We can only begin to fathom
the depths of your love.
How great you are.
How marvelous are your ways!
Alleluia! Amen.

Words: Latin hymn, 9th c.; tr. *Hymnal* 1940, alt. © 1940 Church Pension Fund
Music (CONDITOR ALME SIDERUM 8.8.8.8): Plainsong mode IV; arr. *Lutheran Book of Worship*
© 1978 Lutheran Book of Worship, admin. Augsburg Fortress

72 Imagine

1 Who hears? Who hears the voice of the hun - gry, the
2 Who knows? who knows the hopes that lie hid - den, for -

thir - sty? Who sees? Who sees the
got - ten? Who comes? Who comes to

tears of the suf - fering ones?
lead all the chil - dren home?

Refrain

I - mag - ine a King who would come through the

dark - ness and walk, where I walk, full of great -

Words and Music (IMAGINE): Keith and Kristyn Getty © 2003 Thankyou Music (PRS), admin. worldwide at EMICMGPublishing.com excluding Europe which is admin. by Kingswaysongs

ness, and call me to his side, just like a fa - ther and child.

Dona Nobis Pacem 73

Dona nobis pacem means "grant us your peace."

Optional prayer with spoken or sung refrain using the first 4 measures: **Dona nobis pacem.**

Prince of Peace, as we wait for your coming, we pray fervently: *Refrain*
For all who live with violence and war [specify], we pray: *Refrain*
For all who live with worry and fear [specify], we pray: *Refrain*
For all who live in loneliness and despair [specify], we pray: *Refrain*
For all of us, your children, who long for peace, we pray: *Refrain*
Maranatha: Come, Lord Jesus, we pray. **Amen.**

Words: traditional, Latin
Music (DONA NOBIS PACEM): traditional

74 ## Savior of the Nations, Come

1 Sav - ior of the na - tions, come, show your - self, the
2 Not by hu - man power or seed did the wom - an's
3 Mar - y then was found with child, still a vir - gin,
4 Christ laid down his maj - es - ty, passed through dark Geth -

vir - gin's son. Fill with won - der, all the earth,
womb con - ceive; on - ly by the Spir - it's breath
chaste and mild. God had fa - vored her with grace
sem - a - ne. Though he left his Fa - ther's home,

that our God chose such a birth.
was the Word of God made flesh.
to re - ceive the Prince of Peace.
Christ now sits on God's own throne.

5 Since the star at Bethlehem
brought new light to earth again,
may our faith shine bright each day;
faithful God, keep sin away.

6 Christ in glory, intercede
for your creatures' suffering need.
Let your resurrecting power
soon complete the victory hour.

7 Praise to you, O Lord, we sing.
Praise to Christ, our newborn King!
With the Father, Spirit, one,
let your lasting kingdom come.

Chord symbols represent a simplified harmony.

Words: Ambrose, 4th c.; Martin Luther, 1523; tr. Calvin Seerveld, 1984, © Calvin Seerveld
Music (NUN KOMM DER HEIDEN HEILAND 7.7.7.7): *Enchiridia*, Erfurt, 1524; harm. Seth Calvisius, 1594, P.D.

Lord, You Were Rich Beyond All Splendor 75

1 Lord, you were rich be-yond all splen - dor, yet for love's
2 You are our God be-yond all prais - ing, yet, for love's
3 Lord, you are love be-yond all tell - ing; Sav - ior and

sake, be-came so poor; leav-ing your throne in glad sur - ren - der,
sake, be-came a man; stoop-ing so low, but sin-ners rais - ing
Kind, we wor-ship you. Em-man-u - el, with-in us dwell-ing,

sap - phire-paved courts for sta - ble floor. Lord, you were rich be -
heaven-ward by your e - ter - nal plan. You are our God be -
make us and keep us pure and true. Lord, you are love be -

yond all splen - dor, yet for love's sake, be - came so poor.
yond all prais - ing, yet, for love's sake, be - came a man.
yond all tell - ing; Sav - ior and King, we wor - ship you.

Chord symbols represent a simplified harmony.

Words: Frank Houghton (1894-1972), from 2 Corinthians 8:9 © OMF International(UK)
Music (FRAGRANCE/QUÉLLE EST CETTE ODEUR AGREABLE 9.8.9.8.9.8): Martin Fallas Shaw (1875-1958)
from *Songs of Praise*; arr. reproduced by permission of Oxford University Press

76 O Come, All Ye Faithful

Descant

4 Yea, Lord, we greet thee, born this hap-py morn-ing;

1 O come, all ye faith-ful, joy-ful and tri-um-phant! O
2 God of___ God,___ Light of Light e-ter-nal,
3 Sing, choirs of an-gels, sing in ex-ul-ta-tion,
4 Yea, Lord, we greet thee, born this hap-py morn-ing;

Je-sus, to thee be all glo-ry given;

come ye, O come ye to Beth-le-hem!
lo, he ab-hors not the vir-gin's womb;
sing, all ye cit-i-zens of heaven a-bove:
Je-sus, to thee be all glo-ry given;

Word of the Fa-ther, now in flesh ap-pear-ing;

Come and be-hold him, born the King of an-gels;
Son of the Fa-ther, be-got-ten, not cre-at-ed;
"Glo-ry to God, all glo-ry in the high-est!"
Word of the Fa-ther, now in flesh ap-pear-ing;

Words: attr. John F. Wade, 1743; tr. Frederick Oakeley, 1841, and others, P.D.
Music (ADESTE FIDELES irregular): attr. John F. Wade, 1743; desc. © 1947 *Hymns Ancient and Modern*, admin.
Hope Publishing Company

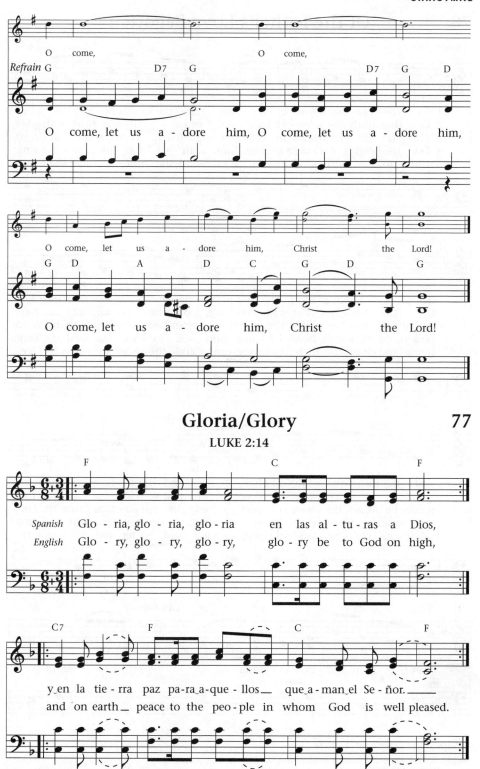

O come,   O come,

Refrain
O come, let us a - dore him, O come, let us a - dore him,

O come, let us a - dore him, Christ the Lord!

O come, let us a - dore him, Christ the Lord!

Gloria/Glory

77

LUKE 2:14

Spanish Glo - ria, glo - ria, glo - ria   en las al - tu - ras a Dios,
English Glo - ry, glo - ry, glo - ry,   glo - ry be to God on high,

y en la tie - rra paz pa - ra a - que - llos que a - man el Se - ñor.
and on earth peace to the peo - ple in whom God is well pleased.

Words: Luke 2:14
Music (CUEQUITA): Pablo Sosa (b. 1947), Argentina © 1990 Pablo Sosa, admin. OCP Publications

78 Of the Father's Love Begotten

Unison

1 Of the Fa-ther's love be-got-ten ere the worlds be-gan to be,
2 O that birth for-ev-er bless-ed, when a vir-gin, blest with grace,
3 This is he whom seers in old time chant-ed of with one ac-cord,
4 Let the heights of heaven a-dore him; an-gel hosts, his prais-es sing:
5 Christ, to you, with God the Fa-ther and the Spir-it, there shall be

he is Al-pha and O-me-ga— he the source, the end-ing he,
by the Ho-ly Ghost con-ceiv-ing, bore the Sav-ior of our race;
> whom the voic-es of the proph-ets prom-ised in their faith-ful word;
powers, do-min-ions, bow be-fore him and ex-tol our God and King;
hymn and chant and high thanks-giv-ing and the shout of ju-bi-lee:

of the things that are, that have been, and that fu-ture years shall see
and the babe, the world's Re-deem-er, first re-vealed his sa-cred face,
> now he shines, the long-ex-pect-ed; let cre-a-tion praise its Lord
let no tongue on earth be si-lent, ev-ery voice in con-cert ring
hon-or, glo-ry, and do-min-ion and e-ter-nal vic-to-ry

ev-er-more and ev-er-more. *Last time* (A - men.)

For an alternate arrangement see 38, 54

Words: Marcus Aurelius Clemens Prudentius (348-413); tr. Composite, P.D.
Music (DIVINUM MYSTERIUM 8.7.8.7.8.7.7): Plainsong mode V, 13th c.; arr. Paul G. Bunjes (1914-1998);
  arr. © 1982 Concordia Publishing House

Lo, How a Rose E'er Blooming

1 Lo, how a rose e'er bloom-ing from ten - der stem hath sprung;
2 I - sa - iah 'twas fore - told it, the rose I have in mind;
3 This flower, so small and ten - der, with fra - grance fills the air;
4 O Sav - ior, child of Mar - y, who felt our hu - man woe;

of Jes - se's lin - eage com - ing, as saints of old have sung.
with Mar - y we be - hold it, the vir - gin moth - er kind.
his bright-ness ends the dark-ness that kept the earth in fear.
O sav - ior, King of glo - ry, who does our weak - ness know:

It came, a flower - et bright, a - mid the cold of
To show God's love a - right, she bore to us a
True God and yet true man, he came to save his
bring us at length, we pray, to the bright courts of

win - ter when half spent was the night.
Sav - ior when half spent was the night.
peo - ple from earth's dark night of sin.
heav - en and in - to end - less day.

Words: German, 15th c.; st. 1-2 tr. Theodore Baker, 1894; st. 3 tr. Gracia Grindal, 1978, © 1978 *Lutheran Book of Worship*, admin. Augsburg Fortress; st. 4 John C. Mattes (1876-1948)

Music (ES IST EIN' ROS' ENTSPRUNGEN 7.6.7.6.6.7.6): from *Alte Catholische Geistliche Kirchengesäng*, Cologne, 1599; harm. Michael Praetorius, 1609, P.D.

80 Hark! The Herald Angels Sing

1 Hark! the her - ald an - gels sing, "Glo - ry to the new - born King;
2 Christ, by high - est heaven a - dored, Christ, the ev - er - last - ing Lord!
3 Hail the heaven - born Prince of Peace! Hail the Sun of Right - eous - ness!

peace on earth and mer - cy mild, God and sin - ners rec - on - ciled!"
Late in time be - hold him come, off - spring of the vir - gin's womb.
Light and life to all he brings, risen with heal - ing in his wings.

Joy - ful, all ye na - tions, rise; join the tri - umph of the skies;
Veiled in flesh the God - head see; hail the in - car - nate De - i - ty,
Mild, he lays his glo - ry by, born that we no more may die,

with the an - gel - ic hosts pro - claim, "Christ is born in Beth - le - hem!"
pleased as man with us to dwell, Je - sus, our Im - man - u - el.
born to raise us from the earth, born to give us sec - ond birth.

Refrain B♭

Hark! the her - ald an - gels sing, "Glo - ry to the new - born King!"

Words: Charles Wesley, 1739, alt., P.D.
Music (MENDELSSOHN 7.7.7.7. D refrain 7.7): Felix Mendelssohn, 1840; adapt. William H. Cummings, 1856, P.D.

Angels, from the Realms of Glory

1 An - gels, from the realms of glo - ry, wing your flight o'er all the earth;
2 Shep-herds, in the fields a - bid - ing, watch-ing o'er your flocks by night,
3 Sa - ges, leave your con - tem-pla-tions; bright-er vi - sions beam a - far;

you, who sang cre - a - tion's sto - ry, now pro-claim Mes - si - ah's birth:
God with us is now re - sid - ing; yon - der shines the in - fant Light:
seek the great de - sire of na - tions; you have seen his na - tal star:

Refrain

come and wor-ship, come and wor-ship, wor-ship Christ, the new-born King!

4 Though an infant now we view him,
   he will share his Father's throne,
   gather all the nations to him;
   every knee shall then bow down:
   Refrain

5 All creation, join in praising
   God the Father, Spirit, Son,
   evermore your voices raising
   to the eternal Three in One:
   Refrain

Optional call to worship

All who come from near and far, **come and worship.**
All who thirst for God, **come and worship.**
All whose hearts overflow with gratitude and hope, **come and worship.**
All whose hearts may be filled with despair or grief, **come and worship.**
All who come with doubts or questions about life in Jesus, **come and worship.**

[Add other phrases as appropriate].

Through the grace of God's Holy Spirit,
come, worship Christ, the newborn King.

Words: James Montgomery, 1816, alt., P.D.
Music (REGENT SQUARE 8.7.8.7 refrain 4.4.6): Henry Smart, 1867, P.D.

82 Les anges dans nos campagnes/ Angels We Have Heard on High

French 1 Les an-ges dans nos cam-pa-gnes, ont enton-né l'hym-ne des cieux,
English 1 An-gels we have heard on high,_ sweet-ly sing-ing o'er the plains
2 Shep-herds, why this ju-bi-lee?_ Why your joy-ous strains pro-long?
3 Come to Beth-le-hem and see_ him whose birth the an-gels sing;

et l'é-cho de nos mon-ta-gnes, re-dit_ce chant mé-lo-di-eux.
and the moun-tains in re-ply,_ ech-o-ing their joy-ous strains.
What the glad-some tid-ings be_ which in-spire your heaven-ly song?
come, a-dore on bend-ed knee_ Christ the Lord, the new-born King.

Refrain

Glo - - - ri-a

in ex-cel-sis De-o. Glo -

Words: French, 18th c.; tr. *Crown of Jesus Music*, 1862, alt., P.D.
Music (GLORIA 7.7.7.7 refrain 3.6.3.6): French, 18th c.; arr. Edward S. Barnes, 1937, P.D.

ri - a in ex - cel - sis De - o.

French

2 Bergers, pour qui cette fête?
Quel est l'objet de tous ces chants?
Quel vainqueur, quelle conguête
mérite ces cris triomphants? *Refrain*

3 Cherchons tous l'heureux village
qui l'a vu naître sous ses toits;
offronslui le tender homage
et de nos voix! *Refrain*

Gloria, Gloria/Glory to God 83

LUKE 2:14

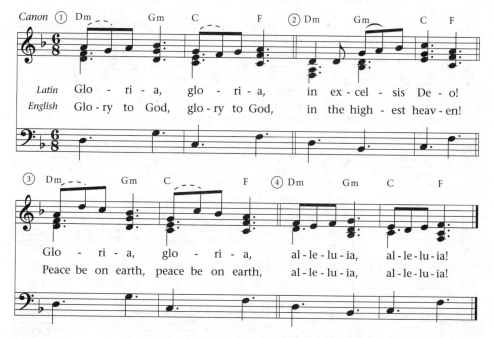

Latin Glo - ri - a, glo - ri - a, in ex - cel - sis De - o!

English Glo - ry to God, glo - ry to God, in the high - est heav - en!

Glo - ri - a, glo - ri - a, al - le - lu - ia, al - le - lu - ia!

Peace be on earth, peace be on earth, al - le - lu - ia, al - le - lu - ia!

Words: Luke 2:14
Music (GLORIA, GLORIA): Jacques Berthier (b. 1923) © 1979 Ateliers et Presses de Taizé, Taizé Community, France, GIA Publications, Inc., exclusive North American agent

84 Ere zij God/Glory to God

LUKE 2:14

Dutch: E - re zij God! E - re zij God in den ho - ge, in den
English: Glo - ry to God! Glo - ry to God in the high - est, in the

ho - ge, in den ho - ge! Vre - de op aar - de, vre - de op
high - est, in the high - est! Peace be on earth, peace be on

2nd time to "Amens"/Coda

aar - de, in de men - sen een wel - be - ha - gen.
earth, to the peo - ple whom God de - lights in.

E - re zij God in den ho - ge! E - re zij God in den ho - ge!
Glo - ry to God in the high - est! Glo - ry to God in the high - est!

Words: Luke 2:14; para. F.A. Schultz, ca. 1870; tr. *Psalter Hymnal,* 1987, © 1987 Faith Alive Christian Resources
Music (ERE ZIJ GOD irregular): F.A. Schultz, ca. 1870, P.D.

85 Silent Night! Holy Night

Words: Joseph Mohr, 1818; tr. John F. Young, 1863, P.D.
Music (STILLE NACHT): Franz Gruber, 1818, P.D.

Away in a Manger

1 A - way in a man-ger, no crib for a bed, the lit - tle Lord
2 The cat - tle are low-ing, the ba - by a-wakes, but lit - tle Lord
3 Be near me, Lord Je - sus; I ask you to stay close by me for -

Je - sus laid down his sweet head; the stars in the bright sky looked
Je - sus, no cry - ing he makes. I love you, Lord Je - sus: look
ev - er and love me, I pray. Bless all the dear child - ren in

down where he lay; the lit - tle Lord Je - sus a - sleep on the hay.
down from the sky and stay by my side un - til morn - ing is nigh.
your ten - der care; pre - pare us for heav - en to live with you there.

Words: North American, 19th c., P.D.
Music (AWAY IN A MANGER 11.11.11.11): James R. Murray (1841-1905), P.D.

Alternate tune

Music (CRADLE SONG 11.11.11.11): William J. Kirkpatrick (1838-1921), P.D.

87 Once in Royal David's City

1 Once in roy-al Da-vid's cit-y stood a low-ly cat-tle shed,
where a moth-er laid her ba-by in a man-ger for his bed:
Ma-ry was that moth-er mild,— Je-sus Christ, her lit-tle child.—

2 He came down to earth from heav-en who is God and Lord of all;
and his shel-ter was a sta-ble, and his cra-dle was a stall:
with the poor, and meek, and low-ly lived on earth our Sav-ior ho-ly.

3 Je-sus is our child-hood's pat-tern, day by day like us he grew;
he was lit-tle, weak, and help-less, tears and smiles like us he knew:
and he feels for all our sad-ness, and he shares in all our glad-ness.

4 And our eyes at last shall see him,
through his own redeeming love,
for that child, so dear and gentle,
is our Lord in heaven above:
and he leads his children on
to the place where he has gone.

5 Not in that poor lowly stable
with the oxen standing by
we shall see him, but in heaven,
set at God's right hand on high;
there his children gather round,
bright like stars, with glory crowned.

Words: Cecil F. Alexander, 1848, P.D.
Music (IRBY 8.7.8.7.7.7): Henry J. Gauntlett, 1849, P.D.

O Little Town of Bethlehem

1 O lit - tle town of Beth - le - hem, how still we see thee lie!
2 For Christ is born of Mar - y, and gath - ered all a - bove,
3 How si - lent - ly, how si - lent - ly the won - drous gift is given!
4 O ho - ly Child of Beth - le - hem, de - scend to us, we pray.

A - bove thy deep and dream-less sleep the si - lent stars go by.
while mor - tals sleep, the an - gels keep their watch of won - dering love.
So God im - parts to hu - man hearts the bless - ings of his heaven.
Cast out our sin and en - ter in; be born in us to - day.

Yet in thy dark streets shin - eth the ev - er - last - ing Light;
O morn - ing stars, to - geth - er pro - claim the ho - ly birth,
No ear may hear his com - ing, but in this world of sin,
We hear the Christ - mas an - gels the great glad tid - ings tell;

the hopes and fears of all the years are met in thee to - night.
and prais - es sing to God the King, and peace to all on earth.
where meek souls will re - ceive him still the dear Christ en - ters in.
O come to us, a - bide with us, our Lord Em - man - u - el.

Chord symbols represent a simplified harmony.

Words: Phillips Brooks (1835-1893), P.D.
Music (ST. LOUIS 8.6.8.6.7.6.8.6): Lewis H. Redner (1831-1908), P.D.

89 On Christmas Night

1 On Christ-mas night all Chris-tians sing to hear the news the
2 Then why should we on earth be sad, since our Re-deem-er
3 When sin de-parts be-fore his face, then life and health come
4 All out of dark-ness we have light, which made the an-gels

an-gels bring. On Christ-mas night all Chris-tians sing to
made us glad? Then why should we on earth be sad, since
in its place. When sin de-parts be-fore his face, then
sing this night. All out of dark-ness we have light, which

hear the news the an-gels bring: news of great joy, news
our Re-deem-er made us glad, when from our sin he
life and health come in its place. An-gels re-joice with
made the an-gels sing this night: "Glo-ry to God in

of great mirth, news of our mer-ci-ful King's birth.
set us free, all for to gain our lib-er-ty?
us and sing, all for to see the new-born King.
high-est heaven, peace on earth, and good-will. A-men."

Words: Luke Wadding (d. 1686), alt., P.D.
Music (SUSSEX CAROL 8.8.8.8 refrain 10.9): English carol; arr. Ralph Vaughan Williams (1872-1958), P.D.

How Great Our Joy

1 While by the sheep we watched at night, glad tid - ings brought an
2 There shall be born, so he did say, in Beth - le - hem a
3 There shall the child lie in a stall, this child who shall re -
4 This gift of God we'll cher - ish well, that ev - er joy our

Refrain

an - gel bright.
child to - day.   How great our joy! Great our joy!
deem us all.
hearts shall fill.

Joy, joy, joy! Joy, joy, joy! Praise we the Lord in

heaven on high! Praise we the Lord in heaven on high!

f = forte/loud
p = piano/soft

Words: traditional German carol, P.D.
Music (JUNGST 8.8 refrain 4.3.3.3.8.8): traditional German melody; arr. Hugo Jungst

91 God Reigns! Earth Rejoices

PSALM 97

Unison

1 God reigns! Earth re - joic - es! O - ceans shout God's might!
2 Fires will blaze the path - way; stars will mark the place,
3 E - vil walks be - side us, crush - es with its grief;
4 Light dawns for the right - eous, joy for God's own heirs—

Clad in truth and joy, God's throne is our de - light.
when God comes in glo - ry, meets us face to face.
yet in God the faith - ful find their sure re - lief.
love all loves ex - cel - ling, grace be - yond com - pare.

Clouds roll a - side, and night be - comes as day.
Moun - tains will shake and worth - less i - dols fall;
Shack - les will break and chains of bon - dage cease;
Daugh - ters and sons, God's maj - es - ty pro - claim!

God will dwell a - mong us; God will show the way!
Zi - on will re - joice, for God is Lord of all!
for - mer lam - en - ta - tions now are songs of peace.
Let your hearts de - clare the Lord's most ho - ly name!

Words: Michael Morgan © 2011 Michael Morgan, admin. Faith Alive Christian Resources
Music (NOËL NOUVELET 11.11.10.11): Medieval French carol, P.D.

Joy to the World

PSALM 98

1 Joy to the world! the Lord is come: let earth re- ceive her
2 Joy to the earth! the Sav-ior reigns: let all their songs em-
3 No more let sin and sor-row grow nor thorns in-fest the
4 He rules the world with truth and grace, and makes the na-tions

King. Let ev-ery heart pre-pare him room, and
ploy, while fields and floods, rocks, hills, and plains re-
ground; he comes to make his bless-ings flow far
prove the glo-ries of his right-eous-ness and

heaven and na-ture sing, and heaven and na-ture
peat the sound-ing joy, re-peat the sound-ing
as the curse is found, far as the curse is
won-ders of his love, and won-ders of his
and heaven and na-ture sing,

sing, and heaven, and heaven and na-ture sing.
joy, re-peat, re-peat the sound-ing joy.
found, far as, far as the curse is found.
love, and won-ders, won-ders of his love.

and

heaven and na-ture sing,

For another setting of Ps. 98 see 547

Words: Isaac Watts (1674-1748), 1719, P.D.
Music (ANTIOCH 8.6.8.6.6.8): Lowell Mason, 1848, P.D.

93 Go, Tell It on the Mountain

Refrain
Unison

Go, tell it on the moun-tain, o-ver the hills and ev-ery-where;

go, tell it on the moun-tain that Je-sus Christ is born.

Harmony

1 While shep-herds kept their watch-ing o'er si-lent flocks by night,
2 The shep-herds feared and trem-bled when lo! a-bove the earth
3 Down in a low-ly sta-ble the hum-ble Christ was born,

be-hold, through-out the heav-ens there shone a ho-ly light.
rang out the an-gel cho-rus that hailed our Sav-ior's birth.
and God sent us sal-va-tion that bless-ed Christ-mas morn.

Words: African American spiritual, 19th c., P.D.
Music (GO TELL IT 7.6.7.6 refrain 7.8.7.6): African American spiritual, 19th c.; arr. © 2012 Faith Alive
   Christian Resources

In the Heavens Shone a Star

1 In the heav-ens shone a star, van-quish-ing the gloom of night, her-ald-ing a won-drous birth; God's own Son now comes to earth.

2 From the an-gels shep-herds heard the good tid-ings of his birth, and to Beth-le-hem they sped to be-hold his man-ger bed.

3 Wise men saw the heaven-ly sign, jour-neyed far from O-rient land, him their Lord and King to greet, of-fering trea-sures at his feet.

4 Filled with won-der and with awe, at his cra-dle low we bow to a-dore the Ho-ly Child, Son of God, and yet so mild.

Refrain
Je-sus Christ is born to-day, Christ-mas Day!

Words: Jonathan Malicsi and Ellsworth Chandlee, Philippines © 1990, 2000 Christian Conference of Asia, admin. GIA Publications, Inc.
Music (KALINGA 7.7.7.7 refrain 7.3): Kalinga traditional melody; arr. Joel Navarro © 2010 Joel Navarro, admin. Faith Alive Christian Resources

95 What Child Is This

1 What child is this, who, laid to rest, on Mar-y's lap is sleep-ing?
2 Why lies he in such mean es-tate where ox and ass are feed-ing?
3 So bring him in-cense, gold, and myrrh; come, pea-sant, king, to own him.

Whom an-gels greet with an-thems sweet while shep-herds watch are keep-ing?
Good Chris-tian, fear; for sin-ners here the si-lent Word is plead-ing.
The King of kings sal-va-tion brings; let lov-ing hearts en-throne him.

This, this is Christ the King, whom shep-herds guard and an-gels sing;
Nails, spear shall pierce him through, the cross be borne for me, for you;
Raise, raise the song on high, the vir-gin sings her lul-la-by;

haste, haste to bring him laud, the babe, the son of Mar-y!
hail, hail for Word made flesh, the babe, the son of Mar-y!
joy, joy, for Christ is born, the babe, the son of Mar-y.

Words: William C. Dix (1837-1898), P.D.
Music (GREENSLEEVES 8.7.8.7.6.8.6.7): English ballad, 16th c., P.D.

What Feast of Love   **96**

1 What feast of love is offered here, what banquet come from heaven?
 What food of everlasting life, what gracious gift is given?
 This, this is Christ the King, the bread come down from heaven.
 Oh, taste and see and sing! How sweet the manna given!

2 What light of truth is offered here, what covenant from heaven?
 What hope of everlasting life, what wondrous word is given?
 This, this is Christ the King, the sun come down from heaven.
 Oh, see and hear and sing! The Word of God is given!

3 What wine of love is offered here, what crimson drink from heaven?
 What stream of everlasting life, what precious blood is given?
 This, this is Christ the King, the sweetest wine of heaven.
 Oh, taste and see and sing! The Son of God is given!

For music see 95

Words: Delores Dufner, OSB (b. 1939) © 1993 Delores Dufner, admin. OCP Publications

Lord, Bid Your Servant Go in Peace   **97**
LUKE 2:29-32

1 Lord, bid your ser - vant go in peace; your word is now ful - filled.
2 This is the Sav - ior of the world, the Gen - tiles' prom - ised light,

These eyes have seen sal - va - tion's dawn, this child so long fore-told.
God's glo - ry dwell - ing in our midst, the joy of Is - ra - el.

Words: Scripture, from Luke 2:29-32; *Nunc dimittis;* tr. James Quinn, S.J., (b. 1919), alt., 1969, 1989, © James Quinn, S.J., admin. Selah Publishing Company, Inc.
Music (LAND OF REST 8.6.8.6): American folk melody; harm. Annabel Morris Buchanan (1889-1983), 1938, P.D.

98 Good Christian Friends, Rejoice

1 Good Chris-tian friends, re-joice with heart and soul and voice;
2 Good Chris-tian friends, re-joice with heart and soul and voice;
3 Good Chris-tian friends, re-joice with heart and soul and voice;

give ye heed to what we say: Je-sus Christ is born to-day.
now ye hear of end-less bliss: Je-sus Christ was born for this!
now ye need not fear the grave: Je-sus Christ was born to save!

Ox and ass be-fore him bow, and he is in the man-ger now.
He has o-pened heav-en's door, and we are blest for-ev-er-more.
Calls you one and calls you all to gain his ev-er-last-ing hall.

Christ is born to-day! Christ is born to-day!
Christ was born for this! Christ was born for this!
Christ was born to save! Christ was born to save!

Words: German/Latin, medieval; tr. John M. Neale, 1853, alt., P.D.
Music (IN DULCI JUBILO 6.6.7.7.7.8.5.5): German, 14th c., P.D.

Jesus, Jesus, Oh, What a Wonderful Child 99

Je-sus, Je-sus, oh, what a won-der-ful child.

Je-sus, Je-sus, so ho-ly, meek, and mild; new

life, new hope new joy he brings. Lis-ten to the

an-gels sing, "Glo-ry, glo-ry, glo - ry"; to the new-born King!

Words: African American traditional, alt., P.D.
Music (WONDERFUL CHILD): African American traditional; arr. Jeffrey Radford (1953-2002) © 1992
Pilgrim Press

100 Jesus, the Light of the World

1 Hark the her - ald an - gels sing.
2 Joy - ful, all ye na - tions, rise.
3 Christ, by high - est heaven a - dored.
4 Hail, the heaven - born Prince of Peace.

Je - sus, the light of the world.

Glo - ry to the new - born King.
Join the tri - umph of the skies.
Christ, the ev - er - last - ing Lord,
Hail, the Sun of right - eous - ness!

Je - sus, the light of the world.

Words: ref. George D. Elderkin; st. Charles Wesley (1707-1788), P.D.
Music (WE'LL WALK IN THE LIGHT 7.7.7.7 refrain 5.4.10.11.7): George D. Elderkin; arr. Evelyn Simpson-Curenton (b. 1953) © 2000 GIA Publications, Inc.

Optional acclamation

By the power of your Spirit, **we'll walk in the light, beautiful light.**
In times of joy and gladness, **we'll walk in the light, beautiful light.**
In times of sorrow and despair, **we'll walk in the light, beautiful light.**
Grateful for the light of your Word, **we'll walk in the light, beautiful light.**
Grateful for the gift of your church, **we'll walk in the light, beautiful light.**
Called to witness to your love, **we'll walk in the light, beautiful light.**

[Add other phrases as appropriate. The words for the congregation can be spoken or sung to the first four measures of the refrain above, which can be repeated like a vamp. Conclude by singing the entire refrain or entire hymn.]

101 How Bright Appears the Morning Star

1 How bright ap-pears the Morn-ing Star, with mer-cy beam-ing
2 Though cir-cled by the hosts on high, he deigned to cast a
3 Re - joice, O heavens, and earth, re-ply; with praise, O sin-ners,

from a - far; the host of heaven re - joic - es.
pit - ying eye up - on his help-less crea - ture.
fill the sky for this, his in - car - na - tion.

O Right-eous Branch, O Jes-se's Rod, the Son of Man and
The whole cre - a-tion's head and Lord, by high-est ser-a-
In - car-nate God, put forth your power; ride on, ride on, great

Son of God! We too will lift our voic - es:
phim a - dored, as - sumed our ver - y na - ture;
Con - quer-or, till all know your sal - va - tion.

Chord symbols represent a simplified harmony.

Words: William Mercer, 1859, after Philipp Nicolai, 1599, alt., P.D.
Music (WIE SCHÖN LEUCHTET 8.8.7.8.8.7.4.8.4.8): Philipp Nicolai, 1599; adapt. and harm. Johann S. Bach (1685-1750), P.D.

Je - sus, Je - sus, ho - ly, ho - ly, yet most low - ly,
Je - sus, grant us, through your mer - it, to in - her - it
A - men, a - men! Al - le - lu - ia, al - le - lu - ia!

come, draw near us; great Em - man - uel, come and hear us.
your sal - va - tion. Hear, O hear our sup - pli - ca - tion.
Praise be giv - en ev - er - more by earth and heav - en.

Arise, Your Light Is Come 102

1 A - rise, your light is come! The Spir - it's call o - bey; show
2 A - rise, your light is come! Fling wide the pris - on door; pro -
3 A - rise, your light is come! All you in sor - row born, bind
4 A - rise, your light is come! The moun - tains burst in song! Rise

forth the glo - ry of your God which shines on you to - day.
claim the cap - tives' lib - er - ty, good tid - ings to the poor.
up the bro - ken - heart - ed ones and com - fort those who mourn.
up like ea - gles on the wing; God's power will make us strong.

Words: Ruth Duck, 1974, © 1992 GIA Publications, Inc.
Music (FESTAL SONG 6.6.8.6): William H. Walter, 1894, P.D.

103 Arise, Shine, for Your Light Is Come

ISAIAH 60:1-5, 14, 20

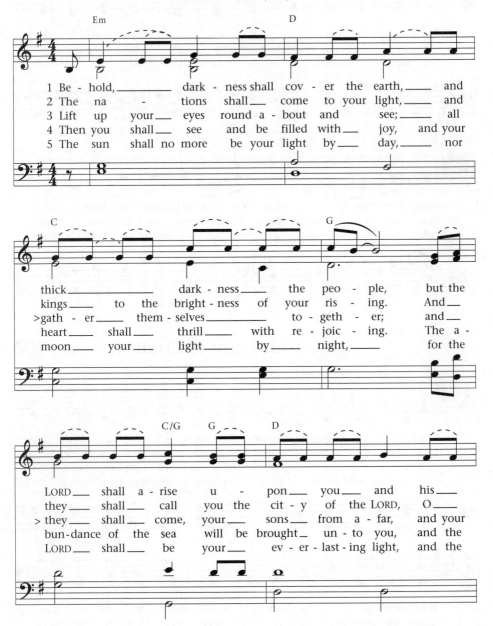

1 Be - hold,_____ dark - ness shall cov - er the earth,____ and
2 The na - tions shall__ come to your light,____ and
3 Lift up your__ eyes round a - bout and see;____ all
4 Then you shall__ see and be filled with__ joy, and your
5 The sun shall no more be your light by__ day,____ nor

thick_____ dark - ness____ the peo - ple, but the
kings____ to the bright - ness of your ris - ing. And__
>gath - er____ them - selves_____ to - geth - er; and__
heart____ shall__ thrill____ with re - joic - ing. The a -
moon__ your__ light____ by____ night,____ for the

LORD__ shall a - rise u - pon__ you__ and his__
they__ shall__ call you the cit - y of the LORD, O__
> they__ shall__ come, your__ sons__ from a - far, and your
bun - dance of the sea will be brought__ un - to you, and the
LORD__ shall__ be your__ ev - er - last - ing light, and the

Words: Isaiah 60:1-5, 14, 20; para. Eric Glass, 1974 (ren.), alt., © 1995 Warner/Chappell Music Canada Ltd.,
admin. Alfred Music Publishing Co., Inc.
Music (ARISE, SHINE irregular): Eric Glass, 1974, © 1974 (ren.) Warner/Chappell Music Canada, Ltd.;
arr. Dale Grotenhuis (1931-2012), 1986, © 2012 Warner/Chappell Music Corp., admin. Alfred Music
Publishing Co., Inc.

glo - ry shall be seen___ up - on you.
Zi - on of the Ho - ly One of Is - rael.
> daugh - ters shall be car - ried at your side.___
wealth___ of the na - tions un - to you.___
days___ of your mourn - ing shall be end - ed.

Refrain

A - rise, shine, for your light is come, and the glo - ry of the

LORD is ris - en. O a - rise, shine, for your

light is come, and the glo - ry of the LORD is up - on you.

104 Songs of Thankfulness and Praise

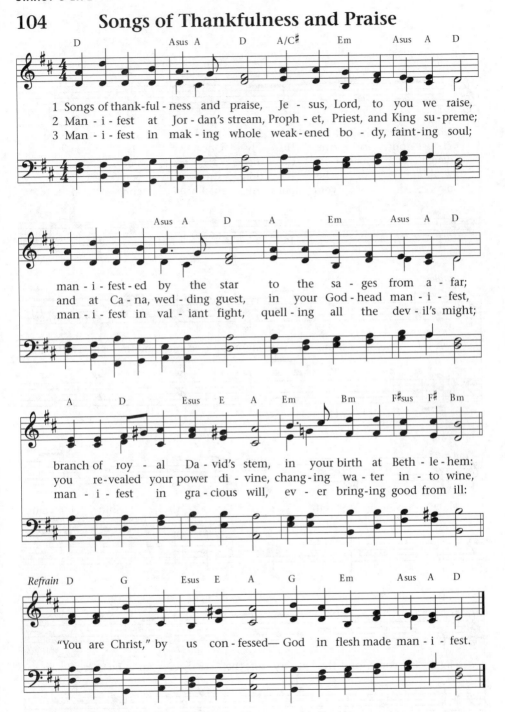

1 Songs of thank-ful-ness and praise, Je - sus, Lord, to you we raise,
2 Man - i - fest at Jor - dan's stream, Proph - et, Priest, and King su - preme;
3 Man - i - fest in mak - ing whole weak-ened bo - dy, faint-ing soul;

man - i - fest-ed by the star to the sa - ges from a - far;
and at Ca - na, wed - ding guest, in your God - head man - i - fest,
man - i - fest in val - iant fight, quell - ing all the dev - il's might;

branch of roy - al Da - vid's stem, in your birth at Beth - le - hem:
you re-vealed your power di - vine, chang-ing wa - ter in - to wine,
man - i - fest in gra - cious will, ev - er bring-ing good from ill:

Refrain
"You are Christ," by us con - fessed— God in flesh made man - i - fest.

For an alternate arrangement see 546

Words: Christopher Wordsorth, 1862, alt., P.D.
Music (SALZBURG 7.7.7.7 D): Jakob Hintze (1622-1702); harm. after Johann S. Bach (1685-1750), P.D.

As with Gladness Men of Old

Descant

5 In that glo-rious cit-y bright none shall need cre-a-ted light;

1 As with glad-ness men of old did the guid-ing star be-hold,
2 As with joy-ful steps they sped to that low-ly man-ger bed,
3 As they of-fered gifts most rare at that man-ger plain and bare,

you its light, its joy, its crown, you its sun which goes not down;

as with joy they hailed its light, lead-ing on-ward, beam-ing bright;
there to bend the knee be-fore Christ, whom heaven and earth a-dore;
so may we with ho-ly joy, pure and free from sin's al-loy,

there for-ev-er may we sing al-le-lu-ias to our King!

so, most gra-cious Lord, may we ev-er-more your splen-dor see.
so may we with will-ing feet ev-er seek your mer-cy seat.
all our cost-liest trea-sures bring, Christ, to you, our heaven-ly King.

4 Holy Jesus, every day
keep us in the narrow way,
and when mortal things are past,
bring our ransomed lives at last
where they need no star to guide,
where no clouds your glory hide.

5 In that glorious city bright
none shall need created light;
you its light, its joy, its crown,
you its sun which goes not down;
there forever may we sing
alleluias to our King!

Words: William C. Dix, 1860, alt., P.D.
Music (DIX 7.7.7.7.7.7): Conrad Kocher, 1838; adapt. William H. Monk, 1861 P.D.; desc. Sydney H. Nicholson, 1944, © The Royal School of Church Music

106 De tierra lejana venimos/From a Distant Home

Spanish 1 De tie-rra le-ja-na ve-ni-mos a ver-te,
2 A re-cién na-ci-do que_es Rey de los rey-es,

English 1 From a dis-tant home the Sav-ior we come seek-ing,
2 Glow-ing gold I bring the new-born babe so ho-ly,

nos sir-ve de guí - a la_es-tre-lla de_O-rien-te.
o-ro le re-ga - lo pa-ra_or-nar sus sien-es.
us-ing as our guide the star, so bright-ly beam-ing.
to-ken of his power to reign a-bove in glo-ry.

Refrain

O bri-llan-te_es-tre - lla que_a-nun-cia la_au-ro - ra
Glo-ria_en las al-tu-ras al Hi-jo de Dios,____
Love-ly east-ern star that tells us of God's morn-ing,
Glo-ry in the high-est to the Son of heav-en,

no nos fal-te nun - ca tu luz bien-he-cho-ra.
glor-ria_en las al-tu-ras
heav-en's won-drous light, O nev-er cease thy shin-ing!
and up-on the earth be

Words: Puerto Rican carol; tr. George K. Evans and Walter Ehret © 1963, 1980 Walter Ehret and George K. Evans, from *The International Book of Christmas Carols*, admin. Licensing Associates
Music (ISLA DEL ENCANTO irregular): Puerto Rican melody, P.D.

Spanish

3 Como_es Dios el niño
   le regalo_incienso,
   Perfume con alma
   que sube_hasta_el_cielo. *Refrain*

4 Al niño del cielo
   que bajó_a la tierra,
   Le regalo mirra
   que_inspira tristeza. *Refrain*

English

3 Frankincense I bring the
   child of God's own choosing,
   token of our prayers to
   heaven ever rising. *Refrain*

4 Bitter myrrh have I to
   give the infant Jesus,
   token of the pain that
   he will bear to save us. *Refrain*

Come, Light, Light of God 107

Words and Music (COME, LIGHT OF GOD): The Sisters of the Community of Grandchamp, Switzerland; tr. Bert Polman (b. 1945); arr. Emily R. Brink (b. 1940) © The Sisters of the Community

108 Blest Are the Innocents

1 Blest are the in-no-cents, Beth-le-hem's own, killed by a
2 Ra-chael is weep-ing, her child is no more, lost to the
3 Where is the com-fort for those who still mourn? Where is as-
4 Where can we turn, Ho-ly God, but to you? Lord, in your

ty-rant who clings to a throne. Not just by Her-od, not
fam-ine, the plague, and the war, lost to the fist and the
sur-ance for those yet un-born? God, hear the blood cry-ing
mer-cy, O make all things new! Cast down the ar-ro-gant,

just long a-go, here and to-day voic-es
curse and the lie— in flesh or spir-it the
out from the ground; shine on the sha-dows where
lift up the least. Gath-er your chil-dren and

cry from be-low.
in-no-cents die.
se-crets re-sound.
grant them your feast.

Final ending

Words: Sylvia Dunstan © 1995 GIA Publications, Inc.
Music (BETA 10.10.10.10): David Landegent and this arr. Albert Chung © 2012 David Landegent, admin. Faith
Alive Christian Resources

Hail to the Lord's Anointed

PSALM 72

1 Hail to the Lord's a-noint-ed, great Da-vid's great-er Son!
2 You come with res-cue speed-y to those who suf-fer wrong,
3 You shall come down like show-ers up-on the fruit-ful earth;
4 Kings shall fall down be-fore you, and gold and in-cense bring;

Hail, in the time ap-point-ed, your reign on earth be-gun!
to help the poor and need-y, and bid the weak be strong;
love, joy, and hope, like flow-ers, spring in your path to birth.
all na-tions shall a-dore you, your praise all peo-ple sing.

You come to break op-pres-sion, to set the cap-tive free,
to give them songs for sigh-ing, their dark-ness turn to light,
Be-fore you on the moun-tains shall peace, the her-ald, go,
To you shall prayer un-ceas-ing and dai-ly vows as-cend,

to take a-way trans-gres-sion, and rule in eq-ui-ty.
whose souls, con-demned and dy-ing, are pre-cious in your sight.
and right-eous-ness in foun-tains from hill to val-ley flow.
your king-dom still in-creas-ing, a king-dom with-out end.

For other settings of Ps. 72 see 219, 953

Words: James Montgomery, 1822, P.D.
Music (ES FLOG EIN KLEINS WALDVÖGELEIN 7.6.7.6 D): German; harm. George Ratcliffe Woodward, 1904, P.D.

110 Behold the Lamb of God

1 As of old God prom-ised us in proph-ets' word and sign,
2-13 *Sing one or more appropriate stanzas and then conclude with stanza 14.*
14 In the life of Je-sus Christ, with eyes of faith, we see

Christ has come, the Lamb of God, so hu-man, yet di-vine.
Love in-car-nate, Word made flesh. The Lamb of God is he!

One of us, how can that be, and of God, a mys-ter-y!
Serv-ant, Sav-ior, Friend, and Guide, Ris-en Pres-ence at our side!

To stanzas 2-14

Ag-nus De-i! Glo-ri-a! Be-hold the Lamb of God!

Words: Mary Nelson Keithahn © 2011, 2012 GIA Publications, Inc.
Music (KENSINGTON 8.5.8.5.7.7): John D. Horman © 2011 GIA Publications, Inc.

hold the Lamb of God! Be-hold the Lamb of God!

2 See him lying in a manger,
  newborn baby boy;
  Joseph sighing, Mary smiling,
  overwhelmed with joy,
  angels singing overhead,
  shepherds kneeling at his bed. *Refrain*

3 See him speaking in the temple,
  only twelve years old;
  scribes and Pharisees astounded
  at a youth so bold,
  probing scripture's holy way,
  seeking answers for his day. *Refrain*

4 See him coming to the Jordan,
  not yet thirty one;
  John the Baptist recognizing
  that his time had come,
  heavens opening from above,
  Spirit falling like a dove. *Refrain*

5 See him reading from Isaiah,
  guest in his hometown;
  Nazareth, attentive, listening,
  many with a frown;
  friends refusing to hear more,
  neighbors showing him the door. *Refrain*

6 See him gathering twelve disciples,
  such a leader he;
  fishermen and tax collectors
  hearing "follow me,"
  leaving boats and fishing nets,
  money bags without regret. *Refrain*

7 See him welcoming the children,
  friend with arms held wide,
  joyfully they all come running
  quickly to his side,
  laughing in his warm embrace,
  smiling at his kindly face. *Refrain*

8 See him touching hopeful people,
  healer with love's hand;
  lame feet dancing, deaf ears hearing,
  music in the land,
  blind eyes seeing what they've known,
  lepers cleansed now, going home. *Refrain*

9 See him sitting at the table,
  Christ the Living Bread;
  sinners wondering, then rejoicing
  when in love they're fed,
  some repenting of their ways,
  others singing psalms of praise. *Refrain*

10 See him listening to his critics,
  strong, yet gentle one;
  angry voices asking him how
  he could be God's Son,
  charging him with blasphemy,
  making death his destiny. *Refrain*

11 See him praying in the garden,
  Truth and Life and Way;
  his friends sleeping, unaware that
  one will soon betray,
  Judas giving out advice,
  Christ the willing sacrifice. *Refrain*

12 See him dying, crucified,
  a man nailed to a tree;
  Mary and the others weeping
  there on bended knee,
  mourning one they could not save,
  bearing him to borrowed grave. *Refrain*

13 See him standing in the morning
  near an empty tomb;
  angels greeting grieving women,
  banishing their gloom;
  alleluias ringing clear,
  "He is risen! Christ is here!" *Refrain*

111 O Love, How Deep, How Broad, How High

1 O love, how deep, how broad, how high, beyond all
thought and fan - ta - sy, that God, the Son of
God, should take our mor - tal form for mor - tals' sake!

2 For us bap - tized, for us he bore his ho - ly
fast and hun - gered sore; for us temp - ta - tion
sharp he knew, for us the tempt - er o - ver - threw.

3 For us he prayed; for us he taught; for us his
dai - ly works he wrought: by words and signs and
ac - tions thus still seek - ing not him - self, but us.

4 For us to e - vil power be - trayed, scourged, mocked, in
pu - ple robe ar - rayed, he bore the shame - ful
cross and death; for us gave up his dy - ing breath.

5 For us he rose from death again;
for us he went on high to reign;
for us he sent his Spirit here
to guide, to strengthen, and to cheer.

6 All glory to our Lord and God
for love so deep, so high, so broad—
the Trinity, whom we adore
forever and forevermore.

Words: Latin, 15th c.; tr. Benjamin Webb, 1854, alt., P.D.
Music (DEO GRACIAS 8.8.8.8): English, 15th c.; harm. Carl Schalk, 1969, © 1969 Concordia Publishing House

When You, O Lord, Were Baptized 112

Unmeasured, sung freely

When you, O Lord, were bap-tized in the Jor-dan, the wor-ship of the Trin-i-ty was made man-i-fest. For the voice of the Fa-ther bore wit-ness un-to you, call-ing you the be-lov-ed Son. And the Spir-it in the form of a dove con-firmed his word as sure and stead-fast. O Christ, our God— who has ap-peared and en-light-ened the world, glo-ry be to you.

Words and Music (WHEN YOU, O LORD, WERE BAPTIZED irregular): *Orthodox Liturgy of Epiphany* from Russia, P.D.

113 Mark How the Lamb of God's Self-Offering

1 Mark how the Lamb of God's self-of-fering our hu-man sin-ful-ness takes on in the birth-wa-ters of the Jor-dan as Je-sus is bap-tized by John. Hear how the voice from heav-en thun-ders, "Lo, this is my be-lov-ed Son." See how in dove-like

2 From this as-sur-ance of God's fa-vor Je-sus goes to the wil-der-ness, there to en-dure a time of test-ing that read-ied him to teach and bless. So we, by wa-ter and the Spir-it bap-tized in-to Christ's min-is-try, are of-ten led to

2 Grant us, O God, the strength and cour-age to live the faith our lips de-clare; bless us in our bap-tis-mal call-ing; Christ's roy-al priest-hood help us share. Turn us from ev-ery false al-le-giance, that we may trust in Christ a-lone: raise up in us a

For an alternate arrangement see 196

Words: Carl P. Daw Jr (b.1944) © 1990 Hope Publishing Company
Music (GENEVAN 98/118 /RENDEZ À DIEU 9.8.9.8 D): *Genevan Psalter,* 1551; harm. Dale Grotenhuis (1931-2012), 1985, © 1987 Faith Alive Christian Resources

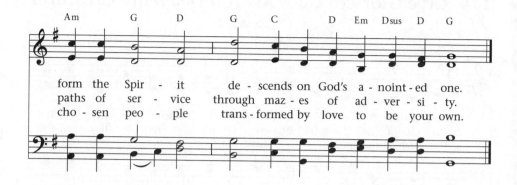

form the Spir - it de - scends on God's a - noint - ed one.
paths of ser - vice through maz - es of ad - ver - si - ty.
cho - sen peo - ple trans - formed by love to be your own.

Optional prayer of confession

God of our salvation,
we marvel that you sent your Son in the world,
that we might become your children.

Yet we confess
that we often rebel against you and your ways.
We fall back into a spirit of fear.
We turn toward false saviors.

Forgive and heal us, we pray.
Help us, once again,
to turn away from all that is false,
and to turn toward you.

Help us to hear and embrace
the identity, the promise and the calling
you give to us in our baptism
as your dearly loved children. Amen.

114 Give Glory to God, All You Heavenly Creatures

PSALM 29

1 Give glo-ry to God, all you heav-en-ly crea-tures; all glo-ry and
2 The voice of the LORD rolls out o-ver the wa-ters; it thun-ders and
3 The voice of the LORD now is break-ing the ce-dars; he shat-ters the

pow-er be-long to the LORD! So drop to your knees and re-
ech-oes his glo-ry a-broad. The voice of the LORD is ma-
trees while Mount Leb-a-non quakes. God speaks: all the hills jump like

spect what is ho-ly; be qui-et and lis-ten: the voice of the LORD!
jes-tic and might-y; its pow-er re-sounds, and his crea-tures are awed.
an-te-lopes star-tled—the voice of the LORD makes us crea-tures to shake.

4 The voice of the LORD whips out lightning-like flashes.
The voice of the LORD makes the desert to reel.
The voice of the LORD sets the oak tree awhirling.
God strips forests bare by the force of his gale.

5 The creatures now worship the God of all power;
all creatures respond, "May God's glory increase."
The LORD gives his people their strength and all blessing;
the LORD shall encircle his people with peace.

For another setting of Ps. 29 see 922

Words: Calvin Seerveld © 1983 Calvin Seerveld
Music (ARLES 12.11.12.11): Charles H. Gabriel (1856-1932), P.D.

Jesus, Tempted in the Desert

115

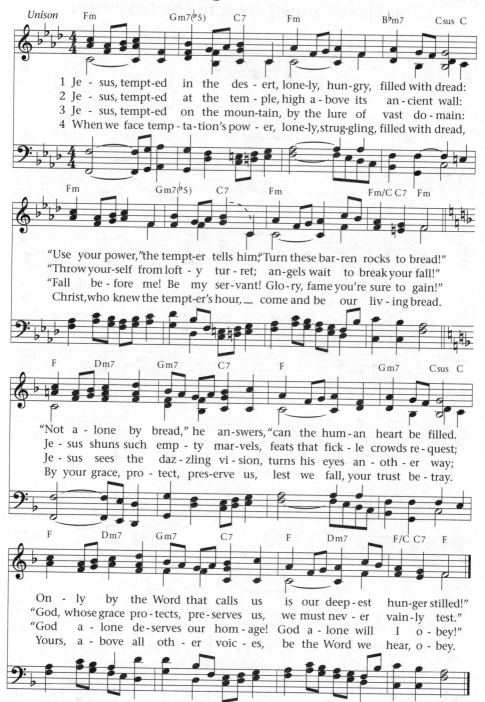

1 Je - sus, tempt-ed in the des - ert, lone-ly, hun-gry, filled with dread:
2 Je - sus, tempt-ed at the tem - ple, high a - bove its an - cient wall:
3 Je - sus, tempt-ed on the moun-tain, by the lure of vast do - main:
4 When we face temp - ta-tion's pow - er, lone-ly, strug-gling, filled with dread,

"Use your power," the tempt-er tells him, "Turn these bar-ren rocks to bread!"
"Throw your-self from loft - y tur - ret; an-gels wait to break your fall!"
"Fall be - fore me! Be my ser-vant! Glo - ry, fame you're sure to gain!"
Christ, who knew the tempt-er's hour, __ come and be our liv - ing bread.

"Not a - lone by bread," he an-swers, "can the hum-an heart be filled.
Je - sus shuns such emp - ty mar-vels, feats that fick - le crowds re - quest;
Je - sus sees the daz - zling vi - sion, turns his eyes an - oth - er way;
By your grace, pro - tect, pres-erve us, lest we fall, your trust be - tray.

On - ly by the Word that calls us is our deep - est hun-ger stilled!"
"God, whose grace pro - tects, pre-serves us, we must nev - er vain-ly test."
"God a - lone de-serves our hom-age! God a - lone will I o - bey!"
Yours, a - bove all oth - er voic - es, be the Word we hear, o - bey.

Alternate tune: EBENEZER see 179, 796

Words: Herman G. Stuempfle Jr (b. 1923) © 1993 GIA Publications, Inc.
Music (GENEVA 8.7.8.7 D): George Henry Day, 1940, © 1943, 1961, 1985 Church Pension Fund

116 Tú has venido a la orilla/ You Have Come Down to the Lakeshore

Spanish 1 Tú has ve - ni - do a la o - ri - lla, no has bus -
2 Tú sa - bes bien lo que ten - go; en mi

English 1 You have come down to the lake - shore, seek - ing
2 You know full well what I have, Lord: nei - ther

ca - do ni a sa - bios ni a ri - cos; tan só - lo
bar - ca no hay o - ro ni es - pa - das, tan só - lo
nei - ther the wise nor the wealth - y, but on - ly
trea - sure nor wea - pons for con - quest, just these my

quie - res que yo te si - ga.
re - des y mi tra - ba - jo.
ask - ing for me to fol - low.
fish - nets and will for work - ing.

Refrain

Se - ñor, me has mi - ra - do a los o - jos,
O Lord, you have looked in - to my eyes;

Words and Music (PESCADOR DE HOMBRES 8.10.10 refrain 9.9.11.9): Cesáreo Gabarain, 1976;
tr. Madeleine Forell Marshall, 1988, © 1977 Cesáreo Gabarain, admin. OCP Publications

son - ri - en - do   has   di - cho mi nom - bre,
kind - ly smil - ing,   you've called out my name._____

en la_a - re - na   he de - ja - do mi bar - ca,
On the sand   I   have a - ban-doned my small boat;

jun - to_a ti   bus - ca - ré o - tro mar.
now with you   I   will seek oth - er   seas.

Spanish

3 Tú necesitas mis manos,
   mi cansancio que_a otros descanse,
   amor que quiera seguir amando.
   Refrain

4 Tú, pescador de_otros lagos,
   ansia_eterna de_almas que_esperan,
   amigo bueno, que_así me llamas.
   Refrain

English

3 You need my hands, my exhaustion,
   working love for the rest of the weary,
   a love that's willing to go on loving.
   Refrain

4 You who have fished other waters,
   you, the longing of souls
      that are yearning:
   O loving Friend,
      you have come to call me. *Refrain*

117 Blest Are They

MATTHEW 5:3-12

1 Blest are they, the poor in spir - it; theirs is the
2 Blest are they, the low - ly ones; ___ they shall in -
3 Blest are they ___ who show mer - cy; mer - cy
4 Blest are they ___ who seek peace; ___ they are the
5 Blest are you who suf - fer hate, ___ all ___ be -

king - dom of God. ___ Blest ___ are they, ___
her - it the earth. ___ Blest ___ are they who
> shall ___ be theirs. ___ Blest ___ are they, the
chil - dren of God. ___ Blest ___ are they who
cause ___ of me. Re - joice and be glad, ___

full ___ of sor - row; ___ they ___ shall be con - soled.
hun - ger and thirst; ___ they ___ shall have their fill.
> pure ___ of heart; ___ they ___ shall see God.
suf - fer in faith; ___ the glo - ry of God is theirs.
yours is the king - dom; ___ shine ___ for all to see.

Words: David Haas (b. 1957), based on Matthew 5:3-12, © 1985 GIA Publications, Inc.
Music (BLEST ARE THEY irregular): David Haas, desc. Michael Joncas (b. 1951) © 1985 GIA Publications, Inc.

118   The Kingdom of Our God Is Like

1 The king-dom of our God is like a trea - sure trove con-
2 The king-dom of our God is like a mus - tard seed in
3 The king-dom of our God is like the yeast a wo - man

cealed be - neath the ground, for which one sells all
size which grows to of - fer nes - ting space for
takes and mix - es in to leav - en each and

else to buy that field, all else to buy that field.
ev - ery bird that flies, for ev - ery bird that flies.
ev - ery loaf she bakes, and ev - ery loaf she bakes.

4 The kingdom of our God is like a merchant who, to own
the rarest pearl, sells everything to gain that pearl alone,
to gain that pearl alone.

5 The kingdom of our God is like a net which has been cast
and draws in good and bad which must be sorted out at last,
be sorted out at last.

Words: Christopher L. Webber, adapt. from Matthew 13:31-33, 44-52, © Theodore Presser, admin. Carl Fischer
Music (DOVE OF PEACE 8.6.8.6.6): American folk melody; harm. Charles H. Webb © 1989 United Methodist
Publishing House

Keep Your Lamps Trimmed and Burning   119

1 Keep your lamps___ trimmed and burn - ing, keep your lamps___ trimmed and burn - ing, keep your lamps ___ trimmed and burn - ing, for the time is draw-ing nigh.

2 Dark - er mid - night lies be - fore us, dark - er mid-night lies be - fore us, dark - er mid-night lies be - fore us, for the time is draw-ing nigh.

3 Lo, the morn - ing soon is break - ing, lo, the morn - ing soon is break - ing, lo, the morn-ing soon is break - ing, for the time is draw-ing nigh.

Refrain

Chil-dren, don't grow wea - ry, chil-dren, don't grow wea - ry, chil-dren, don't grow wea - ry, for the time is draw-ing nigh.

4 Christian journey soon be over,. . .
5 Keep your lamps trimmed and burning,. . .

Words: African American spiritual, P.D.
Music (KEEP YOUR LAMPS irregular): African American spiritual; arr. *New Hymns and Songs* © 2003 Augsburg Fortress

120 Look and Learn

Unison

1 Look and learn from the birds of the air, fly - ing high a - bove
2 Look and learn from the flowers of the field, bring - ing beau - ty and
3 What God wants___ should be___ our will; where God calls___ should

wor - ry and fear; nei - ther sow - ing nor har - vest - ing seed,
col - or to life; nei - ther sew - ing nor tai - lor - ing cloth,
be___ our goal. When we seek___ the king - dom first,

Harmony

yet they're giv - en what - ev - er they need. If the God of
yet they're dressed in the fin - est at - tire. If the God of
all we've lost___ is ours___ a - gain. Let's be done with

earth and heaven cares for birds as much as this,
earth and heaven cares for flowers as much as this,
anx - ious thoughts, set a - side to - mor - row's cares,

Words: Nah Young-Soo, based on Matthew 6:23-24; tr. John L. Bell (b. 1949) © 1991 Wild Goose Resource Group, Iona Community, Scotland, GIA Publications, Inc., exclusive North American agent
Music (LOOK AND LEARN 9.9.9.9.7.7.7.7): Nah Young-Soo; arr. John L. Bell (b. 1949) © 1991 Wild Goose Resource Group, Iona Community, Scotland, GIA Publications, Inc., exclusive North American agent

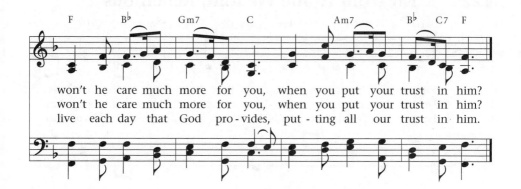

won't he care much more for you, when you put your trust in him?
won't he care much more for you, when you put your trust in him?
live each day that God pro-vides, put-ting all our trust in him.

Jesus Calls Us, O'er the Tumult   121

1 Je - sus calls us, o'er the tu-mult of our life's wild, rest-less sea,
2 Je - sus calls us from the wor-ship of the vain world's gold-en store,
3 Long a - go ap - os - tles heard it by the Gal - i - le - an lake,

day by day his voice is sound-ing, say-ing,"Chris-tian, fol-low me."
from each i - dol that would keep us, say-ing "Chris-tian, love me more."
turned from home and work and fam - ily, leav-ing all for his dear sake.

4 In our joys and in our sorrows,
   days of work and hours of ease,
   still he calls, in cares and pleasures,
   "Christian, love me more than these."

5 Jesus calls us! By your mercy,
   Savior, may we hear your call,
   give our hearts to your obedience,
   serve and love you best of all.

Words: Mrs. Cecil F. Alexander, 1852, P.D.
Music (GALILEE 8.7.8.7): William H. Jude, 1887, P.D.

122   Far from Home We Run, Rebellious

1 Far from home we run, re - bel - lious, seek - ing cit - ies
2 Dreams that lured us on have van - ished; free - dom's road has
3 Long the road that winds us home - ward, faint the hope that

bright with dreams, cast - ing loose from love that claims us,
run its course. All that glit - tered now lies tar - nished,
love still waits; yet the feet that once were way - ward

1, 2

crav - ing life that glit - ters, gleams.
robbed of joy by guilt, re - morse.
lead us toward fa - mil - iar gates.

3   To Stanzas 4 - 6

4 Swift, a fa - ther runs to meet us, bear - ing
5 Arms, long emp - ty, close a - round us, bind - ing
6 Bread and wine for cel - e - bra - tion on the

Words: Herman G. Stuempfle © 1993 GIA Publications, Inc.
Music (GOTT WILL'S MACHEN 8.7.8.7): Johann Ludwig Stelner, 1723, P.D.; sts. 4-6 alt. Norma de Waal
Malefyt © 2007 Faith Alive Christian Resources

love that cov - ers shame.   Sin and guilt no
hearts in warm em - brace.   Love we lost once
ta - ble now are spread.   Songs as - cend in

more de - feat us;   grace re - stores a home, a name.
more has found us,   shines a - gain from face to face.
jub - i - la - tion,   for we live who once were dead!

Optional prayer of confession

Sing stanzas 1-5, use this prayer, then sing stanza 6.

Loving God,
we confess that we, like the younger brother,
often live out prodigal schemes and plans.
We wander from your ways, distance ourselves from you,
and squander your treasures.
Help us turn away from sin and evil,
and turn toward you.
By the power of your Spirit,
renew and restore us;
and help us sense your joyful embrace.

We confess that we, like the older brother,
often resent the grace you have shown to prodigals.
Teach us to marvel at your lavish grace,
and enable us to join the feast of celebration
you spread out before us.
Through Jesus Christ, our Lord. Amen.

123 Come to Me, O Weary Traveler

1 Come to me, O weary traveler; come to me
2 Do not fear, my yoke is ea - sy; do not fear,
3 Take my yoke and leave your trou - bles; take my yoke
4 Rest in me, O wea - ry tra - veler; rest in me

with your dis - tress; come to me, you hea - vy bur - dened;
my bur - den's light; do not fear the path be - fore you;
and come with me. Take my yoke, I am be - side you;
and do not fear. Rest in me, my heart is gen - tle;

come to me and find your rest.
do not run from me in fright.
take and learn hu - mil - i - ty.
rest and cast a - way your care.

Optional reading (Matt. 11:28-30)

Jesus, said,
"Come to me, all you who are weary and burdened,
and I will give you rest.
Take my yoke upon you and learn from me,
for I am gentle and humble in heart,
and you will find rest for your souls.
For my yoke is easy and my burden is light."

Words: Sylvia Dunstan © 1991 GIA Publications, Inc.
Music (AUSTIN 8.7.8.7): William P. Rowan, 1992, © 1993 Selah Publishing Co., Inc.

A Sower's Seed Fell on a Path 124

1 A sow - er's seed fell on a path packed
2 And some fell down where rock - y ground no
3 And some seed fell a - mong the weeds that
4 But some seed fell on fer - tile soil and

hard by foot and cart, and hun - gry spar - rows
sus - te - nance could give. Be - neath the scorch - ing
wove a tan - gling snare to choke the green and
flour - ished more and more un - til the joy - ous

ate their fill be - fore a root could start.
noon - day sun no ten - der plant could live.
bud - ding plants that nev - er fruit would bear.
har - vest time, when hun - dred - fold it bore.

Refrain

Lord, give us ears to hear your Word and hearts where seed can grow.

For an alternate arrangement see 359

Words: Herman G. Stuempfle, adapt. from Mark 4:1-20 © 2000 GIA Publications, Inc.
Music (MORNING SONG 8.6.8.6.8.6): J. Wyeth, *Repository of Sacred Music,* 1813; harm. C. Winfred Douglas (1867-1944), P.D.

125 Jesus the Lord Said, "I Am the Bread"

1 Jesus the Lord said, "I am the bread; the bread of___ life for the
world am I. The bread of___ life for the world am I; the
bread of___ life for the world am I." Jesus the Lord said,
"I am the bread; the bread of___ life for the world am I."

2 Jesus the Lord said, "I am the light; the one true___ light of the
world am I. The one true___ light of the world am I; the
one true___ light of the world am I." Jesus the Lord said,
"I am the light; the one true___ light of the world am I."

3 Jesus the Lord said, "I am the door; the way and the door for the
sheep am I. The way and the door for the sheep am I; the
way and the door for the sheep am I." Jesus the Lord said,
"I am the door; the way and the door for the sheep am I."

4 Jesus the Lord said, "I am the shepherd;
  the one good shepherd
  of the sheep am I. . ."

5 Jesus the Lord said, "I am the life;
  the resurrection and the life am I. . ."

6 Jesus the Lord said, "I am the way;
  the way of truth and the life am I. . ."

7 Jesus the Lord said, "I am the vine;
  the vine that feeds every branch am I. . ."

Words: sts. 1-5 anonymous Urdu, tr. C. Dermott Monahan (1906-1957) © 1969 Christian Conference of Asia, admin. GIA Publications, Inc.; sts. 6-7 Bert Polman (b. 1945); based on "I Am" passages in the Gospel of John © 2001 Faith Alive Christian Resources
Music (YISU NE KAHA irregular): Urdu melody; arr. Andrew Donaldson (b. 1951) © 1997 Andrew Donaldson

Come, One and All

PSALM 49

126

May be sung in canon

1 Come, one and all, from near and far, to share the
2 Some flaunt their gold, some trust its power— but what they
3 Though wealth or learn - ing may be ours, or fame that
4 Be - yond this age of shame and sham we glimpse a
5 Why crave re - nown or o - pu - lence? They fade, those

in - sights I have found: a heart which has been taught by
cher - ish will de - cay; and still the ran - som for a
> spreads through-out the land, the shack - les of mor - tal - i -
bet - ter des - ti - ny: the Lord will lift us free from
things we now pos - sess; our hope, our life are in the

faith in - forms the wis - dom I ex - pound.
soul re - mains a price too great to pay.
> ty pre - vent so much that we have planned.
death to walk with him e - ter - nal - ly.
Lord, the God we hon - or and con - fess.

Bass line can be played by keyboard or xylophones. Possible rhythmic variations of the bass line:

Words: Martin Leckebusch © 2006 Kevin Mayhew Ltd.
Music (KIÚ-JI-IT 8.8.8.8): I-To Loh (b. 1936), 1999, © 1999 and arr. © 2011 I-To Loh

127 Jesus Heard with Deep Compassion

1 Je-sus heard with deep com-pas-sion pleas for heal - ing, cries of pain;
2 Je-sus touched the lives of out-casts, weak or sin - ful, scorned or poor;
3 Je-sus, Lord, our true ex - am - ple, you have shown how we must live.

cured the lame and cleansed the lep - er, gave the blind their sight a - gain.
gave them self - re - spect and cour-age, trust and faith and hope se - cure.
Teach us how to share with oth - ers ev - ery - thing we have to give.

At his voice, tor-ment-ing spir-its fled a mad-man's tor-tured mind;
Tru - ly hear - ing, tru - ly see-ing deep with - in each trou-bled soul,
Let our days be spent in ser-vice; bring us by your grace to know

clothed and healed, he went re - joic-ing, home and fam - i - ly to find.
Je - sus healed their wound-ed spir-its, sent them forth with lives made whole.
heal - ing is the chur-ch's call-ing, and the path that we must go.

Words: Joy F. Patterson (b. 1931) © 1994 Hope Publishing Company
Music (PLEADING SAVIOR 8.7.8.7 D): J. Leavitt's *Christian Lyre*, 1830; harm. Ralph Vaughan Wiliams, 1906,
P.D. in North America, used by permission of Oxford University Press for other territories.

I Heard the Voice of Jesus Calling

128

I heard the voice of Jesus call-ing; here's what he said to me:

1 If you don't let me wash your feet,
2 All that you do for the least of these—
3 If you have ears to hear, then hear;

I can't your Sav - ior be; no, I can't your Sav - ior be.
that's what you do to me; yes, that's what you do to me.
if you have eyes, then see; oh, if you have eyes, then see.

4 Your deepest prayer I will fulfill
where two or three agree; yes,
where two or three agree.

5 I've come that you may know the truth—
that's what will set you free; yes,
that's what will set you free.

6 This is my body, given for you—
why don't you taste and see? Oh,
why don't you taste and see?

7 Believe in me and you will live
through all eternity; yes,
through all eternity.

129 Somlandela/We Will Follow

Zulu 1 Som - lan - de - la, som - lan - del' u - Je - su. Som - lan - de - la,
English 1 We will fol - low, we will fol - low Je - sus. We will fol - low,

yon - ke in - da - wo. Som - lan - de - la, som - lan - del' u - Je - su.
we will fol - low him. We will fol - low, we will fol - low Je - sus.

To stanzas
Leader Som - lan - de - la.
We will fol - low.
Final Ending

La - pho e - ya - kho - na som - lan - de - la. de - la.
We will fol - low Je - sus where he leads us. leads us.

Additional stanzas

2 Through the valleys, we will follow Jesus.
  Through the valleys, we will follow him.
  Through the valleys, we will follow Jesus.
  We will follow Jesus where he leads us.

3 To the mountains. . .

4 In the city. . .

5 In our classroom. . .

6 In our calling. . .

Words: traditional Zulu, P.D.
Music (SOMLANDELA 10.9.10.10): traditional Zulu; arr. Dean McIntyre © 2005 The General Board of
  Discipleship of The United Methodist Church

Jesus on the Mountain Peak

130

1 Je - sus on the moun-tain peak, stands a - lone in glo - ry blaz - ing. Let us, if we dare to speak, join the saints and an - gels prais - ing. Hal - le - lu - jah!

2 Trem - bling at his feet we saw Mo - ses and E - li - jah speak - ing. All the proph - ets and the law shout through them their joy - ful greet - ing. Hal - le - lu - jah!

3 Swift the cloud of glo - ry came, God pro - claim - ing in its thun - der Je - sus as the Son by name! Na - tions, cry a - loud in won - der! Hal - le - lu - jah!

4 This is God's be - lov - ed Son! Law and proph - ets sing be - fore him; first and last and on - ly One. All cre - a - tion shall a - dore him! Hal - le - lu - jah!

Optional prayer of praise

Triune God of glory,
we marvel at the splendor
and majesty of Jesus,
whom saints and angels,
priests and prophets worship as Lord.
We marvel that this Lord
set his face toward Jerusalem
and chose the way of suffering and death.

We marvel that this way
of suffering and death
would become, for us,
the way of life and hope.
Oh, the depths of the riches
of the wisdom and knowledge of God!
How marvelous are your ways, O Lord,
surpassing all human understanding.
**We worship and glorify you,
Father, Son, and Holy Spirit. Amen.**

Words: Brian Wren, 1962, 1988, © 1977, rev. 1995 Hope Publishing Company
Music (MOWSLEY 7.8.7.8.4): Cyril Vincent Taylor (b. 1907) © 1985 Hope Publishing Company

131 Christ, We Climb with You the Mountain

1 Christ, we climb with you the moun-tain where in sol-i-
2 Christ, stay with us on the moun-tain, for our hearts beat
3 Je-sus, send us to the val-ley where the road through
4 Christ, trans-fig-ured on the moun-tain, Christ, who walked the

tude you pray. There your gar-ments white and glist-ening,
fast with fear while a might-y voice that, thun-dering,
suf-fering leads. There we meet your an-guished peo-ple;
earth to save! Christ, the Son of God in glo-ry,

shine more bright-ly than the day. Face a-glow with
brings God's maj-es-ty too near: "Know this man who
there your world from vio-lence bleeds. Give us cour-age,
Christ, who took the form of slave! Help the church, your

God's own glo-ry, you with an-cient proph-ets talk, tak-ing coun-sel
stands be-fore you is the Christ, my Son, my own! Lis-ten, when you
when we fal-ter, not to shrink from pain or loss. Je-sus, grant us,
liv-ing bo-dy, share with you love's cost and pain; till the world, re-

Chord symbols represent a simplified harmony.

Words: Herman G. Stuempfle Jr © 2006 GIA Publications, Inc.
Music (IN BABILONE 8.7.8.7 D): *Oude en Nieuwe Hollantse Boerenlietjes en Contradansen*; arr. Julius Röntgen, and Ralph Vaughn Williams, P.D.

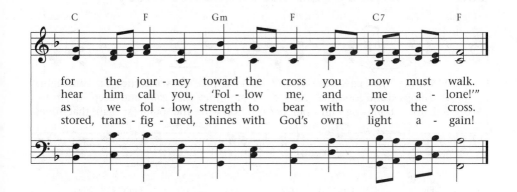

for the jour - ney toward the cross you now must walk.
hear him call you, 'Fol - low me, and me a - lone!'"
as we fol - low, strength to bear with you the cross.
stored, trans - fig - ured, shines with God's own light a - gain!

Lord, Who Throughout These Forty Days   132

1 Lord, who through-out these for - ty days for us did fast and pray,
2 As you with Sa - tan did con-tend, and did the vic - tory win,
3 As you did hun - ger and did thirst, so teach us, gra-cious Lord,

teach us with you to mourn our sins and close by you to stay.
O give us strength in you to fight, in you to con - quer sin.
to die to self, and so to live by your most ho - ly Word.

4 And through these days of penitence,
and through your Passiontide,
forevermore, in life and death,
O Lord, with us abide.

5 Abide with us, that through this life
of doubts and hope and pain,
an Easter of unending joy
we may at last attain!

For an alternate arrangement see 476, 647

Words: Claudia F. Hernaman, 1873, alt., P.D.
Music (MORNING SONG 8.6.8.6): *Sixteen Tune Settings,* 1812; attr. Elkanah Kelsey Dare; harm. David Ashley White, 1994, © 1994 Selah Publishing Company, Inc.

133 Swiftly Pass the Clouds of Glory

1 Swift - ly pass the clouds of glo - ry, heav-en's voice, the daz-zling light;
2 Glimpsed and gone the rev - e - la - tion, they shall gain and keep its truth,
3 Lord, trans - fig - ure our per-cep-tion with the pur - est light that shines,

Mo - ses and E - li - jah van - ish; Christ a - lone com-mands the height!
not by build-ing on the moun-tain an - y shrine or sa - cred booth,
and re - cast our life's in - ten-tions to the shape of your de - signs,

Pe - ter, James, and John fall si - lent, turn - ing from the sum-mit's rise
but by fol - low - ing the Sav - ior through the val - ley to the cross
till we seek no oth - er glor - ry than what lies past Cal-vary's hill

down - ward toward the shad-owed val - ley where their Lord has fixed his eyes.
and by test - ing faith's re - sil - ience through be-tray - al, pain, and loss.
and our liv - ing and our dy - ing and our ris - ing by your will.

Alternate tune: EBENEZER see 179, 796

Words: Thomas H. Troeger, 1985, © Oxford University Press Inc., 1994, assigned to Oxford University Press 2010, reproduced by permission
Music (GENEVA 8.7.8.7 D): George Henry Day, 1940, © 1943, 1961, 1985 Church Pension Fund

Throughout These Lenten Days and Nights 134

May be sung in canon

1 Through - out these Lent - en days and nights we
2 The pil - grim Christ, the Lamb of God, who
3 We bear the si - lence, cross, and pain of
4 And though the road is hard and steep, the

turn to walk the in - ward way, where, meet - ing Christ, our
found in weak - ness great - er power, em - brac - es us, though
hu - man bur - dens, hu - man strife, while sis - ters, bro - thers
Spir - it ev - er calls us on through Cal - vary's dy - ing,

guide and light, we live in hope till Eas - ter day.
lost and flawed, and leads us to his ris - ing hour.
help sus - tain our cou - rage till the feast of life.
dark and deep, un - til we see the com - ing dawn.

5 So let us choose the path of one
who wore, for us, the crown of thorn,
and slept in death, that we might wake
to life on Resurrection Morn!

6 Rejoice, O sons and daughters! Sing
and shout hosannas! Raise the strain!
For Christ, whose death Good Friday brings,
on Easter day will live again!

Words: James Gertmenian (b. 1947) © 1993 Hope Publishing Company
Music (TALLIS CANON 8.8.8.8): Thomas Tallis (1505-1585), ca. 1561, P.D.

135 Jesus Set His Face

Words and Music (FLINT irregular): Gregg DeMey © 2012 Re:Create Music, admin. Faith Alive Christian Resources

136 To My Precious Lord

Korean
2 나를 위해 십자가에 오르신 그 발
흘린 피로 나의 죄를 대속하셨네

3 주님 다시 이 땅 위에 임하실 그 때
주의 크신 사랑으로 날 받아 주소서

English
3 When in clouds of glory you
come back to earth again,
Jesus, with your love, embrace
and claim me as your friend.

Christ, the Life of All the Living 137

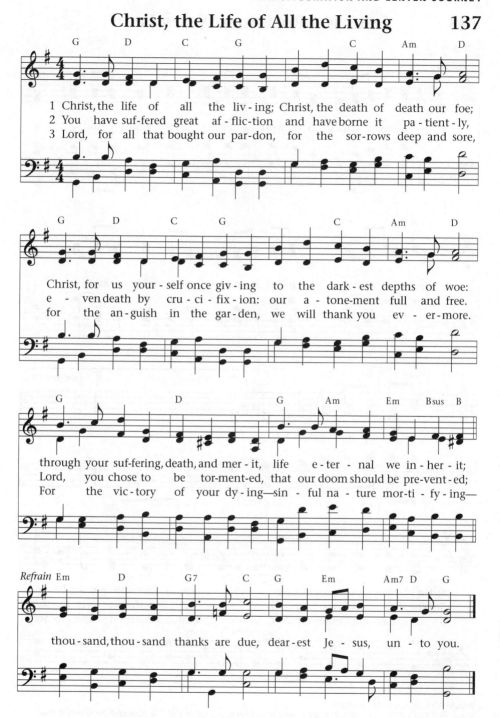

1 Christ, the life of all the liv-ing; Christ, the death of death our foe;
2 You have suf-fered great af-flic-tion and have borne it pa-tient-ly,
3 Lord, for all that bought our par-don, for the sor-rows deep and sore,

Christ, for us your-self once giv-ing to the dark-est depths of woe:
e-ven death by cru-ci-fix-ion: our a-tone-ment full and free.
for the an-guish in the gar-den, we will thank you ev-er-more.

through your suf-fering, death, and mer-it, life e-ter-nal we in-her-it;
Lord, you chose to be tor-ment-ed, that our doom should be pre-vent-ed;
For the vic-tory of your dy-ing—sin-ful na-ture mor-ti-fy-ing—

Refrain
thou-sand, thou-sand thanks are due, dear-est Je-sus, un-to you.

Words: Ernst C. Homburg, 1659; tr. Catherine Winkworth, 1863, alt., P.D.
Music (JESU, MEINES LEBENS LEBEN 8.7.8.7.8.8 refrain 7.7): Das grosse *Cantionale*, Darnstadt, 1687, P.D.

138 Jesus Is a Rock in a Weary Land

Refrain

Je-sus is a rock in a wear-y land, a wear-y land, a wear-y land; Je-sus is a rock in a wear-y land, a shel-ter in the time of storm.

1 Fine last time

2 Fine last time

1 No one can do like Je-sus, not a mum-bling word he said;
2 When Je-sus was on earth_____ the_ flesh was ver-y weak;
3 Yon-der comes my Sav-ior, him_ whom I love so well;

Words: African American spiritual
Music (WEARY LAND irregular): African American spiritual; sts. arr. Wyatt Tee Walker © 2000 Wyatt Tee
Walker © admin. GIA Publications, Inc.; ref. Glen E. Burleigh © 1993 admin. GIA Publications, Inc.

he went walk-ing down to Laz - a - rus' grave, and he
he took a towel and gird - ed him-self, and he
he has the palm of vic - to-ry and the

raised him___ from the dead.
washed his dis - ci - ples' feet. Je - sus is rock.
keys of___ death and hell.

Looking to Jesus 139
HEBREWS 12:1-3

Since we are surrounded
by so great a cloud of witnesses,
let us also lay aside every weight
and the sin that clings so closely,
and let us run with perseverance
the race that is set before us,
looking to Jesus
the pioneer and perfecter of our faith,
who for the sake of the joy that was set before him
endured the cross,
disregarding its shame,
and has taken his seat
at the right hand of the throne of God.
Consider him who endured such hostility
against himself from sinners,
so that you may not grow weary or lose heart.

Text: Hebrews 12:1-3, NRSV

140 I Want Jesus to Walk with Me

Freely

1 I want Je - sus to walk with me;
2 In my tri - als, Lord, walk with me;
3 When I'm in trou - ble, Lord, walk with me;

I want Je - sus to walk with me;
in my tri - als, Lord, walk with me;
when I'm in trou - ble, Lord, walk with me;

all a - long my pil - grim jour - ney,
when my heart is al - most break - ing,
when my head is bowed in sor - row,

Lord, I want Je - sus to walk with me.
Lord, I want Je - sus to walk with me.
Lord, I want Je - sus to walk with me.

Words: African American spiritual
Music (SOJOURNER irregular): African American spiritual, P.D.

Somos pueblo que camina/
We Are People on a Journey

141

Spanish 1 So - mos pue-blo que ca - mi - na   por la sen - da del do - lor.
2 Los hu - mil-des y los po - bres   in - vi - ta - dos son de Dios.

English 1 We are peo-ple on a jour-ney;   pain is with us all the way.
2 God has sent the in - vi - ta - tion   to the hum-ble and the poor.

Refrain

A - cu - da-mos ju - bi - lo - sos   a la san - ta co - mu - nión.
Joy - ful - ly we come to-geth - er   at the ho - ly feast of God.

Spanish

3 Este pan que Dios nos brinda
   alimenta nuestra unión. *Refrain*

4 Cristo aquí se hace presente;
   al reunirnos en su amor. *Refrain*

5 Los sedientos de justicia
   buscan su liberación. *Refrain*

English

3 This is bread that God provides us,
   nourishing our unity. *Refrain*

4 Christ is ever present with us
   to unite us all in love. *Refrain*

5 All who truly thirst for justice
   seek their liberation here. *Refrain*

Optional sending and blessing

Walk, people of God! **Camina, pueblo de Dios!***
With those who are persecuted and oppressed, **camina, pueblo de Dios.**
With those whom the world shuns, **camina, pueblo de Dios.**
With those who hunger and thirst, **camina, pueblo de Dios.**
With those whose hearts are breaking, **camina, pueblo de Dios.**
[With those . . . . . . , **camina, pueblo de Dios.**]

And the blessing of God Almighty,
the Father, the Son, and the Holy Spirit,
be upon you and remain with you forever. **Amen.**

*Alternate response in English could be: Walk, people of God.

Words: *La Misa Popular Nicaragüense,* 20th c.; tr. Carolyn Jennings (b. 1936) © 1993 The Pilgrim Press
Music (SOMOS PUEBLOS irregular): *La Misa Popular Nicaragüense,* 20th c., P.D.

142 We Are People on a Journey

1 We are peo-ple on a jour-ney, fol-lowing where the Mas-ter walks. We are peo-ple on a jour-ney in the sha-dow of the cross. What com-pels? The face of Je-sus!

2 We are peo-ple on a jour-ney, tak-ing up the cross of Christ. We are peo-ple on a jour-ney, mov-ing on from death to life. We re-lease the sin that tan-gles.

3 We are peo-ple on a jour-ney to the ta-ble of the Lord. We are peo-ple on a jour-ney, fed by wa-ter and the Word. We re-mem-ber, we re-mem-ber

4 We are peo-ple on a jour-ney, ris-ing up in life re-born. We are peo-ple on a jour-ney, speak-ing peace, ac-cept-ing scorn. We are walk-ing toward a home-land,

Words and Music (DEEPER JOURNEY 8.7.8.7 D): Gregg DeMey © 2008, 2010 Re:Create Music, admin. Faith Alive Christian Resources

143   Mantos y palmas/Filled with Excitement

Spanish 1 Man - tos y pal - mas es - par - cien - do, va
       2 Co - mo en la en - tra - da de Je - ru - sa - lén,

English 1 Filled with ex - cite - ment, all the hap - py throng
       2 As in that en - trance to Je - ru - sa - lem,

el pue - blo a - le - gre de Je - ru - sa - lén.
to - dos can - ta - mos a Je - sús el Rey,
spread cloaks and branch - es on the cit - y streets.
we sing ho - san - nas to the Christ, our King,

A - llá a lo le - jos se em - pie - za a mi - rar
al Cris - to vi - vo que nos lla - ma hoy
There in the dis - tance they be - gin to see,
to the liv - ing Sav - ior who still calls to - day,

en un po - lli - no al Hi - jo de Dios.
pa - ra se - guir - le con a - mor y fe.
rid - ing on a don - key, comes the Son of God.
ask - ing us to fol - low him with love and faith.

Refrain

Mien - tras mil vo - ces re - sue - nan por do - quier; ho - san - na al que
From ev - ery cor - ner a thou - sand voic - es sing _____ prais - es to

vie - ne en el nom - bre del Se - ñor. Con un a - lien - to de
him who comes in the name of God. With one great shout of __

gran ex - cla - ma - ción pro - rrum - pen con voz triun - fal:
ac - cla - ma - tion loud tri - um - phant _ song breaks forth:

"¡Ho - san - na! ¡Ho - san - na al Rey!
"Ho - san - na! Ho - san - na to the King!

¡Ho - san - na! ¡Ho - san - na al Rey!"
Ho - san - na! Ho - san - na to the King!"

144 Lift Up the Gates Eternal

PSALM 24

Refrain

Lift up the gates e-ter-nal, lift up your voic-es;
the King of glo-ry comes, the na-tion re-joic-es. *Fine*

1 See, all the earth is God's, its peo-ple and na-tions;
2 Who can go up this moun-tain, who stand in prais-ing?
3 They shall re-ceive for-give-ness, and have God's bless-ing

God built it on the deeps and laid its foun-da-tions. *To st. 2*
Those who are pure, who come with clean hands up-rais-ing. *To st. 3*
if they will search for God, their Sav-ior con-fess-ing. *To Refrain*

4 Come, lift your voices high,
be lifted to glory;
the Lord our God approaches,
come, shout the story. *To st. 5*

6 Come, lift your heads with joy;
come, lift up your tower;
the King of glory comes in
full might and power. *To st. 7*

5 Who is this glorious one,
for whom we are waiting?
We wait the mighty Lord,
our God celebrating. *To Refrain*

7 Who is this King of glory
of whom we're singing?
Our God, the Lord of Hosts,
the victory is bringing. *To Refrain*

For another setting of Ps. 24 see 499

Words: sts. Arlo Duba © 1986 Arlo D. Duba; ref. Willard F. Jabusch © 1967 Willard F. Jabusch, admin. OCP Publications
Music (PROMISED ONE 12.12.12.12): Israeli folk melody; arr. John Ferguson © 1974 United Church Press, admin. The Pilgrim Press

Hosanna, Loud Hosanna

145

1 Ho - san - na, loud ho - san - na the lit - tle chil-dren sang;
2 From Ol - i - vet they fol - lowed mid an ex - ul - tant crowd,
3 "Ho - san - na in the high - est!" That an - cient song we sing,

through pil - lared court and tem - ple the love - ly an - them rang.
the vic - tory palm branch wav - ing, and chant - ing clear and loud.
for Christ is our Re - deem - er, the Lord of heaven, our King.

To Je - sus, who had blessed them, close fold - ed to his breast,
The Lord of earth and heav - en rode on in low - ly state,
O may we ev - er praise him with heart and life and voice,

the chil - dren sang their prais - es, the sim - plest and the best.
nor scorned that lit - tle chil - dren should on his bid - ding wait.
and in his bliss - ful pres - ence e - ter - nal - ly re - joice.

For an alternate arrangement see 679. For music in a higher key see 726

Words: Jennette Threlfall, 1873, P.D.
Music (ELLACOMBE 7.6.7.6 D): *Gesangbuch der Herzogl,* Hofkapelle, Würtemberg, 1784, P.D.

146 All Glory, Laud, and Honor

Refrain

All glo-ry, laud, and hon - or to you, Re-deem-er, King,

to whom the lips of chil - dren made sweet ho-san-nas ring. *Fine*

1 You are the King of Is - rael and Da-vid's roy - al Son,
2 The com-pa-ny of an - gels is prais-ing you on high,
3 The peo-ple of the He - brews with palms be - fore you went;

To Refrain

now in the Lord's name com - ing, the King and Bless-ed One.
and we with all cre - a - tion in cho-rus make re - ply.
our praise and prayer and an - thems be-fore you we pre - sent.

4 To you before your passion
they sang their hymns of praise;
to you, now high exalted,
our melody we raise. *Refrain*

5 As you received their praises,
accept the prayers we bring,
for you delight in goodness,
O good and gracious King! *Refrain*

Words: Theodulph of Orelans, ca. 820; tr. John M. Neale, 1851, alt., P.D.
Music (ST. THEODULPH 7.6.7.6 D): Melchoir Teschner, 1615; harm. William H. Monk, 1861, P.D.

Hail and Hosanna

PSALM 118:26

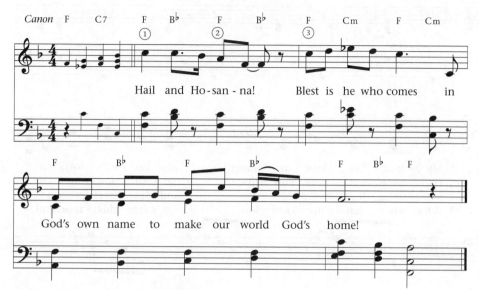

Psalm 118:19-29 for optional use with "Hail and Hosanna"

Refrain
Open for me the gates of the righteous;
I will enter and give thanks to the LORD.
This is the gate of the LORD
through which the righteous may enter.
I will give you thanks, for you answered me;
you have become my salvation.

Refrain

The stone the builders rejected
has become the cornerstone;
the LORD has done this,
and it is marvelous in our eyes.
The LORD has done it this very day;
let us rejoice today and be glad.

LORD, save us!
LORD, grant us success!

Blessed is he who comes
in the name of the LORD.
From the house of the LORD we bless you.

Refrain

The LORD is God,
and he has made his light shine on us.
With boughs in hand,
join in the festal procession
up to the horns of the altar.

You are my God, and I will praise you;
you are my God, and I will exalt you.
Give thanks to the LORD, for he is good;
his love endures forever.

Refrain

Accompaniment pattern for singing in canon; may be played by handbells or on keyboard.

For another setting of Ps. 118 see 196

Words: James Hart Brumm (b. 1962) © 1992 Choristers Guild
Music (HAIL AND HOSANNA): Alfred V. Fedak (b. 1953) © 1992 Choristers Guild

148 My Song Is Love Unknown

1 My song is love un-known, my Sav-ior's love to
2 He came from heav-en's throne sal-va-tion to be-
3 Some-times they crowd his way and his sweet prais-es
4 Why, what has my Lord done to cause this rage and

me. Love to the love-less shown, that
stow; but they re-fused, and none the
sing, re-sound-ing all the day, ho-
spite? He made the lame to run and

they might love-ly be. Oh, who am I that
longed-for Christ would know. This is my friend, my
san-nas to their King. Then, "Cru-ci-fy!" is
gave the blind their sight. What in-jur-ies, yet

Alternate tune: LOVE UNKNOWN *see 315*

For an alternate arrangment see 315

Words: Samuel Crossman, 1664, alt., P.D.
Music (RHOSYMEDRE 6.6.6.6.8.8.8): John D. Edwards, ca. 1840; arr. Albert Chung © 2012 Albert Chung,
admin. Faith Alive Christian Resources

for my sake, oh, who am I that
friend in - deed, this is my friend, my
all their breath, then, "Cru - ci - fy!" is
these are why, what in - jur - ies, yet

for my sake my Lord should take frail flesh and die?
friend in - deed, who at my need, his life did spend.
all their breath, and for his death they thirst and cry.
these are why the Lord Most High so cruel - ly dies.

5 With angry shouts they have my dear Lord done away;
a murderer they save, the Prince of Life they slay.
Yet willingly, he bears the shame,
yet willingly, he bears the shame,
that through his name all might be free.

6 Here might I stay and sing of him my soul adores:
never was love, dear King, never was grief like yours.
This is my friend in whose sweet praise,
this is my friend in whose sweet praise
I all my days would gladly spend.

149 Ride On, Ride On in Majesty

1 Ride on, ride on in maj - es - ty! Hear all the
2 Ride on, ride on in maj - es - ty! In low - ly
3 Ride on, ride on in maj - es - ty! The hosts of
4 Ride on, ride on in maj - es - ty! In low - ly

tribes ho - san - na cry; O Sav - ior meek, your
pomp ride on to die. O Christ, your tri - umphs
an - gels in the sky look down with sad and
pomp ride on to die; bow your meek head to

road pur - sue, with palms and scat - tered gar - ments strewn.
now be - gin o'er cap - tive death and con - quered sin.
won - dering eyes to see the ap - proach - ing sa - cri - fice.
mor - tal pain; then take, O Christ, your power and reign.

Optional reading (Ps. 38:9-15)

All my longings lie open before you, Lord;
my sighing is not hidden from you.

My heart pounds, my strength fails me;
even the light has gone from my eyes.
My friends and companions avoid me
because of my wounds;
my neighbors stay far away.

Those who want to kill me set their traps,
those who would harm me talk of my ruin;
all day long they scheme and lie.

I am like the deaf, who cannot hear,
like the mute, who cannot speak;
I have become like one who does not hear,
whose mouth can offer no reply.
LORD, I wait for you;
you will answer, Lord my God.

Alternate tune: CHICKAHOMINY see 150

Words: Henry Hart Milman, 1821, P.D.
Music (DEO GRACIAS 8.8.8.8): English, 15th c.; harm. Carl Schalk, 1969, © 1969 Concordia Publishing House

Rebuke Me Not in Anger, LORD

150

PSALM 38

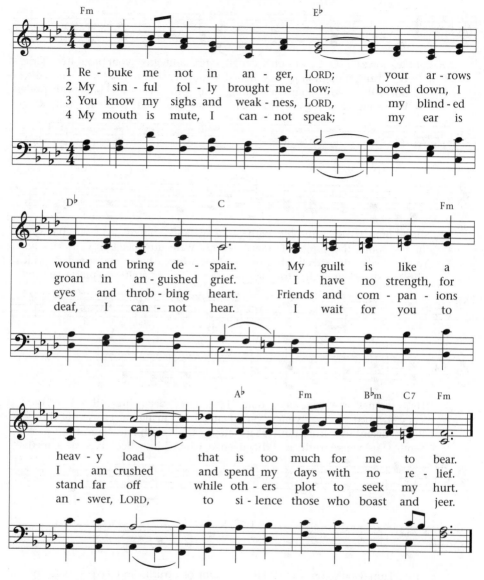

1 Re-buke me not in an-ger, LORD; your ar-rows
2 My sin-ful fol-ly brought me low; bowed down, I
3 You know my sighs and weak-ness, LORD, my blind-ed
4 My mouth is mute, I can-not speak; my ear is

wound and bring de-spair. My guilt is like a
groan in an-guished grief. I have no strength, for
eyes and throb-bing heart. Friends and com-pan-ions
deaf, I can-not hear. I wait for you to

heav-y load that is too much for me to bear.
I am crushed and spend my days with no re-lief.
stand far off while oth-ers plot to seek my hurt.
an-swer, LORD, to si-lence those who boast and jeer.

5 My pain is ever with me, LORD,
for I have sinned against your laws.
My foes are mighty—those who hate
and slander me without a cause.

6 Do not forsake me, O my LORD;
do not go far from me, my God.
Come quickly, help me now, I pray,
O LORD, my Savior and my God.

This entire psalm can be heard as the cry of God's people. Stanzas 3, 4, 6 can also be heard as Jesus' cry in his passion.

Chord symbols represent a simplified harmony.

Alternate tune: DEO GRACIAS *see 149*

Words: Helen Otte (b. 1931), 1985, © 1987 Faith Alive Christian Resources
Music (CHICKAHOMINY 8.8.8.8): Henry B. Hays, 1981, alt. © 1981 Order of St. Benedict, Inc., admin.
 Liturgical Press

151 Rejoice, O Zion's Daughter

1 Re - joice, O Zi - on's daugh - ter, and greet your prom-ised king.
2 O Christ, though king they hailed you, they sent you out to die,
3 But still you come a - mong us in cit - ies built with pride.
4 We shout a - gain, "Ho - san - na!" We hail you as our King!

Spread branch - es in his path - way, and loud ho - san - nas sing!
for soon the songs of prais - es were drowned by "Cru - ci - fy!"
You walk the streets of sor - row where hate and greed di - vide.
Christ, stir our wills to ac - tion to match the praise we sing.

He comes a - stride a don - key in deep hu - mil - i - ty
They stripped a - way your gar - ments, They made a cross your throne,
Re - deem us from our mad - ness, the clash of class and race.
Send us where truth is threat-ened, where jus - tice is de - nied,

to claim God's com - ing king - dom of truth and eq - ui - ty.
and there you died in dark - ness, a - ban-doned and a - lone.
Es - tab - lish soon your king - dom of jus - tice, truth, and grace.
and move our hearts to of - fer the love for which you died.

Words: Herman G. Stuempfle (b. 1923) © 1997 GIA Publications, Inc.
Music (LLANGLOFFAN 7.6.7.6 D): Welsh, 19th c., P.D.

I Love the Lord; He Heard My Cry (refrain) 152
PSALM 116

Refrain

I love the LORD, for he heard my voice;
he heard my cry for mercy.
Because he turned his ear to me,
I will call on him as long as I live.
The cords of death entangled me,
the anguish of the grave came over me;
I was overcome by distress and sorrow.
Then I called on the name of the LORD:
"LORD, save me!"
 The LORD is gracious and righteous;
our God is full of compassion.
The LORD protects the unwary;
when I was brought low, he saved me.
Return to your rest, my soul,
for the LORD has been good to you.
For you, LORD, have delivered me from death,
my eyes from tears,
my feet from stumbling,
that I may walk before the LORD
in the land of the living.

Refrain

I trusted in the LORD when I said,
"I am greatly afflicted";
 in my alarm I said,
"Everyone is a liar."
 What shall I return to the LORD
for all his goodness to me?
I will lift up the cup of salvation
and call on the name of the LORD.
I will fulfill my vows to the LORD
in the presence of all his people.

Refrain

Precious in the sight of the LORD
is the death of his faithful servants.
Truly I am your servant, LORD;
I serve you just as my mother did;
you have freed me from my chains.
I will sacrifice a thank offering to you
and call on the name of the LORD.
I will fulfill my vows to the LORD
in the presence of all his people,
in the courts of the house of the LORD—
in your midst, Jerusalem.
Praise the LORD.

Refrain or sing the full version of "I Love the
Lord" *439*

For other settings of Ps. 116 see 439, 735, 819, 871

Words: Isaac Watts (1674-1748), P.D.
Music (I LOVE THE LORD; HE HEARD MY CRY fragment): African American spiritual; harm. Richard Small-
wood (b. 1948) © 1975 Century Oak Publishing Group/Richwood Music, admin. Conexion Media Group,
Inc.; arr. Dave Maddux

153   Great God, Your Love Has Called Us

1 Great God, your love has called us here, as we, by love, for
2 We come with self-in-flict-ed pains of bro-ken trust and
3 Great God, in Christ you call our name and then re-ceive us

love were made. Your liv-ing like-ness still we bear,
cho-sen wrong, half-free, half-bound by in-ner chains,
as your own, not through some mer-it, right, or claim,

though marred, dis-hon-ored, dis-o-beyed. We come, with all our
by so-cial forc-es swept a-long, by powers and sys-tems
but by your grac-ious love a-lone. We strain to glimpse your

heart and mind your call to hear, your love to find.
close con-fined, yet seek-ing hope for hu-man-kind.
mer-cy seat and find you kneel-ing at our feet.

(continues)

Words: Brian A. Wren (b. 1936) © 1977, rev. 1995 Hope Publishing Company
Music (RYBURN 8.8.8.8.8.8): Norman Cocker (1889-1953) and arr. Al Fedak, 2012, © Oxford University Press.
Reprinted with permission of Oxford University Press

4 Then take the towel, and break the bread,
and humble us, and call us friends.
Suffer and serve till all are fed,
and show how grandly love intends
to work till all creation sings,
to fill all worlds, to crown all things.

5 Great God, in Christ you set us free
your life to live, your joy to share.
Give us your Spirit's liberty
to turn from guilt and dull despair,
and offer all that faith can do
while love is making all things new.

Ubi caritas et amor/Live in Charity   154

Latin U - bi ca - ri - tas et a - mor,
English Live in char - i - ty and stead - fast love,

u - bi ca - ri - tas, De - us i - bi est.
live in char - i - ty; God will dwell with you.

Optional reading (from 1 John 4:7-12)

Let us love one another, for love comes from God.
Everyone who loves has been born of God and knows God.
Whoever does not love does not know God, because God is love.
This is how God showed his love among us:
He sent his one and only Son into the world that we might live through him.
This is love: not that we loved God, but that he loved us
and sent his Son as an atoning sacrifice for our sins.
Since God so loved us, we also ought to love one another.
No one has ever seen God; but if we love one another,
God lives in us and his love is made complete in us.

Words: Scripture; English para. Taizé Community © 1979 Ateliers et Presses de Taizé, Taizé Community, France, GIA Publications, Inc., exclusive North American agent
Music (UBI CARITAS): Jacques Berthier © 1991 Ateliers et Presses de Taizé, Taizé Community, France, GIA Publications, Inc., exclusive North American agent

155 As He Gathered at His Table

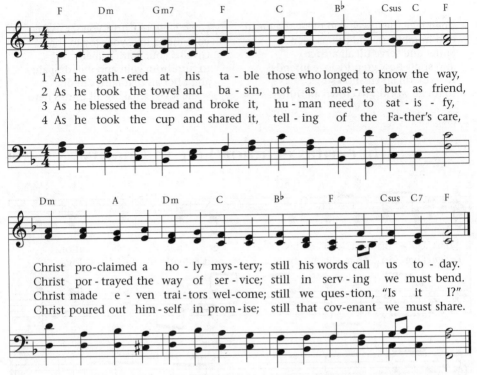

1 As he gath-ered at his   ta - ble those who longed to know the way,
2 As he took the towel and   ba - sin, not as mas - ter but as friend,
3 As he blessed the bread and broke it, hu - man need to sat - is - fy,
4 As he took the cup and shared it, tell - ing of the Fa-ther's care,

Christ pro-claimed a   ho - ly mys-tery; still his words call   us   to - day.
Christ por - trayed the way of ser - vice; still in serv - ing   we must bend.
Christ made   e - ven trai-tors wel-come; still we ques-tion, "Is   it   I?"
Christ poured out him-self in prom-ise; still that cov-enant we must share.

5 As they sang a hymn together,
   praising Israel's saving King,
   hearts and voices made one music;
   still delivering love we sing.

6 As he went into the garden,
   praying, "Father, use your Son,"
   Christ alone could know its meaning;
   still we pray, "God's will be done."

7 Though his feast be one of symbols,
   what we celebrate is real;
   still Christ welcomes to his table;
   still Christ serves us at his meal.

Optional Prayer

Covenant God,
we bless and thank you for the gift of the meal
that Jesus commanded us to share.
We thank you for this sign of your presence with us
and your love for the world that Jesus came to redeem.
**We long to feast with Jesus
in the fullness of the coming kingdom.
May our worship today
deepen our anticipation of that glory.
Amen.**

For descant see 56

Words: Paul A. Richardson, 1986, © 1990 The Hymn Society, admin. Hope Publishing Company
Music (STUTTGART 8.7.8.7): Christian F. Witt's *Psalmodia Sacra*, 1715; adapt. Henry J. Gauntlett, 1861, P.D.

As in That Upper Room You Left Your Seat   156

1 As in that up-per room you left your seat
2 I bow be-fore you, all my sin con-fessed,
3 So in re-mem-brance of your life laid down,

and took a towel and chose a ser-vant's part,
to hear a-gain the words of love you said;
I come to praise you for your grace di-vine;

so for to-day, Lord, wash a-gain my feet,
and at your ta-ble, as your hon-ored guest,
saved by your cross and sub-ject to your crown,

who in your mer-cy died to cleanse my heart.
I take and eat the true and liv-ing bread.
strength-ened for ser-vice by this bread and wine.

Words: Timothy Dudley-Smith (b. 1926) ©1993 Hope Publishing Company
Music (UPPER ROOM 10.10.10.10): Richard VanOss © 2012 Richard VanOss, admin. Faith Alive Christian
   Resources

157 Meekness and Majesty

1 Meek - ness and maj - es - ty, man - hood and De - i - ty
2 Fa - ther's pure ra - di-ance, per - fect in in - no - cence,
3 Wis - dom un - search-a - ble, God the in - vis - i - ble,

in per - fect har-mo - ny, the Man who is God.
yet learns o - be - di-ence to death on a cross,
Love in - de - struct-i - ble in frail - ty ap - pears.

Lord of e - ter - ni - ty dwells in hu - man - i - ty,
suf - fering to give us life, con - quering through sac - ri - fice,
Lord of in - fin - i - ty, stoop - ing so ten-der - ly,

kneels in hu - mil - i - ty, and wash - es our feet.
and, as they cru - ci - fy, prays, "Fa - ther, for - give."
lifts our hu - man - i - ty to the heights of his throne.

Words and Music (MEEKNESS AND MAJESTY 12.11.12.11 refrain 12.5.5): Graham Kendrick © 1986 Thankyou Music (PRS), admin. worldwide at EMICMGPublishing.com excluding Europe which is admin. by Kingswaysongs

Oh, what a mys-ter-y— meek-ness and maj-es-ty;
bow down and wor-ship, for this is your
God.
God.

Optional prayer

God of glory,
in a world drawn
to so many lesser visions of glory,
teach us the greater glory of Jesus,
    who did not grasp power,
    who was obedient to death,
    who did not despise the lowly,
    who stooped to wash his disciples' feet,

[Add other phrases as appropriate].

Then help us to be formed
into the likeness of Jesus.
Help us
    to do nothing out of selfish ambition,
    to seek the interests of others,
    to love our enemies,
    to be servants of your peace,

[Add other phrases as appropriate].

We pray in Jesus' name. **Amen.**

158 Shadows Lengthen into Night

1 Shar-ing Pas-chal bread and wine   as the day-light ebbs a-
2 In a grove of ol-ive trees   un-der-neath a dark-ening
3 In the gar-den, still and deep,   those he asked to watch and
4 Deep-er in the gar-den's chill,   Je-sus kneels to pray a-

way, friends at ta-ble join to dine.
sky, Je-sus warns what he fore-sees:
pray, heav-y lid-ded, fall a-sleep,
lone, wrest-ling with God's ho-ly will,

One of them will soon be-tray.
Pe-ter al-so will den-y.
wea-ry from the anx-ious day.
cry-ing out, "Let it be done!"

Refrain

Sha-dows length-en in-to night.

(continues)

Words: Mary Louise Bringle © 2006 GIA Publications, Inc.
Music (TENEBRAE 7.7.7.7 refrain 7): Sally Ann Morris © 2006 GIA Publications, Inc.

5 All too soon, the silence rends,
   with a crash of club and sword.
   Judas, still received as "Friend,"
   with a kiss betrays his Lord. *Refrain*

6 Christ's disciples, weak with fear,
   fail one further, stringent test—
   so like us, with trouble near—
   fleeing far at his arrest. *Refrain*

7 While the web of darkness grows,
   Jesus suffers through his trial.
   As the herald rooster crows,
   Peter speaks his third denial. *Refrain*

8 Lifted high upon a cross,
   Perfect Love hangs pierced with nails.
   All creation grieves its loss,
   as the very sunlight fails. *Refrain*

When using in the context of a Tenebrae Service (Service of Shadows), each stanza is preceded by a Scripture reading. After each stanza a candle may be extinguished.

1. *Matthew 26:20-25: The Shadow of Betrayal*
2. *Matthew 26:31, 33-35: The Shadow of Impending Faithlessness*
3. *Matthew 26:36-41: The Shadow of Unshared Vigil*
4. *Matthew 26:42-45: The Shadow of Christ's Agony*
5. *Matthew 26:47-50: The Shadow of Arrest*
6. *Mark 14:48-50: The Shadow of Desertion*
7. *Luke 22:54-62: The Shadow of Denial*
8. *Luke 23:33-46: The Shadow of the Cross*

Alternate Lenten stanzas based on texts from Lamentations:

1 God who rules the waning day,
   darkness steals across the land.
   Hear your people as we pray.
   Hold us, trembling, in your hand.
   Refrain

2 Lonely roads to Zion mourn,
   as her enemies prevail.
   All her priests and elders groan;
   all her young girls grieve and wail.
   Refrain

3 Shackled with a heavy chain,
   sorely broken by the rod.
   Days of sorrow and of pain:
   can this be the hand of God?
   Refrain

4 Look, O Lord, on our disgrace:
   captive people live as slaves;
   heartsick, hungering after grace.
   Be for us the God who saves!
   Refrain

5 Look: the Lamb of God appears,
   sinless, to the slaughter led.
   For our sins and griefs, his tears:
   stricken, beaten, bruised, and dead.
   Refrain

159 Stay with Me

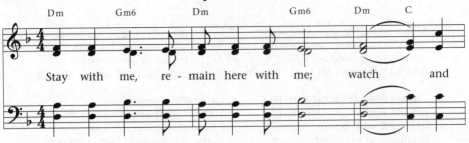

Words: Based on Matthew 26
Music (STAY WITH ME): Jacques Berthier © 1984 Ateliers et Presses de Taizé, Taizé Community, France, GIA
  Publications, Inc., exclusive North American agent

160 A Reflection on Jesus' Prayers

*The following reflection and prayer may be used
with the sung refrain "Stay With Me" 159.*

"In the days of his flesh, Jesus offered up
prayers and supplications, with loud cries and
tears, to the one who was able to save him
from death, and he was heard because of his
reverent submission." *(Heb. 5:7)*

Reader 1: "May they be one as we are one. . . ."
(or additional text from John 17)

Refrain

Reader 2: "My God, my God, why have you
forsaken me"
(or additional text from Ps. 22)

Refrain

Reader 1: "Into your hands I commit my spirit"
(or additional text from Ps. 31)

Refrain

Reader 2: "Thank you for hiding these things
from the wise, revealing them to children."
(Matt.11:25-27)

Refrain

Reader 1: "I will proclaim your name to my
brothers and sisters, in the midst of the congregation I will praise you. . ." *(Ps. 22:22;
Heb. 2:12)*

Refrain

Lord God, by your Spirit help us
to not merely to listen
to the prayers that Jesus prayed,
but also to be united with him
in his death and resurrection.
May we, the praying church,
learn how to pray as Christ's body,
from the one who—
in life and in death—
is the head of the body,
our Lord Jesus Christ. Amen.

Text: scripture, NRSV adapted

Go to Dark Gethsemane

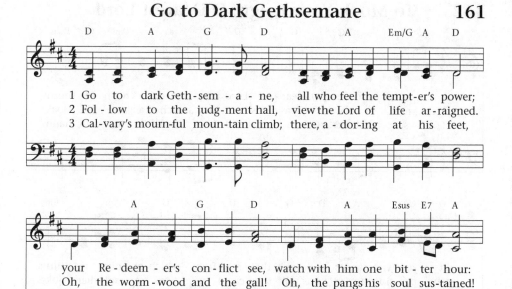

1 Go to dark Geth-sem-a-ne, all who feel the tempt-er's power;
2 Fol-low to the judg-ment hall, view the Lord of life ar-raigned.
3 Cal-vary's mourn-ful moun-tain climb; there, a-dor-ing at his feet,

your Re-deem-er's con-flict see, watch with him one bit-ter hour:
Oh, the worm-wood and the gall! Oh, the pangs his soul sus-tained!
mark the mir-a-cle of time, God's own sac-ri-fice com-plete:

turn not from his griefs a-way— teach us, Lord, how we should pray.
Shun not suf-fering, shame, or loss— help us, Lord, to bear our cross.
"It is fin-ished!" hear him cry— save us, Lord, when death draws nigh.

In some circumstances it may be appropriate to conclude with the following stanza.

4 Early hasten to the tomb
where they laid his breathless clay:
all is solitude and gloom.
Who has taken him away?
Christ is risen! He meets our eyes.
Savior, teach us so to rise.

For this music in a higher key see 623

Words: James Montomery, 1825, alt., P.D.
Music (REDHEAD 7.7.7.7.7.7): Richard Redhead, 1853, P.D.

162 To Mock Your Reign, O Dearest Lord

1 To mock your reign, O dear-est Lord, they made a crown of thorns,
2 In mock ac-claim, O gra-cious Lord, they snatched a pur-ple cloak,
3 A scep-tered reed, O pa-tient Lord, they thrust in-to your hand,

set you with taunts a-long that road from which no one re-turns.
your pas-sion turned, for all they cared in-to a sol-dier's joke.
and act-ed out their grim cha-rade to its ap-point-ed end.

They could not know, as we do now, how glo-rious is that crown,
They could not know, as we do now, that though we mer-it blame,
They could not know, as we do now, though em-pires rise and fall,

that thorns would flower up-on your brow, your sor-rows heal our own.
you will your robe of mer-cy throw a-round our na-ked shame.
your king-dom shall not cease to grow till love em-brac-es all.

For an alternate arrangement see 10

Words: Fred Pratt Green, 1973, © 1973 Hope Publishing Company
Music (KINGSFOLD 8.6.8.6 D): traditional English; adapt. Ralph Vaughan Williams (1872-1958), 1906, P.D.

What Grace Is This

1 What grace is this! My Lord and King has set his
2 What grace is this— that ver-y God would stoop to
3 What grace is this! Though Lord of all, he yields to
4 What grace is this! Rude a-gon-ies! With com-mon

face to suf-fer-ing. The Son e-ter-nal dies to
lift a cross of wood and walk a road of rock and
Pon-tius Pil-ate's law and lets the Ro-man ham-mers
thieves he hangs and bleeds. The sin-less Son bears each mis-

bring e-ter-nal life to me.
blood, a sin-ner's road, for me.
draw a rush of blood for me.
deed. He pays for all, for me.

5 What grace is this! Once wrapped in cloths
and gently laid in manger-trough,
he's taken, dead, from wretched cross
and wrapped again for me.

6 What grace is this? How can it be?
He wears this raw humility
to lift me to eternity.
Such grace—sweet grace—for me.

Words: Laurie F. Gauger © 2005 Laurie F. Gauger, admin. Faith Alive Christian Resources
Music (WHAT GRACE 8.8.8.6): G.A. Hennig © 2005 G.A. Hennig, admin. Faith Aive Christian Resources

164

What Wondrous Love

PSALM 22

1 What won-drous love is this, O my soul, O my soul! What
2 When I was sink-ing down, sink-ing down, sink-ing down, when
3 To God and to the Lamb I will sing, I will sing, to
4 And when from death I'm free, I'll sing on, I'll sing on, and

won-drous love is this, O my soul! What won-drous love is
I was sink-ing down, sink-ing down; when I was sink-ing
God and to the Lamb I will sing; to God and to the
when from death I'm free, I'll sing on; and when from death I'm

this that caused the Lord of bliss to bear the dread-ful curse
down be-neath God's right-eous frown, Christ laid a-side his crown
Lamb, who is the great I AM— while mil-lions join the theme,
free, I'll sing and joy-ful be, and through e-ter-ni-ty

for my soul, for my soul, to bear the dread-ful curse for my soul?
for my soul, for my soul, Christ laid a-side his crown for my soul.
I will sing, I will sing, while mil-lions join the theme, I will sing.
I'll sing on, I'll sing on, and through e-ter-ni-ty I'll sing on.

For other settings of Ps. 22 see 165, 511, 594

Words: S. Mead's *A General Selection*, 1811, P.D.
Music (WONDROUS LOVE 12.9.12.12.9): W. Walker's *Southern Harmony*, 1835; harm. Emily R. Brink, 1986,
© 1987 Faith Alive Christian Resources

Psalm 22:1-11, 22-29

The Psalm reading may begin with WONDROUS LOVE refrain played on an instrument or hummed by the congregation. For the music of the refrain see the bracketed portion of 164.

Voice 1:
My God, my God,
why have you forsaken me?
Why are you so far from saving me,
so far from my cries of anguish?
My God, I cry out by day,
but you do not answer,
by night, but I find no rest.

Voice 2:
Yet you are enthroned as the Holy One;
you are the one Israel praises.
In you our ancestors put their trust;
they trusted and you delivered them.
To you they cried out and were saved;
in you they trusted
and were not put to shame.

All Sing
What wondrous love is this,
O my soul, O my soul!
What wondrous love is this,
O my soul!

Voice 1:
But I am a worm and not a man,
scorned by everyone, despised by the people.
All who see me mock me;
they hurl insults, shaking their heads.
"He trusts in the Lord," they say,
"let the Lord rescue him.
Let him deliver him,
since he delights in him."

All Sing
When I was sinking down,
sinking down, sinking down,
when I was sinking down,
sinking down...

Voice 2:
Yet you brought me out of the womb;
you made me trust in you,
even at my mother's breast.
From birth I was cast on you;
from my mother's womb
you have been my God.

Do not be far from me,
for trouble is near
and there is no one to help.

All Sing
To God and to the Lamb I will sing,
I will sing,
to God and to the Lamb I will sing.

Voice 1:
I will declare your name to my people;
in the assembly I will praise you.
You who fear the Lord, praise him!
All you descendants of Jacob, honor him!
Revere him, all you descendants of Israel!

Voice 2:
For he has not despised or scorned
the suffering of the afflicted one;
he has not hidden his face from him
but has listened to his cry for help.
From you comes the theme
of my praise in the great assembly;
before those who fear you
I will fulfill my vows.
The poor will eat and be satisfied;
those who seek the Lord will praise him—
may your hearts live forever!

Voice 1 and 2 together:
All the ends of the earth
will remember and turn to the Lord,
and all the families of the nations
will bow down before him,
for dominion belongs to the Lord
and he rules over the nations.
All the rich of the earth
will feast and worship;
all who go down to the dust
will kneel before him—
those who cannot keep themselves alive.

All Sing
And when from death I'm free,
I'll sing on, I'll sing on,
and when from death I'm free,
I'll sing on.

For other settings of Ps. 22 see 164, 511, 594

Sung refrain: from "What Wondrous Love is This," S. Mead's *A General Selection*, 1811, P.D.

166 Were You There

1 Were you there when they cru - ci - fied my Lord? *Were you there?*
2 Were you there when they nailed him to the tree?
3 Were you there when they laid him in the tomb?
4 Were you there when the sun re - fused to shine? *Were you there?*

Were you there when they cru - ci - fied my Lord? *Were you there?*
Were you there when they nailed him to the tree?
Were you there when they laid him in the tomb?
Were you there when the sun re - fused to shine? *Were you there?*

Oh, some - times it caus - es me to trem - ble, trem - ble, trem - ble.

Were you there when they cru - ci - fied my Lord? *Were you there?*
Were you there when they nailed him to the tree?
Were you there when they laid him in the tomb?
Were you there when the sun re - fused to shine? *Were you there?*

Optional Easter Stanza
Were you there when God raised him from the tomb?. . .

Words: African American spiritual, P.D.
Music (WERE YOU THERE 10.10.14.10): African American spiritual; harm. C. Winfred Douglas, 1940, P.D.

Beneath the Cross of Jesus 167

1 Be - neath the cross of Je - sus I long to take my stand,
2 Up - on the cross of Je - sus, my eye at times can see
3 I take, O cross, your sha - dow for my a - bid - ing place;

the sha - dow of a might - y rock with - in a wear - y land,
the ver - y dy - ing form of one who suf - fered there for me.
I ask no oth - er sun - shine than the sun - shine of his face;

a home with - in the wil - der - ness, a rest up - on the way,
And from my con - trite heart, with tears, two won - ders I con - fess:
con - tent to let the world go by, to know no gain nor loss,

from the burn - ing of the noon - tide heat and the bur - dens of the day.
the___ won - der of his glor - ious love and___ my un - wor - thi - ness.
my___ sin - ful self my on - ly shame, my___ glo - ry all, the cross.

Words: Elizabeth C. Clephane (1830-1869), P.D.
Music (ST. CHRISTOPHER 7.6.8.6.8.6.8.6): Frederick C. Maker (1844-1927), P.D.

168 O Sacred Head, Now Wounded

1 O sa-cred head, now wound-ed, with grief and shame weighed down,
2 My Lord, what you did suf-fer was all for sin-ners' gain;
3 What lan-guage shall I bor-row to thank you, dear-est Friend,

now scorn-ful-ly sur-round-ed with thorns, your on-ly crown.
mine, mine was the trans-gres-sion, but yours the dead-ly pain.
for this, your dy-ing sor-row, your mer-cy with-out end?

O sa-cred head, what glo-ry and bless-ing you have known!
So here I kneel, my Sav-ior, for I de-serve your place;
Lord, make me yours for-ev-er, a loy-al ser-vant true,

Yet, though de-spised and gor-y, I claim you as my own.
look on me with your fa-vor and save me by your grace.
and let me nev-er, nev-er out-live my love for you.

Chord symbols represent a simplified harmony.

For an alternative arrangement see 656

Words: Latin, medieval; German tr. Paul Gerhardt, 1656; English tr. James W. Alexander, 1830, alt., P.D.
Music (HERZLICH TUT MICH VERLANGEN 7.6.7.6 D): Hans Leo. Hassler, 1601; adapt. and harm. Johann S. Bach in *St. Matthew Passion*, 1729, P.D.

Jesus, Remember Me LUKE 23:42

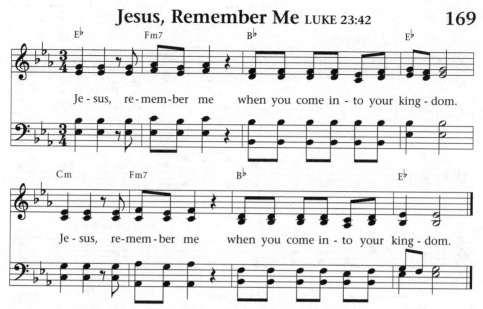

Je - sus, re - mem - ber me when you come in - to your king - dom.

Je - sus, re - mem - ber me when you come in - to your king - dom.

Words: Luke 23:42
Music (JESUS REMEMBER ME 6.8.6.8): Jacques Berthier © 1978, 1980, 1981 Ateliers et Presses de Taizé, Taizé
Community, France, GIA Publications, Inc., exclusive North American agent

Man of Sorrows—What a Name

1 Man of sor - rows—what a name for the Son of God, who came
2 Bear-ing shame and scoff-ing rude, in my place con-demned he stood,
3 Guilt-y, help - less, lost were we; blame-less Lamb of God was he,

ru - ined sin - ners to re - claim: Hal - le - lu - jah, what a Sav - ior!
sealed my par - don with his blood: Hal - le - lu - jah, what a Sav - ior!
sac - ri - ficed to set us free: Hal - le - lu - jah, what a Sav - ior!

4 He was lifted up to die;
"It is finished" was his cry;
now in heaven exalted high:
Hallelujah, what a Savior!

5 When he comes, our glorious King,
all his ransomed home to bring,
then anew this song we'll sing:
Hallelujah, what a Savior!

Words and Music (HALLELUJAH! WHAT A SAVIOR 7.7.7.8): Philip P. Bliss, 1875, alt., P.D.

171

Calvary

*Refrain Cal - va - ry,_____ Cal - va - ry,_____ Cal - va -
1 Ev - ery time I think a - bout Je - sus, ev - ery
2 Sin - ner, do you love____ my Je - sus? Sin - ner,

ry,_____ Cal - va - ry,_____ Cal - va - ry,_____
time I think a - bout Je - sus, ev - ery time I
do you love____ my Je - sus? Sin - ner, do you

Cal - va - ry,_____ sure - ly he died on Cal - va - ry.
think a - bout Je - sus; sure - ly he died on Cal - va - ry.
love____ my Je - sus? Sure - ly he died on Cal - va - ry.

3 Don't you hear him calling his Father? *3x*
Surely he died on Calvary. *Refrain*

4 Don't you hear him say, "It is finished!" *3x*
Surely he died on Calvary. *Refrain*

5 Jesus died for my salvation. *3x*
Surely he died on Calvary. *Refrain*

Refrain should be sung at the beginning and then following each stanza.
Words and Music (CALVARY irregular): African American spiritual, P.D.

Ah, Holy Jesus, How Have You Offended 172

1 Ah, ho-ly Je-sus, how have you of-fend-ed, that mor-tal
2 Who was the guilt-y? Who brought this up-on you? It is my
3 For me, dear Je-sus, was your in-car-na-tion, your mor-tal
4 There-fore, dear Je-sus, since I can-not pay you, I do a-

judg-ment has on you de-scend-ed? By foes de-rid-ed,
trea-son, Lord, that has un-done you. 'Twas I, Lord Je-sus,
sor-row, and your life's ob-la-tion; your death of an-guish
dore you and will ev-er pray you, think on your pit-y

by your own re-ject-ed, O most af-flict-ed!
I it was de-nied you; I cru-ci-fied you.
and your bit-ter pas-sion, for my sal-va-tion.
and your love un-swerv-ing, not my de-serv-ing.

Optional reading (Rom. 5:8-11)

But God demonstrates his own love for us in this:
While we were still sinners, Christ died for us.
Since we have now been justified by his blood,
how much more shall we be saved from God's wrath through him!
For if, when we were God's enemies, we were reconciled to him through the death of his Son,
how much more, having been reconciled, shall we be saved through his life!
Not only is this so, but we also rejoice in God through our Lord Jesus Christ,
through whom we have now received reconciliation.

Words: Johann Heermann, 1630; tr. Robert Bridges, 1899, alt., P.D.
Music (HERZLIEBSTER JESU 11.11.11.5): Johann Crüger, 1640, P.D.

173 Alas! And Did My Savior Bleed

1 A - las! And did my Sav - ior bleed, and did my
2 Was it for sins that I have done he groaned up -
3 Well might the sun in dark - ness hide and shut its
4 Thus might I hide my blush - ing face while his dear

Sov - ereign die? Would he de - vote that
on the tree? A - maz - ing pit - y,
glo - ries in when Christ, the might - y
cross ap - pears, dis - solve my heart in

sa - cred head for sin - ners such as I?
grace un - known, and love be - yond de - gree!
Mak - er, died for his own crea - tures' sin.
thank - ful - ness, and melt mine eyes to tears.

Optional reading (Is. 53:1-5)

Who has believed what we have heard?
And to whom has the arm
of the LORD been revealed?
For he grew up before him like a young plant,
and like a root out of dry ground;
he had no form or majesty
that we should look at him,
nothing in his appearance
that we should desire him.
He was despised and rejected by others;
a man of suffering
and acquainted with infirmity;

and as one from whom others
hide their faces he was despised,
and we held him of no account.
**Surely he has borne our infirmities
and carried our diseases;
yet we accounted him stricken,
struck down by God, and afflicted.
But he was wounded
for our transgressions,
crushed for our iniquities;
upon him was the punishment
that made us whole,
and by his bruises we are healed.**

Text: Isaiah 53:1-5, NRSV
Words: Isaac Watts, 1707, alt., P.D.
Music (MARTYRDOM 8.6.8.6): Hugh Wilson, ca. 1800; adapt. Robert Smith, 1825, P.D.; arr. Nolan Williams Jr
   (b. 1969) © 2000 GIA Publications, Inc.

I Stand Amazed

1 I stand a-mazed in the pres-ence of Je - sus, the Naz - a - rene,
2 He took my sins and my sor - rows; he made them his ver - y own;
3 When with the ran-somed in glo - ry his face I at last shall see,

and won-der how he could love me, a sin - ner, con - demned, un - clean.
he bore the bur - den to Cal - vary and suf - fered and died a - lone.
'twill be my joy through the a - ges to sing of his love for me.

Refrain

How mar - vel - ous, how won - der - ful! And my song shall ev - er be:

How mar - vel - ous, how won - der - ful is my Sav - ior's love for me!

Words and Music (MY SAVIOR'S LOVE 8.7.8.7 refrain 8.7.8.7): Charles H. Gabriel, P.D.

175   When I Survey the Wondrous Cross

1 When I sur-vey the won-drous cross on which the
2 For-bid it, Lord, that I should boast, save in the
3 See, from his head, his hands, his feet, sor-row and
4 Were the whole realm of na-ture mine, that were a

Prince of glo-ry died, my rich-est gain I
death of Christ, my God! All the vain things that
love flow min-gled down. Did e'er such love and
pres-ent far too small. Love so a-maz-ing,

count but loss, and pour con-tempt on all my pride.
charm me most, I sac-ri-fice them through his blood.
sor-row meet, or thorns com-pose so rich a crown?
so di-vine, de-mands my soul, my life, my all.

If continuing on to refrain "The Wonderful Cross," the last note should only be held for two beats.

Alternate key

Words: Isaac Watts, 1707, P.D.
Music (HAMBURG 8.8.8.8): Lowell Mason, 1824, P.D.

The Wonderful Cross

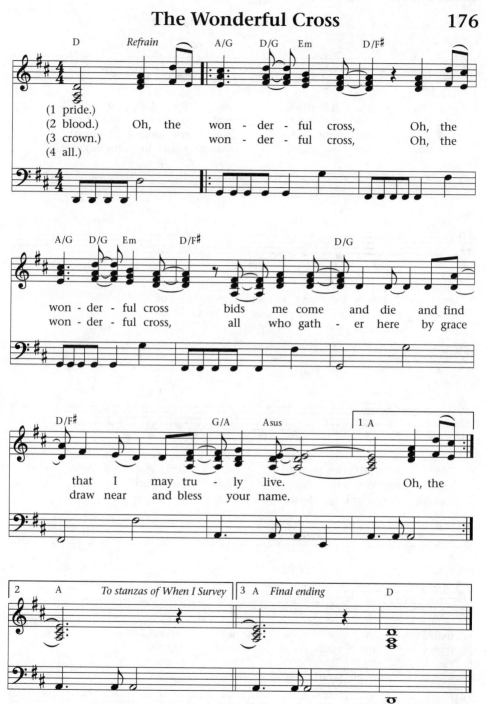

(1 pride.)
(2 blood.) Oh, the won - der - ful cross, Oh, the
(3 crown.) won - der - ful cross, Oh, the
(4 all.)

won - der - ful cross bids me come and die and find
won - der - ful cross, all who gath - er here by grace

that I may tru - ly live. Oh, the
draw near and bless your name.

To stanzas of When I Survey | Final ending

Words and Music (THE WONDERFUL CROSS): Chris Tomlin, J.D. Walt, Jesse Reeves © 2000
worshiptogether.com songs (ASCAP)/sixsteps Music (ASCAP), admin. EMICMGPublishing.com

177 Oh, to See the Dawn

1 Oh, to see the dawn of the darkest day:
2 Oh, to see the pain writ-ten on your face,
3 Now the day-light flees; now the ground be-neath
4 Oh, to see my name writ-ten in the wounds,

Christ on the road to Cal-va-ry.
bear-ing the awe-some weight of sin.
quakes as its Ma-ker bows his head.
for through your suf-fering I am free.

Tried by sin-ful men, torn and beat-en, then
Ev-ery bit-ter thought, ev-ery e-vil deed
Cur-tain torn in two, dead are raised to life,
Death is crushed to death; life is mine to live,

nailed to a cross of wood.
crown-ing your blood-stained brow.
"Fin-ished!" the vic-tory cry.
won through your self-less love!

Words and Music (OH, TO SEE THE DAWN 10.8.10.6 refrain 6.6.6.8): Keith Getty and Stuart Townend © 2005
Thankyou Music (PRS), admin. worldwide at EMICMGPublishing.com excluding Europe which is admin. by
Kingswaysongs; desc. Larry Visser © 2012 Thankyou Music, admin. EMICMGPublishing.com

Descant

Refrain

4 This the pow-er of the cross:

1-3 This the power of the cross: Christ be-
4 This the power of the cross: Son of

Son of God slain for us. What a love, what a

came sin for us. Took the blame,
God slain for us. What a love,

cost! We stand, we stand for-giv-en at the cross.
bore the wrath, we stand for-giv-en at the cross.
what a cost! We stand for-giv-en at the cross.

178 A Prayer for a Service of Vigil and Waiting

Lord of life,
your Son, our Lord Jesus, is the light of the world.
As we remember how your people gathered on this night
to celebrate the Passover feast of deliverance,
kindle our hearts with the fires of your Spirit
so that we may be filled with a holy desire
to shine with the brightness of Christ's rising.
Amen.

179   Alleluia! Alleluia! Hearts to Heaven

1 Al - le - lu - ia, al - le - lu - ia! Hearts to heaven and
2 Al - le - lu - ia, Christ is ris - en! Death at last has
3 Christ is ris - en, Christ the first - fruits of the ho - ly
4 Al - le - lu - ia, al - le - lu - ia! Glo - ry be to

voic - es raise. Sing to God a hymn of glad - ness, sing to
met de - feat. See the an - cient powers of e - vil in con -
har - vest yield, which will all its full a - bun - dance at his
God on high; al - le - lu - ia! to the Sav - ior, who has

God a hymn of praise. He who on the cross a vic - tim
fu - sion and re - treat. Once he died and once was bur - ied;
sec - ond com - ing yield. Then the gold - en ears of har - vest
won the vic - to - ry; al - le - lu - ia! to the Spir - it,

For music in a higher key see 922

Words: Christopher Wordsworth, 1862, alt., P.D.
Music (EBENEZER 8.7.8.7 D): Thomas J. Williams, (1869-1944), 1890, P.D.

for the world's sal - va - tion bled,
now he lives for - ev - er - more—
will their heads be - fore him wave,
fount of love and sanc - ti - ty;

Je - sus Christ, the
Je - sus Christ, the
rip - ened by his
al - le - lu - ia,

King of glo - ry, now is ris - en from the dead.
world's Re - deem - er, whom we wor - ship and a - dore.
glo - rious sun - shine from the fur - rows of the grave.
al - le - lu - ia! to the tri - une Maj - es - ty.

A Prayer of Easter Expectation 180

Merciful God,
on this day we remember
the women who waited at Jesus' tomb,
the fearful disciples gathered again in the upper room,
the despondent pilgrims on their journey to Emmaus.
Who among them could have imagined all that would take place?

We pray, with urgency and expectation,
for all those—among us and around us—who live every day in fear and despondency,
without tasting and seeing the joy of resurrection life in Christ.
As we wait, may your Spirit be on the move.

May many—those we love, those we have never met—
be surprised by joy in this Easter season.
Through the power of the resurrected Christ, we pray. Amen.

181 See, What a Morning

1 See, what a morn - ing, glo - rious-ly bright, with the
2 See Ma - ry weep - ing, "Where is he laid?"— as in
3 One with the Fa - ther, An - cient of Days, through the

dawn - ing of hope in Je - ru - sa - lem;
sor - row she turns from the emp - ty tomb.
Spir - it who clothes faith with cer - tain - ty.

fold - ed the grave - clothes, tomb filled with light, as the
Hears a voice speak - ing, call - ing her name; it's the
Hon - or and bless - ing, glo - ry and praise to the

an - gels an - nounce, "Christ is ris - en!"
Mas - ter, the Lord, raised to life a-gain!
King crowned with power and au - thor - i - ty.

182 Christ the Lord Is Risen Today

1 Christ the Lord is risen to-day! Al - le - lu - ia!
2 Love's re-deem-ing work is done, Al - le - lu - ia!
3 Lives a-gain our glo-rious King; Al - le - lu - ia!

All cre - a - tion, join to say: Al - le - lu - ia!
Fought the fight, the bat-tle won; Al - le - lu - ia!
Where, O death, is now your sting? Al - le - lu - ia!

Raise your joys and tri-umphs high; Al - le - lu - ia!
Death in vain for - bids him rise; Al - le - lu - ia!
Once he died, our souls to save; Al - le - lu - ia!

Sing, O heavens, and earth, re - ply: Al - le - lu - ia!
Christ has o - pened par - a - dise. Al - le - lu - ia!
Where your vic - to - ry, O grave? Al - le - lu - ia!

(continues)

Chord symbols represent a simplified harmony.

Words: Charles Wesley, 1739, alt., P.D.
Music (EASTER HYMN 7.7.7.7 with alleluias): *Lyra Davidica*, 1708, P.D.

4 Soar we now where Christ has led, Alleluia!
Fol<u>low</u>ing our exalted Head; Alleluia!
Made like him, like him we rise; Alleluia!
Ours the cross, the grave, the skies. Alleluia!

5 Hail the Lord of earth and <u>heaven</u>! Alleluia!
Praise to you by both be <u>given</u>; Alleluia!
Risen Christ, triumphant now; Alleluia!
Every knee to you shall bow. Alleluia!

Aleluya/Alleluia 183

Spanish 1 A - le - lu - ya. A - le - lu - ya. A - le - lu - ya. A - le - lu - ya.
English 1 Al - le - lu - ia. Al - le - lu - ia. Al - le - lu - ia. Al - le - lu - ia.

A - le - lu - ya. A - le - lu - ya. El Se - ñor re - su - ci - tó.
Al - le - lu - ia. Al - le - lu - ia. Christ the Lord is risen in - deed.

2 Alleluia, alleluia. *(3x)* Christ, the firstfruits from the grave.
3 Alleluia, alleluia. *(3x)* Christ has given us new life.
4 Alleluia, alleluia. *(3x)* Glory, love, and praise to God.

Words: traditional
Music (ALELUYA HONDURAS 8.8.8.7): Honduran traditional melody; arr. John L. Bell (b. 1949) © 1995 Wild
Goose Resource Group, Iona Community, Scotland, GIA Publications, Inc., exclusive North American agent

184 Good Christians All, Rejoice and Sing

1 Good Chris-tians all, re-joice and sing! Now is the tri - umph of our King! To all the world glad news we bring:
2 The Lord of life is risen to - day. Sing songs of praise a - long his way. Let all the world re - joice and say:
3 Praise we in songs of vic - to - ry that love, that life which can - not die, and sing with hearts up - lift - ed high:

Refrain
Al - le - lu - ia, al - le - lu - ia, al - le - lu - ia!

4 Your name we bless, O risen Lord,
   and sing today with one accord
   the life laid down, the life restored:
   Refrain

5 To God the Father, God the Son,
   to God the Spirit, three-in-one,
   we sing for life in us begun:
   Refrain

Chord symbols represent a simplified harmony.

Words: Cyril A. Alington, 1925, alt. © 1958 *Hymns Ancient and Modern,* admin. Hope Publishing Company
Music (GELOBT SEI GOTT 8.8.8 with alleluias 4.4.4): Melchoir Vulpius, 1609, P.D.

The Strife Is O'er, the Battle Done

Alleluias to be sung at the beginning and conclusion of the hymn

1 The strife is o'er, the bat - tle done; the vic - to -
ry of life is won; the song of tri - umph
has be - gun. Al - le - lu - ia!

2 The powers of death have done their worst, but Christ their
le - gions has dis - persed. Let shouts of ho - ly
joy out - burst. Al - le - lu - ia!

3 The three sad days are quick - ly sped; he ris - es
glo - rious from the dead. All glo - ry to our
ris - en Head. Al - le - lu - ia!

4 He closed the yawning gates of hell;
the bars from heaven's high portals fell.
Let hymns of praise his triumph tell.
Alleluia!

5 Lord, by the stripes which wounded thee,
from death's dread sting thy servants free,
that we may live and sing to thee.
Alleluia!

Words: *Symphonia Sirenum*, Cologne, 1695; tr. Francis Pott, 1861, P.D.
Music (VICTORY 4.4.4.8.8.8.4): Giovanni da Palestrina, 1591; adapt. and arr. William H. Monk, 1861, P.D.

Low in the Grave He Lay

186

1 Low in the grave he lay— Je - sus, my Sav - ior; wait - ing the
2 Vain - ly they watch his bed— Je - sus, my Sav - ior; vain - ly they
3 Death can - not keep its prey— Je - sus, my Sav - ior; he tore the

coming day— Je - sus, my Lord.
seal the dead— Je - sus, my Lord. Up from the grave he a - rose,
bars a - way— Je - sus, my Lord. *He a - rose!*

with a might - y tri - umph o'er his foes. *He a - rose!* He a - rose a vic - tor

from the dark do - main, and he lives for - ev - er with his saints to reign!

He a - rose! *He a - rose!* He a - rose! *He a - rose!* Hal - le - lu - jah! Christ a - rose!

Words and Music (CHRIST AROSE 6.5.6.4 refrain 7.9.11.11.6.7): Robert Lowry, 1874, alt, P.D.

Thine Is the Glory

1 Thine is the glo-ry, ris-en, con-quering Son; end-less is the
2 Lo, Je-sus meets thee, ris-en from the tomb! Lov-ing-ly he
3 No more we doubt thee, glo-rious Prince of life; life is naught with-

vic-tory thou o'er death hast won! An-gels in bright rai-ment
greets thee, scat-ters fear and gloom; let his church with glad-ness,
out thee; aid us in our strife; make us more than con-querors,

rolled the stone a-way, kept the fold-ed grave-clothes where thy
hymns of tri-umph sing, for the Lord now liv-eth; death hath
through thy death-less love; bring us safe through Jor-dan to thy

bod-y lay.
lost its sting! Thine is the glo-ry, ris-en con-quering Son;
home a-bove.

end-less is the vic-tory thou o'er death hast won!

Words: Edmond Budry (1854-1932); tr. R. Birch Hoyle (1875-1939), P.D.
Music (JUDAS MACCABAEUS 5.5.6.5.6.5.6.5 refrain 5.5.6.5): George Frideric Handel (1685-1759), P.D.

188 Mfurahini, haleluya/Christ Has Arisen, Alleluia

Words: Bernard Kyamanywa (b. 1938) © 1968 Lutheran Theological College, Makumira, Tanzania, admin.
Augsburg Fortress; tr. Howard S. Olson (1922-2010) © 1977 Howard S. Olson, admin. Augsburg Fortress
Music (MFURAHNI, HALELUYA 9.9.9 refrain 10.10.9.9): Tanzanian traditional, P.D.

Ka - shi - nda ki - fo, ha - le - lu - ya; Ha - le - lu - ya, Ye - su yu ha - i.
Our sin for - giv - ing, al - le - lu - ia! Je - sus is liv - ing, al - le - lu - ia!

4 "Go spread the news:
   he's not in the grave;
he has arisen this world to save.
Jesus' redeeming labors are done.
Even the battle with sin is won."
Refrain

5 Christ has arisen to set us free.
Alleluia, to him praises be!
Jesus is living! Let us all sing;
he reigns triumphant,
   heavenly king.
Refrain

Alleluia

189

Al - le - lu - ia, al - le - lu - ia, al - le - lu - ia.

Al - le - lu - ia, al - le - lu - ia, al - le - lu - ia.

Words: traditional
Music (ALLELUIA 7): Jacques Berthier © 1984 Les Presses de Taizé, GIA Publications, Inc., exclusive North
  American agent

190   O Sons and Daughters

Alleluias to be sung at the beginning and conclusion of the hymn   *Fine*

Al - le - lu - ia, al - le - lu - ia, al - le - lu - ia, al - le - lu - ia!

1 O sons and daugh - ters of the king, whom heav - en - ly hosts in
2 That Eas - ter morn at break of day, the faith - ful wom - en
3 An an - gel clad in white they see, who sat and spoke un -

glo - ry sing, to - day the grave has lost its sting. Al - le - lu - ia!
went their way to seek the tomb where Je - sus lay. Al - le - lu - ia!
to the three, "Your Lord has gone to Gal - i - lee." Al - le - lu - ia!

The Thomas Narrative

4 At night the apostles met in fear;
among them came their Master dear
and said, "My peace be with you here."
Alleluia!

5 When Thomas first the tidings heard
that some had seen the risen Lord,
he doubted the disciples' word.
Lord, have mercy!

6 "My piercéd side, O Thomas, see,
and look upon my hands, my feet;
not faithless but believing be."
Alleluia!

7 No longer Thomas then denied;
he saw the feet, the hands, the side.
"You are my Lord and God!" he cried.
Alleluia!

8 How blest are they who have not seen
and yet whose faith has constant been,
for they eternal life shall win.
Alleluia!

Words: early 16th c., based on Matthew 28 and John 20; tr. John M. Neale, 1851, alt., P.D.
Music (O FILII ET FILLAE 4.4.4.4.8.8.8.4): *Airs sur les hymnes sacrez, odes et noëls*, Paris, 1623, P.D.

Praise the Savior, Now and Ever

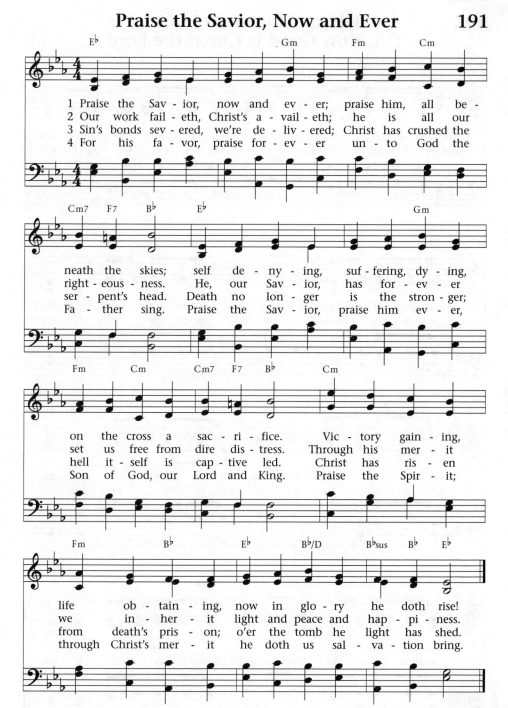

1 Praise the Sav - ior, now and ev - er; praise him, all be -
2 Our work fail - eth, Christ's a - vail - eth; he is all our
3 Sin's bonds sev - ered, we're de - liv - ered; Christ has crushed the
4 For his fa - vor, praise for - ev - er un - to God the

neath the skies; self de - ny - ing, suf - fering, dy - ing,
right - eous - ness. He, our Sav - ior, has for - ev - er
ser - pent's head. Death no lon - ger is the stron - ger;
Fa - ther sing. Praise the Sav - ior, praise him ev - er,

on the cross a sac - ri - fice. Vic - tory gain - ing,
set us free from dire dis - tress. Through his mer - it
hell it - self is cap - tive led. Christ has ris - en
Son of God, our Lord and King. Praise the Spir - it;

life ob - tain - ing, now in glo - ry he doth rise!
we in - her - it light and peace and hap - pi - ness.
from death's pris - on; o'er the tomb he light has shed.
through Christ's mer - it he doth us sal - va - tion bring.

Chord symbols represent a simplified harmony.

Words: Venantius Honorius Fortunatus, 569; tr. Augustus Nelson (1863-1949), alt., P.D.
Music (UPP, MIN TUNGA 8.7.8.7.8.7): *Then Swenska Psalm-Boken*, 1697, P.D.

192 Oh, qué bueno es Jesús/ Oh, How Good Is Christ the Lord

Spanish Oh, qué bue - no es Je - sús. Que por mí mu - rió en la cruz.
English Oh, how good is Christ the Lord! On the cross he died for me.

Mis pe - ca - dos per - do - nó. A su nom - bre glo - ria.
He has par - doned all my sin. Glo - ry be to Je - sus.

A su nom - bre glo - ria. A su nom - bre glo - ria.
Glo - ry be to Je - sus! Glo - ry be to Je - sus!

En tres días re - su - ci - tó. A su nom - bre glo - ria.
In three days he rose a - gain. Glo - ry be to Je - sus.

Words: Puerto Rican folk hymn, P.D.
Music (OH QUÉ BUENO 7.7.7.6.6.6.7.6): Puerto Rican folk hymn; harm. Dale Grotenhuis (1931-2012), 1985,
© 1987 Faith Alive Christian Resources

I Know that My Redeemer Lives

1 I know that my Re - deem - er lives! What joy this
2 He lives tri - um - phant from the grave; he lives e -
3 He lives to sil - ence all my fears; he lives to
3 He lives to bless me with his love; he lives to

blest as - sur - ance gives! He lives, he lives, who
ter - nal - ly to save; he lives ex - alt - ed,
wipe a - way my tears; he lives to calm my
plead for me a - bove; he lives my hun - gry

once was dead; he lives, my ev - er - liv - ing head!
throned a - bove; he lives to rule his church in love.
trou - bled heart; he lives all bless - ing to im - part.
soul to feed; he lives to help in time of need.

5 He lives, my kind, wise, heavenly friend;
he lives and loves me to the end;
he lives, and while he lives, I'll sing;
he lives, my prophet, priest, and king!

6 He lives and grants me daily breath;
he lives, and I shall conquer death;
he lives my mansion to prepare;
he lives to bring me safely there.

7 He lives, all glory to his name!
He lives, my Savior, still the same;
what joy this blessed assurance gives:
I know that my Redeemer lives!

Words: Samuel Medley (1738-1799), alt., P.D.
Music (DUKE STREET 8.8.8.8): John Hatton (1710-1793), 1793, P.D.

194 Refuge and Rock

PSALM 18

1 Ref - uge and Rock, Shield and De - liv - er - er!
2 Earth - quake and fire, thun - der and light - ning!
3 Faith - ful and pure, blame - less and per - fect—
4 Wis - dom and strength, hon - or and tri - umph!
5 Wor - ship and thanks, rev - erence and glo - ry

I love you, LORD, for your un - fail - ing care:
Clothed in such ar - mor you sprang to my aid;
> yet to the crook - ed you show your - self shrewd.
Such are the gifts you are ea - ger to give:
be to the LORD I am hon - ored to know;

fac - ing the grave, fear - ing de - struc - tion,
part - ing the heavens, burst - ing with splen - dor,
> Your ho - ly light shines on my dark - ness;
strength for the fight; wis - dom to lead me;
saved from my foes, called to your ser - vice,

For another setting of Ps. 18 see 436

I called to you and you an - swered my prayer:
you left your foes ov - er - whelmed and dis - mayed.
>my steps are guid - ed, my vig - or re - newed.
tri - umph and more for as long as I live;
I will ex - tol you wher - ev - er I go.

I was dis - tressed— you heard my voice;
Your awe - some power, your ten - der grace
>Your law will shape my heart and mind,
hon - or in - deed to make it known
Your love sur - rounds me all my days:

I will re - joice, for you saved me.
gave me a place where I flour - ish.
> let - ting me find rich - est bless - ing.
that you a - lone are e - ter - nal.
there - fore I praise you, my Sav - ior.

Optional prayer

O God, you are our strength, our rock, our fortress and deliverer.
In Christ you burst forth from the tomb to conquer our foes of sin and death.
We are so deeply grateful for the promise
that we who celebrate with joy his glorious rising from the dead
may also be raised from the death of sin to the life of righteousness,
through him who lives and reigns with you and the Holy Spirit,
one God, now and forever. Amen.

195   Easter Call to Worship

ISAIAH 25:6-9

On this mountain the Lord of hosts will make for all peoples
a feast of rich food, a feast of well-aged wines,
of rich food filled with marrow, of well-aged wines strained clear.
And he will destroy on this mountain
the shroud that is cast over all peoples,
the sheet that is spread over all nations;
he will swallow up death forever.
Then the Lord God will wipe away the tears from all faces,
and the disgrace of his people he will take away from all the earth,
for the Lord has spoken.
It will be said on that day,
Lo, this is our God;
we have waited for him, so that he might save us.
This is the Lord for whom we have waited;
let us be glad and rejoice in his salvation.

Continue with the singing of 196 or another Easter song of praise.

Text: Isaiah 25:6-9, NRSV

196   Give Thanks to God for All His Goodness

PSALM 118

1 Give thanks to God for all his good-ness: "His love for-
2 Brought low, I cried to God; he heard me. He an-swered
3 Hark! right-eous and vic-to-rious sing-ing: "The LORD's right

ev-er is the same." Give thanks to God, O ho-ly
me and set me free. The LORD with me, no one can
hand does val-iant-ly." For life re-stored my prais-es

For an alternate arrangement see 113, 547

For another setting of Ps. 118 see 147

Words: Stanley Wiersma, 1982, © 1987 Faith Alive Christian Resources
Music (GENEVAN 98/118/RENDEZ À DIEU 9.8.9.8 D): *Genevan Psalter*, 1551; harm. Claude Goudimel, 1564, P.D.

4 The stone the builders had rejected
is now the foremost cornerstone.
The LORD has done it, we have seen it—
his ways confound what we had known.
This is the day of days: God made it!
And we are glad, we praise his name:
"Save us and let us know your blessing.
Your love forever is the same."

5 Our voices join in glad confession:
"God's love forever is the same."
Blest is the one in our procession
who comes triumphant in God's name.
Let branches mark the festal highway.
Bring to the altar glad acclaim:
"You are my God, and I will praise you:
Your love forever is the same!"

197 Cristo Vive/Christ Is Risen

Spanish 1 Cris - to vi - ve, fue-ra_el llan - to, los la - men - tos y_el pe - sar!
2 Que si Cris - to no vi - vie - ra va - na fue - ra nues-tra fe.

English 1 Christ is ris - en, Christ is liv - ing. Dry your tears, be un - a - fraid!
2 If the Lord had nev - er ris - en, we'd have noth - ing to be - lieve.

Ni la muer - te ni_el se - pul - cro lo_han po - di - do su - je - tar.
Mas se cum - ple su pro - me - sa: "Por - que vi - vo, vi - vi - réis."

Death and dark - ness could not hold him, nor the tomb where he was laid.
But his prom - ise can be trust - ed: "You will live, be - cause I live."

No bus - quéls en - tre los muer - tos al que siem-pre_ha de vi - vir.
Si_en Ad - án en - tró la muer - te, por Je - sús la vi - da_en - tró;

Do not look a - mong the dead for One who lives for - ev - er - more;
As we share the death of Ad - am, so in Christ we live a - gain.

Cris - to vi - ve! Es - tas nue - vas por do - quier de - jad o - ir.
no te - máis, el triun-fo_es vues-tro: ¡El Se - ñor re - su - ci - tó!

tell the world that Christ is ris - en, make it known he goes be - fore.
Death has lost its sting and ter - ror. Christ the Lord has come to reign.

(continues)

Spanish

3 Si_es verdad que de la muerte
   el pecado_es aguijón,
   no temáis pues Jesucristo
   nos da vida_y salvación.
   Gracias demos al Dios Padre
   que nos de seguridad.
   Que quien cree en Jesucristo
   vive pro la_eternidad.

English

3 Death has lost its old dominion,
   let the world rejoice and shout!
   Christ, the firstborn of the living,
   gives us life and leads us out.
   Let us thank our God who causes
   hope to spring up from the ground.
   Christ is risen, Christ is giving
   life eternal, life profound.

Celtic Alleluia   198

Optional acclamation with spoken "Alleluia" or the singing of all or a portion of the above refrain.

Christ has died, Christ has risen: **Alleluia!**
We lift our hearts to the Lord in song: **Alleluia!**
With Jesus, we have died to self: **Alleluia!**
With Jesus, we are raised to new life: **Alleluia!**
Nothing can separate us from God's love: **Alleluia!**
Where, O death, is your sting? **Alleluia!**
Thanks be to God for this indescribable gift! **Alleluia!**

[Add phrases as appropriate.]

Words and Music (CELTIC ALLELUIA 4.4.4.4): Fintan O'Carroll (1922-1981) and Christopher Walker (b. 1947)
© 1985 Fintan O'Carroll and Christopher Walker, admin. OCP Publications

199   Come, You Faithful, Raise the Strain

1 Come, you faith - ful, raise the strain   of   tri - um - phant glad - ness!
2 'Tis   the spring of   souls to - day: Christ has burst   his   pri - son,
3 Nei - ther could the gates of death, nor   the tomb's dark por - tal,
4 Al - le - lu - ia! Now we cry   to   our Lord im - mor - tal,

God   has brought forth   Is - ra - el   in - to   joy from   sad - ness,
and   from three days' sleep in death   as   a   sun has   ris - en.
nor   the watch - ers,   nor the seal, hold you as   a   mor - tal:
who,   tri - um - phant, burst the bars   of   the tomb's dark   por - tal;

loosed from Phar - aoh's bit - ter yoke   Ja - cob's sons   and   daugh - ters;
All   the win - ter   of   our sins,   long and dark, is   fly - ing
but   to - day, a - mong your own,   you ap - pear, be - stow - ing
Al - le - lu - ia! With the Son,   God the Fa - ther   prais - ing;

led   them with   un - mois-tened foot through the Red Sea   wa - ters.
from the Light   to   whom we give   laud and praise un - dy - ing.
your deep peace, which   ev - er - more pass - es   hu - man know-ing.
Al - le - lu - ia!   Yet a - gain to   the Spir - it   rais - ing.

Words: John of Damascus (ca. 675-749); tr. John Mason Neale (1818-1866), alt., P.D.
Music (ST. KEVIN 7.6.7.6 D): Arthur S. Sullivan, 1872, P.D.

Praise the Lord, the Day Is Won

200

PSALM 105

1 Praise the Lord, the day is won!
Glory, hallelujah!
God for us great things has done.
Sing, shout hallelujah!
Now let all the earth proclaim
resurrection wonder;
in God's all-enduring name,
death is cast asunder!

2 Loosed from chains by bondage cast;
glory, hallelujah!
God has freed our souls at last.
Sing, shout hallelujah!
Slaves held captive for so long,
scarred by sin and sadness,
lift anew their victory song,
filled with joy and gladness!

3 As God's Spirit moved the sea;
glory, hallelujah!
set our hearts at liberty.
Sing, shout hallelujah!
In our darkest, dreadful day,
crushed by grief and mourning;
God will roll the stone away,
radiant love adorning.

4 God's great covenant is sealed!
Glory, hallelujah!
Our salvation is revealed.
Sing, shout hallelujah!
Plagues no more confound the flock,
flames nor flood assail us;
sure as water from the rock,
God will never fail us!

5 Faithful in the Lord rejoice.
Glory, hallelujah!
Raise to God your new-found voice.
Sing, shout hallelujah!
Crowned with full redemption's light,
by God's grace befriended;
life, behold the glorious sight;
death, your reign is ended!

For music see 199
Words: Michael Morgan © 2011 Michael Morgan, admin. Faith Alive Christian Resources

Affirmation: Jesus, Our Hope

201

Jesus Christ is the hope of God's world.
In his death,
the justice of God is established;
forgiveness of sin is proclaimed.
On the day of the resurrection,
the tomb was empty; his disciples saw him;
death was defeated; new life had come.
God's purpose for the world was sealed.

Our ascended Lord gives hope for two ages.
In the age to come, Christ is the judge,
rejecting unrighteousness,
isolating God's enemies to hell,
blessing the new creation in Christ.
In this age, the Holy Spirit is with us,
calling nations to follow God's path,
uniting people through Christ in love.

Text: *Our Song of Hope* st. 4-5 © 2013 Reformed Church Press

202 This Joyful Eastertide

1 This joy-ful Eas-ter-tide, a - way with sin and sad - ness!
   Our Lord, the cru - ci - fied, has filled our hearts with glad - ness.
2 My be - ing shall re - joice, se - cure with - in God's keep - ing,
   un - til the trum-pet voice shall wake us from our sleep - ing.

Refrain

Had Christ, who once was slain, not burst his three - day pris - on, our

faith would be in vain. But now has Christ a - ris - en, a - ris - en, a -

ris - en, but now has Christ a - ris - en.

3 Death's waters lost their chill when Jesus crossed the river.
   His love shall reach me still; his mercy is forever.
   Refrain

Chord symbols represent a simplified harmony.

Words: George R. Woodward, 1894, alt., P.D.
Music (VRUECHTEN 6.7.6.7 refrain 6.7.6.7.6.7): J. Ouden's *David's Psalmen*, 1685; harm. Dale Grotenhuis
(1931-2012), 1984, © 1987 Faith Alive Christian Resources

Now the Green Blade Rises

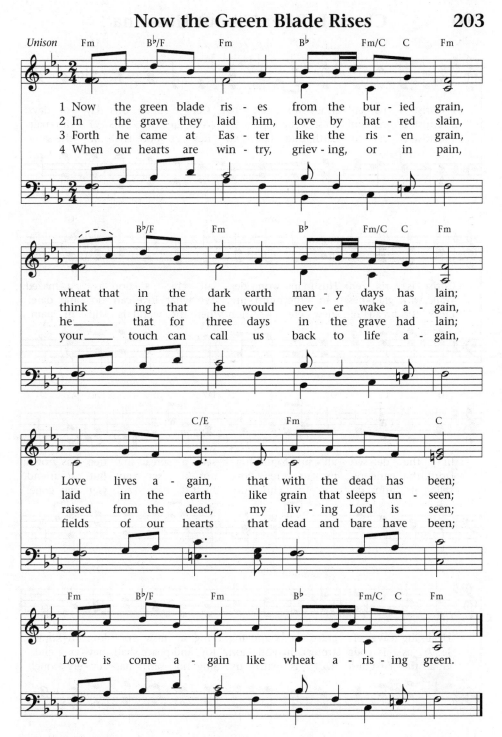

1 Now the green blade ris - es from the bur - ied grain,
2 In the grave they laid him, love by hat - red slain,
3 Forth he came at Eas - ter like the ris - en grain,
4 When our hearts are win - try, griev - ing, or in pain,

wheat that in the dark earth man - y days has lain;
think - ing that he would nev - er wake a - gain,
he____ that for three days in the grave had lain;
your____ touch can call us back to life a - gain,

Love lives a - gain, that with the dead has been;
laid in the earth like grain that sleeps un - seen;
raised from the dead, my liv - ing Lord is seen;
fields of our hearts that dead and bare have been;

Love is come a - gain like wheat a - ris - ing green.

Words: J. M. C. Crum (1872-1958), alt., reproduced by permission of Oxford University Press
Music (NOËL NOUVELET 11.11.10.11): traditional French carol; arr. Martin Shaw, (1875-1958), reproduced by
  permission of Oxford University Press

204   Christ Is Risen! Shout Hosanna

1 Christ is ris - en! Shout ho - san - na! Cel - e - brate this day of days!
2 Christ is ris - en! Raise your spir - its from the cav - erns of des - pair.
3 Christ is ris - en! Earth and heav - en nev - er - more shall be the same.

Christ is ris - en! Hush in won - der; all cre - a - tion is a - mazed.
Walk with glad - ness in the morn - ing. See what love can do and dare.
Break the bread of new cre - a - tion where the world is still in pain.

In the de - sert all - sur - round - ing, see, a spread - ing tree has grown.
Drink the wine of res - ur - rec - tion, not a ser - vant, but a friend.
Tell its grim de - mon - ic cho - rus: "Christ is ris - en! Get you gone!"

Heal - ing leaves of grace a - bound - ing bring a taste of love un - known.
Je - sus is our strong com - pan - ion. Joy and peace shall nev - er end.
God the First and Last is with us. Sing ho - san - na, ev - ery - one!

Words: Brian Wren (b. 1936) © 1986 Hope Publishing Company
Music (HYMN TO JOY 8.7.8.7 D): Ludwig van Beethoven (1770-1827), 1824, adapt. Edward Hodges
(1796-1867), alt., P.D.

Alleluia! Jesus Is Risen

1 Al - le - lu - ia! Jesus is ris - en! Trumpets re - sound-ing in
2 Walk-ing the way, Christ in the cen - ter, tell - ing the sto - ry to
3 Je - sus the vine, we are the branch-es; life in the Spir - it the

glo - ri - ous light! Splen-dor, the Lamb, heav-en for - ev - er!
o - pen our eyes; break-ing our bread, giv - ing us glo - ry:
fruit of the tree; heav - en to earth, Christ to the peo - ple,

Oh, what a mir - a - cle God has in sight!
Je - sus, our bless-ing, our con-stant sur - prise. Je-sus is ris-en and
gift of the fu - ture now flow - ing to me.

we shall a - rise: give God the glo - ry! Al - le - lu - ia!

4 Weeping, be gone; sorrow be silent:
death put asunder, and Easter is bright.
Cherubim sing: "O grave, be open!"
Clothe us in wonder, adorn us in light.
Refrain

5 City of God, Easter forever,
golden Jerusalem, Jesus the Lamb,
river of life, saints, and archangels,
sing with creation to God the I AM!
Refrain

Words: Herbert F. Brokering (1926-2009) © 1995 Augsburg Fortress
Music (EARTH AND ALL STARS 4.5.10 D refrain 10.5.4): David N. Johnson (1922-1987), 1968, © 1968
Augsburg Fortress

206 Christ Is Alive! Let Christians Sing

1 Christ is a - live! Let Chris - tians sing. The cross stands
2 Christ is a - live! No long - er bound to dis - tant
3 In ev - ery in - sult, rift and war, where col - or,

em - pty to the sky. Let streets and homes with
years in Pal - es - tine, but sav - ing, heal - ing,
scorn, or wealth di - vide, Christ suf - fers still, yet

prais - es ring. Love, drowned in death, shall nev - er die.
here and now, and touch - ing ev - ery place and time.
loves the more, and lives, where e - ven hope has died.

4 Women and men, in age and youth,
can feel the Spirit, hear the call,
and find the way, the life, the truth,
revealed in Jesus, freed for all.

5 Christ is alive, and comes to bring
good news to this and every age,
till earth and sky and ocean ring
with joy, with justice, love and praise.

Words: Brian A. Wren (b. 1936) © 1975, rev. 1995 Hope Publishing Company
Music (TRURO 8.8.8.8): T. Williams' *Psalmodia Evangelica*, 1789, P.D.

Come to Us, Beloved Stranger

1 Come to us, be-lov-ed Stran-ger, as you came that East-er day.
2 Stay with us and give us bless-ing, that our hopes a-gain may rise.
3 We would nev-er fail to see you as you walk with us each day.

Walk with us to our Em-ma-us, for we need you still to-day.
Of-fer us your bro-ken bo-dy; o-pen our un-see-ing eyes.
As a friend and not a strang-er you would join us on our way.

Come to us when we are bro-ken, when our dear-est hopes are lost,
Come to us, God's love em-bod-ied; touch our hearts with burn-ing flame.
Help us trust that through your mer-cy we can doubt and fear tran-scend,

speak to us the proph-ets' mes-sage you ful-filled up-on the cross.
Ris-en Christ, once dead, now liv-ing, come to us through joy, through pain.
and to oth-ers be a bless-ing. Keep us faith-ful till life's end.

Words: Edith Sinclair Downing (b. 1922), 1993, 1995 © 1998 Selah Publishing Company, Inc.
Music (BEACH SPRING 8.7.8.7 D): *The Sacred Harp* (1844); harm. James Wood, 1958, © 1958, ren. 1986
    Broadman Press, admin. Music Services

208   A Hymn of Glory Let Us Sing

1 A hymn of glo-ry let us sing! New hymns through-out the world shall ring: Al-le-lu-ia! Al-le-lu-ia! Christ, by a road be-fore un-trod, as-cends un-to the throne of God.

2 The ho-ly ap-os-tol-ic band up-on the Mount of Ol-ives stands, Al-le-lu-ia! Al-le-lu-ia! and with his faith-ful fol-lowers see their Lord as-cend in maj-es-ty.

3 O Lord, our home-ward path-way bend that our un-wea-ried hearts as-cend, Al-le-lu-ia! Al-le-lu-ia! where, seat-ed on your Fa-ther's throne, you reign as King of kings a-lone.

4 O ris-en Christ, as-cend-ed Lord, all praise to you let earth ac-cord: Al-le-lu-ia! Al-le-lu-ia! You are, while end-less a-ges run, with Fa-ther and with Spir-it one.

Refrain

Al-le-lu-ia! Al-le-lu-ia, al-le-lu-ia, al-le-lu-ia, al-le-lu-ia!

For an alternate arrangement see 317, 551, 847

Words: Bede (673-735); tr. *Lutheran Book of Worship* © 1978 *Lutheran Book of Worship*, admin. Augsburg Fortress
Music (LASST UNS ERFREUEN 8.8.8.8 with alleluias): *Auserlesen Catholische Geistliche Kirchengesänge*, Cologne, 1623; arr. © 1978 *Lutheran Book of Worship*, admin. Augsburg Fortress

Hail the Day that Sees Him Rise

209

1 Hail the day that sees him rise, Al - le - lu - ia!
2 There for him high tri - umph waits; Al - le - lu - ia!
3 High - est heaven its Lord re - ceives; Al - le - lu - ia!
4 Still for us he in - ter - cedes; Al - le - lu - ia!
5 There we shall with you re - main, Al - le - lu - ia!

to his throne be - yond the skies. Al - le - lu - ia!
lift your heads, e - ter - nal gates. Al - le - lu - ia!
> yet he loves the earth he leaves. Al - le - lu - ia!
his a - ton - ing death he pleads, Al - le - lu - ia!
part - ners of your end - less reign, Al - le - lu - ia!

Christ, the Lamb for sin - ners given, Al - le - lu - ia!
He has con - quered death and sin; Al - le - lu - ia!
> Though re - turn - ing to his throne, Al - le - lu - ia!
near him - self pre - pares our place, Al - le - lu - ia!
see you with un - cloud - ed view, Al - le - lu - ia!

en - ters now the high - est heaven. Al - le - lu - ia!
take the King of glo - ry in. Al - le - lu - ia!
> still he calls us all his own. Al - le - lu - ia!
he the first fruits of our race. Al - le - lu - ia!
find our heaven of heavens in you. Al - le - lu - ia!

Words: Charles Wesley, 1739, and Thomas Cotterill, 1820, alt., P.D.
Music (LLANFAIR 7.4.7.4.7.4.7.4): Robert Williams, 1817, P.D.

210 Since Our Great High Priest, Christ Jesus

HEBREWS 1:3-4; 2:8-11; 4;14-16

1 Since our great high priest, Christ Je-sus, bears the name a-
2 Since we have a priest who suf-fered, know-ing weak-ness,
3 Sac-ri-fice and suf-fering o-ver, now he sits at
4 Love's ex-am-ple, hope's at-trac-tion, faith's be-gin-ning

bove all names, reign-ing Son of God, sur-pass-ing
tears, and pain; who, like us, was tried and temp-ted;
God's right hand, crowned with praise, no more an out-cast,
and its end, pi-o-neer of our sal-va-tion,

oth-er ti-tles, powers, and claims; since to heaven our
un-like us, with-out a stain; since he shared our
his pre-em-i-nence long planned; such a great high
might-y ad-vo-cate and friend: Je-sus, now in

Lord has passed, let us hold our wit-ness fast!
low-ly place, let us bold-ly seek his grace!
priest we have, strong to help, su-preme to save!
glo-ry raised, our as-cend-ed Lord, be praised!

Alternate tune: IRBY see 87

Words: Hebrews 1:3-4; 2:8-11; 4:14-16, para. Christopher Idle © 1973 The Jubilate Group, admin. Hope Publishing Company
Music (UNSER HERRSHER 8.7.8.7.7.7): Joachim Neander, 1680; harm. *The Chorale Book for England*, 1863, alt., P.D.

Lift Up Your Voices

PSALM 68:1-19

211

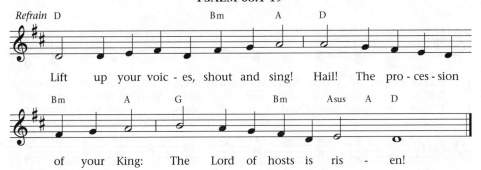

Lift up your voic - es, shout and sing! Hail! The pro - ces - sion
of your King: The Lord of hosts is ris - en!

For accompaniment see 212

Refrain

May God arise,
may his enemies be scattered;
may his foes flee before him.
May you blow them away like smoke—
as wax melts before the fire,
may the wicked perish before God.
But may the righteous be glad
and rejoice before God;
may they be happy and joyful.
Sing to God, sing in praise of his name,
extol him who rides on the clouds;
rejoice before him—his name is the LORD.

Refrain

A father to the fatherless,
a defender of widows,
is God in his holy dwelling.
God sets the lonely in families,
he leads out the prisoners with singing;
but the rebellious live
in a sun-scorched land.
When you, God,
went out before your people,
when you marched
through the wilderness,
the earth shook,
the heavens poured down rain,
before God, the One of Sinai,
before God, the God of Israel.
You gave abundant showers, O God;
you refreshed your weary inheritance.
Your people settled in it,
and from your bounty,
God, you provided for the poor.

Refrain

The Lord announces the word,
and the women who proclaim it
are a mighty throng:
"Kings and armies flee in haste;
the women at home divide the plunder.
Even while you sleep
among the sheep pens,
the wings of my dove
are sheathed with silver,
its feathers with shining gold."
When the Almighty scattered
the kings in the land,
it was like snow
fallen on Mount Zalmon.
Mount Bashan, majestic mountain,
Mount Bashan, rugged mountain,
why gaze in envy,
you rugged mountain,
at the mountain where God
chooses to reign,
where the LORD himself
will dwell forever?

Refrain

The chariots of God are tens of
thousands and thousands of thousands;
the Lord has come from Sinai
into his sanctuary.
When you ascended on high,
you took many captives;
you received gifts from people,
even from the rebellious —
that you, LORD God,
might dwell there.
Praise be to the Lord,
to God our Savior,
who daily bears our burdens.

Refrain or continue by singing 212

For another setting of Ps. 68 see 212

Words: ref. Martin Tel © 2011 Martin Tel, admin. Faith Alive Christian Resources
Music (GENEVAN 68/OLD 113th fragment): *Genevan Psalter*, 1539, P.D.

212 Give Praise to God with Reverence Deep

PSALM 68:20-35

1 Give praise to God with rev-erence deep; he dai-ly comes our
2 Pro-ces-sions come with God the King; with shouts of joy the
3 Show us your strength, O LORD of hosts, so ev-ery king who
4 All na-tions of the earth, ex-ult, raise psalms of praise to

lives to keep and kind-ly bears our bur - dens. Our God up-
por-tals ring as God comes to his tem - ple. With harps and
comes to boast will ho-nor and o-bey you. LORD, for your
heav-en's vault, God's an-cient throne and dwell - ing. God rides his

holds us in the strife; to us he grants e-ter-nal life
tim-brels, choirs___ sing, and maid-ens dance be-fore their King,
tem-ple's sake make right those waste-land lives now filled with blight;
char-iot in the height, he thun-ders forth his roy-al right;

and saves from all that threat - ens. God crush-es heads of
while all Mount Zi-on trem - bles. Praise God, praise God, you
stop those who would de-fy you. Tram-ple to dust be-
God reigns, all kings ex-cel - ling. Pro-claim the awe-some

For another setting of Ps. 68 see 211

Chord symbols represent a simplified harmony.

Words: Psalm 68:20-35, *Psalter Hymnal*, 1987, © 1987 Faith Alive Christian Resources
Music (GENEVAN 68/OLD 113TH | 8.8.7.8.8.7 D): *Genevan Psalter*, 1539, P.D.; harm. Howard Slenk © 1987
  Faith Alive Christian Resources

en - e - mies; he brings them back from far - thest seas for Is - rael's
ho - ly throng, with prais - es lift his name in song; bless God, O
neath your feet those who de - light in war's de - ceit, all those who
power of God, make known his might - y deeds a - broad; all Is - rael

ju - bi - la - tion. He hears the need - y when they cry; he saves their
con - gre - ga - tion. Here Ben - ja - min, the least, leads on; there Ju - dah's
lust for plun - der. Let plun-derers bring their ill-gained hoard; let ev - ery
shall ex - tol him. For he is pow - er - ful and great: all earth and

souls when death draws nigh: this God is our sal - va - tion.
princ - es, Zeb - u - lun, and Naph - ta - li— one na - tion.
na - tion praise the LORD, lift up their hands in won - der.
skies are his es - tate; his maj - es - ty ex - cels them.

Optional prayer (1 Cor. 15:57)

Mighty God,
you have delivered us from sin's captivity
and freed us from the power of death.
Thanks be to you for giving us the victory
through our Lord Jesus Christ!

Inspire now our songs of extravagant praise
so that the entire world may know
that Jesus is Lord. **Amen.**

213 Affirmation: The Benefits of the Ascension

How does Christ's ascension to heaven benefit us?

**First, he is our advocate in heaven
in the presence of his Father.**

**Second, we have our own flesh in heaven
as a sure pledge that Christ our head
will also take us, his members, up to himself.**

**Third, he sends his Spirit to us on earth
as a corresponding pledge.
By the Spirit's power we seek not earthly things
but the things above, where Christ is,
sitting at God's right hand.**

Text: Heidelberg Catechism Q&A 49

214 Why This Dark Conspiracy

PSALM 2

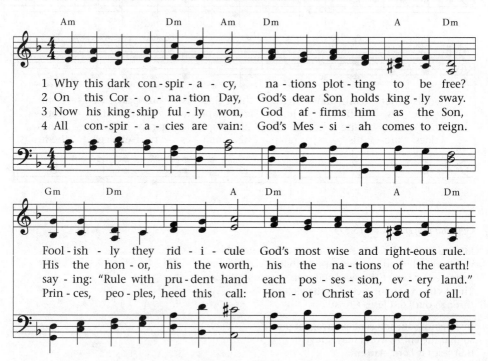

1 Why this dark con-spir-a-cy, na-tions plot-ting to be free?
2 On this Cor-o-na-tion Day, God's dear Son holds king-ly sway.
3 Now his king-ship ful-ly won, God af-firms him as the Son,
4 All con-spir-a-cies are vain: God's Mes-si-ah comes to reign.

Fool-ish-ly they rid-i-cule God's most wise and right-eous rule.
His the hon-or, his the worth, his the na-tions of the earth!
say-ing: "Rule with pru-dent hand each pos-ses-sion, ev-ery land."
Prin-ces, peo-ples, heed this call: Hon-or Christ as Lord of all.

Words: Norman J. Goreham © 2010 Norman J. Goreham, admin. Faith Alive Christian Resources
Music (CHRIST IST ERSTANDEN 7.7.7.7.4 refrain 4.4.4.7.7.4): J. Klug's *Geistliche Lieder*, 1533; harm. Dale
  Grotenhuis (1931-2012) © 1987 Faith Alive Christian Resources

Lord, have mer - cy! Lord, have mer - cy; Christ, have mer - cy;
Al - le - lu - ia! Al - le - lu - ia! Al - le - lu - ia!
Al - le - lu - ia! Al - le - lu - ia! Al - le - lu - ia!

Lord, have mer - cy! Fool - ish - ly they rid - i - cule
Al - le - lu - ia! His the hon - or, his the worth,
Al - le - lu - ia! Now his king - ship ful - ly won,
Al - le - lu - ia! Prin - ces, peo - ples, heed this call:

God's most wise and right - eous rule. Lord have mer - cy!
his the na - tions of the earth! Al - le - lu - ia!
God af - firms him as the Son. Al - le - lu - ia!
Hon - or Christ as Lord of all. Al - le - lu - ia!

A Prayer in Times of International Strife 215

Lord God Almighty,
as we offer praise to our ascended Lord,
the nations conspire; the people make plots.
Today we pray especially for [_____].

Pour out your Spirit, we pray:
Strengthen us with the conviction that Jesus is Lord.
Correct us for our complicit participation
in the world's vain plots.
Guide every leader, every nation,
and every people into the path of
righteousness, justice, and truth.

Teach us, O Lord, to be wise.
Teach us to take refuge in you.
Amen.

216

Nations, Clap Your Hands

PSALM 47

1 Na - tions, clap your hands; shout with joy, you lands! Awe-some is the LORD;
2 God goes up on high with a joy-ful cry, with a might-y shout;
3 God reigns o - ver all rul - ers great and small. Lead - ers of the world,

spread his fame a - broad. He rules ev - ery land with a might-y hand.
peo - ple, sing it out! Let your voic - es bring prais-es to our King.
ser - vants of the LORD, ral - ly round his throne; he is God a - lone.

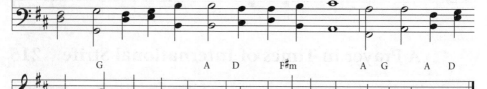

God brings na - tions low; he sub - dues each foe. From his might-y
Praise him with a song; praise with heart and tongue; praise with ev - ery
Sing be - fore him now, in his pres - ence bow. God of A - bra -

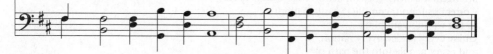

throne God pro - tects his own. Our in - her - i - tance is our sure de-fense.
skill; praise with mind and will. God rules all the earth; mag-ni - fy his worth.
ham! God of ev - ery land! Wor-ship and a - dore God for - ev - er-more.

Words: *Psalter Hymnal*, 1987, alt. © 1987 Faith Alive Christian Resources
Music (GENEVAN 47 | 5.5.5.5.5.5 D): Louis Bourgeois, 1551; harm. Claude Goudimel, 1564, P.D.

The Lord unto My Lord Has Said

PSALM 110

1 The LORD un-to my Lord has said, "Sit here at my right hand
2 "Your peo-ple will be glad-ly yours when you a-rise in might,
3 "You shall sub-due the kings of earth, with God at your right hand;

un-til I make your en-e-mies sub-mit to your com-mand.
like dawn-ing day, like hope-ful youth, with ho-ly beau-ty bright.
the na-tions you shall rule in might and judge in ev-ery land."

A scep-ter pros-pered by the LORD your might-y hand shall wield;
The priest-hood of Mel-chiz-e-dek the LORD has giv-en you;
The Lord, re-freshed by liv-ing streams, shall nei-ther faint nor fall,

from Zi-on you shall rule the world, and all your foes shall yield.
it shall re-main for-ev-er-more; God's word is al-ways true.
and he shall be the glo-rious head, ex-alt-ed o-ver all.

Words: *Psalter,* 1912, alt., P.D.
Music (ALL SAINTS NEW 8.6.8.6 D): Henry S. Cutler, 1872, P.D.

218   To Your Unequaled Strength

PSALM 21

1 To your un - e - qualed strength, O Lord, your
2 The rul - ers of the Lord's e - lect wear
3 The ones who hon - or you as Lord, to
4 In wrath our en - e - mies will fall, your

cho - sen ones as - pire; bring to the just sure
crowns of fin - est gold; their lives, once emp - ty,
such shall hon - or come; and those in whom good-
arm puts them to flight; we gain our bless - ings

vic - to - ry, and grant their hearts' de - sire.
now through faith shall burst with wealth un - told.
will a - bides in you will find a home.
by your grace, and vic - tory through your might.

Optional prayer

Almighty God, you have given victory to Christ, your Anointed One.
Keep us from stumbling into lesser loyalties, and give us strength to stand firm,
trusting in the grace and peace of Jesus Christ our Lord. **Amen.**

For an alternate harmonization see 34

Words: Michael Morgan © 1999, 2011 Michael Morgan, admin. Faith Alive Christian Resources
Music (DETROIT 8.6.8.6): *Supplement to Kentucky Harmony,* 1820; harm. Hal H. Hopson © 2002 Selah
  Publishing Company, Inc.

Jesus Shall Reign

PSALM 72

1 Je - sus shall reign wher - e'er the sun does its suc -
2 To him shall end - less prayer be made, and prais - es
3 Peo - ple and realms of ev - ery tongue dwell on his
4 Bless - ings a - bound wher - e'er he reigns: the pris - oners

ces - sive jour - neys run, his king - dom stretch from
throng to crown his head. His name like sweet per -
love with sweet - est song, and in - fant voic - es
leap to lose their chains, the wea - ry find e -

shore to shore, till moons shall wax and wane no more.
fume shall rise with ev - ery morn - ing sac - ri - fice.
shall pro - claim their ear - ly bless - ings on his name.
ter - nal rest, and all who suf - fer want are blest.

5 Let every creature rise and bring
the highest honors to our King,
angels descend with songs again,
and earth repeat the loud amen.

For other settings of Ps. 72 see 109, 953

Words: Isaac Watts, 1719, alt., P.D.
Music (DUKE STREET 8.8.8.8): John Hatton, (1710-1793), 1793, P.D.

220 At the Name of Jesus

PHILIPPIANS 2:5-11

1 At the name of Je - sus ev - ery knee shall bow,
2 At his voice cre - a - tion sprang at once to sight:
3 Hum - bled for a sea - son, to re - ceive a name
4 bore it up tri - um - phant with its hu - man light,

ev - ery tongue con - fess him King of glo - ry now;
all the an - gel fac - es, all the hosts of light,
from the lips of sin - ners, un - to whom he came;
through all ranks of crea - tures, to the cen - tral height,

'tis the Fa - ther's plea - sure we should call him Lord,
thrones and dom - i - na - tions, stars up - on their way,
faith - ful - ly he bore it spot - less to the last,
to the throne of God - head, to the Fa - ther's breast;

who from the be - gin - ning was the might - y Word.
all the heaven - ly or - ders in their great ar - ray.
brought it back vic - to - rious when from death he passed;
filled it with the glo - ry of that per - fect rest.

Words: Caroline M. Noel, 1870. alt., P.D.
Music (KING'S WESTON 6.5.6.5 D): Ralph Vaughan Wiliams (1872-1958) from *Enlarged Songs of Praise*, 1931, reproduced by permission of Oxford University Press

(continues)

5 In your hearts enthrone him; there let him subdue
all that is not holy, all that is not true.
Look to him, your Savior, in temptation's hour;
let his will enfold you in its light and power.

6 Christians, this Lord Jesus shall return again,
with his Father's glory, o'er the earth to reign;
for all wreaths of empire meet upon his brow,
and our hearts confess him King of glory now.

For the Honor of Our King 221
PSALM 45

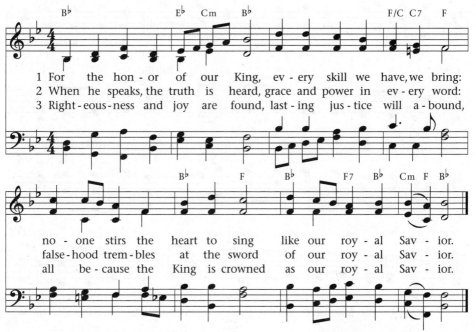

1 For the hon-or of our King, ev-ery skill we have, we bring:
2 When he speaks, the truth is heard, grace and power in ev-ery word:
3 Right-eous-ness and joy are found, last-ing jus-tice will a-bound,

no-one stirs the heart to sing like our roy-al Sav-ior.
false-hood trem-bles at the sword of our roy-al Sav-ior.
all be-cause the King is crowned as our roy-al Sav-ior.

4 See the splendor of Christ's bride
led in honor to his side—
chosen, loved, and beautified
by her royal Savior.

5 Now, and to eternal days,
all God's people join to raise
one unending song of praise
to our royal Savior.

Words: Martin Leckebusch © 2002 Kevin Mayhew Ltd.
Music (MONKLAND 7.7.7.6): J. Freylinghausen's *Geistreiches Gesangbuch,* 1704; adapt. John Antes, ca. 1800;
arr. John Wilkes, 1861, P.D.

222

He Is King of Kings

The leader may improvise additional words.

Words: African American spiritual, P.D.
Music (HE IS KING irregular): African American spiritual; arr. Joseph T. Jones (1902-1983); adapt. Melva W. Costen, 1989, © 1990 Melva W. Costen

Crown Him with Many Crowns

223

1 Crown him with man-y crowns, the Lamb up-on his throne; Hark!
2 Crown him the Lord of life, who tri-umphed o'er the grave, who
3 Crown him the Lord of love; be-hold his hands and side, rich
4 Crown him the Lord of years, the po-ten-tate of time, cre-

how the heaven-ly an-them drowns all mu-sic but its own;
rose vic-to-rious in the strife for those he came to save;
wounds, yet vi-si-ble a-bove, in beau-ty glo-ri-fied;
a-tor of the rol-ling spheres, in-ef-fa-bly sub-lime.

a-wake, my soul, and sing of him who died for thee
his glo-ries now we sing who died and reigns on high,
no an-gels in the sky can ful-ly bear that sight,
All hail, Re-deem-er, hail! for thou hast died for me;

and hail him as thy match-less King through all e-ter-ni-ty.
who died e-ter-nal life to bring, and lives that death may die.
but down-ward bend their burn-ing eyes at mys-ter-ies so bright.
thy praise shall nev-er, nev-er fail through-out e-ter-ni-ty.

Words: sts. 1, 3, 4 Matthew Bridge, 1851; st. 2 Godfrey Thring, 1874, alt., P.D.
Music (DIADEMATA 6.6.8.6 D): George J. Elvey, 1868, P.D.

224   Rejoice, the Lord Is King

Descant

4 Re - joice in glo - rious hope; for Christ, the Judge, shall come to

1 Re - joice, the Lord is King! Your Lord and King a - dore. Re-
2 His king-dom can - not fail; he rules o'er earth and heaven; the
3 He sits at God's right hand till all his foes sub - mit, bow
4 Re - joice in glo - rious hope; for Christ, the Judge, shall come to

gath - er all his saints to their e - ter-nal home. We soon shall

joice, give thanks and sing and tri-umph ev - er - more. Lift up your
keys of death and hell to Christ the Lord are given. Lift up your
down at his com - mand, and fall be-neath his feet. Lift up your
gath - er all his saints to their e - ter - nal home. We soon shall

hear the arch - an - gel's voice; the trump of God shall sound, re - joice!

heart, lift up your voice. Re - joice, a - gain I say, re - joice!
heart, lift up your voice. Re - joice, a - gain I say, re - joice!
heart, lift up your voice. Re - joice, a - gain I say, re - joice!
hear the arch - an - gel's voice; the trump of God shall sound, re - joice!

Words: Charles Wesley, 1744, alt., P.D.
Music (DARWALL'S 148th 6.6.6.6.8.8): John Darwall, 1770; desc. Sydney H. Nicholson (1875-1947), P.D.

You, Lord, Are Both Lamb and Shepherd 225

1 You, Lord, are both Lamb and Shep-herd. You, Lord, are both prince and slave. You, peace-mak-er and sword-bring-er of the way you took and gave. You, the ev-er-last-ing in - stant; you, whom we both scorn and crave.

2 Clothed in light up-on the moun-tain, stripped of might up-on the cross, shin-ing in e-ter-nal glo-ry, beg-gared by a sol-dier's toss, you, the ev-er-last-ing in - stant; you, who are both gift and cost.

3 You, who walk each day be-side us, sit in pow-er at God's side. You, who preach a way that's nar-row, have a love that reach-es wide. You, the ev-er-last-ing in - stant; you, who are our pil-grim guide.

4 Wor-thy is our earth-ly Je-sus! Wor-thy is our cos-mic Christ! Wor-thy your de-feat and vic-to-ry. Wor-thy still your peace and strife. You, the ev-er-last-ing in - stant; you, who are our death and life.

Words: Sylvia Dunstan (1955-1993) © 1991 GIA Publications, Inc.
Music (PICARDY 8.7.8.7.8.7): French, 17th c., P.D.

226 Jesus Is Lord

1 Je-sus is Lord! Be-hold, the King of kings, ex-al-ted
2 (This is my) God. Be-hold his hands and side, the wounds of
3 (For me, to) live is Christ, to die is gain, for Christ has
4 (Yes, sud-den)-ly, my God shall come a-gain. And ev-ery

high, the name a-bove all names. I sing his
love that healed my bro-ken-ness. What God is
died that I might gain his life. He is my
knee shall bow be-fore his name. And he shall

praise, the Lamb u-pon the throne, who reigns in glo-ry,
this? What kind of sac-ri-fice would give so much to
all, my joy, my right-eous-ness, my hope of glo-ry
reign for-ev-er on the throne. And in his glo-ry

power, and ma-jes-ty. 2 This is my
gain a love-less soul? 3 For me, to
when he comes to reign. 4 Yes, sud-den-
there I shall pro- claim: "Je-sus is

He Is Lord

227

1 He is Lord, he is Lord, he is ris-en from the dead, and he is Lord! Ev-ery knee shall bow, ev-ery tongue con-fess that Je-sus Christ is Lord.

2 He is King, he is King, he will draw all na-tions to him; he is King! And the time shall be when the world shall sing that Je-sus Christ is King.

3 He is Love, he is Love, he has shown us by his life that he is Love! All his peo-ple sing with one voice of joy that Je-sus Christ is Love.

4 He is Life, he is Life, he has died to set us free, and he is Life! And he calls us all to live ev-er-more, for Je-sus Christ is Life.

Words: st. 1 Marvin Frey © 1977 Marvin Frey; sts. 2, 3, 4 anonymous
Music (HE IS LORD 3.3.11.10.6): Marvin Frey © 1977 Marvin Frey; harm. Dale Grotenhuis (1931-2012)
© 1987 Marvin Frey

228 Send Us Your Spirit

Refrain may be sung in a canon

Refrain ① D G/D ② D G/D D

Come, Lord Je - sus, send us your Spir - it, re - new the

Em G2 A D G/D

face of the earth. Come, Lord Je - sus,

D G/D D Em G

send us your Spir - it, re - new the face of the earth.

Asus D G/D *To stanzas* | D *Final ending*

Stanzas D Am7/D

1 Come___ to us, Spir - it of God; breathe in us
2 Fill us with__ the fire of your love; burn in us
3 Send__ us__ the wings of new birth; fill all the

Words and Music (SEND US YOUR SPIRIT irregular): David Haas (b. 1957) © 1981, 1982, 1987 GIA Publications, Inc.

now,_____ we sing to - geth - er.
now;_____ bring us to - geth - er.
earth with the love you have taught us. Let

Spir - it of hope and of light,_____ fill___ our lives;
Come to us, dwell in us, change our lives,___ O Lord;
all_____ cre - a - tion now be shak-en with love;

come to us, Spir - it of God.

Affirmation: The Holy Spirit   229

What do you believe concerning "the Holy Spirit"?

**First, that the Spirit,
with the Father and the Son,
is eternal God.**

**Second, that the Spirit
is given also to me,
so that, through true faith,
he makes me share in Christ
and all his benefits,
comforts me,
and will remain with me forever.**

Text: Heidelberg Catechism Q&A 53

230 Come, Holy Spirit

Come, Holy Spirit, Our Souls Inspire 231

1 Come, Ho- ly Spir-it, our souls in-spire and light-en with ce-
2 Thy bless- ed unc- tion from a- bove is com-fort, life, and
3 Teach us to know the Fa- ther, Son, and thee, of both, to

les- tial fire; thou the a- noint- ing Spir- it art,
fire of love; en- a- ble with per-pet- ual light
be but one; that through the a- ges all a- long

who dost thy sev- en- fold gifts im- part.
the dull- ness of our mor- tal sight.
this may be our end- less song:

4 Praise to thine e- ter- nal mer- it, Fa- ther, Son and

Ho- ly Spir- it. A- men.

Words: attr. Rabanus Maurus, 9th c.; tr. John Cosin, 1627, alt., P.D.
Music (VENI, CREATOR SPIRITUS 8.8.8.8): Plainsong Mode VIII; arr. Healey Willan (1880-1968) © the Estate of Healey Willan

232

Come, Holy Ghost

1 Come, Ho-ly Ghost, Cre-a-tor blest, and in our hearts take up thy rest; come with thy grace and heaven-ly aid to fill our hearts which thou hast made, to fill our hearts which thou hast made.

2 O Com-fort-er, to thee we cry, thou heaven-ly gift of God most high; thou fount of life, and fire of love, and sweet a-noint-ing from a-bove, and sweet a-noint-ing from a-bove.

3 O Ho-ly Ghost, through thee a-lone, know we the Fa-ther and the Son; be this our firm un-chang-ing creed, that thou dost from them both pro-ceed, that thou dost from them both pro-ceed.

4 Praise we the Lord: Fa-ther and Son, and Ho-ly Spir-it with them one; and may the Son on us be-stow all gifts that from the Spir-it flow, all gifts that from the Spir-it flow.

Words and Music (BE NOT AFRAID 8.8.8.8.8 refrain 4.8.4.8): from *Veni Creator Spiritus*, attr. Rhabanus Maurus (776-856), Bruce Benedict, Ray Mills, 2005, © 2006 Cardiphonia Music/Raymond G. Mills; arr. Diane Dykgraaf © 2012 Cardiphonia Music/Raymond G. Mills

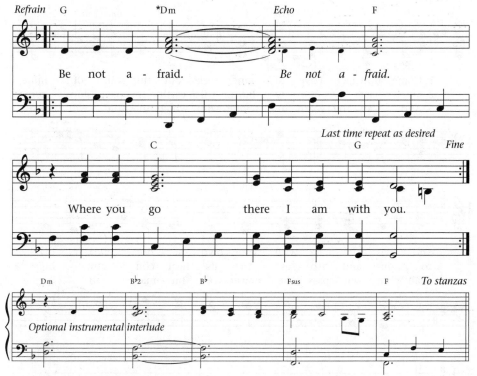

Refrain G   *Dm   Echo   F

Be not a - fraid.   Be not a - fraid.

Last time repeat as desired

C   G   Fine

Where you go   there   I   am   with   you.

Dm   B♭2   B♭   Fsus   F   *To stanzas*

Optional instrumental interlude

Optional ending: bracketed portion of the stanza can be sung layered with the Refrain,
coming in at the *asterisk.

Haleluya, Puji Tuhan/Alleluia, Praise the Lord 233

Descant

Pu - ji   Tu - han.   Pu - ji   Tu - han.
Praise — the — Lord.   Praise — the — Lord.
Lou - ez   le   Seig-neur.   Lou - ez   le   Seig-neur.
Lo - bet   den — Herrn.   Lo - bet   den — Herrn.
A - la - bar a Dios!   A - la - bar a Dios!

G   D   G   C   G

Indonesian Ha - le - lu - ya   Pu - ji   Tu - han. Ha-le-lu-ya, ha-le-lu-ya, Pu-ji Tu - han.
English Al - le - lu - ia, praise — the — Lord. Al-le-lu-ia, al-le-lu-ia praise — the — Lord.
French Al - lé - lu - ia,   lou-ez le Seig-neur. Al-lé-lu-ia, al-lé - lu - ia, lou-ez le Seig-neur.
German Hal-le - lu - ja,   lo-bet den — Herrn. Hal-le-lu - ja, hal-le-lu - ja,   lo-bet den — Herrn.
Spanish A - le - lu - ya,   a - la-bar a Dios! A-le-lu-ya, a-le-lu-ya,   a - la-bar a Dios!

Words and Music (PUJI TUHAN): traditional Soahuku, Seram Island, Indonesia; adapt. Christian I. Tamaela

234 Come Down, O Love Divine

1 Come down, O Love di - vine; seek out this soul of mine,
2 Oh, let it free - ly burn, till earth - ly pas - sions turn
3 And so the yearn - ing strong, with which the soul will long,

and vis - it it with your own ar - dor glow - ing;
to dust and ash - es in its heat con - sum - ing;
shall far out - pass the power of hu - man tell - ing;

O Com - fort - er, draw near; with - in my heart ap - pear,
and let your glo - rious light shine ev - er on my sight,
for none can guess God's grace, till Love cre - ates a place

and kin - dle it, your ho - ly flame be - stow - ing.
and clothe me round, the while my path il - lum - ing.
where - in the Ho - ly Spir - it makes a dwell - ing.

Words: Bianco da Siena (ca. 1350-1434); tr. Richard F. Littledale (1833-1890), P.D.
Music (DOWN AMPNEY 6.6.11.6.6.11): Ralph Vaughan Williams (1872-1958), P.D.

Spirit, Working in Creation

1 Spir-it, work-ing in cre-a-tion, bring-ing or-der out of strife,
2 Spir-it, com-ing from the Fa-ther as a dove up-on our Lord,
3 Spir-it, breathed on the dis-ci-ples, giv-ing peace where there was fear,

come a-mong God's gath-ered peo-ple, giv-ing har-mo-ny and life.
come up-on your cho-sen peo-ple, may your bless-ings be out-poured.
come a-mong us, touch us, send us, mak-ing Je-sus' pres-ence near.

Spir-it, speak-ing through the proph-ets so the voice of God was heard,
Spir-it, driv-ing to the des-ert e-ven God's An-oint-ed One,
Praise and glo-ry, Ho-ly Spir-it, for your love on us out-poured,

come, in-spire, a-lert your peo-ple to this day's pro-phet-ic word.
come to us in trial and test-ing, that God's will in us be done.
giv-ing hon-or to the Fa-ther and pro-claim-ing Je-sus "Lord."

Words: John Richards, 1978, © John Richards/Renewal Servicing
Music (SUNRISE 8.7.8.7 D): *Kyriale*, Luxembourg, 1768, P.D.

236   Praise the Spirit in Creation

1 Praise the Spirit in creation, breath of God, life's origin: Spirit, moving on the waters, quickening worlds to life within, source of breath to all things breathing, life in whom all lives begin.

2 Praise the Spirit, close companion of our inmost thoughts and ways: who, in showing us God's wonders, is for us the power to gaze; and God's will to those who listen, by a still small voice conveys.

3 Praise the Spirit, who enlightened priests and prophets with the word; holy truth behind the wisdoms which as yet knew not our Lord; by whose love and power in Jesus, God by us was seen and heard.

(continues)

Words: Michael Hewlett (1916-2000) © Michael Hewlett/Oxford Univeristy Press from *English Praise* 1975, reproduced by permission of Oxford University Press
Music (JULION 8.7.8.7.8.7): David Hurd © 1983 GIA Publications, Inc.

4 Tell of how the ascended Jesus
  armed a people for his own;
  how a hundred men and women
  turned the known world upside down,
  to its dark and farthest corners
  by the wind of heaven blown.

5 Pray we then, O Lord the Spirit,
  on our lives descend in might;
  let your flame break out within us,
  fire our hearts and clear our sight
  till, white-hot in your possession,
  we, too, set the world alight.

Spirit of God, Unleashed on Earth   237

1 Spir - it of God, un-leashed on earth with rush of
2 You came in power, the church was born; O Ho - ly
3 With burn - ing words of vic - tory won in - spire our

wind and roar of flame! With tongues of fire saints
Spir - it, come a - gain! From liv - ing wa - ters
hearts grown cold with fear, re - vive in us bap -

spread good news; earth, kin - dling, blazed its loud ac - claim.
raise new saints, let new tongues hail the ris - en Lord.
tis - mal grace, and fan our smol - dering lives to flame.

Words: John W. Arthur, 1972, alt. © John W. Arthur, used by permission of Mary Arthur
Music (TRURO 8.8.8.8): T. Williams' *Psalmodia Evangelica*, 1789, P.D.

238 Spirit, Spirit of Gentleness

Words and Music (SPIRIT irregular): James K. Manley, 1975, © 1978 James K. Manley

then you coaxed up the moun-tains from the "val - leys of sleep,
and you gift - ed your peo - ple with a law and a land;
then you whis-pered in si - lence when the whole world was still.
from the bond - age of sor - row all the cap - tives dream dreams;

and o - ver the e - ons you called to each thing,
and when they were blind - ed with i - dols and lies,
And down in the cit - y you called once a - gain,
our wom - en see vi - sions; our men clear their eyes.

To Refrain

"A - wake from your slum - bers and__ rise on your wings."
then you spoke through your proph - ets to__ o - pen their eyes.
when you blew through your peo - ple on the rush of the wind.
With__ bold new de - ci - sions your__ peo - ple a - rise.

Optional charge and blessing (Gal. 5:22-23, 25; Rom. 15:13)

The fruit of the Spirit is love, joy, peace, forbearance,
kindness, goodness, faithfulness, gentleness and self-control.
Against such things there is no law.
Since we live by the Spirit,
let us keep in step with the Spirit.

May the God of hope fill you
with all joy and peace as you trust in him,
so that you may overflow with hope
by the power of the Holy Spirit.

239 Wind Who Makes All Winds That Blow

1 Wind who makes all winds that blow—gusts that bend the sap-lings low,
2 Fire who fuels all fires that burn—suns a-round which plan-ets turn,
3 Ho - ly Spir - it, wind and flame, move with-in our mor - tal frame.

gales that heave the sea in waves, stir-rings in the mind's deep caves—
bea - cons mark-ing reefs and shoals, shin-ing truth to guide our souls—
Make our hearts an al - tar pyre. Kin - dle them with your own fire.

aim your breath with stead - y power on your church, this day, this hour.
come to us as once you came: burst in tongues of sa - cred flame!
Breathe and blow up - on that blaze till our lives, our deeds, and ways

Raise, re - new the life we've lost, Spir - it God of Pen - te - cost.
Light and pow - er, might and strength, fill your church, its breadth and length.
speak that tongue which ev-ery land by your grace shall un - der - stand.

Words: Thomas H. Troeger (b. 1945) © Oxford University Press Inc., 1986, assigned to Oxford University Press
  2010, reproduced by permission
Music (ABERYSTWYTH 7.7.7.7 D): Joseph Parry (1841-1903); 1879, alt., P.D.

Fear Not, Rejoice and Be Glad

240

JOEL 2-3

Refrain

Fear not, re-joice and be glad: the LORD has done a great thing, has poured out his Spir-it on all who live, on those who con-fess his name. *Fine*

1 The fig tree is bud-ding, the vine bear-ing fruit, the wheat fields are gold-en with grain. Thrust in the sick-le, the har-vest is ripe; the LORD has giv-en us rain.

2 We shall eat in plen-ty and be sat-is-fied, the moun-tains will drip with new wine. "My chil-dren will drink of the foun-tain of life; my chil-dren will know they are mine."

3 "My peo-ple will know that I am the LORD; their shame I have tak-en a-way. My Spir-it will lead them to-geth-er a-gain, my Spir-it will show them the way." *To Refrain*

Words: based on Joel 2-3; vers. Priscilla Wright, 1971, alt. © 1971, 1975 Celebration
Music (CLAY irregular): Priscilla Wright, 1971; harm. Dale Grotenhuis (1931-2012), 1986, © 1971, 1975
Celebration

241 Santo Espíritu, excelsa paloma/ Holy Spirit, from Heaven Descended

Spanish
1 San-to Es-pí-ri-tu, ex-cel-sa pa-lo-ma, in-mu-
2 San-to Es-pí-ri-tu, fue-go ce-les-te, en el

English
1 Ho-ly Spir-it, from heav-en de-scend-ed, in the
2 Ho-ly Spir-it, with flame you a-noint-ed the be-

ta-ble ser del Tri-no Dios; men-sa-je-ro de paz, que pro-
dí-a de Pen-te-cos-tés, cual la nu-be de glo-ria, ba-
form of a dove you were seen; with a mes-sage of love from the
liev-ers on that Pen-te-cost, bring-ing heav-en-ly light and im-

ce-des del Pa-dre, hoy con-sué-la-nos con sua-ve voz.
jas-te a la i-gle-sia co-mo al tem-plo de Sión o-tra vez.
Fa-ther a-bove,_ giv-ing com-fort to all who be-lieve.
part-ing great might_ to be-liev-ers as sign to the lost.

Tu fra-gan-cia y lle-nu-ra an-he-la-mos; em-bal-sa-ma tu
Pa-ra el nue-vo cris-tia-no e-res se-llo; ca-da u-no de
How we long for your fra-grance to fill us; we con-fess our deep
As the tow-er of fire was for Is-rael, fill our lives now with

Words and Music (EXCELSA PALOMA irregular): Philip W. Blycker (b. 1939) © 1977 Philip W. Blycker; arr. Albert Chung © 2012 Philip W. Blycker

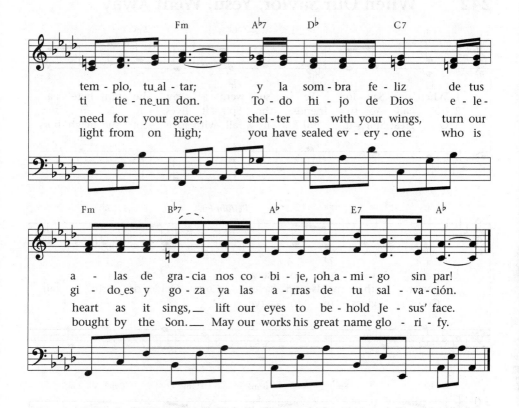

tem - plo, tu_al - tar;   y   la   som - bra   fe - liz   de tus
ti   tie - ne_un don.   To - do   hi - jo   de Dios   e - le-
need for   your grace;   shel - ter   us   with your wings,   turn our
light from   on   high;   you have sealed ev - ery - one   who is

a   -   las   de   gra - cia   nos co - bi - je, ¡oh_a - mi - go   sin par!
gi   -   do_es   y   go - za   ya   las   a - rras   de   tu   sal - va - ción.
heart   as   it   sings, __ lift our eyes   to   be - hold   Je - sus' face.
bought   by   the   Son. __ May our works his great name glo   -   ri - fy.

Spanish

3 Santo_Espíritu,_aceite bendito,
   cual producto del verde_olivar;
   luminaria_y calor
   en la tienda sagrada
   donde_Aarón se_acercaba_a_adorar.
   Agua viva_y regeneradora,
   santifícanos contra el mal;
   somos uno_en Jesús,
   los creyentes del mundo,
   por tu santa labor bautismal.

4 Santo_Espíritu, viento potente,
   fuente_y fuerza de paz y de_amor;
   paracleto veraz
   que consuelo nos brindas
   y abogas a nuestro favor.
   Sénos luz que_ilumine la Biblia,
   nuestros pies dirigiendo_al andar.
   Hoy rendimos a ti
   nuestras almas ansiosas;
   sólo_ungidos podremos triunfar.

English

3 Holy Spirit, flow freely among us,
   sacred oil giving sight where sin blinds;
   just as Aaron of old
   lit the lamps in the cold,
   warm our hearts and illumine our minds.
   You have baptized us into one body;
   Living Water, now cleanse and renew.
   Sanctify us, we pray,
   that God's Word we obey,
   and to Christ may we ever be true.

4 Holy Spirit of God, breathe upon us,
   fill our hearts with your love, joy, and peace;
   Paraclete, you are nigh,
   interceding on high;
   grant that our meager faith would increase.
   Be our lamp to interpret the Scriptures,
   be our guide to instruct in the way.
   We surrender our will
   as our cup you refill
   to victoriously live every day.

242　When Our Savior, Yesu, Went Away

1 When our Sav - ior, Ye - su, went a - way, he sent here a
2 In all Ye - su's friends the Spir - it lives; it is Ye - su's
3 O great Spir - it, fill us all with love for the neigh - bors

friend with us to stay. Come, Guide on earth, our
power that molds and saves.
God gives us to serve.

Spir - it - friend; come to in - spire, di - rect, de - fend.

4 Come, great Spirit, fire the church on earth,
to your whole creation give new birth.
Refrain

5 Praise be to our Maker, and the Son,
with whom now and ever you are one.
Refrain

Words: Ghanaian; adapt. Tom Colvin (1925-2000) © 1969, rev. 1997 Hope Publishing Company
Music (NYOHENE 9.9 refrain 8.8): Ghanaian (Dagomba) melody; arr. John L. Bell (b. 1949) © 1969, rev. 1997
  Hope Publishing Company

One People, Here, We Gather

1 One peo - ple, here, we gath - er; one gos - pel here up - lifts
2 One teach - er calls dis - ci - ples to Ma - ry's "bet - ter part":
3 One world in - vites our nur - ture, a stew - ard - ship of care
4 One Spir - it sends us on - ward in wit - ness to the earth,

a Pen - te - cost of na - tions, va - ri - e - ties of gifts.
to lis - ten to Christ's les - sons; to learn with o - pen heart;
for o - ceans, fields, and for - ests—one hab - i - tat we share.
as min - is - ters of jus - tice and mid - wives for re - birth:

When Ba - bel tongues con - found us or dif - fer - en - ces di - vide,
to live with hon - est ques - tions; to knock, to seek, to find;
We tend one sa - cred gar - den, as God's own breath im - plores,
to lead the church with cour - age on ven - tures new be - gun,

we break one loaf to - geth - er of Christ the cru - ci - fied.
to love the God of wis - dom with soul and strength and mind.
from coast - al bays to moun - tains, from east to west - ern shores.
re - formed yet still re - form - ing, till God's whole will is done.

Chord symbols represent a simplified harmony.

Words: Mary Louise Bringle (b. 1953) © 2006 GIA Publications, Inc.
Music (MUNICH 7.6.7.6 D): *Neu-vermehrtes Gesangbuch,* Meiningen, 1693; adapt. and harm. Felix Mendelssohn, 1847, P.D.

244 Sopla, sopla fuerte/Blow Wild and Blow Freely

Spanish 1 Sop - la, sop - la fuer - te, Es - pí - ri - tu Di - vi - no.
English 1 Blow wild and blow free - ly, O liv - ing Ho - ly Spir - it.
2 Blow wild and blow free - ly, O liv - ing Ho - ly Spir - it.
3 Blow wild and blow free - ly, O liv - ing Ho - ly Spir - it.

Ven has - ta no - so - tros con to -
Come, breathe in and through us with your
Come kin - dle and warm us with your
Let love reap the har - vest as your

do vi - gor. Plan - ta tu si -
strength and power. Pre - pare here the
ra - diant fires. Spur us with the
fruits in - crease. Draw us to each

mien - te de vi - da a - bun - dan - te y haz -
soil___ for life in all a - bun - dance, and___
cour - age to speak and work for jus - tice. Make us
oth - er in fel - low - ship and ser - vice.

Words: Maria Inés Simeone © Maria Inés Simeone; tr. Mary Louise Bringle © 2010 GIA Publications, Inc.
Music (SOPLA FUERTE irregular): Horacio Vivares, arr. Joel Navarro © Horacio Vivares

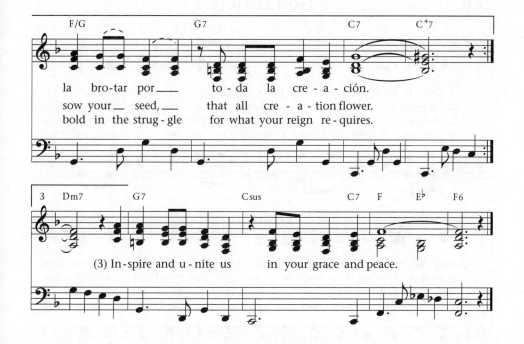

la bro-tar por____ to - da la cre - a - ción.
sow your__ seed, __ that all cre - a - tion flower.
bold in the strug - gle for what your reign re - quires.

(3) In-spire and u - nite us in your grace and peace.

Spanish

2 Sopla, sopla fuerte, Espíritu Divino.
  Mueve nuestros seres con fuego y valor
  dándonos coraje para gritar muy fuerte
  la Palabra de Vida que provoca acción.

3 Sopla, sopla fuerte, Espíritu Divino.
  Haz que fructifique el don del amor
  aquel que bien vivido nos trae la justicia
  y engendra en nosotros paz y comunión.

Affirmation: The Communion of Saints   245

What do you understand by
"the communion of saints"?

**First, that believers one and all,
as members of this community,
share in Christ
and in all his treasures and gifts.**

**Second, that each member
should consider it a duty
to use these gifts readily and joyfully
for the service and enrichment
of the other members**

Text: Heidelberg Catechism Q&A 55

246

God Is Here

1 God is here! As we, your peo-ple, meet to of - fer praise and prayer,
2 Here are sym-bols to re-mind us of our life - long need of grace;
3 Here our chil-dren find a wel-come in the Shep-herd's flock and fold;
4 Lord of all, of church and king-dom, in an age of change and doubt,

may we find in full - er mea-sure what it is in Christ we share.
here are ta - ble, font, and pul - pit; here the Word has cen - tral place.
here, as bread and wine are tak - en, Christ sus-tains us as of old.
keep us faith - ful to the gos - pel; help us work your pur-pose out.

Here, as in the world a - round us, all our var - ied skills and arts
Here in hon - es - ty of preach-ing, here in si - lence as in speech,
Here the ser-vants of the Ser - vant seek in wor-ship to ex - plore
Here, in this day's cel - e - bra - tion, all we have to give, re - ceive;

wait the com - ing of your Spir - it in - to o - pen minds and hearts.
here in new - ness and re - new - al God the Spir - it comes to each.
what it means in dai - ly liv - ing to be - lieve and to a - dore.
we who can - not live with-out you, we a - dore you! We be - lieve.

(continues)

Words: st. 1-4 Fred Pratt Green, 1977, © 1979 Hope Publishing Company; st. 5 Henrietta Ten Harmsel © 1979
  Hope Publishing Company
Music (NETTLETON 8.7.8.7 D): J. Wyeth's *Repository of Sacred Music,* Part II, 1813, P.D.

Optional stanza for a church anniversary

5 In this time of celebration we would offer special praise.
As we think of past and future, vow anew to walk your ways.
Times of triumph, times of failure—still this song keeps ringing through:
Lord, your works cannot be numbered, **Lord, our church* belongs to you.

*Can substitute the name of your church.

Optional prayer for church anniversary or dedication

Lord of the church,
what a privilege it is to be welcomed into your family,
to be called together to love and serve you
and the world that you so love.
Thank you for the many ways you have blessed this community
as one part of your worldwide body . . .
Strengthened for service by gratitude,
we dedicate ourselves to you.
Help us to walk in step with your Spirit,
our comforter and guide. **Amen.**

I Love Your Church, O Lord 247

1 I love your church, O Lord! Her saints be - fore you stand,
2 Be - yond my high - est joy I prize her heaven - ly ways,
3 I love your church, O God, the peo - ple you have called,

dear as the ap - ple of your eye and grav - en on your hand.
her sweet com - mu - nion, sol - emn vows, her hymns of love and praise.
the church our blest Re - deem - er saved with his own pre - cious blood.

Words: Timothy Dwight, 1800, alt., P.D.
Music (ST. THOMAS 6.6.8.6): Aaron Williams, 1770, P.D.

248   We Are Your People

1 We are your peo - ple, Spir - it of grace; you dare to make us
2 Joined in com - mu - ni - ty, treas - ured and fed, may we dis - cov - er
3 Rich in di - ver - si - ty, help us to live clos - er than neigh - bors,
4 Glad of tra - di - tion, help us to see in all life's chang - ing

to all our neigh-bors Christ's liv - ing voice, hands, and face;
gifts in each oth - er, will - ing to lead and be led;
o - pen to stran - gers, a - ble to clash and for - give;
where you are lead - ing, where our best ef - forts should be;

Christ's liv - ing voice, hands, and face.
will - ing to lead and be led.
a - ble to clash and for - give.
where our best ef - forts should be.

race.

5 Give, as we venture, justice and care
(peaceful, resisting, waiting, or risking)
wisdom to know when and where;
wisdom to know when and where.

6 Spirit, unite us; make us, by grace,
willing and ready, Christ's living body,
loving the whole human race;
loving the whole human race.

Great Is the LORD Our God

249

PSALM 48

1 Great is the LORD our God, and great-ly to be praised.
2 God makes his cit-y strong by liv-ing in her halls.
3 With-in your tem-ple, LORD, in your most ho-ly place,

Up-on a hill God's cit-y stands in glo-rious beau-ty raised—
When kings join forc-es and ad-vance, they mar-vel at her walls.
we on your lov-ing-kind-ness dwell, the won-ders of your grace.

his ho-ly moun-tain high, the cit-y of our King,
God scat-ters those a-round whose pride makes them so sure.
Your peo-ple sing your praise wher-e'er your name is known;

the joy of all the earth be-low. In praise to God we sing.
As we have heard, so have we seen: God's cit-y is se-cure.
by ev-ery deed your hand has done your right-eous-ness is shown.

4 Let Zion now rejoice and all her people sing;
   let them with thankfulness proclaim the judgments of their King.
   Mount Zion's walls behold, about her ramparts go,
   and number all the lofty towers that guard her from the foe.

5 Observe her palaces, mark her defenses well,
   that to the children following you her glories you may tell.
   For God as our own God forever will abide,
   and till life's journey close in death will be our faithful guide.

Words: st. 1-2 *Psalter Hymnal*, 1987; st. 3-5 *Psalter*, 1887, rev., 1987, © 1987 Faith Alive Christian Resources
Music (DIADEMATA 6.6.8.6 D): George J. Elvey, 1868, P.D.

250 Christ Is Made the Sure Foundation

1 Christ is made the sure foun-da-tion, Christ, our head and
2 To this tem-ple, where we call you, come, O Lord of
3 Here be-stow on all your ser-vants what they seek from
4 Praise and hon-or to the Fa-ther, praise and hon-or

cor-ner-stone, cho-sen of the Lord and pre-cious,
hosts, and stay; come with all your lov-ing-kind-ness,
you to gain. What they gain from you, for-ev-er
to the Son, praise and hon-or to the Spir-it,

bind-ing all the Church in one; ho-ly Zi-on's
hear your peo-ple as they pray, and your full-est
with the bless-ed to re-tain; and here-af-ter
ev-er three and ev-er one: one in might and

help for-ev-er and our con-fi-dence a-lone.
ben-e-dic-tion shed with-in these walls to-day.
in your glo-ry ev-er-more with you to reign.
one in glo-ry while un-end-ing a-ges run!

Chord symbols represent a simplified harmony.

Words: Latin, ca. 8th c.; tr. John Mason Neale (1818-1866), alt., P.D.
Music (WESTMINSTER ABBEY 8.7.8.7.8.7): Henry Purcell (1659-1695), adapt., PD.

The Church's One Foundation

251

1 The chur-ch's one foun-da-tion is Je-sus Christ, her Lord;
2 E-lect from ev-ery na-tion, yet one o'er all the earth;
3 Though with a scorn-ful won-der the world sees her op-pressed,
4 Mid toil and trib-u-la-tion, and tu-mult of her war,

she is his new cre-a-tion by wa-ter and the Word.
her char-ter of sal-va-tion: one Lord, one faith, one birth.
by schi-sms rent a-sun-der, by her e-sies dis-tressed,
she waits the con-sum-ma-tion of peace for-ev-er-more,

From heaven he came and sought her to be his ho-ly bride;
One ho-ly name she bless-es, par-takes one ho-ly food,
yet saints their watch are keep-ing; their cry goes up: "How long?"
till with the vi-sion glo-rious her long-ing eyes are blest,

with his own blood he bought her, and for her life he died.
and to one hope she press-es, with ev-ery grace en-dued.
and soon the night of weep-ing shall be the morn of song.
and the great church vic-to-rious shall be the church at rest.

5 Yet she on earth has union with God the Three in One,
and mystic sweet communion with those whose rest is won:
O happy ones and holy! Lord, give us grace that we,
like them, the meek and lowly, may live eternally.

Words: Samuel J. Stone, 1866, P.D.
Music (AURELIA 7.6.7.6 D): Samuel S. Wesley, 1864, P.D.

252 Church of God, Elect and Glorious

1 Church of God, e- lect and glo- rious, ho- ly na - tion,
2 God has called you out of dark- ness in - to his most
3 Once you were an a - lien peo- ple, strang - ers to God's
4 Church of God, e- lect and ho- ly, be the peo - ple

cho - sen race, called as God's own spe - cial peo- ple,
mar - velous light, brought his truth to life with- in you,
heart of love, but he brought you home in mer - cy,
he in- tends, strong in faith and swift to an - swer

roy - al priests and heirs of grace; know the
turned your blind - ness in - to sight. Let your
cit - i - zens of heaven a - bove. Let his
each com - mand your Mas - ter sends. Roy - al

pur - pose of your call - ing, show to all his
light so shine a - round you that God's name is
love flow out to oth - ers, let them feel the
priests, ful - fill your call - ing through your sac - ri -

Words: based on I Peter 2:9-10, James E. Seddon © 1982 The Jubilate Group, admin. Hope Publishing
   Company
Music (ABBOT'S LEIGH 8.7.8.7 D): Cyril V. Taylor © 1942, ren. 1970, Hope Publishing Company

might - y deeds, tell of love that knows no
glo - ri - fied and all find fresh hope and
Fa - ther's care, that they too may know his
fice and prayer; give your lives in joy - ful

lim - its, grace that meets all hu - man needs.
pur - pose in Christ Je - sus cru - ci - fied.
wel - come and his count - less bless - ings share.
ser - vice, sing his praise, his love de - clare.

Affirmation: The Church Universal   253

What do you believe
concerning "the holy catholic church"?

**I believe that the Son of God
through his Spirit and Word,
out of the entire human race,
from the beginning of the world to its end,
gathers, protects, and preserves for himself
a community chosen for eternal life
and united in true faith.
And of this community
I am and always will be
a living member.**

Text: Heidelberg Catechism Q&A 54

254 For All the Saints

1 For all the saints who from their la - bors rest,
2 Thou wast their rock, their for - tress, and their might;
3 O blest com - mu - nion, fel - low - ship di - vine!

who thee by faith be - fore the world con - fessed,
thou, Lord, their cap - tain in the well - fought fight;
We feeb - ly strug - gle, they in glo - ry shine;

thy name, O Je - sus, be for - ev - er blest.
thou in the dark - ness drear their one true light.
yet all are one in thee, for all are thine.

Al - le - lu - ia, al - le - lu - ia!

4 And when the strife is fierce,
    the warfare long,
steals on the ear the distant triumph song,
and hearts are brave again,
    and arms are strong.
Alleluia, alleluia!

5 From earth's wide bounds,
    from ocean's farthest coast,
through gates of pearl
    streams in the countless host,
singing to Father, Son, and Holy Ghost:
Alleluia, alleluia!

Words: William W. How, 1864, alt., P.D.
Music (SINE NOMINE 10.10.10 with alleluias): Ralph Vaughan Williams, 1906, P.D.

Somos uno en Cristo/
We Are One in Christ Jesus

Spanish So-mos u-no en Cris-to, so-mos u-no, so-mos u-no, u-no só-lo.

English We are one in Christ Je-sus, all one bod-y, all one spir-it, all to-geth-er.

só-lo. Un so-lo Dios, un so-lo Se-ñor, u-na so-la fe, un so-lo_a-mor, un so-lo bau-tis-mo, —— un so-lo_Es-pí-ri-tu y é-se es el Con-so-la-dor.

geth-er. We share one God, one might-y Lord, one a-bid-ing faith, one bind-ing love, one sin-gle bap-ti-sm, one Ho-ly Com-fort-er, the Ho-ly Spir-it, u-nit-ing all.

Words: Anonymous; English tr. Alice Parker (b. 1925) © 1996 Abingdon Press, admin. The Copyright Company
Music (SOMOS UNO irregular): Anonymous; arr. Philip W. Blycker (b. 1939) © 1992 Celebremos/Libros Alianza

256 # They'll Know We Are Christians

1 We are one in the Spir-it, we are one in the Lord.
We are one in the Spir-it, we are one in the Lord,
and we pray that all u-ni-ty may one day be re-stored.

Refrain

And they'll know we are Chris-tians by our love, by our love.

Yes, they'll know we are Chris-tians by our love.

2 We will walk with each other, we will walk hand in hand. *2x*
and together we'll spread the news that God is in our land. *Refrain*

3 We will work with each other, we will work side by side. *2x*
and we'll guard each one's dignity and save each one's pride. *Refrain*

4 All praise to the Father, from whom all things come,
and all praise to Christ Jesus, his only Son,
and all praise to the Spirit, who makes us all one. *Refrain*

Blest Be the Tie That Binds

1 Blest be the tie that binds our hearts in
2 Be - fore our Fa - ther's throne we pour our
3 We share our mu - tual woes, our mu - tual
4 When we are called to part, it gives us

Chris - tian love; the fel - low - ship of
ar - dent prayers; our fears, our hopes, our
bur - dens bear, and of - ten for each
in - ward pain; but we shall still be

kin - dred minds is like to that a - bove.
aims are one, our com - forts and our cares.
oth - er flows the sym - pa - thiz - ing tear.
joined in heart, and hope to meet a - gain.

5 This glorious hope revives
  our courage by the way;
  while each in expectation lives
  and waits to see the day.

6 From sorrow, toil, and pain,
  and sin, we shall be free;
  and perfect love and friendship reign
  through all eternity.

Words: John Farrell, 1782, P.D.
Music (DENNIS 6.6.8.6): attr. Johann C. Nägeli, 1828, P.D.

258

Koinonia*

How can I say that I love the Lord whom I've
-get to say that I love the one whom I

nev - er, ev - er seen be-fore; and for-
walk be - side each and

ev - ery day? How can I look up - on your face

and ig - nore God's love? You I must em - brace! You're my

broth-er; you're my sis - ter; and I

Koinonia, from the Greek word κοινωνία, means "fellowship."

Words and Music (KOINONIA): V. Michael McKay © Schaff Music Publishing, LLC

Affirmation: The Unity of the Body   259

We believe in one holy,
universal Christian church,
**the communion of saints
called from the entire human family.**

We believe that Christ's work of reconciliation
is made manifest in the church
as the community of believers
**who have been reconciled
with God and with one another.**

We believe that this unity of the people of God
must be manifested and be active
in a variety of ways:
in that we love one another;
that we experience, practice, and pursue
community with one another;
that we are obligated to give ourselves willingly
and joyfully to be of benefit
and blessing to one another;
**that we share one faith,
have one calling,
are of one soul and one mind;
have one God and Father,
are filled with one Spirit,
are baptized with one baptism,**

**eat of one bread
and drink of one cup,
confess one name,
are obedient to one Lord,
work for one cause,
and share one hope.**

That together we come to know
the height and the breadth
and the depth of the love of Christ;
**together are built up
to the stature of Christ,**
to the new humanity;
**together know and bear
one another's burdens,**
thereby fulfilling the law of Christ
that we need one another
and upbuild one another,
admonishing and comforting one another;
**that we suffer with one another
for the sake of righteousness;
pray together;
together serve God in this world;
and together fight against all
which may threaten or hinder this unity.**

Text: from the Belhar Confession

260 Miren qué bueno/Oh, Look and Wonder

PSALM 133

Spanish
2 ¡Miren qué bueno es cuando
las hermanas están juntas!
Se parece al rocío
sobre los montes de Sión. *Refrain*

3 ¡Miren qué bueno es cuando
nos reunimos todos juntos!
Porque el Señor ahí manda
vida eterna y bendición. *Refrain*

Words: from Psalm 133, Pablo Sosa (b. 1933) © 1972 GIA Publications, Inc.
Music (MIREN QUÉ BUENO irregular): Pablo Sosa (b. 1933) © 1972 GIA Publications, Inc.

Shout, for the Blessed Jesus Reigns

261

1 Shout, for the bless - ed Je - sus reigns; through dis - tant
lands his tri - umphs spread. And sin - ners freed from
end - less pains, own him their Sav - ior and their Head.

2 He calls his cho - sen from a - far; they all at
Zi - on's gates ar - rive. Those who were dead in
sin be - fore by sov - ereign grace are made a - live.

3 Gen - tiles and Jews his laws o - bey. All lands and
na - tions of - ferings bring and, un - con - strained, their
hom - age pay to their ex - al - ted God and King.

4 Oh, may his holy church increase,
his Word and Spirit still prevail,
while angels celebrate his praise
and saints his growing glories hail.

5 Loud hallelujahs to the Lamb
from all below and all above!
In lofty songs exalt his name,
in songs as lasting as his love.

Words: Benjamin Beddome, 1769, P.D.
Music (TRURO 8.8.8.8): T. Williams' *Psalmodia Evangelica*, 1789, P.D.

262   # I Love to Tell the Story

1 I love to tell the sto - ry of un - seen things a - bove,
2 I love to tell the sto - ry; 'tis pleas - ant to re - peat
3 I love to tell the sto - ry, for those who know it best

of Je - sus and his glo - ry, of Je - sus and his love.
what seems, each time I tell it, more won - der - ful - ly sweet.
seem hun - ger - ing and thirst - ing to hear it, like the rest.

I love to tell the sto - ry be - cause I know 'tis true;
I love to tell the sto - ry, for some have nev - er heard
And when, in scenes of glo - ry, I sing the new, new song,

it sat - is - fies my long - ings as noth - ing else can do.
the mes - sage of sal - va - tion from God's own ho - ly Word.
'twill be the old, old sto - ry that I have loved so long.

Words: A. Catherine Hankey, 1866, P.D.
Music (HANKEY 7.6.7.6 D refrain): William G. Fisher, 1869, P.D.

Refrain

I love to tell the sto-ry; 'twill be my theme in glo-ry
to tell the old, old sto-ry of Je-sus and his love.

Affirmation: Joining The Mission of God   263

Joining the mission of God,
the church is sent
with the gospel of the kingdom
**to call everyone to know
and follow Christ
and to proclaim to all
the assurance that in the name of Jesus
there is forgiveness of sin
and new life for all
who repent and believe.**

The Spirit calls all members
**to embrace God's mission
in their neighborhoods
and in the world:**
to feed the hungry,
bring water to the thirsty,
welcome the stranger,
clothe the naked,
care for the sick,

and free the prisoner.
**We repent of leaving this work to a few,
for this mission is central to our being.**

In a world estranged from God,
where happiness and peace
are offered in many names
and millions face confusing choices,
**we witness—
with respect for followers
of other ways—
to the only one
in whose name salvation is found:
Jesus Christ.
In Jesus, God reconciles
the world to himself.
God loves all creation;
his compassion knows no bounds.**

Text: from stanzas 41, 42, *Our World Belongs to God*

264   Lift High the Cross

Descant

Lift high the cross, the love of Christ pro - claim till

Refrain
Unison

Lift high the cross, the love of Christ pro - claim till

all the world a - dore his sa - cred name.

all the world a - dore his sa - cred name.   *Fine*

Harmony

Em	Am	D	Bm	C	Em	B

1 Come, Chris - tians, fol - low where our Sav - ior trod,
2 All new - born ser - vants of the Cru - ci - fied
3 From north and south, from east and west we raise
4 O Lord, once lift - ed on the tree of pain,

Words: George W. Kitchin, 1887, rev. Michael R. Newbolt, 1916, alt. © 1974 Hope Publishing Company
Music (CRUCIFER 10.10 refrain 10.10): Sydney H. Nicholson, 1916, © 1974 Hope Publishing Company; desc.
  Richard Proulx © 1974 Hope Publishing Company

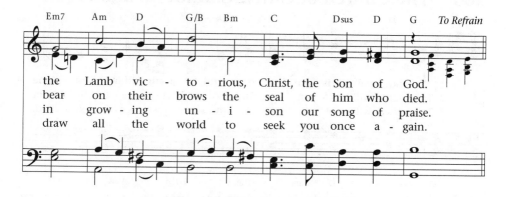

the	Lamb	vic -	to -	rious,	Christ,	the	Son	of	God.
bear	on	their	brows	the	seal	of	him	who	died.
in	grow -	ing	un - i -	son	our	song	of	praise.
draw	all	the	world	to	seek	you	once	a -	gain.

5 Let every race and every language tell
of him who saves our lives from death and hell. *Refrain*

6 Set up your throne, that earth's despair may cease
beneath the shadow of its healing peace. *Refrain*

7 So shall our song of triumph ever be:
praise to the Crucified for victory! *Refrain*

A Prayer for the Mission of the Church   265

Lord God,
we bless you for your charge to us
to "make disciples from every nation
and to teach them to obey all
that you have commanded us."
**How grateful we are
for your promise to never leave us
or forsake us.**

*[Add other prayers that rehearse God's commissioning,
and promises]*

As we seek to plant the seed of your word,
and to water the seed once planted,
**teach us to trust and to testify
that you are the source of all the growth.**

[Add other prayers that rehearse dependence on God]

As the seed of your Word
is planted in our hearts,
**help us—and all those around us—
to be good soil,**

**receptive to all that you desire for us
to know, to love, and to do.**

*[Add other prayers for receptive hearts, among both those
who minister and those who are ministered to]*

By your Spirit,
increase our "love and knowledge
and depth of insight:
**so that
"we may discern what is best,
and be pure and blameless
for the day of Christ,
filled with the harvest of righteousness
that comes through Jesus,
to the glory and praise of God."**

[Add other prayers for discernment and wisdom in ministry]

We pray,
through Jesus Christ, our Lord. Amen.

Text: from Matt. 28:18-20; 1 Cor. 3:6, Matt. 13:1-23; Phil. 1:9-11

266 The Church of Christ Cannot Be Bound

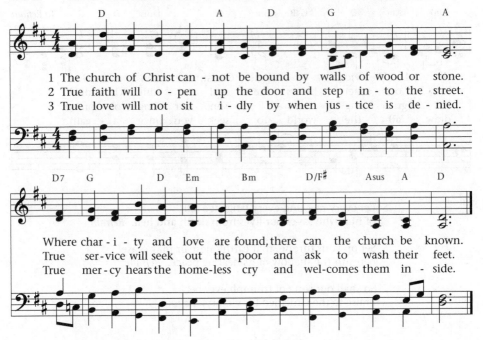

1 The church of Christ can - not be bound by walls of wood or stone.
2 True faith will o - pen up the door and step in - to the street.
3 True love will not sit i - dly by when jus - tice is de - nied.

Where char - i - ty and love are found, there can the church be known.
True ser - vice will seek out the poor and ask to wash their feet.
True mer - cy hears the home-less cry and wel-comes them in - side.

4 If what we have we freely share
   to meet our neighbor's need,
   then we extend the Spirit's care
   through every selfless deed.

5 The church of Christ cannot be bound
   by walls of wood or stone.
   Where charity and love are found,
   there can the church be known.

Alternate tune: MCKEE *see 268*

Words: Adam M. L. Tice (b. 1979) © 2005 GIA Publications, Inc.
Music (ST. PETER 8.6.8.6) Alexander R. Reinagle, 1836, P.D.

267 The Great Commission

MATTHEW 28:18-20

Jesus said, "All authority in heaven and on earth has been given to me."
With gratitude and expectation, we hear Jesus' command:
Therefore go and make disciples of all nations,
baptizing them in the name of the Father and of the Son and of the Holy Spirit,
and teaching them to obey everything I have commanded you.
With joy and trust, we hear Jesus' promise:
"Surely I am with you always, to the very end of the age."

Text: adapted from Matt. 28:18-20

For additional songs about the mission of the church, see the sections *Offering Our Lives*
and *Sending,* and look under *Missions* in the index.

In Christ There Is No East or West

268

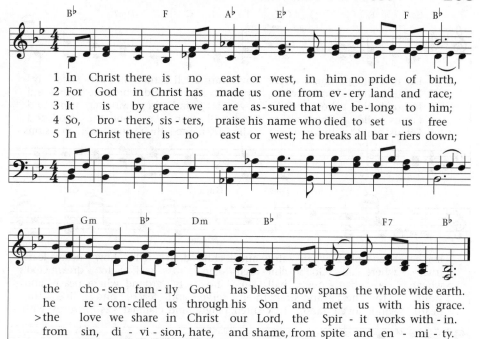

1 In Christ there is no east or west, in him no pride of birth,
2 For God in Christ has made us one from ev-ery land and race;
3 It is by grace we are as-sured that we be-long to him;
4 So, bro-thers, sis-ters, praise his name who died to set us free
5 In Christ there is no east or west; he breaks all bar-riers down;

the cho-sen fam-i-ly God has blessed now spans the whole wide earth.
he re-con-ciled us through his Son and met us with his grace.
>the love we share in Christ our Lord, the Spir-it works with-in.
from sin, di-vi-sion, hate, and shame, from spite and en-mi-ty.
by Christ re-deemed, by Christ pos-sessed, in Christ we live as one.

German

1 In Christus ist nicht Ost noch West,
nicht Süden oder Nord,
nur eine groß' Geschwisterschaft
die ganze Erde fort.

French

1 Gens de tous pays, du sud au nord,
vous êtes invités:
De l'ouest à l'est, du sud au nord,
accourez du monde entière.

Dutch

1 In Christus is noch west noch oost,
in Hem noch zuid noch noord,
één broederschap rust in zijn troost,
één wereld in zijn woord.

Spanish

1 Orient ni occidente hay,
en Cristo y su bondad,
incluida en su amor está
la entera humanidad.

Korean

1 예수 안에는 동과 서 없네
주 안에 귀천 없네
주가 축복하신 백성들
온 세계에 퍼지네

Arabic

1 في المسيح لا شرق و
لا غرب، فيه لا نفتخر بجنسنا
العائلة المختارة التي بار
كها الله الآن تملأ كل الأرض

Alternate tune: ST. PETER see 266

Words: John Oxenbam, 1908, alt., P.D.; Korean tr. Eunae Chung © 2012 Faith Alive Christian Resources;
Arabic tr. Maged Dakdouk and Anne Zaki © 2012 Faith Alive Christian Resouces; Dutch tr. J.W. Schulte
Nordholt (b. 1920); French Nicole Berthet, German M. Liesengag, 1924; Spanish J. R. de Balloch
Music (MCKEE 8.6.8.6): African American spiritual, adapt. and harm. Harry T. Burleigh, 1939, P.D.

269 **All Are Welcome**

1 Let us build a house where love can dwell and all can safe-ly
2 Let us build a house where proph-ets speak, and words are strong and
3 Let us build a house where love is found in wa-ter, wine, and
4 Let us build a house where hands will reach be-yond the wood and
5 Let us build a house where all are named, their songs and vi-sions

live, a place where saints and chil-dren tell how hearts learn
true, where all God's chil-dren dare to seek to dream God's
>wheat: a ban-quet hall on ho-ly ground, where peace and
stone to heal and strength-en, serve and teach, and live the
heard and loved and trea-sured, taught and claimed as words with-

to for-give. Built of hopes and dreams and vi-sions, rock of
reign a-new. Here the cross shall stand as wit-ness and as
>jus-tice meet. Here the love of God, through Je-sus, is re-
Word they've known. Here the out-cast and the stran-ger bear the
in the Word. Built of tears and cries and laugh-ter, prayers of

faith and vault of grace; here the love of Christ shall end di-vi-sions:
sym-bol of God's grace; here as one we claim the faith of Je-sus:
>vealed in time and space, as we share in Christ the feast that frees us:
im-age of God's face; let us bring an end to fear and dan-ger:
faith and songs of grace, let this house pro-claim from floor to raf-ter:

Words and Music (TWO OAKS 9.6.8.6.8.7.10 refrain 8.7): Marty Haugen (b. 1950) © 1994
GIA Publications, Inc.

A Prayer of Indigenous Peoples, Refugees, Immigrants, and Pilgrims 270

Triune God
Father, Son, and Holy Spirit,
we come before you
as many parts of a single body;
people drawn from every tribe,
every nation, every language;
some indigenous - peoples of the land;
some refugees, immigrants, pilgrims -
people on the move;
some hosts, some guests;
some both hosts and guests;
all of us searching for an eternal place
where we can belong.

Creator, forgive us.
The earth is yours and everything that is in it.
But we forget.
In our arrogance we think we own it.
In our greed we think we can steal it.
In our ignorance we worship it.
In our thoughtlessness we destroy it.
We forget that you created it
to bring praise and joy to you.
That you gave it as a gift, for us to steward,
for us to enjoy,
for us to see more clearly
your beauty and your majesty.

Jesus, save us.
We wait for your kingdom.
We long for your throne.
We hunger for your reconciliation,
for that day when people, from every tribe
and every tongue will gather
around you and sing your praises.

Holy Spirit, teach us.
Help us to remember that the body
is made up of many parts;
each one unique and every one necessary.
Teach us to embrace the discomfort
that comes from our diversity
and to celebrate the fact that we are unified,
not through our sameness,
but through the blood of our LORD
and Savior, Jesus Christ.

Triune God, we love you.
Your creation is beautiful.
Your salvation is merciful.
And your wisdom is beyond compare.
We pray this all in Jesus' name. Amen.

271   Earth and All Stars

1 Earth and all stars! Come, rush-ing plan-ets!
2 Hail, wind, and rain! Come, blow-ing snow-storms!
3 Trum-pet and pipes! Come, clash-ing cym-bals!
4 En-gines and steel! Come, pound-ing ham-mers!

Sing to the Lord a new song!

Oh, vic-to-ry! Or-der from cha-os!
Flow-ers and trees! Soft rus-tling dry leaves!
Harp, lute, and lyre! Low hum-ming cel-los!
Lime-stone and beams! Strong build-ing work-ers!

Sing to the Lord a new song!

Words: Herbert Brokering (1926-2009) alt. © 1968 Augsburg Fortress
Music (EARTH AND ALL STARS 4.5.7 D refrain 7.7.9): David Johnson, (1922-1987) © 1968 Augsburg Fortress;
  harm. Dale Grotenhuis (1931-2012)© 1984 Augsburg Fortress

He has done mar - vel-ous things.

I too will praise him with a new song!

5 Classrooms and labs!
   Come, boiling test tubes!
   Sing to the Lord a new song!
   Athlete and band! Loud cheering people!
   Sing to the Lord a new song! *Refrain*

6 Knowledge and truth!
   Come, piercing wisdom!
   Sing to the Lord a new song!
   Children of God, dying and rising,
   Sing to the Lord a new song! *Refrain*

A Prayer for Our Work 272

Lord God,
We pray for all
   who work in business and industry,
   who work in homemaking,
   who work in medicine,
   who work in education,
   who work in agriculture,
   who work in government,
   who work in service to others,
   who are beginning a new career,
   who struggle in their work,
   who are seeking new or different jobs,
   who are retired or anticipating retirement,
   who are unemployed or underemployed.

   [Add other categories as appropriate]

Give us joy in our work, and in using gifts and talents we receive from you.
Give us joy in doing all our work to your honor and glory.
Equip us to labor in ways that promote justice and peace.
Equip us to be ministers of your peace in a world that cries for peace.
Through Jesus Christ, our Lord. Amen.

273 Tout est fait pour la gloire de Dieu/ All Is Done for the Glory of God

French 1 Tout est fait pour la gloi-re de Dieu. A - men ! A - men !
2 Le vie c'est pour la gloi-re de Dieu. A - men ! A - men !

English 1 All is done for the glo-ry of God. A - men! A - men!
2 Life is lived for the glo-ry of God. A - men! A - men!

Tout dé - pend de ce que tu en fais. A - men ! A -
All de - pends up-on our glo - rious God. A - men! A -

men ! A - men ! A - men ! A - men !
men! A - men! A - men! A - men!

Tout est fait pour la gloi-re de Dieu. A - men ! A - men !
All is done for the glo-ry of God. A - men! A - men!

French

3 Le culte est pour la gloire de Dieu.
   Amen ! Amen !

4 L'offrande est pour la gloire de Dieu.
   Amen ! Amen !

English

3 Worship is for the glory of God.
   Amen! Amen!

4 All is given for the glory of God.
   Amen! Amen!

O God, Who Gives to Humankind

274

1 O God, who gives to hu - man-kind a search-ing heart and quest - ing mind, grant us to find your truth and laws, and wis - dom to per - ceive their cause.

2 In all our learn - ing give us grace to bow our - selves be - fore your face; as knowl - edge grows, Lord, keep us free from self - de - struc - tive van - i - ty.

3 Some-times we think we un - der - stand all work-ings of your might - y hand; then through your Son help us to know those truths which you a - lone can show.

4 Teach us to joy in things re - vealed, to search with care all yet con - cealed, as through Christ's light your truth we find and wor - ship you with heart and mind.

Optional prayer for teachers and learners

We bless you, Lord, for the privilege of growing in grace and knowledge.
Help us to be hungry for your truth, and to mature as your dearly loved children.
Keep us faithful, and save us from false and distorted teaching.
By your Spirit, lead us into all truth
in the name of Jesus, the way, the truth, and life. Amen.

For an alternate arrangement see 502

Words: Edward J. Burns, 1969, © Edward J. Burns
Music (GERMANY 8.8.8.8): W. Gardiner's *Sacred Melodies*, 1815; arr. Paul Detterman © 2012 Paul Detterman,
admin. Faith Alive Christian Resources

275

No hay dios tan grande/
There's No God as Great

Spanish: No hay dios tan gran-de co-mo tú, no lo hay, no lo hay.
English: There's no god as great as you, O Lord, O__ Lord, my__ God.

Spanish: No hay dios que pue-da_ha-cer las o-bras co-mo las que ha-ces
English: There's no god who works the might-y won-ders, all the won-ders that you

Spanish: tú. tú. No_es con es-pa-da, ni con e-jér-ci-to, mas con tu
English: do. do. Not by our weap-ons, nor by our pow-er, but by your

Spanish: San-to_Es-pí-ri-tu. tu. Y es-ta_i-gle-sia se mo-ve-
English: Spir-it we are led. led. The Ho-ly Spir-it will move the

Words and Music (NO HAY DIOS irregular): Spanish traditional; tr. *Psalter Hymnal*, 1987, © 1987 Faith Alive
Christian Resources

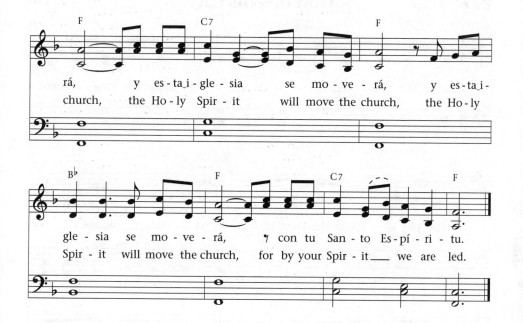

rá,   y es-ta_i-gle-sia   se mo-ve-rá,   y es-ta_i-
church,   the Ho-ly Spir-it   will move the church,   the Ho-ly

gle-sia se mo-ve-rá,   y con tu San-to Es-pí-ri-tu.
Spir-it will move the church,   for by your Spir-it___ we are led.

A Prayer for the Common Good 276

Lord, our God,
help us to be agents of your peace in *[town, city, township, region]*.
We pray for all who work
   to provide housing,
   to resist racism,
   to provide fruitful employment,
   to provide safe schools and places of training and learning,
   to develop artistic gifts,
   to provide health care,
   to provide spiritual care
   to minister to refugees
   to bear witness to your love for us in Jesus Christ . . .

[Add other petitions as appropriate]

May we be your agents of peace and renewal,
that all your children may flourish.
Through Jesus Christ, our Lord,
Amen.

277 **God of This City**

You're the God of this cit-y, You're the King of these

peo-ple, You're the Lord of this na - tion, you are.

You're the light in this dark - ness, You're the hope to the

hope-less, You're the peace to the rest - less, you are.

There is no one like our God.

Words and Music (GOD OF THIS CITY): McCann, Boyd, Jordan, Comfort, Kernaghan, Bleakley, and arr.
Denise Miersma © 2006 Bluetree Publishing, admin. Exchange Church Media Ltd.

278 The City Is Alive, O God

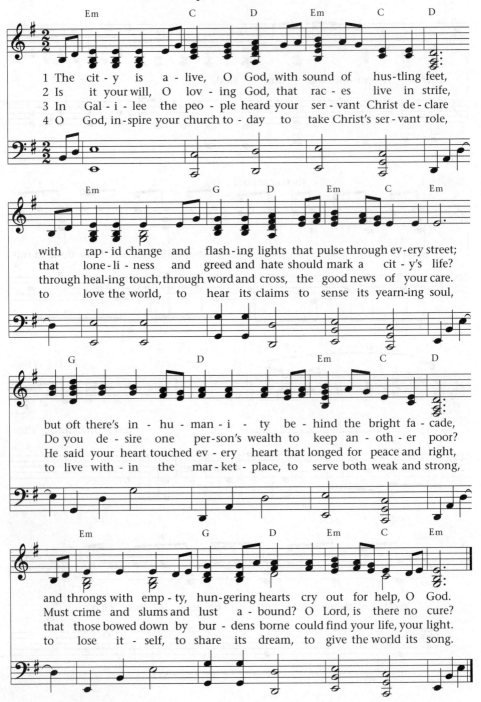

1 The cit-y is a-live, O God, with sound of hus-tling feet,
2 Is it your will, O lov-ing God, that rac-es live in strife,
3 In Gal-i-lee the peo-ple heard your ser-vant Christ de-clare
4 O God, in-spire your church to-day to take Christ's ser-vant role,

with rap-id change and flash-ing lights that pulse through ev-ery street;
that lone-li-ness and greed and hate should mark a cit-y's life?
through heal-ing touch, through word and cross, the good news of your care.
to love the world, to hear its claims to sense its yearn-ing soul,

but oft there's in-hu-man-i-ty be-hind the bright fa-cade,
Do you de-sire one per-son's wealth to keep an-oth-er poor?
He said your heart touched ev-ery heart that longed for peace and right,
to live with-in the mar-ket-place, to serve both weak and strong,

and throngs with emp-ty, hun-ger-ing hearts cry out for help, O God.
Must crime and slums and lust a-bound? O Lord, is there no cure?
that those bowed down by bur-dens borne could find your life, your light.
to lose it-self, to share its dream, to give the world its song.

Words: William W. Reid Jr, alt. © 1969 The Hymn Society, admin. Hope Publishing Company
Music (STAR OF COUNTY DOWN 8.6.8.6 D): Irish traditional; arr. Rory Cooney (b. 1952) © 1990
GIA Publications, Inc.

Alabad al Señor/Praise the Lord
PSALM 117

279

For other settings of Ps. 117 see 570, 588, 589, 591

Words: Psalm 117, Sp. traditional; tr. Mary Louise Bringle, 2011, © 2011 GIA Publications, Inc.
Music (ALABAD AL SEÑOR irregular): Sp. traditional; arr. Marcus Hong, alt. © 2011 Faith Alive Christian
  Resources

280 My Song Forever Shall Record

PSALM 89

1 My song for-ev-er shall re-cord the ten-der
2 I sing of mer-cies that en-dure, for-ev-er
3 Al-might-y God, your loft-y throne has jus-tice

mer-cies of the Lord; your faith-ful-ness will
build-ed firm and sure, of faith-ful-ness that
for its cor-ner-stone, and shin-ing bright be-

I pro-claim, and ev-ery age shall know your name.
nev-er dies, es-tab-lished change-less in the skies.
fore your face are truth and love and bound-less grace.

4 With blessing is the nation crowned
whose people know the joyful sound;
they in the light, O Lord, shall live,
the light your face and favor give.

5 All glory unto God we yield,
who is our constant help and shield;
all praise and honor we will bring
to you, the Holy One, our King.

For use with all of Psalm 89 sing stanzas 1-4, read vv. 19-37 sing st. 5, read vv. 38-51 sing st. 5 again.
Conclude by reading v. 52.

Words: *Psalter*, 1912, alt., P.D.
Music (WINCHESTER NEW 8.8.8.8): *Musikalisches Hand-buch*, Hamburg, 1690, P.D.

God of The Ages, Whose Almighty Hand 281

1 God of the a-ges, whose al-might-y hand
2 Thy love di-vine hath led us in the
3 From war's a-larms, from dead-ly pes-ti-
4 Re-fresh thy peo-ple on their toil-some

hand leads forth in beau-ty all the star-ry band
past; in this free land by thee our lot is cast;
lence, be thy strong arm our ev-er sure de-fense;
way; lead us from night to nev-er-end-ing day;

of shin-ing worlds in splen-dor through the skies:
be thou our rul-er, guard-ian, guide, and stay;
may true re-li-gion in our hearts in-crease,
fill all our lives with love and grace di-vine;

our grate-ful songs be-fore thy throne a-rise.
thy Word our law, thy paths our chos-en way.
thy boun-teous good-ness nour-ish us in peace.
all glo-ry, laud, and praise be ev-er thine.

Words: Daniel C. Roberts, 1876, alt., P.D.
Music (NATIONAL HYMN 10.10.10.10): George W. Warren, 1892, P.D.

282 O God of Every Nation

1 O God of ev-ery na - tion, of ev-ery race and land,
2 From search for wealth and pow - er and scorn of truth and right,
3 Lord, strength-en all who la - bor that we may find re - lease
4 Keep bright in us the vi - sion of days when war shall cease,

re - deem the whole cre - a - tion with your al - might - y hand.
from trust in bombs that show - er de - struc-tion through the night,
from fear of rat - tling sa - ber, from dread of war's in - crease.
when ha - tred and di - vi - sion give way to love and peace,

Where hate and fear di - vide us and bit - ter threats are hurled,
from pride of race and na - tion and blind-ness to your way,
When hope and cour - age fal - ter, Lord, let your voice be heard;
till dawns the morn - ing glo - rious when truth and jus - tice reign,

in love and mer - cy guide us, and heal our strife - torn world.
de - liv - er ev - ery na - tion, e - ter - nal God, we pray!
with faith that none can al - ter, your ser - vants un - der - gird.
and Christ shall rule vic - to - rious o'er all the world's do - main.

Words: William W. Reid Jr, alt. © 1958, ren. 1986 The Hymn Society, admin. Hope Publishing Company
Music (LLANGLOFFAN 7.6.7.6 D): Welsh, 19th c., P.D.

O God of Love, Forever Blest

PSALM 120

1 O God of love, for-ev-er blest, pit-y my suf-fering state.
2 I cried in trou-ble to the Lord, and he has an-swered me.

When will you set my soul at rest from lips that love de-ceit?
From ly-ing lips and craft-y tongue, O Lord, my soul set free.

Refrain

Too long my soul has made its home with those who lift the who lift the

sword. I am for peace; they make for war.
sword. but when I speak, they make for war.

Optional concluding prayer

God of peace, in the middle of a world filled with warfare and violence, we pray for the coming of the Prince of Peace. We cling to your promise that you will break the bow and shatter the spear. We long to live up to our calling as instruments of peace. Through our prayers and through our actions, help us to plant seeds of peace. Then, by your Spirit, turn them into blossoms of hope, the fruit of righteousness. **Amen.**

Words: Isaac Watts, alt., P.D.
Music (SHALOM 120 | 8.6.8.6 refrain 8.8.8.4): Bruce Benedict © 2009 Cardiphonia Music; arr. Greg Scheer
© 2011 Greg Scheer

284 God Is Known Among His People

PSALM 76

1 God is known a-mong his peo-ple; his name shines in
2 God, most ex-cel-lent and awe-some, more than moun-tains,
3 When from heaven your judg-ment sound-ed, all the earth in
4 Make your vows to God and keep them, pay the LORD what

Is - ra - el; for of old he has es - tab - lished
firm and high, you have stripped the val - iant - heart - ed
fear was still— when, to save the meek and low - ly,
is his own. Might - y ones come now be - fore him,

his own house on Zi - on's hill. There he broke the
who on their own strength re - ly. Who can stand be -
you worked out your right - eous will. E - ven hu - man
hum - bly kneel be - fore God's throne. Come and bring your

sword and ar - row, bade the noise of war be still.
fore your an - ger or your might - y hand de - fy?
wrath shall praise you: your de - sign it shall ful - fill.
gifts be - fore him; wor - ship God and God a - lone.

Words: *Psalter*, 1912; *Psalter Hymnal*, 1987, rev. © 1987 Faith Alive Christian Resources
Music (LAUDA ANIMA 8.7.8.7.8.7): John Goss, 1869, P.D.

Blest Be God

1 Blest be God, blest be God for - ev - er.
2 God will ban - dage the wounds of the bro - ken,
3 Come, O Lord, come and save the op - pressed,_____

Who in time and e - ter - ni - ty lives,
and pay heed to each bod - y and soul;
lift the poor from the doors of de - spair;

God the Lord who loves jus - tice and mer - cy
God has asked hu - man - kind not to fear_____
put a song in the hearts of your peo - ple,

and who heals and for - gives those who fall.
but be - lieve that the king - dom's at hand.
those whose hope and whose trust is in you.

Words: Salvador T. Martinez (b. 1939), Payap University, Chiang-Mai, Thailand; adapt. John L. Bell (b. 1949)
© Salvador T. Martinez
Music (DANDASOY 10.9.10.9): Philipine melody from the island of Negros, arr. John L. Bell (b. 1949)
© 1990 Wild Goose Resource Group, Iona Community, Scotland, GIA Publications, Inc., exclusive North
American agent

286 Glorious Things of Thee Are Spoken

PSALM 87

1 Glo - rious things of thee are spo - ken, Zi - on, cit - y of our God.
2 See, the streams of liv - ing wa - ters, spring - ing from e - ter - nal love,
3 Round each hab - i - ta - tion hov - ering, see the cloud and fire ap - pear
4 Sav - ior, since of Zi - on's cit - y I through grace a mem - ber am,

He, whose word can - not be bro - ken formed thee for his own a - bode.
well sup - ply thy sons and daugh - ters and all fear of want re - move.
for a glo - ry and a cov - ering, show - ing that the Lord is near.
let the world de - ride or pit - y, I will glo - ry in your name.

On the Rock of A - ges found - ed, what can shake thy sure re - pose?
Who can faint while such a riv - er ev - er flows their thirst to as-suage?
Thus de - riv - ing from their ban - ner light by night and shade by day,
Fad - ing are the world's best plea-sures, all its boast - ed pomp and show;

With sal - va-tion's walls sur-round-ed, thou may'st smile at all thy foes.
Grace, which like the Lord, the giv - er, nev - er fails from age to age.
safe they feed up - on the man - na which God gives them on their way.
sol - id joys and last - ing trea-sures none but Zi - on's chil-dren know.

Words: John Newton, 1779, alt., P.D.
Music (AUSTRIAN HYMN 8.7.8.7 D): Franz Joseph Haydn (1732-1809), 1797, P.D.

A Prayer for the Nations 287

Glorious things are spoken of you,
God, the source of all springs.
**Our names are known by you
and recorded in your book.**

Your blessing was pronounced on all families
through your servant Abraham,
**and you have established
a home for all of us.**

We pray, O God,
for all the nations of the earth,
lands physically separated by geography—
peoples divided by language,
culture, custom, and color—
yet united as your children.

As of old you claimed your people
from all lands and nations—
from Egypt and Babylon,
Philistia and Ethiopia—
even so, look with mercy upon your church
in this land and in every nation.
Guide us in your ways of justice and peace.

**We call upon you—
from every tribe and every nation,
in every tongue and language,
joining our voices together
in song proclaiming,
all our springs are in you. Amen.**

Text: based on Psalm 87, Melissa Haupt, 2011, © Creative Commons Attribution-NonCommercial-ShareAlike

Shalom/Bring Peace 288

ISAIAH 2:4

Words: Isaiah 2:4
Music (LO YISA GOI irregular): folk song, P.D.

289

For the Healing of the Nations

Gm   Dm   Eᵇsus

1 For the heal-ing of the na-tions, Lord, we pray with one ac-
2 Lead us for-ward in-to free-dom, from de-spair your world re-
3 All that kills a-bun-dant liv-ing, let it from the earth be
4 You, Cre-a-tor God, have writ-ten your great name on hu-man-

Bᵇ   Cm7   Bᵇ6

cord,   for a just and e-qual shar-ing of the
lease,   that, re-deemed from war and ha-tred, all may
banned: pride of sta-tus, race or school-ing, dog-mas
kind;   for our grow-ing in your like-ness bring the

Cm6   Dsus   D   Gm

things that earth af-fords.   To a life of love in
come and go in peace.   Show us how through care and
that ob-scure your plan.   In our com-mon quest for
life of Christ to mind;   that by our re-sponse and

Dm   Cm   D   Gm

ac-tion help us rise and pledge our word.
good-ness fear will die and hope in-crease.
jus-tice may we hal-low life's brief span.
ser-vice earth its des-ti-ny may find.

Words: Fred Kaan © 1968 Hope Publishing Company
Music (HUACO 8.7.8.7.8.7): Swee Hong Lim © 2012 Swee Hong Lim, admin. Faith Alive Christian Resources

Hear Us, O Lord, As We Voice Our Laments 290

PSALM 64

1 Hear us, O Lord, as we voice our la - ments;
2 Heal those who have been pierced by wick - ed lies;
3 Un - do the plans that wick - ed ones de - vise;

help the op - pressed and be their sure de - fense;
shield them from e - vil lurk - ing in dis - guise,
let all their schem - ing bring their own de - mise;

guard them from plots of schem - ing en - e - mies;
and from op - pres - sors think - ing "No one sees;"
then with great fear all peo - ples will a - gree:

be a strong ref - uge for all ref - u - gees.
be a strong ref - uge for all ref - u - gees.
God is a ref - uge for all ref - u - gees.

Words: David Landegent © 2010 David Landegent, admin. Faith Alive Christian Resources
Music (LANGRAN 10.10.10.10): James Langran, 1861, P.D.

291 How Long, O Lord, How Long

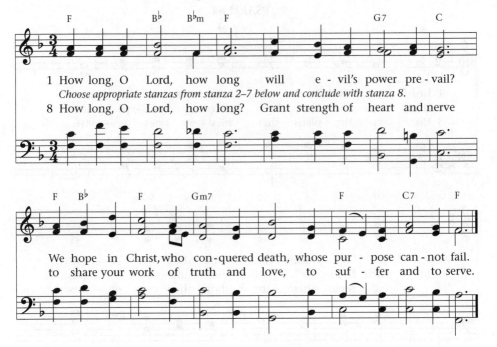

1 How long, O Lord, how long will e-vil's power pre-vail?
Choose appropriate stanzas from stanza 2–7 below and conclude with stanza 8.
8 How long, O Lord, how long? Grant strength of heart and nerve

We hope in Christ, who con-quered death, whose pur-pose can-not fail.
to share your work of truth and love, to suf-fer and to serve.

2 "How long, O Lord, how long,"
the starving millions cry,
"Shall famine's blight our lives destroy,
our children waste and die?"

3 How long, O Lord, how long
must homeless people lie
without a bed in street and camp
while others pass them by?

4 How long, O Lord, how long
will justice bow to greed,
and wealth and power forge the chains
that hold the poor in need?

5 How long, O Lord, how long
will walls we build divide,
and pride of gender, race, or class
another's worth deride?

6 How long, O Lord, how long
must war its carnage spread
and leave behind in ruined rows
the harvest of the dead?

7 "How long, O Lord, how long?"
we cry in our despair;
yet, nailed upon the cross we see
the emblem of your care.

Optional prayer

After stanza 2: we pray for the hungry and those who minister among them *[specify ministries]*
After stanza 3: we pray for the homeless and those who minister among them *[specify ministries]*
After stanza 4: we pray for the poor and those who minister among them *[specify ministries]*
After stanza 5: we pray for victims of prejudice and those who minister among them *[specify ministries]*
After stanza 6: we pray for victims of warfare and those who minister among them *[specify ministries]*

For this music in a lower key see 747

Words: Herman G. Stuempfle Jr (1923-2007) © 1993 GIA Publications, Inc.
Music (TRENTHAM 6.6.8.6): Robert Jackson (1840-1914), 1878, P.D.

There Where the Judges Gather

PSALM 82

292

1 There where the judg - es gath - er, a great - er takes his seat;
2 "Deal just - ly with the need - y, pro - tect the par - ent - less,
3 God speaks: "I named you rul - ers, to serve the Most High God;

"How long," he asks the judg - es, "will you pro - nounce de - ceit?
de - liv - er the af - flict - ed from those who would op - press.
but you shall die as mor - tals and per - ish by my rod."

How long show spe - cial fa - vor to those of ill re - pute?
But you are whol - ly blind - ed, you do not un - der - stand;
A - rise, O God, in judg - ment, your sov - ereign - ty make known;

How long ne - glect the or - phaned, the poor and des - ti - tute?
there - fore foun - da - tions tot - ter, in - jus - tice rocks the land."
for yours are all the na - tions; the peo - ples are your own.

Chord symbols represent a simplified harmony.

Words: Henry Zylstra, 1953, alt., © 1976 Faith Alive Christian Resources
Music (MEIRIONYDD 7.6.7.6 D): William Lloyd, 1840, P.D.

293   O Great God and Lord of the Earth

PSALM 94

1 O great God and Lord of the earth, rouse your-
self and de-mon-strate jus - tice; give the ar - ro - gant
what they de - serve, si - lence all ma - le - vo - lent
boast - ing. See how some you love are bro - ken,

2 Those who crush your peo - ple de - light, claim-ing
God a - bove takes no no - tice; they pro - claim___ that
heav - en is blind, that the God of Ja - cob is
si - lent. Stu - pid fools, when will you lis - ten?

3 God the Lord will not stay a - way nor for -
sake his well - be - loved peo - ple; heav - en's jus - tice
soon will ap - pear, and the pure in heart will em -
brace it. Yes, the ones whom God in - struc - ted,

4 Should the wrong change plac - es with right and the
courts play host to cor - rup - tion; should the in - no - cent
fear for their lives while the guilt - y smile at their
schem - ing; still the Lord will be your ref - uge,

Words: Psalm 94; para. and arr. John L. Bell © 2002 Wild Goose Resource Group, Iona Community, Scotland,
GIA Publications, Inc., exclusive North American agent
Music (VOS SOS EL DESTAZADO 8.9.8.9.8.9.8.9): Guillermo Cuellar © 1996 GIA Publications, Inc.; acc.
Marcus Hong © 2011 GIA Publications, Inc.

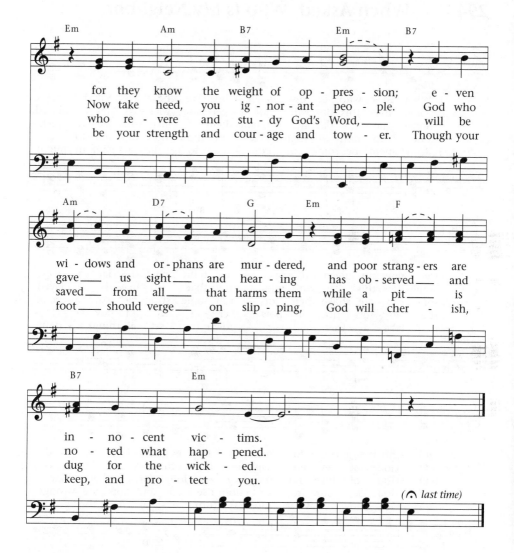

for they know the weight of op - pres - sion; e - ven
Now take heed, you ig - nor - ant peo - ple. God who
who re - vere and stu - dy God's Word,___ will be
be your strength and cour - age and tow - er. Though your

wi - dows and or - phans are mur - dered, and poor strang - ers are
gave___ us sight___ and hear - ing has ob - served___ and
saved___ from all___ that harms them while a pit___ is
foot___ should verge___ on slip - ping, God will cher - ish,

in - no - cent vic - tims.
no - ted what hap - pened.
dug for the wick - ed.
keep, and pro - tect you.

(⌒ last time)

Optional prayer of lament

God of justice and mercy,
in our pain and sorrow,
help us to hold on to your sure promise
that you will never leave or forsake us.
**Give us courage to forsake revenge,
to testify to the beauty of your justice,
and to place our hope in you. Amen.**

Optional prayer of confession

God of justice and mercy,
we confess that we, too often,
are arrogant and indifferent.
**We are the guilty.
We have sinned by what we have done
and what we have left undone.
Clothe us in Christ's righteousness
and teach us to act justly, to love mercy,
and to walk humbly with you. Amen.**

294 When Asked, Who Is My Neighbor

1 When asked, who is my neigh - bor? We hear the Sav - ior say:
2 Some live this day with an - ger at wick - ed - ness dis-played.
3 Some rue the day that brought them to live with deep re - gret,
4 Cor - rup - tion in high plac - es, those choos-ing not to see
5 Re - mem - ber now your prom - ise to come a - gain in might

the one in need of mer - cy, both near and far a - way.
Some live this day with griev - ing that jus - tice is de - layed.
> some can - not shake their sor - row, some strug-gle to re - pent.
the vi - o - lence of pow - er, ef - fects of pov - er - ty—
to take a - way all sor - row, to set all things a - right.

O Christ, still come in mer - cy to ev - ery-one in need,
O God, of ev - ery neigh-bor, on both sides of the walls
> O God, of love and mer - cy, we long for your em - brace.
O God, see our fru - stra - tion; rise up and stop the wrongs
O God, show us your glo - ry; turn e - vil in - to good

your Spir - it work-ing through us, your love in word and deed.
that shield us from each oth - er, bring jus - tice to their cause.
> You of - fer us for - give - ness; help us re - ceive your grace.
of neigh-bor a - gainst neigh - bor to whom our love be - longs.
un - til your love and jus - tice reach ev - ery neigh-bor - hood.

Words: Emily R. Brink © 2012 The Center for Christian Ethics, Baylor University
Music (LLANGLOFFAN 7.6.7.6 D): Welsh, 19th c., P.D.

Let Justice Flow

Let jus - tice flow down, down like a riv - er, down to the val - leys where the help - less cry. Let right - eous - ness flow through us for - ev - er, lead us to the stream that will nev - er run dry.

1 Flow to the mouths of the hun - gry; flow to the hands of the poor.
2 Flow to the streets of the home - less, find - ing no place they can go.
3 Flow through the courts of our na - tion, guide us in love's __ de - crees.

Flow to the hearts of the or - phans, heal __ the wounds of war.
Flow to the cells of the pris - on - ers fac - ing each day a - lone.
Lead us to streams of sal - va - tion; fill __ our land with peace.

Words (from Amos 5:24) and Music (LET JUSTICE FLOW irregular): Douglas Romanow © 1994 Douglas
Romanow & Citizens for Public Justice

296

We Are Called

1 Come! Live in the light! Shine with the joy and the love of the Lord! We are called to be light for the king-dom, to live in the free-dom of the cit-y of God.

2 Come! O-pen your heart! Show your mer-cy to all those in fear! We are called to be hope for the hope-less so ha-tred and blind-ness will be no more. We are called to act with

3 Sing! Sing a new song! Sing of that great day when all will be one! God will reign, and we'll walk with each oth-er as sis-ters and broth-ers u-nit-ed in love.

Words and Music (WE ARE CALLED 5.10.10.10 refrain 8.8.9.6): David Haas (b. 1957) © 1988
GIA Publications, Inc.

justice, we are called to love ten-der - ly;

we are called to serve one an - oth-er, to

walk hum-bly with God.

297

Open Our Eyes

Refrain

Come and bring light to a peo-ple in dark-ness. Come, set us

free from the chains we have made. We are your peo-ple, the

Last time to Coda

flock that you tend. Lord, o - pen our eyes once a - gain.

Stanzas

1 To the ones bro - ken - heart - ed:
2 To the vic - tims of vio - lence:
3 When a col - or di - vides us: O - pen our eyes.
4 To those full of life's sor - row:
5 To those suf - fer - ing ill - ness:

These stanzas could be done as a Call and Response with the leader(s) singing the words in italics and the congregation responding with "Open our eyes."

Words and Music (OPEN OUR EYES 7.4.6.4.7.4.7 refrain 11.10.10.8): Kevin Keil © 1998 Lorenz Publishing Company

298 Salaam/Peace

Instrumental introduction, interlude, and ending

1 Your peace with-in us, Lord, will stand, sur-pass-ing all we
2 When walk-ing we are led a-stray, your Spir-it in us
3 God's peace you of-fered us to live, a peace the world can

un-der-stand. E-ven when fears sur-round our land you
lights the way to bring us back and guard our days. You
nev-er give, and while your Spir-it in us lives, you

fill our lives with peace. Sa-laam, sa-laam, the
laam, sa-laam, the

peace of God to ev-ery race. Sa-
peace of God in ev-ery place.

Words: Manal Samir, Egypt © 2002 *Songs of the Evangelical Presbyterian Church of Egypt,* Synod of the Nile, Council of Pastoral Work and Evangelism, admin. Faith Alive Christian Resources; tr. Anne Emile Zaki, adapt. Emily Brink © 2008 Faith Alive Christian Resources

Music (SALAAM 8.8.8.6 refrain 4.8 D): Manal Samir, Egypt © 2002 *Songs of the Evangelical Presbyterian Church of Egypt,* Synod of the Nile, Council of Pastoral Work and Evangelism, admin. Faith Alive Christian Resources; arr. Greg Scheer © 2008 Greg Scheer

Jesu, Jesu, Fill Us with Your Love

299

Refrain

Je - su, Je - su, fill us with your love, show
us how to serve the neigh-bors we have from you.

1 Kneels at the feet of his friends, si - lent-ly wash - es their
2 Neigh-bors are rich folk and poor, neigh-bors are black, brown, and
3 These are the ones we should serve, these are the ones we should
4 Lov - ing puts us on our knees, serv - ing as though we are

feet, Mas - ter who acts as a slave to them.
white, neigh-bors are near - by and far a - way.
love; all these are neigh-bors to us and you.
slaves: this is the way we should live with you.

Optional rhythm

or

Words: Tom Colvin, 1963, © 1969 Hope Publishing Company
Music (CHEREPONI 7.7.9 refrain 9.12): Ghanian folk song; adapt. Tom Colvin, 1963, © 1969 Hope Publishing
Company; arr. Diane Dykgraaf © 2012 Hope Publishing Company

300 Come Now, You Blessed, Eat at My Table

1 "Come now, you bless - ed; eat at my ta - ble," said Je - sus
2 When did we see you hun - gry or thirs - ty? When were you
3 "When you gave bread to earth's hun - gry chil - dren, when you gave
4 Christ, when we see you out on life's road - ways, look - ing to

Christ to the right-eous a - bove. "When I was hun - gry, thirs - ty and
home-less, a stran - ger a - lone? When did we see you sick or in
shel - ter to war's ref - u - gees, when you re - mem - bered those most for -
us in the fa - ces of need, then may we know you, wel - come, and

home - less, sick and in pri - son, you showed me your love."
pri - son? What have we done that you call us your own?
got - ten, you cared for me in the small - est of these."
show you love that is faith - ful in word and in deed.

Optional interlude

Words: Ruth Duck © 1992 GIA Publications, Inc.
Music (COME NOW, YOU BLESSED 10.10.10.10): Jeeva Sam © 1995 Jeeva Sam; arr. © 1995 Musiklus

How Blest Are Those Who Fear the Lord   301

PSALM 112

1 How blest are those who fear the LORD and great - ly
2 A - bound-ing wealth shall bless their home, their right - eous -
3 The peo - ple who be - friend the weak in jus - tice
4 By e - vil tid - ings not dis - mayed, the right - eous

love God's ho - ly will. Their chil - dren share their
ness for - e'er en - dure. To them shall light a -
shall their cause main - tain. True peace shall their whole
trust in God a - lone. Their heart is stead - fast,

great re - ward, and bless - ings all their days shall fill.
rise in gloom, for they are mer - ci - ful and pure.
life at - tend, and long their mem - ory shall re - main.
un - a - fraid, for they shall see their foes o'er - thrown.

5 Dispersing gifts among the poor,
  the righteous for their needs provide.
  Their righteousness shall thus endure;
  their strength in honor shall abide.

6 The wicked will be brought to shame,
  while righteous ones will see the LORD.
  Unrighteous hopes will not see gain,
  for sin will find its due reward.

Words: *Psalter,* 1887; rev. *Psalter Hymnal,* 1987, © Faith Alive Christian Resources
Music (MELCOMBE 8.8.8.8): Samuel Webbe, 1782, P.D.

302 **Hear Our Praises**

1 May our homes be filled with danc - ing,
(2 May your light) shine in the dark - ness

may our streets be filled with joy.
as we walk be - fore the cross.

May in - jus - tice bow to Je - sus
May your glo - ry fill the whole earth

as the peo - ple turn and pray.
as the wa - ter over the seas.

Words and Music (HEAR OUR PRAISES 8.7.8.7 refrain 8.7.8.7): Reuben Morgan © 1998 Hillsong Publishing (APRA), admin. US & Canada at EMICMGPublishing.com

Refrain

From the moun-tain to the val-ley, hear our

prais-es rise to you. From the

heav-ens to the na-tions, hear our

sing-ing fill the air.

2 May your light

303   # Healer of Our Every Ill

Heal-er of our ev-ery ill, light of each to-mor-row,

give us peace be-yond our fear and hope be-yond our sor-row.

1 You who know our fears and sad-ness, grace us with your
2 In the pain and joy, be-hold-ing how your grace is
3 Give us strength to love each oth-er, ev-ery sis-ter,
4 You who know each thought and feel-ing, teach us all your

peace and glad-ness. Spir-it of all com-fort, fill our hearts.
still un-fold-ing, give us all your vis-ion, God of love.
ev-ery broth-er. Spir-it of all kind-ness, be our guide.
way of heal-ing. Spir-it of com-pas-sion, fill each heart.

To use with Psalm 6: Sing the refrain, read vv. 1-3, refrain, vv. 4-5, refrain, vv. 6-7, refrain, vv. 8-10, and conclude with the refrain.

For another setting of Ps. 6 see 409

A Prayer for Healing in Relationships 304

For use with "Healer of Our Every Ill" 303

God, giver of all good things,
your desire is for us to have life,
and have it abundantly.
We trust in your promises
and believe you make everything beautiful in its time,
yet we live in the midst of a hurting and broken world.
Grant us patience,
that we may wait in hope for your healing and redemption.

Refrain

[For those seeking new relationships]
We pray for those who are lonely and seeking relationships—
    those who would like to be married,
    those who yearn for a child,
    those who desire true friendship.
Be present in our waiting,
and may our loneliness and longing be met by your love.

Refrain and/or sing stanza 1

[For those grieving ended relationships]
Some of us cannot see the hope beyond our sorrow,
because we are losing or have lost loved ones.
We grieve the loss of those separated from us
through death or broken relationships.
Comfort us in our pain
and give us hope beyond our sorrow.
We also pray for those whom we love
who have turned away from you.
In your grace and mercy open eyes
and turn hearts to your love.

Refrain and/or sing stanza 2

[For those experiencing strained relationships]
You are the light of each tomorrow,
but we also experience the shadows of despair.
We lament strained relationships.
We may feel lonely though surrounded by people,
    indifferent toward those we love,
    or misunderstood by those who love us.
Shine in our lives and guide us to love like you.

Refrain and/or sing stanza 3

You know our circumstances
and the desires of our hearts.
Help us to remember
that in our pain and in our sorrow you are with us.
Teach us to become
more aware of the needs of those around us
and how we can better care for and love one another.

Refrain and/or sing stanza 4

305 God Is Love

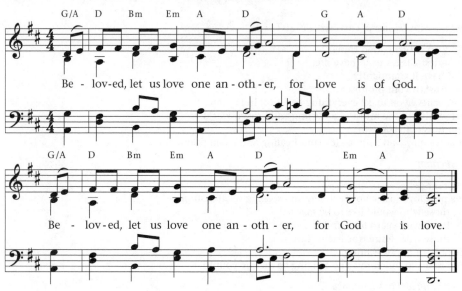

Words and Music (GOD IS LOVE 10.5.10.4): Samuel Batt Owens (1928-1998) © 1998 MorningStar Music Publishers

306 Let Us Love One Another

1 JOHN 4:7-16

Dear friends,
let us love one another,
for love comes from God.

**Everyone who loves
has been born of God and knows God.
Whoever does not love
does not know God,
because God is love.**

This is how God showed his love among us:
He sent his one and only Son into the world
that we might live through him.

**This is love:
not that we loved God,
but that he loved us
and sent his Son
as an atoning sacrifice for our sins.**

Dear friends,
since God so loved us,
we also ought to love one another.

**No one has ever seen God;
but if we love one another,
God lives in us
and his love is made complete in us.**

This is how we know
that we live in him and he in us:
He has given us of his Spirit.
And we have seen and testify
that the Father has sent his Son
to be the Savior of the world.

**If anyone acknowledges
that Jesus is the Son of God,
God lives in them and they in God.
And so we know and rely on
the love God has for us.**

Not for Tongues of Heaven's Angels 307

1 CORINTHIANS 13

Introduction and optional interlude

Unison

1 Not for tongues of heav-en's an-gels, not for wis-dom to dis-cern,
2 Love is hum - ble, love is gen-tle, love is ten - der, true and kind;
3 Nev - er jeal - ous, nev - er self-ish, love will not re-joice in wrong;
4 In the day this world is fad-ing faith and hope will play their part;

not for faith that mas-ters moun-tains, for this bet - ter gift we yearn:
love is gra - cious, ev - er pa - tient, gen - er - ous of heart and mind:
nev - er boast - ful nor re - sent - ful, love be-lieves and suf - fers long:
but when Christ is seen in glo - ry love shall reign in ev - ery heart:

Harmony

may love be ours, O Lord.

Words: Timothy Dudley-Smith (b. 1926), based on I Corinthians 13 © 1985 Hope Publishing Company
Music (REINLYN 8.7.8.7.6): Roy Hopp (b. 1951), 1988, © 1990 Selah Publishing, Inc.

308 A Prayer for Discipleship in Home and Family

Sung Refrain: for full accompaniment, see bracketed portions of 309.

Help us, Lord, to serve each oth - er; bind our hearts in Chris - tian love.

Alternate spoken refrain:
May your Spirit encourage and minister to them, and equip them for service.

Prayer:
Lord, our God,
wherever we live, we need you.
Wherever we live, you call us to serve you.
We pray for all those
 who live alone, *Refrain*
 who live in community, as family or friends, *Refrain*
 who live in foster homes, *Refrain*
 who live in college or university housing, *Refrain*
 who live on military bases or camps, *Refrain*
 who live in prisons, *Refrain*
 who live as refugees, *Refrain*
 who live in group homes, nursing homes, or care facilities, *Refrain*
 who are displaced from their homes, *Refrain*
 who live with conflict,
 who do not have a home. *Refrain*
 [Add other categories as appropriate]

We pray for all those who in their home
 care for children or aging adults, *Refrain*
 provide foster care, *Refrain*
 care for people with special needs, *Refrain*
 make room for the guest among us. *Refrain*

We pray that you will provide for all of your children
—those among us and those around us—
homes of shelter and safety,
communities of loving encouragement and support,
opportunities to serve others as faithful disciples of Jesus,
ministers of Christ's peace. **Amen.**

This outline for prayer can be further expanded by naming people or expressing more detailed prayers for those in each category, and/or adding additional categories as circumstances require. The prayers may be concluded by singing "The Servant Song" 309.

Words and Music (THE SERVANT SONG fragment): Richard Gillard (b. 1953); harm. Betty Pulkingham
(b. 1929) © Scripture in Song, a div. of Integrity Music/Maranatha Music, admin. Music Services

The Servant Song
309

1 Will you let me be your ser-vant, let me be as Christ to you?
2 We are pil-grims on a jour-ney; we are trav-elers on the road.
3 I will hold the Christ-light for you in the night-time of your fear.

Pray that I may have the grace to let you be my ser - vant too.
We are here to help each oth - er walk the mile and bear the load.
I will hold my hand out to you, speak the peace you long to hear.

4 I will weep when you are weeping;
  when you laugh, I'll laugh with you.
  I will share your joy and sorrow
  till we've seen this journey through.

5 Will you let me be your servant,
  let me be as Christ to you?
  Pray that I may have the grace to
  let you be my servant too.

Words and Music (THE SERVANT SONG 8.7.8.7): Richard Gillard (b. 1953); harm. Betty Pulkingham (b. 1929)
© 1977 Scripture in Song, a div. of Integrity Music/Maranatha Music, admin. Music Services

Love in Action
310

ROMANS 12:9-21

Let love be genuine; hate what is evil,
hold fast to what is good;
love one another with mutual affection;
outdo one another in showing honor.
Do not lag in zeal, be ardent in spirit,
serve the Lord.
Rejoice in hope, be patient in suffering,
persevere in prayer.
Contribute to the needs of the saints;
extend hospitality to strangers.

Bless those who persecute you;
bless and do not curse them.
Rejoice with those who rejoice,
weep with those who weep.
Live in harmony with one another;
do not be haughty,
but associate with the lowly;
do not claim to be wiser than you are.

Do not repay anyone evil for evil,
but take thought for what is
noble in the sight of all.
If it is possible, so far as it depends on you,
live peaceably with all.
Beloved, never avenge yourselves,
but leave room for the wrath of God,
for it is written,
"Vengeance is mine, I will repay,
says the Lord."
No, "if your enemies are hungry, feed them;
if they are thirsty,
give them something to drink;
for by doing this you will heap
burning coals on their heads."
Do not be overcome by evil,
but overcome evil with good.

Text: Romans 12:9-21, NRSV

311   Unless the LORD Builds the House

PSALM 127

Un - less the LORD builds the house,

all of it comes to noth - ing. All of it comes to noth - ing.

Un - less the LORD watch-es o - ver the cit-y,

all of it comes to noth - ing. All of it comes to noth - ing.

(continues)

Words and Music (NADA 7.7.7.11.7.7): Gregg DeMey © 2011 Re:Create Music, admin. Faith Alive Christian Resources; arr. Paul Detterman © 2011 Re:Create Music, admin. Faith Alive Christian Resources

Refrain (see previous page)

Unless the LORD builds the house,
the builders labor in vain.
Unless the LORD watches over the city,
the guards stand watch in vain.
In vain you rise early
and stay up late,
toiling for food to eat—
for he grants sleep to those he loves.

Refrain

Children are a heritage from the LORD,
offspring a reward from him.
Like arrows in the hands of a warrior
are children born in one's youth.
Blessed is the one
whose quiver is full of them.
They will not be put to shame
when they contend
with their opponents in court.

Refrain

In Our Households, Heavenly Father   312

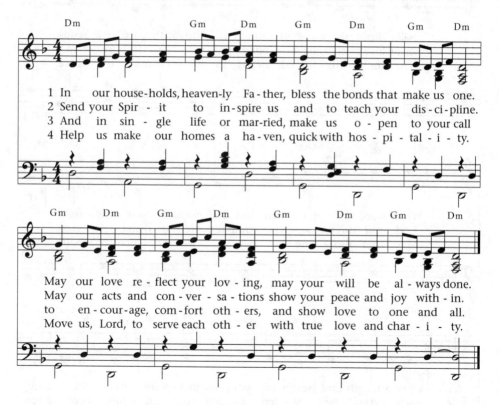

1 In our house-holds, heaven-ly Fa-ther, bless the bonds that make us one.
2 Send your Spir-it to in-spire us and to teach your dis-ci-pline.
3 And in sin-gle life or mar-ried, make us o-pen to your call
4 Help us make our homes a ha-ven, quick with hos-pi-tal-i-ty.

May our love re-flect your lov-ing, may your will be al-ways done.
May our acts and con-ver-sa-tions show your peace and joy with-in.
to en-cour-age, com-fort oth-ers, and show love to one and all.
Move us, Lord, to serve each oth-er with true love and char-i-ty.

Words: sts. 1, 2, 4 Marie J. Post, 1974, 1986, © 1987 Faith Alive Christian Resources; st. 3 Rolf Bouma © 2012
Rolf Bouma, admin. Faith Alive Christian Resources
Music (HATIKVAH 8.7.8.7): traditional Hebrew melody; arr. Hal H. Hopson © 2008 Birnamwood Publications,
a division of MorningStar Music Publishers

313 Whoever Fears the Lord
PSALM 128

1 Who-ev-er fears the Lord and lives as God in-tends
2 We cel-e-brate the joys of home and fam-i-ly,
3 His kind-ness is re-vealed where bit-ter con-flicts cease;

will find the whole of life is filled with gifts he sends.
where love's en-dur-ing bonds pro-vide se-cu-ri-ty.
far more, with-in our hearts, his mer-cy brings us peace.

When work is more than toil and reaps a just re-ward,
God nur-tures ev-ery child for life's de-mand-ing race;
May God pro-long our days to see our chil-dren's heirs,

when strength and health are ours, all these are from the Lord!
each day he of-fers us new fruit-ful-ness, new grace.
and may his gra-cious gifts be ours and al-so theirs.

Text: Martin Leckebusch © 2003 Kevin Mayhew Ltd.
Music (OLD DOMINION 6.6.6.6 D): Roy Hopp © 2011 Roy Hopp

Tell Your Children

1 God the Fa-ther, God of glo-ry, mir-a-cles, and mys-te-ry;
2 Lift the fal-len, feed the hun-gry; God pro-vides for ev-ery-thing.
3 Awe-in-spir-ing deeds of splen-dor— these pro-claim his might-y power;

gen-er-a-tions all a-dore him, God the same through his-to-ry.
He is fair and full of kind-ness, sav-ing those who call him King.
in-ter-wov-en with com-pas-sion is his strength for ev-ery hour.

Refrain

Par-ents, tell your chil-dren, age to age the same.

Glo-ri-fy the liv-ing Lord a-bove, mag-ni-fy his

ho-ly name, mag-ni-fy his ho-ly name.

Words: Grace Hawthorne, 1980, alt., based on Psalm 145 © 1980 Pilot Point Music, admin. Music Services
Music (TELL YOUR CHILDREN 8.7.8.7 refrain 6.5.9.7.7): Tom Fetke, 1980, © 1980 Pilot Point Music, admin.
Music Services

315   Where Love Is, God Abides

1 Where love is, God a - bides: and God shall sure - ly bless
2 How slow to take of - fense love is! How quick to heal!
3 And when time lays its hand on all we hold most dear,

a home where trust and care give birth to hap - pi - ness.
How read - y in dis - tress to know how oth - ers feel!
and life, by life con - sumed, ful - fills its pur - pose here:

May we, O Lord, to - geth - er prove the last - ing joy of such a love.
May we, O Lord, to - geth - er prove the last - ing joy of such a love.
May we, O Lord, to - geth - er prove the last - ing joy of Chris - tian love.

Optional wedding text

The grace of life is theirs who on this wedding day
delight to make their vows and for each other pray.
May they, O Lord, together prove
   the lasting joy of Christian love.

Alternate tune: RHOSYMEDRE *see 148*

When Love Is Found

1 When love is found and hope comes home, sing and be glad
2 When love has flowered in trust and care, build both each day
3 When love is tried as loved-ones change, hold still to hope

that two are one. When love ex-plodes and fills the
that love may dare to reach be-yond home's warmth and
though all seems strange, till ease re-turns and love grows

sky, praise God and share our Mak-er's joy.
light, to serve and strive for truth and right.
wise through lis-tening ears and o-pened eyes.

4 When love is torn and trust betrayed,
pray strength to love till torments fade,
till lovers keep no score of wrong
but hear through pain love's Easter song.

5 Praise God for love, praise God for life,
in age or youth, in calm or strife.
Lift up your hearts, let love be fed
through death and life in broken bread.

For descant see 904

Words: Brian Wren (b. 1936) © 1983 Hope Publishing Company
Music (O WALY WALY 8.8.8.8): English folk melody; arr. © 2001 Faith Alive Christian Resources

317 God, Who Created Hearts to Love

1 God, who cre-a-ted hearts to love, show-er-ing all bless-ings from a-bove—
Al-le-lu-ia! Al-le-lu-ia—give these, who come to you with praise, peace, love, and laugh-ter all their days.

2 Je-sus at Ca-na gave a sign, turn-ing the wa-ter in-to wine:
Al-le-lu-ia! Al-le-lu-ia! Sign that con-tin-ues as he said— love, liv-ing, ris-en from the dead.

3 Spir-it of God, be at their side: Wis-dom and Com-fort, Guard-ian, Guide.
Al-le-lu-ia! Al-le-lu-ia! Make of their hearts a rest-ing place; in ev-ery tri-al, gen-tle grace.

Refrain

Al-le-lu-ia! Al-le-lu-ia! Al-le-lu-ia! Al-le-lu-ia! Al-le-lu-ia!

4 Sing, friends and family gathered here,
voices in witness ringing clear;
Alleluia! Alleluia!
Here is the mystery begun:
woman and man becoming one. *Refrain*

5 God, let our joyful singing be
sign of our faith community.
Alleluia! Alleluia!
Baptized in water, we are fed,
sharing the living wine and bread. *Refrain*

For an alternate arrangement see 208, 551, 847

Words: M.D. Ridge © 1992 M.D. Ridge, admin. OCP Publications
Music (LASST UNS ERFREUEN 8.8.8.8.8.8.6.4.4.4): *Auserlesen Catholische Geistliche Kirchengesänge,* Cologne, 1623, P.D.

Help Us Accept Each Other

318

1 Help us ac-cept each oth-er as Christ ac-cept-ed us;
2 Teach us, O Lord, your les-sons, as in our dai-ly life
3 Let your ac-cept-ance change us, so that we may be moved
4 Lord, for to-day's en-coun-ters with all who are in need,

teach us as sis-ter, broth-er each per-son to em-brace.
we strug-gle to be hu-man and search for hope and faith.
in liv-ing sit-u-a-tions to do the truth in love,
who hun-ger for ac-cept-ance, for right-eous-ness and bread,

Be pres-ent, Lord, a-mong us and bring us to be-lieve
Teach us to care for peo-ple, for all, not just for some,
to prac-tice your ac-cept-ance un-til we know by heart
we need new eyes for see-ing, new hands for hold-ing on;

we are our-selves ac-cept-ed, and meant to love and live.
to love them as we find them, or as they may be-come.
the ta-ble of for-give-ness, and laugh-ter's heal-ing art.
re-new us with your Spir-it, Lord, free us, make us one!

Words: Fred Kaan, 1975, © 1975 Hope Publishing Company
Music (NYLAND 7.6.7.6 D): Finnish; harm. David Evans (1874-1948) from the *Revised Church Hymnary*,
1927, reproduced by permission of Oxford University Press

319 God, My Help and Hiding Place

PSALM 71

Unison

1 God, my help and hid - ing place, res - cue me from shame.
2 From my youth I praised your name, trust - ing you to save.
3 Let me live to teach the young what your love can do,

Be my strength as I grow old; come and clear my name.
Now that I am turn - ing gray, lift me from the grave.
so may peo - ple yet to come place their trust in you.

False ac - cus - ers seek my life, think - ing you have left,
God, my ref - uge and my rock, hide me now. Make haste!
Show once more that you are God: raise me from de - spair!

leav - ing me with no de - fense, help - less and be - reft.
Deal with those who wish me harm; may they be dis - graced.
Then my soul will sing your name, praise your stead - fast care.

A simple accompaniment pattern could be alternating between Gm and Cm each measure or alternating between G and C on an Orff instrument.

Words: Ruth C. Duck © 2011 GIA Publications, Inc.
Music (TOKYO 7.5.7.5 D): Isao Koizumi (1907-1992) © 1958 Isao Koizumi, admin. JASRAC

Gracious Spirit, Heed Our Pleading

1 Gra-cious Spir-it, heed our plead-ing, fash-ion us all a-new.
2 Come to teach us, come to nour-ish those who be-lieve in Christ.
3 Guide our think-ing and our speak-ing done in your ho-ly name.

It's your lead-ing that we're need-ing; help us to fol-low you.
Bless the faith-ful; may they flour-ish, strength-ened by grace un-priced.
Mo-ti-vate all in their seek-ing, free-ing from guilt and shame.

Refrain

English Come, ___ come, ___ come, Ho-ly Spir-it, come.
Swahili Njo-o, njo-o, njo-o, Ro-ho mwe-ma.

4 Not mere knowledge, but discernment, nor rootless liberty;
   turn disquiet to contentment, doubt into certainty.
   Refrain

5 Keep us fervent in our witness, unswayed by earth's allure.
   Ever grant us zealous fitness, which you alone assure.
   Refrain

Words and Music (NJOO KWETU ROHO MWEMA 8.6.8.6 refrain 8): Wilson Niwaglia, 20th c., Tanzania; tr. Howard S. Olson (1922-2010): arr. C. Michael Hawn (b. 1948) © Lutheran Theological College, Makumira, Tanzania, admin. Augsburg Fortress

321   We Need the Power of the Holy Spirit

Chord symbols represent a simplified harmony.

Words: Richard Smallwood © Century Oak/Richwood Music, admin. Conexion Media Group
Music (WE NEED THE POWER): Richard Smallwood; arr. Nolan Williams Jr © Century Oak/Richwood Music,
  admin. Conexion Media Group

I Need Thee Every Hour

1 I need thee ev-ery hour, most gra - cious Lord;
2 I need thee ev-ery hour, stay thou near by;
3 I need thee ev-ery hour, in joy or pain;

no ten - der voice like thine can peace af - ford.
temp - ta - tions lose their power when thou art nigh.
come quick - ly and a - bide, or life is vain.

Refrain

I need thee, O I need thee; ev - ery hour I need thee.

O bless me now, my Sav - ior; I come to thee.

4 I need thee every hour,
   teach me thy will;
   and thy rich promises
   in me fulfill. *Refrain*

5 I need thee every hour,
   most Holy One;
   O make me thine indeed,
   thou Blessed Son! *Refrain*

Words: Annie S. Hawks, 1872; ref. Robert Lowry, 1872, P.D.
Music (NEED 6.4.6.4 refrain 7.6.7.4): Robert Lowry, 1872, P.D.

323   With All My Heart I Thank You, Lord

PSALM 138

1 With all my heart I thank you, LORD. I wor-ship you with
2 The kings of earth shall praise you, LORD. They all have heard your
3 When I must walk a trou - bled way, when I am weak, O

song and prais - ing. Be - fore the "gods" I bless your name
won - drous sto - ry. Now they will sing what they have heard:
LORD, re - vive me. Stretch out your hand a - gainst all hate.

and praise you for your love un - fail - ing. Your stead - fast
"Great is the LORD and great his glo - ry." The LORD is
From sin and all things harm - ful save me. Your right hand

love, your faith - ful - ness, your name, your word are
high in maj - es - ty, yet he re - spects the
gives me vic - to - ry. Work in my life your

For another setting of Ps. 138 see 585

Words: Stanley Wiersma (1930-1986), 1981, © 1987 Faith Alive Christian Resources
Music (GENEVAN 138/MIT FREUDEN ZART 8.9.8.9 D): *Genevan Psalter,* 1551; harm. Dale Grotenhuis
  (1931-2012), 1985, © 1987 Faith Alive Christian Resources

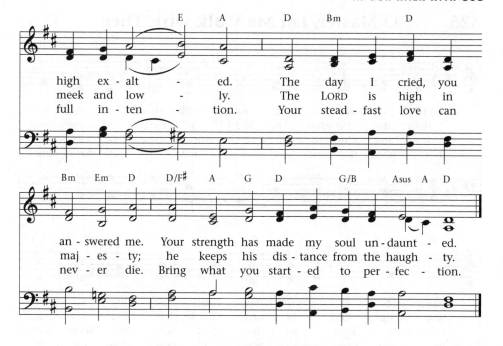

high ex - alt - ed. The day I cried, you
meek and low - ly. The LORD is high in
full in - ten - tion. Your stead - fast love can

an - swered me. Your strength has made my soul un - daunt - ed.
maj - es - ty; he keeps his dis - tance from the haugh - ty.
nev - er die. Bring what you start - ed to per - fec - tion.

O For a Closer Walk with God 324

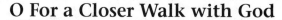

1 O for a clos - er walk with God, a calm and heaven - ly frame,
2 Where is the bless - ed - ness I knew when first I sought the Lord?
3 What peace - ful hours I once en - joyed! How sweet their mem - ory still!

a light to shine up - on the road that leads me to the Lamb!
Where is the soul - re - fresh - ing view of Je - sus and his Word?
But they have left an ach - ing void the world can nev - er fill.

4 The dearest idol I have known,
whate'er that idol be,
help me to tear it from thy throne
and worship only thee.

5 So shall my walk be close with God,
calm and serene my frame;
so purer light shall mark the road
that leads me to the Lamb.

Words: William Cowper, 1772, P.D.
Music (BEATITUDO 8.6.8.6): John B. Dykes, 1875, P.D.

325   O Master, Let Me Walk with Thee

1 O Master, let me walk with thee in low - ly
2 Help me the slow of heart to move by some clear,
3 Teach me thy pa - tience; still with thee in clos - er,
4 In hope that sends a shin - ing ray far down the

paths of ser - vice free; tell me thy se - cret;
win - ning word of love; teach me the way - ward
dear - er com - pa - ny, in work that keeps faith
fu - ture's broad - ening way, in peace that on - ly

help me bear the strain of toil, the fret of care.
feet to stay, and guide them in the home - ward way.
sweet and strong, in trust that tri - umphs o - ver wrong.
thou canst give, with thee, O Mas - ter, let me live.

Words: Washington Gladden (1836-1918), P.D.
Music (MARYTON 8.8.8.8): H. Percy Smith (1825-1898), P.D.

Take Up Your Cross

1 Take up your cross, the Savior said, if you would my disciple be; take up your cross with willing heart, and humbly follow after me.

2 Take up your cross, let not its weight fill your weak spirit with alarm; Christ's strength shall bear your spirit up and brace your heart and nerve your arm.

3 Take up your cross, heed not the shame, and let your foolish heart be still; the Lord for you accepted death upon a cross, on Calvary's hill.

4 Take up your cross, then, in Christ's strength, and calmly every danger brave: it guides you to abundant life and leads to victory o'er the grave.

Words: Charles W. Everest (1814-1877), alt., P.D.
Music (ERHALT UNS, HERR 8.8.8.8): J. Klug's *Geistliche Lieder*, Wittenberg, 1543; harm. Johann Sebastian Bach
  (1685-1750), alt., P.D.

327   When We Walk with the Lord

1 When we walk with the Lord in the light of his Word, what a
2 But we nev-er can prove the de-lights of his love un-til
3 Then in fel-low-ship sweet we will sit at his feet, or we'll

glo-ry he sheds on our way! While we do his good will he a-
all on the al-tar we lay; for the fa-vor he shows and the
walk by his side in the way; what he says we will do, where he

bides with us still, and with all who will trust and o-bey.
joy he be-stows are for those who will trust and o-bey.
sends we will go— nev-er fear, on-ly trust and o-bey.

Refrain

Trust and o-bey, for there's no oth-er way to be

hap-py in Je-sus but to trust and o-bey.

Words: John H. Sammis, 1887, P.D.
Music (TRUST AND OBEY 6.6.9 D refrain 4.6.7.6): Daniel B. Towner, 1887, P.D.

Lead On, O King Eternal

328

1 Lead on, O King e - ter - nal, the day of march has come;
2 Lead on, O King e - ter - nal, till sin's fierce war shall cease,
3 Lead on, O King e - ter - nal; we fol - low, not with fears,

hence - forth in fields of con - quest your tents will be our home.
and ho - li - ness shall whis - per the sweet a - men of peace.
for glad - ness breaks like morn - ing wher - e'er your face ap - pears.

Through days of prep - a - ra - tion your grace has made us strong;
For not with swords' loud clash - ing or roll of stir - ring drums—
Your cross is lift - ed o'er us, we jour - ney in its light;

and now, O King e - ter - nal, we lift our bat - tle song.
with deeds of love and mer - cy the heaven - ly king - dom comes.
the crown a - waits the con - quest; lead on, O God of might.

Words: Ernest W. Shurtleff, 1888, alt., P.D.
Music (LANCASHIRE 7.6.7.6 D): Henry T. Smart, 1836, P.D.

329

Lead Me, Guide Me

Lead me, guide me, a-long the way, for if you lead me, I can-not stray. Lord, let me walk each day with you; lead me my whole life through.

330 Savior, Like a Shepherd Lead Us

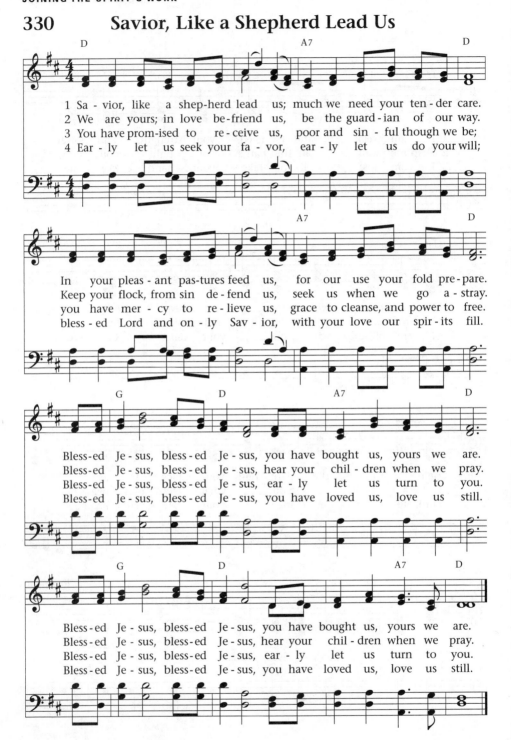

1 Sa - vior, like a shep-herd lead us; much we need your ten - der care.
2 We are yours; in love be-friend us, be the guard - ian of our way.
3 You have prom-ised to re - ceive us, poor and sin - ful though we be;
4 Ear - ly let us seek your fa - vor, ear - ly let us do your will;

In your pleas - ant pas-tures feed us, for our use your fold pre - pare.
Keep your flock, from sin de - fend us, seek us when we go a - stray.
you have mer - cy to re - lieve us, grace to cleanse, and power to free.
bless - ed Lord and on - ly Sav - ior, with your love our spir - its fill.

Bless-ed Je - sus, bless - ed Je - sus, you have bought us, yours we are.
Bless-ed Je - sus, bless - ed Je - sus, hear your chil - dren when we pray.
Bless-ed Je - sus, bless - ed Je - sus, ear - ly let us turn to you.
Bless-ed Je - sus, bless - ed Je - sus, you have loved us, love us still.

Bless-ed Je - sus, bless - ed Je - sus, you have bought us, yours we are.
Bless-ed Je - sus, bless - ed Je - sus, hear your chil - dren when we pray.
Bless-ed Je - sus, bless - ed Je - sus, ear - ly let us turn to you.
Bless-ed Je - sus, bless - ed Je - sus, you have loved us, love us still.

Words: *Hymns for the Young*, 1836; attr. Dorothy A. Thrupp, P.D.
Music (BRADBURY 8.7.8.7 D): William B. Bradbury, P.D.

To the Hills I Lift My Eyes

331

PSALM 121

1 To the hills I lift my eyes; whence shall help for me a-rise?
2 Your pro-tec-tor is the LORD; shade for you he will af-ford.

From the LORD comes all my aid, who the heavens and earth has made.
Nei-ther sun nor moon shall smite; God shall guard by day and night.

He will guard through dan-gers all, will not let you slip or fall.
He will ev-er keep your soul; what would harm he will con-trol.

He who safe his peo-ple keeps nev-er slum-bers, nev-er sleeps.
In the home and by the way God will keep you day by day.

For another setting of Ps. 121 see 652

Words: *Psalter*, 1912, alt., P.D.
Music (GUIDE 7.7.7.7 D): Marcus M. Wells, 1858, P.D.

332   As the Deer Pants for the Water

PSALM 42 AND 43

1 As the deer pants for the wa- ter
2 Day af- ter day he sends his love; I
3 Send me your light and truth to guide me

so my soul longs_ for you, my Lord.
feel his peace come_ rain - ing down.
as I trav - el_ through this land.

When can I come to you a - gain to
I raise a song to him at night like
Lead_ me to your ho - ly dwell - ing

praise you as be - fore?
fire_ from the ground.
at my jour - ney's end.   Why should I

Refrain

For other settings of Ps. 42 see 503, 504; Ps. 43 see 616

Words and Music (CERVUS INDOMITUS irregular): Greg Scheer © 2005 Augsburg Fortress

333
All My Life

PSALM 73

1 All my life I've sung a jeal-ous song.
2 All my life I've walked the way of God.
3 All my life I've watched the wick-ed rule.
4 All my life I've tried to rea-son why.

All my life I've sung a jeal-ous song.
All my life I've walked the way of God.
All my life I've watched the wick-ed rule.
All my life I've tried to rea-son why.

All my life I've sung a jeal-ous song. The
All my life I've walked the way of God. But
All my life I've watched the wick-ed rule. They
All my life I've tried to rea-son why. I

e - vil peo-ple flour-ish, and the good folks suf-fer wrong.
walk - ing got me no-where, and I thought it nev-er would.
look down on the god-ly, and they call us sil - ly fools.
could not find the an-swers and I lost the will to try.

Read Ps. 73:17-28 after stanza 4 or have a soloist or small group sing the interlude found in the accompaniment edition. Then conclude with the singing of stanza 5 at a slower tempo.

5 Now my song is altogether new. *3x*
   For God has changed my vision, as only God could do.

For another setting of Ps. 73 see 346

May the Mind of Christ, My Savior 334

4 May the love of Je - sus fill me as the wa - ters fill the sea.
5 May we run the race be - fore us, strong and brave to face the foe,

1 May the mind of Christ, my Sav-ior, live in me from day to day,
2 May the word of God dwell rich-ly in my heart from hour to hour,
3 May the peace of God, my Fa-ther, rule my life in ev-ery-thing,

Him ex - alt - ing, self a - bas - ing: this is vic - to - ry.
look - ing on - ly un - to Je - sus as we on - ward go.

by his love and power con - trol - ling all I do and say.
so that all may see I tri - umph on - ly through his power.
that I may be calm to com - fort sick and sor - row - ing.

4 May the love of Jesus fill me
as the waters fill the sea.
Him exalting, self abasing:
this is victory.

5 May we run the race before us,
strong and brave to face the foe,
looking only unto Jesus
as we onward go.

Chord symbols represent a simplifed harmony.

Words: Kate B. Wilkinson, 1925, P.D.
Music (ST. LEONARDS 8.7.8.5): A. Cyril Barham-Gould, 1925, © Estate of A.C. Barham-Gould; desc. Emily R. Brink, 1986, © 1987 Faith Alive Christian Resources

335 Like a Child Rests

PSALM 131

Like a child rests in its moth-er's arms, so will I rest in you.

Like a child rests in its moth-er's arms, so will I rest in you.

To Refrain

1 My God, I am not proud. I do not look for things too great.
2 My God, I trust in you. You care for me; you give me peace.
3 O Is - rael, trust in God;_____ now and al - ways trust in God.

Optional prayer

Loving God,
**may our words be simple,
our hearts humbled,
our attention focused,
and our thoughts pure.
Thank you that we may lean upon you,
as a child with its mother.
You are our hope and we praise you.
now and forever. Amen.**

For another setting of Ps. 131 see 447

Words and Music (LIKE A CHILD RESTS 6.8 refrain 9.6.9.6): Christopher Walker (b. 1947) © 1988, 1989
Christopher Walker, admin. OCP Publications

You Are Before Me, Lord

336

PSALM 139

For another setting of Ps. 139 see 337

Words; Ian Pitt-Watson (1923-1995) © 1973 Ian Pitt-Watson Trust
Music (HIGHLAND CATHEDRAL 10.10.10.10): Uli Roever and Michael Korb © Universal Music Publishing
Group (Germany), admin. in the U.S. by Hal Leonard

337 Lord, You Have Searched Me

PSALM 139

1 LORD, you have searched me, and you know where I take
2 If I the wings of morn - ing take and far a -
3 All that I am I owe to you; you knit me,

rest and where I go. LORD, you know all that
way my dwell - ing make, if I should sink in
LORD, with - in the womb. I give my Mak - er

I have planned, and all my ways are in your hand.
deep - est sea, your right hand keeps its hold on me.
thank - ful praise, whose won - drous works my soul a - maze.

4 When I was formed within the earth,
   you knew my frame before my birth.
   My life in all your perfect plan
   was known before my days began.

5 Search me, O God, my heart discern;
   try me, my inmost thoughts to learn;
   and lead me, if in sin I stray,
   to choose the everlasting way.

For another setting of Ps. 139 see 336

Words: *Psalter*, 1912; rev. Marie J. Post, 1986, © 1987 Faith Alive Christian Resources
Music (FEDERAL STREET 8.8.8.8): Henry K. Oliver, 1832, P.D.

I Will Trust in the Lord

2 I'm gonna treat everybody right . . . till I die.
3 I'm gonna stay on bended knee . . . till I die.

Words: African American spiritual
Music (TRUST IN THE LORD irregular): African American spiritual; arr. Jeffrey Radford and Nolan Williams Jr
(b. 1969) © 2000 GIA Publications, Inc.

339   He Knows My Name

1 I have a Mak - er,
2 I have a Fa - ther,

he formed_____ my heart,
he calls me his own.

be - fore ev - en time be - gan, my
He'll nev - er leave_____ me, no

life was in his hand.
mat - ter where I go.

Words and Music (HE KNOWS MY NAME): Tommy Walker © 1996 Doulos Publishing, admin. Music Services; arr. Diane Dykgraaf © 2012 Doulos Publishing, admin. Music Services

Refrain

He knows my name, he knows my ev-ery thought, he sees each tear that falls and hears me when I call.

D.C. *Fine*

Optional prayer (based on Ps. 139)

You are before me, Lord. **You know all about me.**
Before I was born, **you knit me together.**
Before I lived one day, **you wrote the book of my life.**
Even before I speak a word, **you know all about it.**
You are before me, Lord. I trust in you. Amen.

340 I Give You My Heart

This is my de-sire: to ho-nor you.

Lord, with all my heart I wor-ship you.

All I have with-in me— I give you praise.

All that I a-dore is in you.

Refrain

Lord I give you my heart, I give you my soul, I

live for you a-lone. Ev-ery breath that I take, ev-ery

mom-ent I'm a-wake, Lord, have your way in me.

3rd time to Coda

D.S. (Refrain) al Coda

Coda

341   We've Come This Far by Faith

(continues)

Words: Albert A. Goodson © 1965, 1995 Manna Music, Inc., admin. ClearBox Rights, LLC
Music (WE'VE COME THIS FAR irregular): Albert A. Goodson and arr. Jimmie Abbington © 1965, 1993 Manna
    Music, Inc., admin. ClearBox Rights, LLC

Don't be dis-cour-aged with trou-ble in your life; he'll bear your bur - dens and move all mis - er - y and strife. That's why we've

Affirmation: True Faith 342

What is true faith?

**True faith is
not only a sure knowledge
by which I hold as true all that God
has revealed to us in Scripture;
it is also a wholehearted trust,
which the Holy Spirit
creates in me by the gospel,
that God has freely granted,
not only to others but to me also,
forgiveness of sins,
eternal righteousness,
and salvation.**

**These are gifts of sheer grace,
granted solely by Christ's merit.**

Text: Heidelberg Catechism Q&A 21

343 **Blessed Be Your Name**

Words and Music (BLESSED BE YOUR NAME): Matt and Beth Redman © 2002 Kingsway's Thankyou Music, admin. EMI CMG Publishing

name of the Lord, bless - ed be your name.

Bless-ed be the name of the Lord, bless-ed be your

glo - ri - ous name."

Optional prayer (could be read antiphonally)

Blessed are you, Lord our God, King of the universe.
You have created this world in splendor,
and your Spirit renews the face of the earth.
You have made us in your image,
and you renew us in the image of your Son.
You have given us your law,
and your Spirit leads us in the ways of righteousness.
You have grafted us into your covenant of grace,
and you have written your law on our hearts.
You promise to make all things new,
and you give us your Spirit as the firstfruits of a renewed creation.
All glory be to you, Lord our God, giver of every good and perfect gift.
Alleluia! Amen.

344 In Thee Is Gladness

1 In thee is glad - ness a - mid all sad - ness, Je - sus, day - star of my heart! By thee are giv - en the gifts of heav - en, thou the true Re - deem - er art! Our souls thou wak - est; our bonds thou break - est.

2 Je - sus is ours!___ We fear no pow - ers, not of earth or sin or death. He sees and bless - es in worst dis - tress - es; he can change them with a breath. Where - fore the sto - ry— tell of his glo - ry with hearts and voic - es;

Words: Johann Lindemann, 1598; tr. Catherine Winkworth, 1858, alt., P.D.
Music (IN DIR IST FREUDE 5.5.7 D 5.5.5.5.5.4 D): Giovanni G. Gastoldi, 1591, P.D.

has built se - cure - ly and stands for - ev - er: Al - le - lu - ia!
all heaven re - joic - es in him for - ev - er: Al - le - lu - ia!

Our hearts are long - ing to see thy dawn - ing. Liv - ing or dy - ing,
We shout for glad - ness, tri - umph o'er sad - ness, love him and praise him,

in thee a - bid - ing, naught can us sev - er: Al - le - lu - ia!
and still shall raise him glad hymns for - ev - er: Al - le - lu - ia!

Rejoice in the Lord 345

PHILIPPIANS 4:4-7

Rejoice in the Lord always.
I will say it again: Rejoice!
Let your gentleness be evident to all.
The Lord is near.
Do not be anxious about anything,
but in every situation, by prayer and petition,
with thanksgiving, present your requests to God.
And the peace of God,
which transcends all understanding,
will guard your hearts and your minds in Christ Jesus.

346 In Sweet Communion, Lord, with You

PSALM 73

The following may be read before the singing of "In Sweet Communion"

Surely God is good to Israel,
to those who are pure in heart.

But as for me,
my feet had almost slipped;
I had nearly lost my foothold.
For I envied the arrogant
when I saw the prosperity of the wicked.

This is what the wicked are like—
always free of care, they go on amassing wealth.
Surely in vain I have kept my heart pure
and have washed my hands in innocence.

All day long I have been afflicted,
and every morning brings
new punishments.
When I tried to understand all this,
it troubled me deeply

till I entered the sanctuary of God;
then I understood their final destiny.

Surely you place them on slippery ground;
you cast them down to ruin.
How suddenly are they destroyed,
completely swept away by terrors!
They are like a dream when one awakes;
when you arise, Lord,
you will despise them as fantasies.

When my heart was grieved
and my spirit embittered,
I was senseless and ignorant;
I was a brute beast before you.
Yet I am always with you;
you hold me by my right hand.

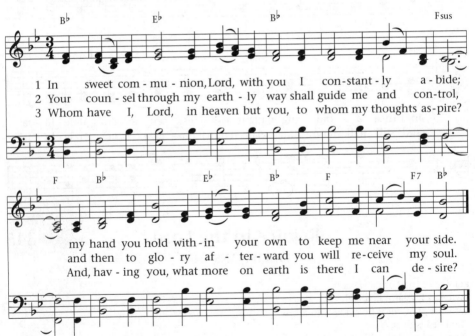

1 In   sweet com-mu-nion, Lord, with you   I   con-stant-ly   a-bide;
2 Your   coun-sel through my earth-ly   way shall guide me and   con-trol,
3 Whom have   I,   Lord,   in heaven but you,   to   whom my thoughts as-pire?

   my hand you hold with-in   your own   to keep me near   your side.
   and then to glo-ry af-ter-ward you will re-ceive   my soul.
   And, hav-ing you, what more   on earth   is there I can   de-sire?

4 Though flesh and heart should faint and fail,
   the Lord will ever be
   the strength and portion of my heart,
   my God eternally.

5 To live apart from God is death;
   'tis good his face to seek.
   My refuge is the living God;
   his praise I long to speak.

For another setting of Ps. 73 see 333

Words: *Psalter*, 1912, alt., P.D.
Music (PRAYER 8.6.8.6): William U. Butcher, 1860, P.D.

The Steadfast Love of the Lord 347

LAMENTATIONS 3:22-23

The stead-fast love of the Lord nev-er ceas-es; God's mer-cies nev-er come to an end. They are new ev-ery morn-ing, new ev-ery morn-ing; great is your faith-ful-ness, O Lord, great is your faith-ful-ness.

Words: Lamentations 3:22-23
Music (STEADFAST LOVE 11.9.7.5.8.6): Edith McNeill (b. 1920) © 1974, 1975 Celebration

348 Great Is Thy Faithfulness

LAMENTATIONS 3:22-23

1 Great is thy faith-ful-ness, O God my Fa-ther; there is no
2 Sum-mer and win-ter and spring-time and har-vest, sun, moon, and
3 Par-don for sin and a peace that en-dur-eth, thy own dear

shad-ow of turn-ing with thee; thou chang-est not, thy com-
stars in their cours-es a-bove join with all na-ture in
pres-ence to cheer and to guide, strength for to-day and bright

pas-sions, they fail not; as thou hast been thou for-ev-er wilt be.
man-i-fold wit-ness to thy great faith-ful-ness, mer-cy, and love.
hope for to-mor-row— bless-ings all mine, with ten thou-sand be-side!

Refrain

Great is thy faith-ful-ness! Great is thy faith-ful-ness! Morn-ing by

Words: Thomas O Chisholm, 1923, © 1923, ren. 1951 Hope Publishing Company
Music (FAITHFULNESS 11.10.11.10 refrain 5.5.10.11.10): William M. Runyan, 1923, © 1923, ren. 1951 Hope Publishing Company

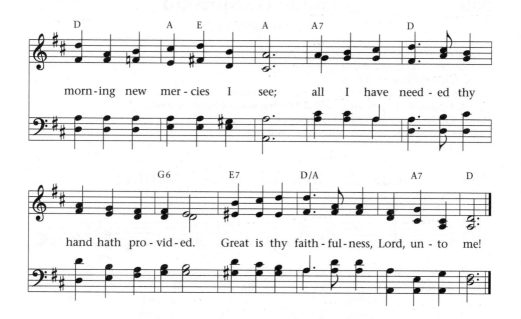

morn-ing new mer-cies I see; all I have need-ed thy

hand hath pro-vid-ed. Great is thy faith-ful-ness, Lord, un-to me!

I Will Sing a Song of Triumph   349
PSALM 129

1 I will sing a song of tri-umph, sing to re-as-sert the truth,
2 When the con-flicts I en-coun-tered left me wound-ed, scarred, and sore,
3 Those who hate what God has cho-sen: in the end, how can they thrive?
4 Those who trust the Lord to save them: may they find, in-stead of shame,

sing al-though un-num-bered trou-bles have be-set me since my youth.
God the Right-eous One was with me to de-stroy the chains I bore.
Plants with nei-ther earth nor mois-ture, what can help them to sur-vive?
kind-ness from the One they wor-ship, end-less bless-ings in God's name.

350 A Call to Discipleship

COLOSSIANS 3:1-4

Since, then, you have been raised with Christ,
set your hearts on things above, where Christ is,
seated at the right hand of God.
Set your minds on things above, not on earthly things.
For you died, and your life is now hidden with Christ in God.
When Christ, who is your life, appears,
then you also will appear with him in glory.

351 Love Divine, All Loves Excelling

1 Love divine, all loves ex-cel-ling, joy of heaven, to
2 Breathe, oh, breathe thy lov-ing Spir-it in-to ev-ery
3 Come, Al-might-y to de-liv-er, let us all thy
4 Fin-ish, then, thy new cre-a-tion; pure and spot-less

earth come down; fix in us thy hum-ble dwell-ing, all thy
troub-led breast; let us all in thee in-her-it; let us
life re-ceive; sud-den-ly re-turn, and nev-er, nev-er-
let us be; let us see thy great sal-va-tion per-fect-

faith-ful mer-cies crown. Je-sus, thou art all com-pas-sion,
find thy prom-ised rest. Take a-way the love of sin-ning;
more thy tem-ples leave. Thee we would be al-ways bless-ing,
ly re-stored in thee: changed from glo-ry in-to glo-ry,

Words: Charles Wesley, 1747, P.D.
Music (HYFRYDOL 8.7.8.7 D): Rowland H. Prichard, 1831, P.D.

pure, un-bound-ed love thou art; vis-it us with
Al-pha and O-me-ga be; end of faith, as
serve thee with thy hosts a-bove, pray and praise thee
till in heaven we take our place,

thy sal-va-tion, en-ter ev-ery trem-bling heart.
its be-gin-ning, set our hearts at lib-er-ty.
with-out ceas-ing, glo-ry in thy per-fect love.
crowns be-fore thee, lost in won-der, love and praise.

Optional readings

A. 2 CORINTHIANS 3:17-4:1

Now the Lord is the Spirit, and where the
    Spirit of the Lord is, there is freedom.
And we all, who with unveiled faces
    contemplate the Lord's glory,
are being transformed into his image with
    ever-increasing glory,
which comes from the Lord, who is the Spirit.
**Therefore, since through God's mercy
    we have this ministry,
we do not lose heart.**

B. 2 CORINTHIANS 4:5-6

For what we preach is not ourselves, but Jesus
    Christ as Lord,
and ourselves as your servants for Jesus' sake.
For God, who said, "Let light shine out of
    darkness,"
made his light shine in our hearts to give us
    the light of
the knowledge of God's glory displayed in the
    face of Christ.
**But we have this treasure in jars of clay
    to show
that this all-surpassing power is from
    God and not from us.**

C. 2 CORINTHIANS 4:14-18

We know that the one who raised the Lord
    Jesus from the dead
will also raise us with Jesus and present us
    with you to himself.
All this is for your benefit,
so that the grace that is reaching more and
    more people
may cause thanksgiving to overflow to the
    glory of God.
Therefore we do not lose heart.
Though outwardly we are wasting away,
yet inwardly we are being renewed day by day.
**For our light and momentary troubles
are achieving for us an eternal glory
    that far outweighs them all.
So we fix our eyes not on what is seen,
    but on what is unseen,
since what is seen is temporary, but
    what is unseen is eternal.**

352 · O Jesus, I Have Promised

1 O Je - sus, I have prom - ised to serve you to the end;
2 O let me feel you near me; the world is ev - er near:
3 O let me hear you speak - ing in ac - cents clear and still,
4 O Je - sus, you have prom - ised to all who fol - low you

be now and ev - er near me, my Mas - ter and my Friend.
I see the sights that daz - zle, the tempt - ing sounds I hear.
a - bove the storms of pas - sion, the mur - murs of self - will.
that where you are in glo - ry your ser - vants shall be too.

I shall not fear the bat - tle if you are by my side,
My foes are ev - er near me, a - round me and with - in;
O speak to re - as - sure me, to has - ten or con - trol;
O guide me, call me, draw me, up - hold me to the end,

nor wan - der from the path - way if you will be my guide.
but, Je - sus, draw still near - er and shield my soul from sin!
and speak to make me lis - ten, O Guard - ian of my soul.
when you in glo - ry take me, my Sav - ior and my friend.

Words: John Ernest Bode, 1869, alt., P.D.
Music (ANGEL'S STORY 7.6.7.6 D): Arthur H. Mann (1850-1929), P.D.

Rejoice, O Pure in Heart

1 Re - joice, O pure in heart! Re - joice, give thanks, and sing!
2 Yes, on through life's long path, still chant - ing as you go;
3 At last the march shall end; the wea - ried ones shall rest;
4 Praise God, who reigns on high, the Lord whom we a - dore:

Your fes - tal ban - ner wave on high, the cross of Christ your King.
from youth to age, by night and day, in glad-ness and in woe.
the pil - grims find their home at last, Je - ru - sa - lem the blest.
the Fa - ther, Son, and Ho - ly Ghost, one God for - ev - er-more.

Refrain

Re - joice, re - joice, re - joice, give thanks, and sing!

re - joice, re - joice,

Optional charge and blessing (1 Thess. 5:16-24)

Rejoice always, pray continually, give thanks in all circumstances;
for this is God's will for you in Christ Jesus.
Do not quench the Spirit.
Do not treat prophecies with contempt but test them all;
hold on to what is good, reject every kind of evil.

May God himself, the God of peace, sanctify you through and through.
May your whole spirit, soul and body be kept blameless
at the coming of our Lord Jesus Christ.
The one who calls you is faithful, and he will do it.

Words: Edward H. Plumpre, 1866, alt., P.D.
Music (MARION 6.6.8.6 refrain 4.6): Arthur H. Messiter, 1883, P.D.

354 LORD, I Gladly Trust

PSALM 25

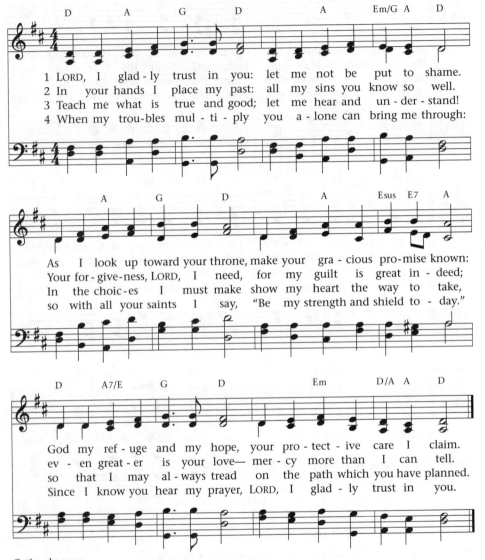

1 LORD, I glad-ly trust in you: let me not be put to shame.
2 In your hands I place my past: all my sins you know so well.
3 Teach me what is true and good; let me hear and un-der-stand!
4 When my trou-bles mul-ti-ply you a-lone can bring me through:

As I look up toward your throne, make your gra-cious pro-mise known:
Your for-give-ness, LORD, I need, for my guilt is great in-deed;
In the choic-es I must make show my heart the way to take,
so with all your saints I say, "Be my strength and shield to-day."

God my ref-uge and my hope, your pro-tect-ive care I claim.
ev-en great-er is your love— mer-cy more than I can tell.
so that I may al-ways tread on the path which you have planned.
Since I know you hear my prayer, LORD, I glad-ly trust in you.

Optional prayer

Loving God, you teach us, you lead us,
you protect us, you forgive us.
In life and in death we belong to you.
We long for your Holy Spirit
to strengthen us in our walk with you.
Give us joy, peace, and patience
as we learn, more and more,
to place our full trust in you. Amen.

For this music in a higher key see 623. For another setting of Ps. 25 see 625

Words: Martin Leckebusch © 2006 Kevin Mayhew Publishers Ltd.
Music (REDHEAD 76 | 7.7.7.7.7.7): Richard Redhead, 1853, P.D.

Be Gracious to Me, Lord

355

PSALM 57

1 Be gra - cious to me, Lord, and hold my spir - it
2 Though snares are set for me, yet I will sleep in
3 My soul, a - wake and sing— such bound - less love re -

fast, that I may shel - ter by your side un -
peace, for I have asked the care of God whose
call, ex - alt God's name a - bove the skies, God's

til the storm is past, un - til the storm is past.
love shall nev - er cease, whose love shall nev - er cease.
glo - ry o - ver all, God's glo - ry o - ver all.

Optional prayer for times of natural disaster

Loving God,
in the middle of all our grief and confusion,
shelter and protect us.
We long for your help: *[specify unique needs]*
Teach us to take refuge in the shadow of your sheltering wings.
**By your Holy Spirit,
open our lips that we may, even now,
testify to your love and faithfulness. Amen.**

Words: Michael Perry © 1973 The Jubilate Group, admin. Hope Publishing Company
Music (MIKTAM 6.6.8.6. with repeat): Larry Visser © 2011 Wayne Leupold Editions, Inc.

356 Fill Thou My Life, O Lord, My God

1 Fill thou my life, O Lord, my God, in ev-ery part with praise,
2 Praise in the com-mon words I speak, life's com-mon looks and tones,
3 So shall each fear, each fret, each care be turned in-to a song,

that my whole be-ing may pro-claim thy be-ing and thy ways.
in fel-low-ship en-joyed at home with my be-lov-ed ones,
and ev-ery wind-ing of the way the ech-o shall pro-long.

Not for the lip of praise a-lone, nor e'en the prais-ing heart
en-dur-ing wrong, re-proach, or loss with sweet and stead-fast will,
So shall no part of day or night from sa-cred-ness be free,

descant st. 3

I ask, but for a life made up of praise in ev-ery part.
for-giv-ing free-ly those who hate, re-turn-ing good for ill.
but all my life, in ev-ery step, be fel-low-ship with thee.

For an alternate arrangement see 679. For music in a higher key see 726

Words: Horatius Bonar, 1863, alt., P.D.
Music (ELLACOMBE 8.6.8.6 D): *Gesangbuch der Herzogl*, Hofkapelle, Würtemberg, 1784, P.D.

In the Lord I'll Be Ever Thankful

Spanish
El Señor es me fortaleza,
el Señor es mi canción.
Él nos da la salvación.
En él confío, no temeré.
En él confío, no temeré.

Portuguese
El Senyor és la meva força,
el Senyor el meu cant.
Ell m'ha estat la salvació.
En ell confio i no tinc por,
en ell confio i no tinc por.

Words: English based on Philippians 4:4-6, Spanish and Portuguese based on Psalm 118:14, The Community of Taizé © 1991 Ateliers et Presses de Taizé, Taizé Community, France, GIA Publications, Inc., exclusive North American agent
Music (IN THE LORD, I'LL BE EVER THANKFUL): Jacques Berthier (1923-1994) © 1991 Ateliers et Presses de Taizé, Taizé Community, France, GIA Publications, Inc., exclusive North American agent

358   Give Thanks

Words and Music (GIVE THANKS): Henry Smith (b. 1952) © 1978 Integrity's Hosanna! Music (ASCAP), admin.
EMICMGPublishing.com

Give Thanks to God, Who Hears Our Cries 359

PSALM 107

1 Give thanks to God, who hears our cries and saves in trou-bled days
2 If you have ev - er wan-dered where no hu-man help was near,
3 If you have ev - er lived in - side the pris-on of your gloom
4 If you drew near the gates of death, too sick to eat or dress,

with won-drous works to hu - man-kind that call for high-est praise.
and in your trou-ble cried to God, who res - cued you from fear,
and cried to God, who broke your bonds and raised you from your tomb,
and cried to God, who heard your voice and healed all your dis - tress,

Let all who know God's sav - ing love sing grate - ful songs al - ways.
then thank the God of stead-fast love who dries your ev - ery tear.
then praise the One who sets you free, who makes dry plac - es bloom.
then sing with sounds of ho - ly joy; God's won-drous works pro - fess.

5 If you have felt your courage fail
before a violent sea
and cried to God, who stilled the storm
and made the wild wind flee,
then in the congregation praise
the God who heard your plea.

6 So praise the One whose love is great,
whose kindness is well known,
consider well the healing hand
and help you have been shown,
and tell the world what God has done.
Praise God and God alone!

For an alternate arrangement see 174

Words: Ruth Duck © 2011 GIA Publications, Inc.
Music (MORNING SONG 8.6.8.6.8.6): J. Wyeth's *Repository of Sacred Music*, 1813; harm. Jack Grotenhuis, 1983,
© 1987 Faith Alive Christian Resources

360   You Are My King (Amazing Love)

I'm for-giv-en be-cause you were for-sak - en.

I'm ac-cept-ed; you were con - demned.

I'm a-live and well, your Spir-it is with-in me be-

cause you died and rose a-gain. A-maz-ing love, how

can it be that you, my King, would die for me?

Words and Music (YOU ARE MY KING): Billy James Foote © 1999 worshiptogether.com songs (ASCAP), admin. EMICMGPublishing.com

361

Because He Lives

God sent his Son, they called him Je - sus; he came to love,
heal, and for - give. He lived and died to buy my
par - don, an emp-ty grave is there to prove my Sav - ior lives.

Refrain
Be - cause he lives I can face to - mor-row, be-cause he lives
all fear is gone, be - cause I know he holds the

Words and Music (RESURRECTION 9.8.9.12 refrain 10.8.9.12): Gloria Gaither (b. 1942) and William J. Gaither (b. 1936) © 1971 William J. Gaither, Inc.

I'm So Glad 362

fu - ture, and life is worth the liv-ing just be-cause he lives.

1 I'm so glad Je - sus lift-ed me. I'm so glad
Je-sus lift-ed me. I'm so glad Je-sus lift-ed me,

I'm glad that

sing-ing glo-ry, hal - le - lu - jah! Je - sus lift-ed me.

2 Satan had me bound;
Jesus lifted me. . . .
singing glory, hallelujah!
Jesus lifted me.

3 When I was in trouble,
Jesus lifted me. . . .
singing glory, hallelujah!
Jesus lifted me.

Words and Music (JESUS LIFTED ME irregular): African American traditional; arr. Evelyn Simpson-Curenton (b. 1953) © 2000 GIA Publications, Inc.

363   Blessed Assurance: Jesus Is Mine

1 Bless-ed as-sur-ance: Je-sus is mine! Oh, what a fore-taste of
2 Per-fect sub-mis-sion, per-fect de-light, vi-sions of *rap-ture now
3 Per-fect sub-mis-sion: all is at rest, I in my Sav-ior am

glo-ry di-vine! Heir of sal-va-tion, pur-chase of God, born of his
burst on my sight; an-gels de-scend-ing bring from a-bove echo-es of
hap-py and blest; watch-ing and wait-ing, look-ing a-bove, filled with his

Refrain

Spir - it, washed in his blood.
mer - cy, whis-pers of love. This is my sto-ry, this is my
good - ness, lost in his love.

song, prais-ing my Sav-ior all the day long; this is my

sto-ry, this is my song, prais-ing my Sav-ior all the day long.

Used here in the sense of glory, ecstatic joy

Words: Fanny Crosby, 1873, P.D.
Music (ASSURANCE 9.10.9.9 refrain 9.9.9.9): Phoebe P. Knapp, 1873, P.D.

Tell Out, My Soul

LUKE 1:46-55

1 Tell out, my soul, the great - ness of the Lord!
2 Tell out, my soul, the great - ness of his name!
3 Tell out, my soul, the great - ness of his might!
4 Tell out, my soul, the glo - ries of his Word!

Un - num - bered bless - ings give my spir - it voice;
Make known his might, the deeds his arm has done;
Powers and do - min - ions lay their glo - ry by.
Firm is his prom - ise, and his mer - cy sure.

ten - der to me the prom - ise of his Word;
his mer - cy sure, from age to age the same;
Proud hearts and stub - born wills are put to flight,
Tell out, my soul, the great - ness of the Lord

in God my Sav - ior shall my heart re - joice.
his ho - ly name, the Lord, the Might - y One.
the hun - gry fed, the hum - ble lift - ed high.
to chil - dren's chil - dren and for - ev - er - more!

Words: Timothy Dudley-Smith (b. 1926), 1961; based on the *Song of Mary*, Luke 1:46-55, © 1962, ren. 1990
  Hope Publishing Company
Music (WOODLANDS 10.10.10.10): Walter Greatorex, 1916, alt., P.D.

365   I Serve a Risen Savior

1 I serve a ris - en Sav - ior, he's in the world to - day;
2 In all the world a - round me I see his lov - ing care,
3 Re - joice, re - joice, O Chris - tian, lift up your voice and sing

I know that he is liv - ing, what - ev - er peo - ple say;
and though my heart grows wea - ry, I nev - er will de - spair;
e - ter - nal hal - le - lu - jahs to Je - sus Christ the King!

I see his hand of mer - cy, I hear his voice of cheer,
I know that he is lead - ing through all the storm - y blast;
The hope of all who seek him, the help of all who find;

and ev - ery time I need him he's al - ways near.
the day of his ap - pear - ing will come at last.
no oth - er is so lov - ing, so good and kind.

Words and Music (ACKLEY 7.6.7.6.7.6.7.5 refrain 10.8.6.10.8.6): Alfred H. Ackley, 1933, © 1933 Homer A.
Rodeheaver, ren. 1961 The Rodeheaver Company, a div. of WORD, LLC.

366 My Jesus, I Love Thee

1 My Je - sus, I love thee, I know thou art mine;
2 I love thee be - cause thou hast first lov - ed me
3 I'll love thee in life, I will love thee in death,
4 In man - sions of glo - ry and end - less de - light,

for thee all the fol - lies of sin I re - sign;
and pur - chased my par - don on Cal - va - ry's tree;
and praise thee as long as thou lend - est me breath,
I'll ev - er a - dore thee in heav - en so bright;

my gra - cious Re - deem - er, my Sav - ior art thou;
I love thee for wear - ing the thorns on thy brow;
and say when the death - dew lies cold on my brow:
I'll sing with the glit - ter - ing crown on my brow:

if ev - er I loved thee, my Je - sus, 'tis now.
if ev - er I loved thee, my Je - sus, 'tis now.
If ev - er I loved thee, my Je - sus, 'tis now.
If ev - er I loved thee, my Je - sus, 'tis now.

Words: William R. Featherstone, ca. 1862, P.D.
Music (GORDON 11.11.11.11) Adoniram J. Gordon, 1876, P.D.

O God, You Are My God Alone

PSALM 63

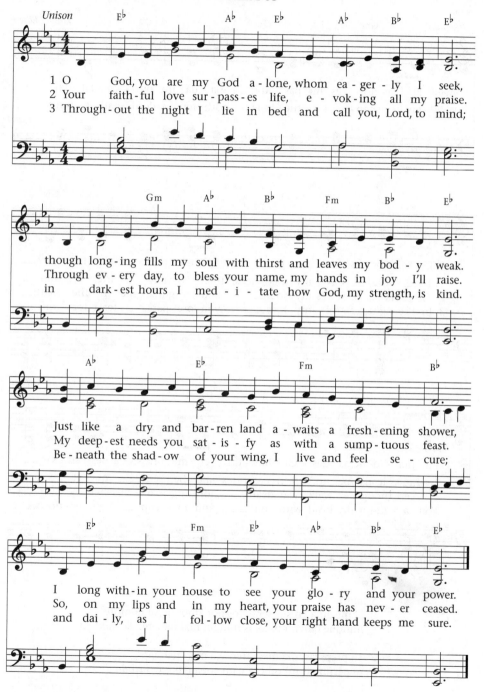

Unison

1 O God, you are my God a - lone, whom ea - ger - ly I seek,
2 Your faith - ful love sur - pass - es life, e - vok - ing all my praise.
3 Through - out the night I lie in bed and call you, Lord, to mind;

though long - ing fills my soul with thirst and leaves my bod - y weak.
Through ev - ery day, to bless your name, my hands in joy I'll raise.
in dark - est hours I med - i - tate how God, my strength, is kind.

Just like a dry and bar - ren land a - waits a fresh - ening shower,
My deep - est needs you sat - is - fy as with a sump - tuous feast.
Be - neath the shad - ow of your wing, I live and feel se - cure;

I long with - in your house to see your glo - ry and your power.
So, on my lips and in my heart, your praise has nev - er ceased.
and dai - ly, as I fol - low close, your right hand keeps me sure.

Words: The Iona Community © 1993 Wild Goose Resource Group, Iona Community, Scotland, GIA
Publications, Inc., exclusive North American agent
Music (GRATUS 8.6.8.6 D): Mary Kay Beall © 1991 Hope Publishing Company

368 El Señor es mi pastor/My Shepherd Is the LORD

PSALM 23

Spanish El Se-ñor es mi pas-tor; na-da me pue-de fal-tar.
English My__ shep-herd is the LORD; noth-ing in-deed shall I want.

1 El Se-ñor es mi pas-tor.__ ¿Qué me pue - de fal-tar?__
1 The__ LORD__ is my shep-herd; there is noth - ing I want.__
2 The__ LORD re-stores my soul__ and guides me in the right;__
3 In the sight__ of my foes__ you pre-pare a feast for me.__

En pra - de - ras des - cu - bier-tas él me lle - va_a des-can - sar.__
God__ leads me in green pas-tures and be - side__ qui - et wa-ters.
e - ven though I walk near death,__ noth-ing e - vil shall I fear.__
You a - noint my head with oil,__ and my cup__ ov - er - flows.__

Spanish

2 El me guía_en sus senderos por amor de su nombre.
Aunque cruce a oscuras ningún mal temeré. *Refrain*

3 Tú preparas una mesa frente_a mis enemigos;
tú perfumas mi cabeza y mi copa rebosa. *Refrain*

For other settings of Psalm 23 see 369, 456, 732, 824

Words: Ricardo Villarreal, 1975; tr. *Psalter Hymnal*, 1987, © 1987 Faith Alive Christian Resources
Music (PASTOR irregular): Ricardo Villarreal, 1975; harm. Delbert Asay, 1975

My Shepherd Will Supply My Need

PSALM 23

369

1 My Shep-herd will sup-ply my need; the LORD God is his name:
in pas-tures fresh he makes me feed, be-side the liv-ing stream.
He brings my wan-dering spir-it back, when I for-sake his ways;
and leads me, for his mer-cy's sake, in paths of truth and grace.

2 When I walk through the shades of death your pres-ence is my stay;
one word of your sup-port-ing breath drives all my fears a - way.
Your hand, in sight of all my foes, shall still my ta - ble spread;
my cup with bless-ings o - ver-flows, your oil a-noints my head.

3 The sure pro-vi-sions of my God at-tend me all my days;
O may your house be my a - bode, and all my work be praise.
There would I find a set-tled rest, while oth - ers go and come;
no more a strang - er or a guest, but like a child at home.

For other settings of Psalm 23 see 368, 456, 732, 824

Words: Isaac Watts (1674-1748), 1719, alt., P.D.
Music (RESIGNATION 8.6.8.6 D): W. Walker's *Southern Harmony*, 1835; harm. Dale Grotenhuis (1931-2012)
© 1990 Dale Grotenhuis

370 My Soul Finds Rest

PSALM 62

1 My soul finds rest in God a-lone, my rock and my sal - va - tion;
(2 Find) rest, my soul, in God a-lone a - mid the world's temp - ta - tions;
(3 I'll) set my gaze on God a-lone and trust in him com-plete-ly;

a for-tress strong a-gainst my foes, and I will not be
when e - vil seeks to take a hold, I'll cling to my sal -
with ev - ery day pour out my soul, and he will prove his

shak - en. Though lips may bless and hearts may curse, and
va - tion. Though rich - es come and rich - es go, don't
mer - cy. Though life is but a fleet - ing breath, a

lies like ar - rows pierce me, I'll fix my heart on
set your heart up - on them; the fields of hope in
sigh too brief to mea - sure, my King has crushed the

For other settings of Ps. 62 see 433, 435

Words and Music (MY SOUL FINDS REST 8.7.8.7 D refrain 7.7.8.6): Psalm 62:1-2, 4-8, 10, 12; Galatians 3:13, Aaron Keyes, Stuart Townend © 2008 ThankYou Music (PRS), admin. worldwide at EMICMGPublishing.com (excl. Europe admin. by Kingswaysongs)

371 Tu fidelidad/I Depend upon Your Faithfulness

Spanish Tu fi-de-li-dad es gran-de,
English I de-pend up-on your faith-ful-ness.

tu fi-de-li-dad in-com-par-a-ble es.
I can jour-ney on, for you are al-ways there.

Na-die co-mo tú, ben-di-to Dios.
None com-pares with you, O bless-ed One;

Gran-de_es tu fi-de-li-dad.
Oh, how great your faith-ful-ness.

When Morning Gilds the Sky

1 When morn - ing gilds the sky, our hearts a - wak - ing cry:
2 To God, the Word on high, the hosts of an - gels cry:
3 Let earth's wide cir - cle round in joy - ful notes re - sound:
4 Be this, when day is past, of all our thoughts the last:

May Je - sus Christ be praised! In all our work and prayer
May Je - sus Christ be praised! Let mor - tals too up - raise
May Je - sus Christ be praised! Let air and sea and sky
May Je - sus Christ be praised! The night be - comes as day

we ask his lov - ing care: May Je - sus Christ be praised!
their voice in hymns of praise: May Je - sus Christ be praised!
from depth to height re - ply: May Je - sus Christ be praised!
when from the heart we say: May Je - sus Christ be praised!

Optional prayer

Faithful God, in joy we declare,
"The sun of righteousness rises
with healing in its wings!" *(Mal. 4:2)*
We pray for your Spirit to help many,
both far and near,
to experience this healing power,
and to join us as we say,
"May Jesus Christ be praised!" Amen.

Words: German, ca. 1800; tr. Edward Caswall, 1858, alt., P.D.
Music (LAUDES DOMINI 6.6.6 D): Joseph Barnby, 1868, P.D.

373   A Service of Morning Prayer

Opening
Our help is in the name of the Lord,
who made heaven and earth.
O Lord, open my lips,
**and my mouth shall
declare your praise.**
The Lord's unfailing love
and mercy never cease,
**fresh as the morning
and sure as the sunrise.**

Morning Hymn

*Psalm(s) (Psalms often used at morning prayer: 3, 5,
19, 34, 36, 51, 63, 90, 95, 100, and 119.)*

O come, let us sing to the Lord;
**let us make a joyful noise
to the rock of our salvation!**
Let us come into his presence
with thanksgiving;
**let us make a joyful noise to him
with songs of praise!**
For the LORD is a great God,
and a great King above all gods.
In his hand are the depths of the earth;
**the heights of the mountains
are his also.**
The sea is his, for he made it,
**and the dry land,
which his hands have formed.**
O come, let us worship and bow down,
let us kneel before the LORD, our Maker!
For he is our God,
**and we are the people of his pasture,
and the sheep of his hand.** (Ps. 95:1-7)

Scripture Reading

Canticle (See p 67 for a setting of the Song of
Zechariah *(Luke 1:68-79).)*

Prayers of the People
Gracious God, rejoicing in your blessings,
trusting in your loving care for all,
we bring you our prayers for the world.
We pray for the created world:
for those who rebuild
where things have been destroyed;
for those who fight hunger,
poverty, and disease;
for those who have power to bring change
for the better and to renew hope.
In the life of our world,
your kingdom come, your will be done.

We pray for our country:
for those who frame our laws
and shape our common life;
for those who keep the peace
and administer justice;
for those who teach, those who heal,
and all who serve the community.
In the life of our land,
your kingdom come, your will be done.

We pray for people in need:
those for whom life is a bitter struggle;
those whose lives are clouded by death and
loss, by pain or disability,
by discouragement or fear,
by shame or rejection.
In the lives of those in need,
your kingdom come, your will be done.

We pray for those in the circle
of friendship and love around us:
children and parents; sisters and brothers;
friends and neighbors;
and for those especially in our thoughts today.
In the lives of those we love,
your kingdom come, your will be done.

We pray for the church:
in its stand with the poor,
in its love for the outcast and the ashamed,
in its service to the sick and neglected,
in its proclamation of the gospel,
in this land, in this place.
In the life of your church,
your kingdom come, your will be done.

Almighty and everlasting God,
we thank you that you have brought us safely
to the beginning of this new day.
Keep us from falling into sin
or running into danger.
Guide us to do always
what is right in your sight.
Through Jesus Christ, our Lord. **Amen.**

The Lord's Prayer (See 911-919)

Closing Hymn

Closing
May we continue to grow in the grace
and knowledge of Jesus Christ,
our Lord and Savior. **Amen.**
Let us bless the Lord. **Thanks be to God.**

Passing of the Peace

Text: Prayers of the People, adapt. from the *Book of Common Order,* Church of Scotland, St. Andrews Press and
Celebrating Common Prayer. Reprinted by permission.

O Splendor of God's Glory Bright

1 O splen-dor of God's glo-ry bright, from light e-ter-nal bring-ing light, O Light of light, the foun-tain spring, O Day, all days il-lu-mi-ning.

2 Come, ver-y Sun of heav-en's love, in last-ing ra-diance from a-bove, and pour the Ho-ly Spir-it's ray on all we think or do to-day.

3 Teach us to love with all our might; drive en-vy out, re-move all spite; turn to the good each trou-bling care, and give us grace your name to bear.

4 All glo-ry be to God Most High; to God the Son let prais-es rise; whom with the Spir-it we a-dore for-ev-er and for-ev-er-more.

Optional reading (Lam. 3:21-26)

Yet this I call to mind
and therefore I have hope:
**Because of the LORD's great love
we are not consumed,
for his compassions never fail.
They are new every morning;
great is your faithfulness.**

I say to myself, "The LORD is my portion;
therefore I will wait for him."
**The LORD is good to those
whose hope is in him,
to the one who seeks him;
it is good to wait quietly
for the salvation of the LORD.**

For an alternate arrangement see 900

Words: Ambrose of Milan, 4th c.; tr. composite, P.D.
Music (PUER NOBIS 8.8.8.8): *Trier manuscript,* 15th c.; adapt. Michael Praetorius, 1609; harm. George Ratcliffe
Woodward, 1910, P.D.

375 **Your Name**

1 As morn-ing dawns and eve-ning fades, you in-spire
2 Je - sus, in your name we pray, come and fill our

songs of praise that rise from earth to touch your heart and
hearts to - day. Lord, give us strength to live for you and

glo - ri - fy your name.
glo - ri - fy your name. Your name is a

strong and might - y tow - er; your name is a

shel - ter like no oth - er. Your name, let the

Words and Music (YOUR NAME 8.7.8.6 refrain 10.10.10.12): Paul Baloche and Glenn Packiam © 2006
Integrity's Hosanna! Music (ASCAP)/Vertical Worship Songs (ASCAP), admin. EMICMGPublishing.com

na - tions sing it loud - er, 'cause noth - ing has the pow -

- er to save but your name.

Hear, O LORD, My Urgent Prayer 376

PSALM 5

1 Hear, O LORD, my ur - gent prayer as I come to seek your care.
2 You do not de - light in sin or in tales that li - ars spin.
3 By your mer - cy and your grace I will come be - fore your face.

With each morn - ing light I raise voice and heart in prayer and praise.
Haugh-ty ones you will de-feat with all those who love de - ceit.
Fear - ing foes, I bow to pray: lead me, LORD; make straight my way.

4 Save me from deceitful ways;
liars' throats are open graves.
Make them bear their guilt, O LORD,
for by choice they spurn your word.

5 Let those trusting you sing praise;
grant them joy to fill their days.
Those who always seek the right
are protected by your might.

For this music in a higher key see 864, 894

Words: Marie J. Post, 1983, © 1987 Faith Alive Christian Resources

Music (TEBBEN 7.7.7.7): Timothy Hoekman, 1979, alt. © 1987 Faith Alive Christian Resources

377
Lord, as the Day Begins

1 Lord, as the day be - gins, lift up our hearts in praise;
2 Christ be in work and skill, serv - ing each oth - er's need;
3 Grant us the Spir - it's strength; teach us to walk his way;
4 Now as the day be - gins, make it the best of days;

take from us all our sins; guard us in all our ways.
Christ be in thought and will, Christ be in word and deed.
so bring us all at length safe to the close of day.
take from us all our sins; guard us in all our ways.

Our ev - ery step di - rect and guide,
Our minds be set on things a - bove
From hour to hour sus - tain and bless,
Our ev - ery step di - rect and guide,

that Christ in all be glo - ri - fied.
in joy and peace, in faith and love.
and let our song be thank - ful - ness.
that Christ in all be glo - ri - fied.

Lord of All Hopefulness

1 Lord of all hope - ful - ness, Lord of all joy, whose
2 Lord of all ea - ger - ness, Lord of all faith, whose
3 Lord of all kind - li - ness, Lord of all grace, your
4 Lord of all gen - tle - ness, Lord of all calm, whose

trust, ev - er child - like, no cares could de - stroy: be
strong hands were skilled at the plane and the lathe: be
hands swift to wel - come, your arms to em - brace: be
voice is con - tent - ment, whose pres - ence is balm: be

there at our wak - ing, and give us, we pray, your
there at our la - bors, and give us, we pray, your
there at our hom - ing, and give us, we pray, your
there at our sleep - ing, and give us, we pray, your

bliss in our hearts, Lord, at the break of the day.
strength in our hearts, Lord, at the noon of the day.
love in our hearts, Lord, at the eve of the day.
peace in our hearts, Lord, at the end of the day.

Chord symbols represent a simplified harmony.

Words: Jan Struther (1901-1953) from *Enlarged Songs of Praise,* 1931, used by permission of Oxford University Press
Music (SLANE 10.11.11.12): Irish; harm. *Hymnal,* 1982 © Church Pension Group/Church Publishing, Inc.

379 Let the Giving of Thanks

PSALM 50

For another setting of Ps. 50 see 9

to	its set - ting	in	the	west.___
and	re - fus - es	to	keep	si - lent.
> to	the judg - ing	of	his	peo - ple.
that___	you may	ev - er	praise	me.
shall___	see my	great	sal -	va - tion."

To Refrain

Midday Prayers   380

A

Sovereign God,
in the midst of this day we pause
to acknowledge that you are Lord.
You are Lord over all creation,
over time, and money,
due dates, and relationships.
You are Lord in times of busyness
and times of rest,
times of health and times of illness.
Wherever you call us to be today,
and in whatever situations face us,
help us in our words and actions
to declare that you are Lord.
In the name of your son, Jesus Christ,
Amen.

B

Almighty and loving God,
from the rising of the sun to its setting,
your name is great among the nations,
your majesty extends to all of creation,
and your call embraces all of our lives.
As we continue to walk with you,
help us to be deeply aware
of your beauty and majesty,
and to honor you
in every thought, word, and deed.
We praise you,
Father, Son, and Holy Spirit—
one God, now and forever. Amen.

C

Ever-present God,
we offer you all of the activities of this day,
a sacrifice of praise and thanks to you,
giver of every good and perfect gift.
By your Spirit,
bless all that we have begun,
correct us
when we fail to honor you,
and use all that we do
to equip each other to live
as your faithful children and servants. Amen.

381   A Service of Evening Prayer

Opening
Our help is in the name of the Lord,
who made heaven and earth.
Jesus Christ is the light of the world,
the light no darkness can overcome.
Stay with us, Lord, for it is evening
and the day is almost over.
Let your light scatter the darkness
and illumine your church.

Evening Hymn

Prayer of Thanksgiving

Psalm(s) *(Psalms often used at evening prayer: 4, 5, 8, 23, 36, 46, 66, 81, 93, 113, 117, 121, 134, 139, and 141.)*

I call upon you, O LORD; come quickly to me;
hear my voice when I call to you.
Let my prayer be as incense before you,
and the lifting up of my hands
as an evening sacrifice.
Set a guard over my mouth, O LORD;
watch over the door of my lips.
Keep my heart from all evil
and my hands from wicked deeds.
Do not let me be tempted by evildoers.
But turn my eyes toward you, O God.
O God, my LORD;
in you I seek refuge;
save me from all danger. *(From Psalm 141)*

Scripture Reading

Canticle (See the Song of Mary, *69, 364, 383 (Luke 1:46-55).)*

Prayers of the People
For the peace from above,
and for our salvation,
*let us pray to the Lord.
Lord, hear our prayer.

For the peace of the whole world,
for the well-being of the church of God,
and for the unity of all,
let us pray to the Lord.
Lord, hear our prayer.

For this place of worship,
and for all who offer here
their worship and praise,
let us pray to the Lord.
Lord, hear our prayer.

For the health of the creation,
for abundant harvests that all may share,
and for peaceful times,
let us pray to the Lord.
Lord, hear our prayer.

For public servants, the government,
and those who protect us;
for those who work to bring peace,
justice, healing, and protection
in this and every place,
let us pray to the Lord.
Lord, hear our prayer.

For those who travel,
for those who are sick and suffering,
and for those who are in captivity,
let us pray to the Lord.
Lord, hear our prayer.

For deliverance in the time of affliction,
wrath, danger, and need,
let us pray to the Lord.
Lord, hear our prayer.

For all servants of the church,
for this gathering,
and for all people who await from the Lord
great and abundant mercy,
let us pray to the Lord.
Lord, hear our prayer.

God of all who fear you,
make us one with all your saints
and with any who are in need.
Teach us to befriend the weak,
and welcome the outcast,
that we may serve the Lord Jesus Christ
and live to offer him glory.
In his holy name we pray. **Amen.**

The Lord's Prayer (See 911-919.)

Closing hymn

Closing
May the peace of God,
which surpasses all understanding,
guard our hearts and minds in Christ Jesus.
Amen.
Let us bless the Lord. **Thanks be to God.**

Passing of the Peace

*May be sung to 887 "Let Us Pray to the Lord"

Text: Prayers of the People, taken from Eastern Liturgies of St. Basil and St. Chrysostom, P.D.; concluding prayer adapt. from the *Book of Common Worship* © 1993 Westminster John Knox Press. Reprinted by permission.

You, O Lord, Are a Shield About Me 382
PSALM 3:3

To use with Psalm 3: Sing the first half of the song, read Ps 3:1-4, repeat the first half of the song, read Ps 3:5-8, sing the whole song with the "hallelujahs".

Words and Music (SHIELD ABOUT ME): from Psalm 3:3, Donn Thomas and Charles Williams © 1980 Spoone Music, Word Music, LLC, admin. Word Music Group, LLC

383 My Spirit Glorifies the Lord

1 My spir - it glo - ri - fies the Lord; in God my
2 All gen - er - a - tions from now on shall call me
3 His mer - cy shall ex - tend to those who fear the

Sav - ior I re - joice, for he be - held my
blest and spread my fame, for he has done great
Lord from age to age; he has re - vealed his

hum - ble state and in his love made me his choice.
things for me— might - y and ho - ly is his name.
might - y arm, scat - tering the proud in all their rage.

4 He brought down rulers from their thrones,
   but lifted those of low degree.
   He filled the hungry with good things,
   but empty sent the rich away.

5 He helped his servant Israel,
   remembering to be merciful,
   keeping his word to Abraham
   and to his seed forevermore.

Chord symbols represent a simplified harmony.

Words: Luke 1:46-55; vers. Dewey Westra, 1931; rev. *Psalter Hymnal*, 1987, © 1987 Faith Alive Christian Resources
Music (PENTECOST 8.8.8.8): William Boyd (1868), P.D.

O Lord, Come Quickly; Hear Me Pray   384

PSALM 141

1 O LORD, come quick - ly; hear me pray
2 Guard lips and heart, with - out, with - in,
3 Let right - eous ones lash out at me—
4 When e - vil deeds dis - rupt my days,
5 Keep me from traps that sin - ners set;

with lift - ed hands at close of day.
so that I do not rel - ish sin.
> a bet - ter oint - ment such would be
my prayers con - demn those e - vil ways.
may they be caught in their own net.

May all my eve - ning prayers a - rise
LORD, let my foot - steps nev - er stray
>than an - y pleas - ure, balm, or cure
The wick - ed heed my words too late,
Though I am bur - dened and dis - tressed,

like in - cense from the sac - ri - fice.
where e - vil - do - ers point the way.
>that wick - ed hands or hearts con - jure.
when they are faced with death's dark gate.
I look, O LORD, to you for rest.

For an accompaniment consider using an open fifth on a D and A, repeating every two measures on the downbeat.

Words: sts. 1,2,4,5 Marie J. Post, 1985, © 1987 Faith Alive Christian Resources; st. 3 Martin Tel © 2011 Martin Tel, admin. Faith Alive Christian Resources
Music (WHEN JESUS WEPT 8.8.8.8): William Billings, *The New England Psalm Singer*, 1770, P.D.

385   A Service of Night Prayer

Opening
Our help is in the name of the Lord,
who made heaven and earth.
It is good to give thanks to the Lord,
to sing your praise, O Most High;
to declare your steadfast love in the morning,
and your faithfulness at night.

Night Hymn

Confession and Assurance
Let us confess our sins to God.
Almighty God, our heavenly Father:
We have sinned against you,
in thought, word, and deed,
by what we have done,
and by what we have left undone.
For the sake of your Son,
our Lord Jesus Christ,
forgive us all our sins
so that we may serve you
in newness of life,
to the glory of your name. Amen.

Quiet

For as the heavens are high above the earth,
so great is God's steadfast love.
As far as the east is from the west,
so far does God remove our sins from us.
Amen.

Psalm(s) (Psalms often used at night prayer: 3, 4, 16,
17, 23, 33, 34, 63, 91, 121, 136, and 139.)

Scripture Reading

Quiet

Prayers of the People
I call upon you, for you will answer me, O God;
turn your ear to me and hear my prayer.
Guard me as the apple of your eye;
hide me in the shadow of your wings.
I will see your face,
and when I awake I will be satisfied.
(From Ps. 17)

[Spoken and/or silent prayer]

O God our Creator,
by whose mercy and might
the world turns safely into darkness
and returns again to light;
we give into your hands our unfinished tasks,
our unsolved problems,
and our unfulfilled hopes.
We know that only those things
which you bless will prosper.
To your great love and protection
we commit each other
and all for whom we have prayed.
You alone are our sure defender,
through Jesus Christ, our Lord. **Amen.**

The Lord's Prayer (or see 911-919)

Our Father in heaven,
hallowed be your name,
your kingdom come,
your will be done
on earth as it is in heaven.
Give us this day our daily bread.
Forgive us our debts,
as we also have forgiven our debtors.
And lead us not into temptation,
but deliver us from the evil one.
For yours is the kingdom
and the power and the glory forever.
Amen.

Canticle (See The Song of Simeon 97, 935 (Luke 2:29-
32).)

Closing

Guide us while we are awake, O Lord,
and guard us while we sleep,
that awake we may watch with Christ,
and asleep rest in his peace.
May almighty God bless, preserve,
and keep us, this night and forevermore.
Amen.

Let us bless the Lord.
Thanks be to God.

Passing of the Peace

Christ, Mighty Savior

1 Christ, might-y Sav-ior, Light of all cre-a-tion, you make the
2 Now comes the day's end as the sun is set-ting, mir-ror of
3 There-fore we come now eve-ning rites to of-fer, joy-ful-ly

day-time ra-diant with the sun-light and to the night give
day-break, pledge of res-u-rec-tion; while in the heav-ens
chant-ing ho-ly hymns to praise you, with all cre-a-tion

glit-ter-ing a-dorn-ment, stars in the heav-ens.
choirs of stars ap-pear-ing hal-low the night-fall.
join-ing hearts and voic-es, sing-ing your glo-ry.

4 Give heed, we pray you,
   to our supplication,
   that you may grant us
   pardon for offenses,
   strength for our weak hearts,
   rest for aching bodies,
   soothing the weary.

5 Though bodies slumber,
   hearts shall keep their vigil,
   forever resting
   in the peace of Jesus,
   in light or darkness
   worshiping our Savior
   now and forever.

Chord symbols represent a simplified harmony.

Words: Mozarabic, 10th c.; tr. Alan McDougall (1895-1964); para. Anne LeCroy (b. 1930) © 1982 The United Methodist Publishing House, admin. The Copyright Company
Music (INNISFREE FARM 11.11.11.5): Richard W. Dirksen (1921-2003) © 1984 Washington National Cathedral Music Program

387 The Day You Gave Us, Lord, Is Ended

1 The day you gave us, Lord, is end-ed;
the dark - ness falls at your be - hest.
To you our morn - ing hymns as - cend - ed;
your praise shall sanc - ti - fy our rest.

2 We thank you that your church, un - sleep - ing
while earth rolls on - ward in - to light,
through all the world her watch is keep - ing,
and nev - er rests by day or night.

3 As o - ver con - ti - nent and is - land
each dawn leads to an - oth - er day,
the voice of prayer is nev - er si - lent,
nor do the prais - es die a - way.

4 So be it, Lord: your throne shall nev - er,
like earth's proud king - doms, pass a - way.
Your king - dom stands and grows for - ev - er,
un - til there dawns your glo - rious day.

Words: John Ellerton, 1870, alt., P.D.
Music (ST. CLEMENT 9.8.9.8): Clement C. Scholefield, 1874, P.D.

Every Heart Its Tribute Pays

PSALM 65

388

1 Ev - ery heart its trib-ute pays, ev - ery tongue its song of praise;
2 Ev - er while his deeds en - dure our sal - va - tion stands se - cure;
3 Year by year, the sea-sons 'round sees the land with bless-ing crowned,

sin and sor - row, guilt and care, brought to him who an - swers prayer;
he whose fin - gers spun the earth, gave the seas and moun-tains birth,
where ca - ressed by sun and rain bar - ren earth gives life a - gain;

there by grace may hu - man - kind full and free for - give-ness find;
tamed the o - cean, formed the land, spread the skies with might - y hand:
sun - lit val - leys burn with gold, na - ture smiles on field and fold,

called and cho - sen, loved and blest, in his pres - ence be at rest.
far - off shores re - vere his Name, day and night his power pro - claim.
gifts of God in plen - ty poured: all things liv - ing, praise the Lord!

For other settings of Ps. 65 see 398, 545

Words: Timothy Dudley-Smith (b. 1926) © 1984 Hope Publishing Company
Music (ST. GEORGE'S WINDSOR 7.7.7.7 D): George J. Elvey, 1858, P.D.

389 Joyous Light of Heavenly Glory

1 Joy-ous light of heaven-ly glo - ry, lov-ing glow of God's own
2 In the stars that grace the dark - ness, in the blaz-ing sun of
3 You who made the heav- en's splen - dor, ev-ery danc-ing star of

face, you who sing cre - a-tion's sto - ry, shine on
dawn, in the light of peace and wis - dom, we can
night, make us shine with gen - tle jus - tice; let us

ev - ery land and race. Now as eve - ning falls a -
hear your qui - et song. Love that fills the night with
each re - flect your light. Might - y God of all cre -

round us, we shall raise our songs to you. God of day-break,
won - der, love that warms the wea - ry soul, love that bursts all
a - tion, gen - tle Christ who lights our way, lov-ing Spir - it

Words: Marty Haugen © 1987 GIA Publications, Inc.
Music (JOYOUS LIGHT 8.7.8.7 D): Marty Haugen © 1987 GIA Publications, Inc.

God of shad - ows, come and light our hearts a - new.
chains a - sun - der, set us free and make us whole.
of sal - va - tion, lead us on to end - less day.

Night Has Fallen 390

Leader F   All

1 *Night has fal - len.* Night has fal - len.
2 *You have kept us, Lord.* You have kept us, Lord.
3 *We will trust in you.* We will trust in you.
4 *Night has fal - len.* Night has fal - len.

God our ma - ker, guard us sleep - ing.

Optional prayer

Loving God,
we rest in your embrace.
We entrust to you all our unfinished tasks,
unsolved problems, and unfulfilled hopes *[name as appropriate]*.
By your Spirit, free us from worry,
and teach us to place our full trust in you. **Amen.**

To use with Psalm 4: read vv. 1-3, sing refrain, read vv. 4-5, sing refrain, read vv. 7-8 and conclude with the singing of the refrain.

391 Awit sa Dapit-Hapon/When Twilight Comes

Filipino 1 Nga - yong nag - da - da - pit ha - pon at lu -

English 1 When twi - light comes and the sun sets, moth - er
2 One day the Rab - bi, Lord Je - sus, called the
3 So gath - er round once a - gain, friends, touched by

mu - lu - bog ang a - raw hu - ma - ha - pon

hen pre - pares for night's rest. As her brood shel - ters
twelve to share his last meal. As the hen tends her
fad - ing glow of sun's gold, and re - count all our

ang i - na - hin at ang kan - yang ma - nga i - na -

un - der her wings, she gives the love of God to her
young, so for them he spent him - self to seek and to
frail hum - an hopes: the dreams of young and sto - ries of

kay ti - ni - ti - pon u - pang mag -

nest. Oh! what joy to feel her warm
heal. Oh! what joy to be with Christ
old. Oh! what joy to pray close to -

Words: Filipino hymn; Moises Andrade; tr. and para. James Minchin © James Minchin, admin. Asian Institute for Liturgy & Music
Music (DAPIT HAPON 8.8.9.9.9.9.7.7): Francisco F. Feliciano (b. 1941) © Francisco F. Feliciano, admin. Asian Institute for Liturgy & Music

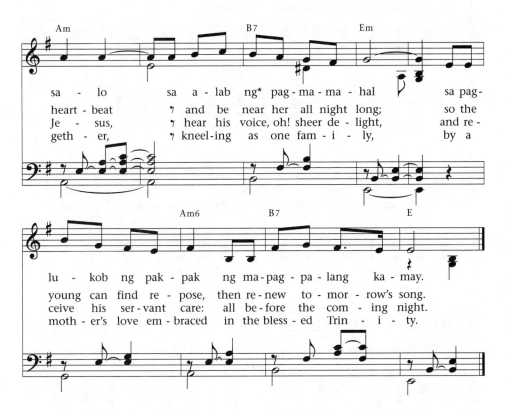

sa - lo   sa a - lab ng* pag - ma - ma - hal   sa pag-
heart - beat   ⁊ and be near her all night long;   so the
Je - sus,   ⁊ hear his voice, oh! sheer de - light,   and re-
geth - er,   ⁊ kneel-ing as one fam - i - ly,   by a

lu - kob ng pak - pak   ng ma - pag - pa - lang ka - may.
young can find re - pose,   then re - new to - mor - row's song.
ceive his ser - vant care: all be - fore the com - ing night.
moth - er's love em - braced   in the bless - ed Trin - i - ty.

Filipino

2 Noon din ay dapit hapon
   at nagwawakas ang araw
   naghapunan ang guro at
   pati kan yang mga** alagad
   nagtipon sila at nagsalo
   sa tinapay at sa alak
   sa piging ng buhay n'yang
   inialay sa lahat.

3 Ngayong nagdadapit hapon
   at lumulubog ang araw
   ang manga magulang at ang
   manga anak ay naghahapunan
   nagtitpon at nagsasalo
   sa ligaya't pagdiriwang
   sa Ama't Anak na Diyos,
   Diyos Espiritung Banal.

*ng (of) pronounced nang
**mga (plural form of "the") pronounced manga

392 O Joyous Light of Glory

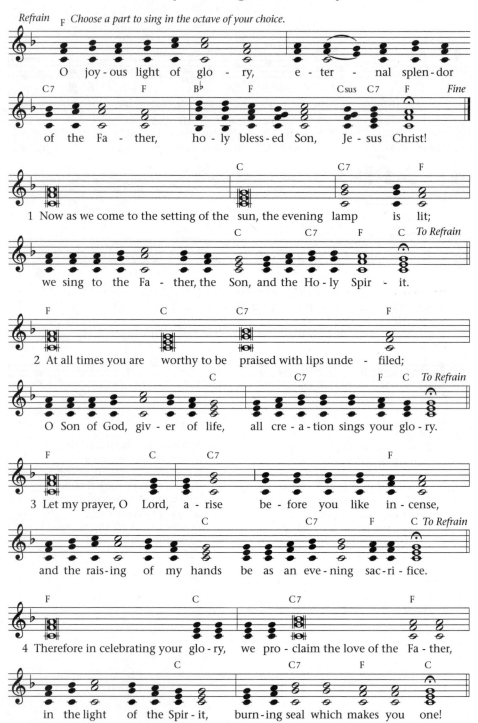

Words: *Phos Hilaron*, attr. Athenogenes (2nd c.); tr. Mepkin Abbey, P.D.
Music (JOYEUSE LUMIERE): A. Gouzes © 1983 *Les Editions de l'Abbaye de Sylvanès*

O Gladsome Light, O Grace

393

1 O glad - some light, O grace of our Cre - a - tor's face,
2 As fades the day's last light, we see the lamps of night
3 To you of right be - longs all praise of ho - ly songs,

the e - ter - nal splen - dor wear - ing: cel - es - tial, ho - ly, blest,
our com - mon hymn out - pour - ing; O God of might un - known,
O Son of God, Life - giv - er; you, there - fore, O Most High,

our Sav - ior Je - sus Christ, joy - ful in your ap - pear - ing.
you, the in - car - nate Son, and Spir - it blest a - dor - ing.
the world does glo - ri - fy and shall ex - alt for - ev - er.

Optional reading (2 Cor. 4:6)

For God, who said, "Let light shine out of darkness,"
made his light shine in our hearts to give us the light of
the knowledge of the glory of God in the face of Christ.

Words: *Phos Hilaron*, Greek hymn; tr. Robert Seymour Bridges (1844-1930), P.D.
Music (NUNC DIMITTIS 6.6.7.6.6.7): Louis Bourgeois (ca. 1510-1561), 1551; harm. Claude Goudimel
  (ca. 1505-1574), 1564, P.D.

394 All Praise to You, My God, This Night

Canon ① G   Dsus   D   Em   ②   D   G   ③   Am

1 All   praise   to   you,   my   God,   this   night,   for   all   the
2 For - give   me,   Lord,   for   this   I   pray,   the   wrong   that
3 Lord,   may   I   be   at   rest   in   you   and   sweet - ly
4 Praise   God,   from whom   all   bless - ings   flow;   praise   him,   all

G   D7   G   Am   G

bless - ings   of   the   light.   Keep   me,   O   keep   me,
I   have   done   this   day.   May   peace   with   God   and
sleep   the   whole   night   through.   Re - fresh   my   strength,   for
crea - tures   here   be - low.   Praise   him   a - bove,   you

D7   G   Am   G   D7   G

King   of   kings,   be - neath   the   shel - ter   of   your   wings.
neigh - bor   be,   be - fore   I   sleep,   re - stored   to   me.
your   own   sake,   so   I   may   serve   you   when   I   wake.
heaven - ly   host;   praise   Fa - ther,   Son,   and   Ho - ly   Ghost.

Optional reading (Ps. 42:8, 11)

By day the Lord directs his love,
at night his song is with me—
a prayer to the God of my life.
Why my soul, are you downcast?
Why so disturbed within me?
Put your hope in God,
for I will yet praise him,
my Savior and my God.

Words: Thomas Ken, 1709, alt., P.D.
Music (TALLIS CANON 8.8.8.8): Thomas Tallis (1505-1585), ca. 1561, P.D.

When Evening Falls and Labors Cease 395

1 When eve-ning falls and la-bors cease, we turn to
2 As dawn will sure-ly fol-low night, so will you
3 Like birds re-turn-ing to their nest, we find in
4 Safe shel-tered by your might-y wings, we praise you,

you in qui-et peace with grate-ful hearts for
make our dark-ness light. New warmth will breathe up-
your strong arms our rest. And as we sleep you
ma-ker of all things, with Christ, our bro-ther

bless-ings past and hope for fu-ture joys that last.
on our land; new life will spring from your own hand.
will re-store our health and strength and joy once more.
and our friend, and Ho-ly Spir-it, with-out end.

Optional reading (Ps. 36:7-9)

How priceless is your unfailing love, O God!
People take refuge in the shadow of your wings.
They feast on the abundance of your house;
you give them drink from your river of delights.
For with you is the fountain of life;
in your light we see light.

For an alternate arrangement see 502

Words: Delores Dufner, OSB, © 2011 GIA Publications, Inc.
Music (GERMANY 8.8.8.8): W. Gardiner's *Sacred Melodies*, 1815; arr. Paul Detterman © 2012 Paul Detterman, admin. Faith Alive Christian Resources

396   For the Fruit of All Creation

1 For the fruit of all cre-a-tion, thanks be to God.
2 In the just re-ward of la-bor, God's will is done.
3 For the har-vests of the Spir-it, thanks be to God.

For his gifts to ev-ery na-tion, thanks be to God.
In the help we give our neigh-bor, God's will is done.
For the good we all in-her-it, thanks be to God.

For the plow-ing, sow-ing, reap-ing, si-lent growth while we are sleep-ing,
In our world-wide task of car-ing for the hun-gry and des-pair-ing,
For the won-ders that as-tound us, for the truths that still con-found us,

fu-ture needs in earth's safe-keep-ing, thanks be to God.
in the har-vests we are shar-ing, God's will is done.
most of all, that love has found us, thanks be to God.

For a descant see 946

Words: Fred Pratt Green, 1970, © 1970 Hope Publishing Company
Music (AR HYD Y NOS 8.4.8.4.8.8.8.4): Welsh melody (c. 1784), P.D.

Praise God for the Harvest of Orchard and Field 397

1 Praise God for the har-vest of or-chard and field,
2 Praise God for the har-vest that comes from a-far,
3 Praise God for the har-vest that's quar-ried and mined,

praise God for the peo-ple who ga-ther their yield,
from mar-ket and har-bor, the sea and the shore:
se-lect-ed and smelt-ed, or shaped and re-fined:

the long hours of la-bor, the skills of a team,
foods packed and trans-port-ed, and ga-thered and grown
for oil and i-ron, for cop-per and coal,

the pa-tience of sci-ence, the power of ma-chine.
by God-giv-en neigh-bors, un-seen and un-known.
praise God, who in love has pro-vid-ed them all.

4 Praise God for the harvest
   of science and skill,
   the urge to discover, create, and fulfill:
   for plans and inventions
      that promise to gain
   a future more hopeful,
      a world more humane.

5 Praise God for the harvest
   of mercy and love
   from leaders and peoples
      who struggle and serve
   with patience and kindness,
      that all may be led
   to freedom and justice,
      and all may be fed.

Words: Brian Wren © 1974, rev. 1996 Hope Publishing Company
Music (STOWEY 11.11.11.11): English folk melody, arr. *Common Ground* editors © 1998 Church of Scotland
   Panel on Worship

398 Sing to the Lord of Harvest

1 Sing to the Lord of har - vest, sing songs of love and praise;
2 God makes the clouds drop fat - ness, the des - erts bloom and spring;
3 Heap on his sa - cred al - tar the gifts his good-ness gave,

with joy - ful hearts and voic - es your al - le - lu - ias raise.
the hills leap up in glad - ness, the val - leys laugh and sing.
the gold - en sheaves of har - vest, the souls Christ died to save.

By him the rol - ling sea - sons in fruit - ful or - der move;
God fills from his great full - ness all things with large in - crease;
Your hearts lay down be - fore him when at his feet you fall,

sing to the Lord of har - vest a joy - ful song of love.
he crowns the year with good - ness, with plen - ty, and with peace.
and with your lives a - dore him who gave his life for all.

Chord symbols represent a simplified harmony.

For other settings of Ps. 65 see 388, 545

Words: John S. B. Monsell, 1866, alt., P.D.; based on Psalm 65:9-13
Music (WIE LIEBLICH IST DER MAIEN 7.6.7.6 D): Johann Steurlein, 1575, P.D.

Bless the LORD, O Saints and Servants

399

PSALM 113

1 Bless the LORD, O saints and ser - vants; praise the might of
2 Who in heaven can be God's e - qual, who on earth with

God's great name: age - less, match - less, filled with won - der, yes - ter -
God com - pare? Who can raise the poor from ash - es, lift the

day, to - day, the same. When the dawn re - ceives the sun - rise
need - y from de - spair? God a - lone in - vites the help - less

till the night re - turns its rays, shall the glo - ry
with the strong to share re - ward; fields once bar - ren

of God's good - ness be the theme of all our praise.
yield a har - vest, tongues once si - lent praise their LORD.

Chord symbols represent a simplified harmony.

Words: Michael Morgan © 2011 Michael Morgan, admin. Faith Alive Resources
Music (AUSTRIAN HYMN 8.7.8.7 D): Franz Joseph Haydn (1732-1809), 1797, P.D.

400　Greet Now the Swiftly Changing Year

1 Greet now the swift - ly chang - ing year with
2 Re - mem - ber now the Son of God and
3 This Je - sus came to end sin's war; the
4 His love a - bun - dant far ex - ceeds the

joy and pen - i - tence sin - cere. Re - joice! Re - joice!
how he shed for us his blood. Re - joice! Re - joice!
name of names for us he bore. Re - joice! Re - joice!
vol - ume of a whole year's needs. Re - joice! Re - joice!

With thanks em - brace an - oth - er year of grace.
With thanks em - brace an - oth - er year of grace.
With thanks em - brace an - oth - er year of grace.
With thanks em - brace an - oth - er year of grace.

5 With him as Lord to lead our way
in want and in prosperity,
what need we fear in earth or space
in this new year of grace!

6 "All glory be to God on high,
and peace on earth!" the angels cry.
Rejoice! Rejoice! With thanks embrace
another year of grace.

7 God, Father, Son, and Spirit, hear!
To all our pleas incline your ear;
upon our lives rich blessing trace
in this new year of grace.

Words: Slovak, 1636; tr. Jaroslav J. Vajda, 1968, alt. © 1969 Concordia Publishing House
Music (SIXTH NIGHT 8.8.8.6): Alfred V. Fedak, 1984, © 1990 Selah Publishing Company

Hours and Days and Years and Ages 401

1 Hour and days and years and a-ges swift as mov-ing shad-ows flee;
2 But from sin your mer-cy drew us, would not leave our souls a-lone.
3 Though swift time keeps march-ing on-ward, it will not de-cide our end.
4 Speed a-long, then, years and a-ges, with your glad-ness and your pain;

as we scan life's fleet-ing pa-ges, noth-ing last-ing do we see.
Gra-cious Lord, you did re-new us; in Christ's death we are your own.
You will al-ways be our Fa-ther, lov-ing God, e-ter-nal Friend.
when our deep-est sor-row ra-ges, God our Fa-ther will re-main.

On the paths our feet are walk-ing, foot-prints all will fade a-way;
Through the mer-cy of your lead-ing, each short step a-long our way
When life's dan-gers o-ver-whelm us, you will ev-er be our stay;
Though all friends on earth for-sake us and our trou-bles shall in-crease,

each to-day as we en-joy it soon be-comes a yes-ter-day.
now be-comes a path to guide us to the land of end-less day.
through your Son you are our Fa-ther, al-ways change-less, come what may.
God with his right hand will take us to our ev-er-last-ing peace.

Words: Rhijivis Feith (1753-1824); tr. Leonard P. Brink, 1929; rev. Henrietta Ten Harmsel (1921-2012), 1984,
© 1987 Faith Alive Christian Resources
Music (O DU LIEBE MEINER LIEBE 8.7.8.7 D): *Moravian Chorale Book* manuscript, Herrnhut, 1735, P.D.

402 Lord, Show Me How to Count My Days

PSALM 39

1 Lord, show me how to count my days, for life is like a
single breath: so swift, the passing of the years,
so brief, the course from birth to death; and all my labor
seems in vain, however great the wealth I gain.

2 I have no hope, except in you, so show me mercy
for my sin; let not my heart be overwhelmed
as I receive your discipline. In hushed and holy
awe I stand: I feel my pain; I sense your hand.

3 But why should those who scorn your name derive enjoyment
from my fear? I keep my feelings to myself
whenever godless ears are near; yet how the fires within
in me burn until, at last, to you I turn.

4 A stranger in the midst of life, a rootless traveler
passing through, I ask you, Lord, to hear my prayer,
and not to spurn my cry to you; but let me find, in-
stead of tears, sufficient joys for all my years.

Words: Martin Leckebusch © 2006 Kevin Mayhew Ltd.
Music (RYBURN 8.8.8.8.8.8.8): Norman Cocker (1889-1953) © Oxford University Press, reproduced by permission of Oxford University Press; arr. Alfred Fedak (b. 1953) © 2011 Oxford University Press

Wildflowers Bloom and Fade

PSALM 90

403

1 Wild-flow-ers bloom and fade, soon come and gone,
2 Your love will nev-er end; our days are brief.
3 Our lives are like the rose that quick-ly dies.
4 Fill us with faith-ful love as morn-ing wakes.

but God, from age to age you still live on.
Our years are full of sin, lab-or, and grief.
Teach us to count our days; God, make us wise.
Let us re-joice in you as each day breaks.

Old-er than time and space, you are our dwell-ing place.
You turn us back to dust, yet all your ways are just,
Though time flies swift-ly past, God, let our good work last.
May your great work be known, your power on earth be shown.

Keep us in your em-brace, O God, our home.
so we will live in trust, O God, our home.
Your strong arms hold us fast, O God, our home.
Do not for-get your own, O God, our home.

For another setting of Ps. 90 see 405

Words: Ruth C. Duck, 1995, © 1996 The Pilgrim Press
Music (INCARNATION 6.4.6.4.6.6.6.4): John L. Bell, 1987, © 1987 Wild Goose Resource Group,
Iona Community, Scotland, admin. by GIA Publications, Inc., exclusive North American agent

404 ## God of Our Life

1 God of our life, through all the cir - cling years we trust in
2 God of the past, our times are in thy hand; with us a -
3 God of the com - ing years, through paths un - known we fol - low

thee; in all the past, through all our hopes and fears, thy
bide. Lead us by faith to hope's true prom - ised land; be
thee; when we are strong, Lord, leave us not a - lone; our

hand we see. With each new day, when morn - ing lifts the veil,
thou our guide. With thee to bless, the dark - ness shines as light,
re - fuge be. Be thou for us in life our dail - ly bread,

we own thy mer - cies, Lord, which nev - er fail.
and faith's fair vi - sion chang - es in - to sight.
our heart's true home when all our years have sped.

Words: Hugh T. Kerr, 1916, P.D.
Music (SANDON 10.4.10.4.10.10): Charles H. Purday, 1860, P.D.

O God, Our Help in Ages Past

PSALM 90

1 O God, our help in a-ges past, our hope for years to come,
2 Un-der the shad-ow of your throne your saints have dwelt se-cure;
3 Be-fore the hills in or-der stood or earth re-ceived its frame,
4 A thou-sand a-ges in your sight are like an eve-ning gone,

our shel-ter from the storm-y blast, and our e-ter-nal home:
suf-fi-cient is your arm a-lone, and our de-fense is sure.
from ev-er-last-ing you are God, to end-less years the same.
short as the watch that ends the night be-fore the ris-ing sun.

5 Time, like an ever-rolling stream,
soon bears us all away;
we fly forgotten, as a dream
dies at the opening day.

6 O God, our help in ages past,
our hope for years to come,
still be our guard while troubles last,
and our eternal home!

Sing stanzas 1-3

We are consumed by your anger
and terrified by your indignation.

**You have set our iniquities before you,
our secret sins in the light of your
presence.**

If we only knew the power of your anger!
**Your wrath is as great as the fear that
is your due.**

Sing stanzas 4-5

Teach us to number our days,
that we may gain a heart of wisdom.

**Relent, LORD! How long will it be?
Have compassion on your servants.**

Satisfy us in the morning with your unfailing
love, that we may sing for joy and be glad all
our days.

**Make us glad for as many days as you
have afflicted us, for as many years as
we have seen trouble.**

May your deeds be shown to your servants,
your splendor to their children.

**May the favor of the Lord our God rest
on us; establish the work of our hands
for us—yes, establish the work of our
hands.**

Sing stanza 6

For another setting of Ps. 90 see 403

Words: Isaac Watts (1674-1719), 1719, alt., P.D.
Music (ST. ANNE 8.6.8.6): William Croft, 1708, P.D.

406

LORD, I Bring My Songs to You

PSALM 34

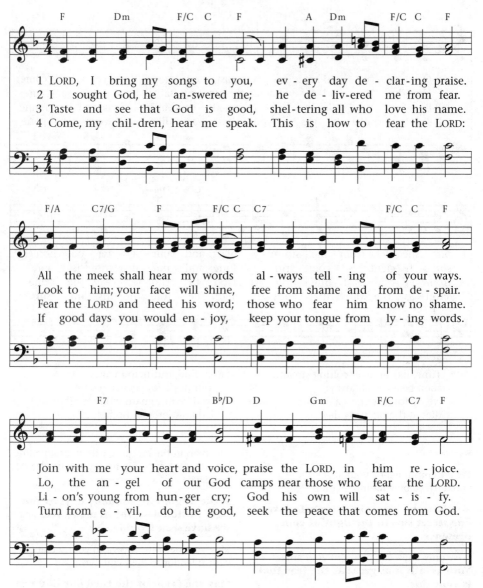

1 LORD, I bring my songs to you, ev - ery day de - clar - ing praise.
2 I sought God, he an - swered me; he de - liv - ered me from fear.
3 Taste and see that God is good, shel - ter - ing all who love his name.
4 Come, my chil - dren, hear me speak. This is how to fear the LORD:

All the meek shall hear my words al - ways tell - ing of your ways.
Look to him; your face will shine, free from shame and from de - spair.
Fear the LORD and heed his word; those who fear him know no shame.
If good days you would en - joy, keep your tongue from ly - ing words.

Join with me your heart and voice, praise the LORD, in him re - joice.
Lo, the an - gel of our God camps near those who fear the LORD.
Li - on's young from hun - ger cry; God his own will sat - is - fy.
Turn from e - vil, do the good, seek the peace that comes from God.

5 God the LORD sees all our needs;
he will answer us in grace.
But against all evil ones
God will surely turn his face.
When the contrite cry, he hears,
saving them and ending fears.

6 Though our troubles multiply,
God the LORD will save his own.
He will turn the wrong aside,
keep unbroken every bone.
Wicked ones the LORD condemns,
but his servants he defends.

For another setting of Ps. 34 see 817

Words: Marie J. Post, 1985, © 1987 Faith Alive Christian Resources
Music (LUX PRIMA 7.7.7.7.7.7): Charles F. Gounod (1818-1893), 1872, P.D.

If You But Trust in God to Guide You 407

1 If you but trust in God to guide you and place your con-fi-
2 On-ly be still and wait his plea-sure in cheer-ful hope with
3 Sing, pray, and keep his ways un-swerv-ing, of-fer your ser-vice

dence in him, you'll find him al-ways there be-side you
heart con-tent. He fills your needs to full-est mea-sure
faith-ful-ly, and trust his word; though un-de-serv-ing,

to give you hope and strength with-in; for those who trust God's
with what dis-cern-ing love has sent; doubt not our in-most
you'll find his prom-ise true to be. God nev-er will for-

change-less love build on the rock that will not move.
wants are known to him who chose us for his own.
sake in need the soul that trusts in him in-deed.

Chord symbols represent a simplifed harmony.

Words: Georg Neumark, 1641; tr. composite
Music (NEUMARK/WER NUR DEN LIEBEN GOTT 9.8.9.8.8.8): Georg Neumark, 1657, P.D.

408   What a Privilege to Carry

PSALM 41

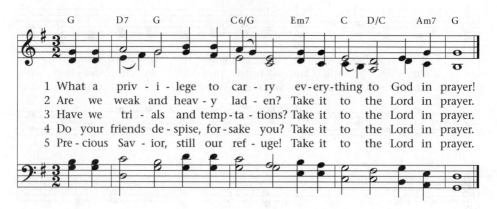

1 What a priv - i - lege to car - ry ev-ery-thing to God in prayer!
2 Are we weak and heav - y lad - en? Take it to the Lord in prayer.
3 Have we tri - als and temp-ta - tions? Take it to the Lord in prayer.
4 Do your friends de - spise, for-sake you? Take it to the Lord in prayer.
5 Pre - cious Sav - ior, still our ref - uge! Take it to the Lord in prayer.

Sing stanza 1

Blessed are those who have regard for the weak;
the Lord delivers them in times of trouble.
**The Lord protects and preserves them—
they are counted among the blessed in
the land—he does not give them over to
the desire of their foes.**
The Lord sustains them on their sickbed
and restores them from their bed of illness.
**I said, "Have mercy on me, Lord;
heal me, for I have sinned against you."**

Sing stanza 1 or 2

My enemies say of me in malice,
"When will he die and his name perish?"
**When one of them comes to see me,
he speaks falsely, while his heart
gathers slander; then he goes out and
spreads it around.**
All my enemies whisper together against me;
they imagine the worst for me, saying,
**"A vile disease has afflicted him;
he will never get up from the place
where he lies."**

Sing stanza 1 or 3

Even my close friend,
someone I trusted,
one who shared my bread,
has turned against me.
**But may you have mercy on me, Lord;
raise me up, that I may repay them.**

Sing stanza 1 or 4

I know that you are pleased with me,
for my enemy does not triumph over me.
**Because of my integrity you uphold me
and set me in your presence forever.**

Sing stanza 1 or 5

Praise be to the Lord, the God of Israel,
from everlasting to everlasting.
Amen and Amen.

For the complete hymn see 898

Words: Joseph M. Scriven, 1855, P.D.
Music (BEACH SPRING fragment): *The Sacred Harp,* Philadelphia, 1833; harm. A. Royce Eckhardt, 1972,
  © 1972, 1996 Covenant Publications

LORD, Chasten Not in Anger

409

PSALM 6

1 LORD, chas-ten not in an - ger, nor in your wrath re - buke me.
2 Turn to me now, up - hold me; for your love's sake re - store me.
3 Pain and dis-tress o'er-whelm me, I cry all night for mer - cy,
4 All who love e - vil, leave me, for God has heard my weep-ing:

Give me your heal-ing word. My soul and bod - y lan - guish;
O save me by your grace. For death ends all re - mem - brance;
my bed is wet with tears. My eyes can weep no lon - ger;
my foes are put to shame. Turned back, no more to grieve me,

I wait for you in an - guish. How long, how long, O LORD?
it wraps the tongue in si - lence. How can the dead sing praise?
my en - e - mies seem stron - ger, my aw - ful foes and fears.
they sud - den - ly shall leave me. All glo - ry to God's name!

Optional concluding prayer

Compassionate healer,
you know the depths of human grief,
the intensity of human pain.
We boldly pray
for healing,
for comfort,
for strength,
and for the peace that surpasses understanding.
We place our hope in you. Amen.

For another setting of Ps. 6 see 303

Words: Clarence P. Walhout, 1982, © 1987 Faith Alive Christian Resources
Music (GENEVAN 6 | 7.7.6.7.7.6): *Genevan Psalter*, 1542; harm. Howard Slenk, 1985, © 1987 Faith Alive
Christian Resources

410 How Long Will You Forget Me, Lord

PSALM 13

1 How long will you for - get me, Lord,
2 Look on my need, O Lord my God,
3 Look on their threats and hear my cry,
4 Lord, in your mer - cy is my trust;

and hide your face a - way?
who grants my ev - ery breath;
and an - swer when I call:
I shall be glad and free:

How long shall e - vils tear my heart
give light that I may see your light,
or they will claim the vic - to - ry
then shall I sing with all my heart

and trou - bles fill my day?
nor sleep the sleep of death.
who long to see me fall.
how you have dealt with me.

Words: Christopher Idle © 1990 The Jubilate Group, admin. Hope Publishing Company
Music (MARTYRDOM 8.6.8.6): Hugh Wilson, ca. 1800; adapt. Robert Smith, 1825, P.D.; arr. Nolan Williams Jr
(b. 1969) © 2000 GIA Publications, Inc.

Protect Me, God: I Trust in You

411

PSALM 16

1 Pro - tect me, God: I trust in you. I tell you now,
2 Your peo - ple are a cho - sen race, and I de - light
3 LORD God, you are my food and drink; my work for you
4 Thank you, my LORD, for warn-ing me; by night and day

"You are my Lord; on you my hap - pi - ness de - pends."
in faith - ful friends, but pa - gan ways I will not share.
is joy in - deed; glad is the her - i - tage that's mine.
you guide my thoughts. With you be - fore me, I stand firm.

Refrain

Pro - tect me, God: I trust in you.

5 So now I'm glad in heart and soul,
for I have found security—
among the dead I shall not lie.
Refrain

6 Not death, but life, shall be my path;
abundant joy your presence grants,
an honored place, and happiness.
Refrain

412 You Are My Hiding Place

PSALM 32:7

For another setting of Ps. 32 see 669

Words and Music (HIDING PLACE): Michael Ledner (b. 1952) © 1981 Universal Music--Brentwood-Benson Publishing (ASCAP)/CCCM Music, admin. Universal Music--Brentwood-Benson Publishing

Lord, You Are My Strength

PSALM 54

413

Lord, you are my strength; has-ten to help me.

Refrain

Save me, O God, by your name;
vindicate me by your might.
Hear my prayer, O God;
listen to the words of my mouth.
Arrogant foes are attacking me;
ruthless people are trying to kill me —
people without regard for God.

Refrain

Surely God is my help;
the Lord is the one who sustains me.
Let evil recoil on those who slander me;
in your faithfulness destroy them.
I will sacrifice a freewill offering to you;
I will praise your name, LORD, for it is good.
You have delivered me from all my troubles,
and my eyes have looked in triumph on my foes.

Refrain

Optional prayer in solidarity with those who suffer injustice

Faithful God,
we boldly pray...
    for all who are victims of war—hasten to help them.
    for all who are taken into slavery—hasten to help them.
    for all who are victims of violence and abuse—hasten to help them.
    for all those, young and old, who are bullied—hasten to help them.
    [other victims, as appropriate]—hasten to help them.

When we forget you and become ruthless ourselves,
forgive us, and hasten to help us,
through the power of Jesus Christ, our Lord.
Amen.

414 All Will Be Well

All will be well, and all will be well, all man-ner of things will be well.

To beginning — *Final ending* — well. well, will be well, will be well.

Optional lament for use with "All Will Be Well"

Refrain

Loving God,
we gather in worship, offering our praise,
yet also acknowledging there is pain in our midst.
In whatever situation we may find ourselves,
you graciously welcome us into your presence.
Held in your Spirit, we can sing:

Refrain

Held in your Spirit, we can also admit
that it is not always easy to sing these words,
and there are times when we cannot sing them.
While we yearn to trust in your promises,
we have experienced the reality of lies, deceit, and dishonesty.
Some of us have been left wounded by the words and actions of others,
so much so that our voices fall silent.
For those who cannot join in the song today, we sing on their behalf:

Refrain

Sometimes all we can do
is cling desperately to these words as life around us changes.
We pray for those among us who are in transition,
those who are mourning losses, those who are sick,
and those experiencing the turbulence of the seasons of life.

[Specific prayers may be added or time allowed for silent prayer.]

(continues)

Text: Melissa Haupt, 2011 © Creative Commons Attribution-NonCommercial-ShareAlike
Words: from *The Revelations of Divine Love*, Julian of Norwich, adapt. S.C.W.; Steven C. Warner © 1993 World
   Library Publications
Music (ALL WILL BE WELL 4.5.8.4.5.8): Steven C. Warner © 1993 World Library Publications

May this community be a place of safety for all seeking refuge,
and may we find comfort and rest in your Word:

Refrain

In all manner of things,
when praise resounds from our lips,
when pain silences our souls,
and all moments in between,
your love endures and sustains.
Give us the faith to trust in your love
and hope in your Word
that all will be well. **Amen.**

Refrain

Listen to My Cry, LORD

PSALM 61

415

1 Lis - ten to my cry, LORD; hear my hum - ble prayer.
2 From the earth's far cor - ners you will hear my cry.
3 You are my pro - tec - tion when my foes ap - pear;
4 In your tent for - ev - er may my dwell - ing be;

When my soul is trou - bled, keep me in your care.
Set me on your rock, LORD, high - er rock than I.
keep me in your tow - er, safe from ev - ery fear.
with your wings of mer - cy gent - ly shel - ter me.

5 All my cries you've answered,
kept me safe from shame.
I am richly blest with
those who fear your name.

6 Bless with life forever
your anointed king.
Through the generations
may he always reign.

7 May your love and mercy
keep him all his days.
Then with joy forever
I will sing your praise.

For another setting of Ps. 61 see 906

Words: Henrietta Ten Harmsel (1921-2012), 1985, © 1987 Faith Alive Christian Resources
Music (WEM IN LEIDENSTAGEN 6.5.6.5): F. Filitz, 1847, P.D.

416
In My Day of Fear

PSALM 56

In my day of fear, I put my trust in you, God Most High.

1 All day long I am un-der at-tack; my
2 In God's Word I have put my faith, in
3 All day long they wound me with words, and
4 But you, O Lord, you have not-ed my grief and
5 I will de-clare with due grat-i-tude how

en-e-mies are al-ways near, ly-ing in wait,
you I trust, O Lord, Most High. There-fore I need no
ev-ery word is meant to harm; band-ing to-geth-er,
seen my end-less mis-er-y; keep all my tears
God has kept my soul from death; thus in God's pres-ence

wait-ing their chance, in-tend-ing to ha-rass and fight.
long-er fear, for what could mor-tals ev-er do?
plot-ting their worst, they sly-ly watch my ev-ery move.
stored in your flask, the tears re-cord-ed in your book.
I glad-ly walk, in pres-ence of the light of life.

Words: The Iona Community © 1993 Wild Goose Resource Group, Iona Community, Scotland,
GIA Publications, Inc., exclusive North American agent
Music (DISTANT OAKS): The Iona Community © 1993 Wild Goose Resource Group, Iona Community,
Scotland, GIA Publications, Inc., exclusive North American agent

Dans nos obscurités/Within Our Darkest Night 417

French Dans nos ob-scu-ri-tés al-lu-me le feu qui ne s'é-teint ja-

English With-in our dark-est night, you kin-dle the fire that nev-er dies a-

Spanish En nues-tra_os-cu-ri-dad, en-cien-de la lla-ma de tu_a-mor, Se-

German Im Dun-kel uns-rer Nacht, ent-zün-de das Feu-er, das nie mehr er-

mais, ne s'é-teint ja-mais. Dans nos ob-scu-ri-tés, al-lu-me le

way, nev-er dies a-way. With-in our dark-est night, you kin-dle the

ñor, de tu_a-mor, Se-ñor. En nues-tra_os-cu-ri-dad, en-cien-de la

lischt, das nie mehr er-lischt. Im Dun-kel uns-rer Nacht, ent-zün-de das

feu qui ne s'é-teint ja-mais, ne s'é-teint ja-mais.

fire that nev-er dies a-way, nev-er dies a-way.

lla-ma de tu_a-mor, Se-ñor, de tu_a-mor, Se-ñor.

Feu-er, das nie mehr er-lischt, das nie mehr er-lischt.

Mandarin
在幽暗黑夜中，你所点燃之火，
永不熄灭，永远不熄灭。

Korean
어두운 밤을 지날 때
영원히 꺼지지 않는 불 밝혀 주소서

Hungarian
Gyújts éjszakánkba fényt,
hadd égjen a soha Ki nem alvó, tűz,
ki nem alvó tűz!

Swahili
Katika giza letu,
washa mo-oto isiozimika,
isiozimika.

For use with Psalm 88: Sing refrain, read vv. 1-7, refrain, read vv. 8-10, refrain, read vv. 11-18 and conclude with the refrain

418 If You Love Me

PSALM 69

Refrain: If you love me, come and an-swer me; O turn to me, O God.

1 I suf-fer shame and in-sult be - cause I know you well; re - ject - ed by my loved ones, and strang - er to my moth - er's chil-dren.

2 Ob - sessed with your dwell-ing, I am shat-tered with no strength; the scorn once meant for you turns a - bout and falls on me.

3 O God, hear my prayer, for I long to know your love, in your kind - ness come to me, you a - lone are my help.

4 Re - joice, come and see, there is rea - son to re - joice, for all who seek God: your hearts will learn to hope a - gain.

Words and Music (IF YOU LOVE ME irregular): David Haas (b. 1957) © 1997 GIA Publications, Inc.

Come Quickly, Lord, to Rescue Me 419

PSALM 70

1 Come quick-ly, LORD, to res-cue me, and has-ten
2 May all who seek your name re-joice, your praise in
3 Yet I am poor and need-y, LORD; be quick to

to my help, I pray. May all who seek to
grat-i-tude re-cord. May those who love your
hear my ur-gent plea. You are my help, my

take my life be put to shame with-out de-lay.
sav-ing power say ev-er-more, "Ex-alt the LORD!"
Sav-ior God! Do not de-lay; re-mem-ber me.

Optional prayer

God of justice and mercy,
we pray for all who are poor and needy,
for all who long for you to hear their urgent plea.
Especially today, we pray for their needs . . .

We pray also as the poor and needy.
We long for you to hear our urgent plea.
Especially today, we pray for our needs . . . .

Help us and all for whom we pray to say:
"You, Lord, are our help and our salvation." Amen.

Chord symbols represent a simplifed harmony.

Words: Bert Polman, 1983, © 1987 Faith Alive Christian Resources
Music (CHICKAHOMINY 8.8.8.8): Henry B. Hays, 1981, alt. © 1981 Order of St. Benedict, Inc., admin.
Liturgical Press

420 Total Praise

With reverence

Lord, I will lift mine eyes to the hills, know - ing my help is com - ing from you. Your peace you give me in time of the storm. You are the source of my strength. You are the strength of my life. I lift my hands in to - tal praise to you. you.

Words and Music (TOTAL PRAISE): Richard Smallwood, arr. Stephen Key © 1996 Bridge Building Music (BMI)/T Autumn Music (BMI), admin. Bridge Building Music

Optional acclamations

You are the source of my strength.
You are the strength of my life.
You are the joy of my heart.
You are the peace of our lives.
You are the light on our path.

[Add other phrases as appropriate]

421 Up to You I Lift My Eyes

PSALM 123

1 Up to you I lift my eyes, high en-throned a-
2 As a ser-vant watch-es still, set to know his
3 As a maid re-ceives com-mand from her grac-ious
4 When in ar-ro-gance de-spised, when re-buffed or

bove the skies: teach me, Lord, to fol-low you,
mas-ter's will: so we fix our eyes on you,
mis-tress' hand: so, our God, we look to you,
vic-tim-ized— we seek mer-cy, Lord, from you:

see your hand in all _____ I do.
seek your hand in all _____ we do.
seek your hand in all _____ we do.
be our guide in all _____ we do.

Optional concluding prayer

Lord Jesus,
our only comfort in life and in death,
the world's contempt
did not dissuade you from accomplishing our salvation.
**We look to no one but you to sustain us now
and through all that is yet to come. Amen.**

Words: Emma Turl, 2001, rev. 2011, © Emma Turl, admin. Praise Trust
Music (THE CALL 7.7.7.7): Ralph Vaughan Williams; adapt. E. Harold Geer © 1911, 1956 Stainer & Bell Ltd

Pass Me Not, O Gentle Savior

422

1 Pass me not, O gen-tle Sav-ior; hear my hum-ble cry;
2 Let me at thy throne of mer-cy find a sweet re-lief;
3 Trust-ing on-ly in thy mer-it, would I seek thy face;
4 Thou the spring of all my com-fort, more than life to me,

while on oth-ers thou art call-ing, do not pass me by.
kneel-ing there in deep con-tri-tion, help my un-be-lief.
heal my wound-ed, bro-ken spir-it, save me by thy grace. *I'm call-ing*
whom have I on earth be-side thee? Whom in heaven but thee?

Refrain

Sav - ior, Sav - ior, hear my hum - ble cry;

while on oth - ers thou are call - ing, do not pass me by.

Words: Fanny J. Crosby, P.D., st. 4 from Psalm 73:25
Music (PASS ME NOT 8.6.8.6 refrain 4.5.8.5): William H. Doane, P.D.

423 Give Me Jesus

1 In the morn-ing when I rise, in the morn-ing when I rise,
2 Dark____ mid-night was my cry, dark____ mid-night was my cry,
3 Just a-bout the break of day, just a-bout the break of day,
4 Oh,____ when I come to die, oh,____ when I come to die,

in the morn-ing when I rise, give me Je - sus.
dark____ mid-night was my cry, give me Je - sus.
just a-bout the break of day, give me Je - sus.
oh,____ when I come to die, give me Je - sus.

Refrain

Give me Je - sus, give me Je - sus;

you may have all this world; give me Je - sus.

Words: African American spiritual, P.D.
Music (GIVE ME JESUS 6.6.6.4 refrain 4.4.6.4): African American spiritual; arr. Diane Dykgraaf © 2012 Diane Dykgraaf, admin. Faith Alive Christian Resources

Jesus, Lover of My Soul

424

1 Je - sus, lov - er of my soul, let me to thy bos - om fly,
2 Oth - er re - fuge have I none; hangs my help-less soul on thee;
3 Thou, O Christ, art all I want, more than all in thee I find:
4 Plen - teous grace with thee is found, grace to co - ver all my sin;

while the near - er wa - ters roll, while the tem - pest still is high;
leave, ah! leave me not a - lone, still sup - port and com - fort me.
raise the fal - len, cheer the faint, heal the sick and lead the blind.
let the heal - ing streams a - bound; make and keep me pure with - in.

hide me, O my Sav - ior, hide, till the storm of life is past;
All my trust on thee is stayed, all my help from thee I bring;
Just and ho - ly is thy name; I am all un - right-eous-ness;
Thou of life the foun-tain art; free - ly let me take of thee;

safe in - to the ha - ven guide, O re - ceive my soul at last.
co - ver my de-fense - less head with the shad - ow of thy wing.
false and full of sin I am, thou art full of truth and grace.
spring thou up with - in my heart, rise to all e - ter - ni - ty.

Words: Charles Wesley (1707-1788), P.D.
Music (MARTYN 7.7.7.7 D): Simeon B. Marsh (1798-1875); arr. Nolan Williams Jr (b. 1969) © 2000
GIA Publications, Inc.

425   Jesus, Priceless Treasure

1 Je - sus, price - less trea - sure, source of pur - est plea - sure, friend most
2 Let your arms en - fold me: those who try to wound me can - not
3 Hence, all world - ly trea - sure! Je - sus is my plea - sure; Je - sus
4 Ban - ish thoughts of sad - ness, for the Lord of glad - ness, Je - sus,

sure and true: long my heart was burn - ing, faint - ing much and
reach me here. Though the earth be shak - ing, ev - ery heart be
is my choice. Hence, all emp - ty glo - ry! What to me your
en - ters in; though the clouds may gath - er, those who love the

yearn - ing, thirst - ing, Lord, for you. Yours I am, O spot - less Lamb,
quak - ing, Je - sus calms my fear. Fires may flash and thun - der crash;
sto - ry told with tempt - ing voice? Pain or loss or shame or cross
Sav - ior still have peace with - in. Though I bear much sor - row here,

so will I let noth - ing hide you, seek no joy be - side you!
yea, though sin and hell as - sail me, Je - sus will not fail me.
shall not from my Sav - ior move me, since he chose to love me.
still in you lies pur - est plea - sure, Je - sus, price - less trea - sure!

Words: Johann Franck, 1653; tr. Catherine Winkworth, 1863, P.D.
Music (GUD SKAL ALTING MAGE/LINDEMAN 6.6.5.6.6.5.7.8.6): Ludvig M. Lindeman (1812-1887), P.D.

My Faith Looks Up to Thee

426

1 My faith looks up to thee, thou Lamb of Cal - va - ry,
2 May thy rich grace im-part strength to my faint - ing heart,
3 While life's dark maze I tread and griefs a - round me spread,
4 When life's swift race is run, death's cold work al - most done,

Sav - ior di - vine! Now hear me while I pray, take all my
my zeal in - spire. As thou hast died for me, O may my
be thou my guide. Bid dark-ness turn to day, wipe sor - row's
be near to me. Blest Sav - ior, then in love fear and dis -

guilt a - way. O let me from this day be whol - ly thine!
love to thee, pure, warm, and change - less be, a liv - ing fire!
tears a - way, nor let me ev - er stray from thee a - side.
trust re - move. O bear me safe a - bove, re - deemed and free!

Optional prayer (based on Ps. 141:8; 2 Cor. 4:6)

Our eyes turn to you, O sovereign Lord;
in you we take refuge.
**By the illumining power of your Holy Spirit,
help us to see the light of the knowledge of your glory
in the face of Jesus Christ, our Lord and Savior. Amen.**

Words: Ray Palmer, 1830, alt., P.D.
Music (OLIVET 6.6.4.6.6.6.4): Lowell Mason, 1832, P.D.

427 How Firm a Foundation

ISAIAH 43:1-5

To use with Psalm 11: Sing st. 1, read Psalm 11:1-3, sing st. 2, read Ps. 11:4-7, sing st. 5

Words: Isaiah 43:1-5; J. Rippon's *Selection of Hymns*, 1787, alt., P.D.
Music (FOUNDATION 11.11.11.11): J. Funk's *A Compilation of Genuine Church Music*, 1832; harm. Dale
  Grotenhuis (1931-2012), 1985, © 1987 Faith Alive Christian Resources

O Lord, Be Our Refuge

428

PSALM 11

1 O Lord, be our refuge,
  when evils assail;
  your justice is sure,
  and your strength will prevail.
  Yet wicked ones rise,
  and the good are laid low.
  Your mercy reveal
  and your righteousness show.

2 O God, send your fire;
  come to judge humankind;
  our evil consume
  and our virtue refine.
  Then crowns of oppression
  will fall to the dust,
  and saints will delight
  in the reign of the just.

3 How firm a foundation we find in God's Word!
  We fashion our lives in the way of the Lord.
  When all else gives way, God's salvation remains;
  and even in death, God's great glory sustains.

For music see 427

Words: Michael Morgan and Martin Tel © 2011 Michael Morgan and Martin Tel, admin. Faith Alive Christian Resources

Don't Be Afraid

429

Words and Music (DON'T BE AFRAID): John L. Bell (b. 1949) © 1995 Wild Goose Resource Group, Iona Community, Scotland, GIA Publications, Inc., exclusive North American agent

430 You Are Mine

1 "I will come to you in the si-lence.
2 "I am hope for all who are hope-less,
3 "I am strength for all the de-spair-ing,
(4 "I) am the Word that leads all to free-dom.

I will lift you from____ all your fear.
I am eyes for all who long to see. In the
heal-ing for the ones who dwell in shame.
am the peace the world____ can-not give.

You will hear my voice. I claim you as my choice. Be
shad-ows of the night____ I will be your light.____
All the blind will see, the lame will all run free, and
I will call your name, em-brac-ing all your pain. Stand

still and know I am here. *To stanza 2*
Come and rest in__ me. *To Refrain*
all will know my__ name. *To Refrain*
up, now walk, and__ live! *To Refrain*

Words: David Haas (b. 1957) © 2005 GIA Publications, Inc.
Music (YOU ARE MINE irregular): David Haas (b. 1957) © 2005 GIA Publications, Inc.

431

The Lord Is My Light

PSALM 27:1, 5, 14

1 The Lord is my light and my__ sal - va - tion; the Lord is my
3 ‌ Wait on the Lord and be of good cour - age; oh, wait on the

light and my__ sal - va - tion; the Lord is my light and
Lord and be of good cour - age;__ wait on the Lord and

my__ sal - va - tion; whom__ shall I__ fear?
be of good cour - age; he shall strength - en thy heart.

Refrain

Whom shall I fear, whom shall I fear? The

For other settings of Ps. 27 see 773, 774, 885

Words: Lillian Bouknight © 1981 Peermusic III, Ltd. and Savgos Music, Inc., admin. Hal Leonard Corporation
Music (THE LORD IS MY LIGHT): Lillian Bouknight; arr. Paul Gainer © 1980 Peermusic III, Ltd. and Savgos
  Music, Inc., admin. Hal Leonard Corporation

Optional prayer in times of tragedy

God, our provider,
thank you for ancient songs
about your faithfulness in times of trouble.
Even when our hearts are numb,
strengthen us to sing your praise.
When our lips are unable to sing,
help us to hear the songs of others who sing on our behalf.
Even now, hide us in the shelter of your wings. **Amen.**

432 God Is Our Refuge and Our Strength

PSALM 46

1 God is our ref - uge and our strength, our ev - er - pres - ent aid,
2 A riv - er flows whose streams make glad the cit - y of our God,
3 The na - tions rage, the king - doms move, but when his voice is heard,
4 O come and see what won - drous works the hand of God has done;
5 "Be still and know that I am God, the LORD whom all must claim;

and there - fore, though the earth be moved, we will not be a - fraid—
the ho - ly place where - in the LORD Most High has his a - bode.
> earth melts with trem - bling fear be - fore the thun - der of his word.
come, see what de - so - la - tion great he brings be - neath the sun.
and ev - ery na - tion of the earth shall mag - ni - fy my name."

though hills in - to the seas be cast, though foam - ing wa - ters roar,
Since God is in the midst of her, un - moved her walls shall stand;
> The LORD of hosts is on our side, our safe - ty to se - cure;
In ev - ery cor - ner of the earth he caus - es wars to cease;
The LORD of hosts is on our side, our safe - ty to se - cure;

though all the might - y bil - lows shake the moun - tains on the shore.
for God will has - ten to her aid when trou - ble is at hand.
> the God of Ja - cob is for us a ref - uge strong and sure.
the wea - pons of the strong de - stroyed, he makes a - bid - ing peace.
the God of Ja - cob is for us a re - fuge strong and sure.

For another setting of Ps. 46 see 892

Words: *Scottish Psalter,* 1650, alt., P.D.
Music (GERARD/NOEL 8.6.8.6 D): English; adapt. Arthur S. Sullivan, 1874, P.D.

In God Alone

433

To use with Psalm 62: Sing the above before reading each of the following sections, Ps. 62:1-4, 5-6, 7-8, and 9-12 and then conclude with singing.

For other settings of Ps. 62 see 370, 435

Words: Psalm 62:1
Music (IN GOD ALONE): Jacques Berthier (1923-1994) © 1991 Ateliers et Presses de Taizé, Taizé Community,
France, GIA Publications, Inc., exclusive North American agent

Affirmation: My Only Comfort

434

What is your only comfort in life and in death?

**That I am not my own,
but belong—
body and soul,
in life and in death—
to my faithful Savior, Jesus Christ.**

**He has fully paid for all my sins
with his precious blood,
and has set me free
from the tyranny of the devil.**

**He also watches over me in such a way
that not a hair can fall from my head
without the will of my Father in heaven;
in fact, all things must work together
for my salvation.**

**Because I belong to him,
Christ, by his Holy Spirit,
assures me of eternal life
and makes me wholeheartedly
willing and ready
from now on to live for him.**

For a sung version of this text see 781
Text: Heidelberg Catechism Q&A 1

435 My Soul Finds Rest in God Alone

PSALM 62

1 My soul finds rest   in God a - lone;   on him   my help de - pends.
2 Find rest, my soul,   in God a - lone;   on him   my hope de - pends.
3 The great of earth   are less than dust;   all   mor - tal strength is vain.

God is my for - tress and my rock;   sal - va - tion sure he   sends.
God is my for - tress and my rock;   sal - va - tion sure he   sends.
And fools a - lone   re - ly on wealth or   prize ill - got - ten gain.

My foes   con - spire to bring me down; they scorn my trou - bled state.
My aid   and hon - or come from God,   my ref - uge strong and sure.
I   know,   O   God, that you are strong, a faith - ful, lov - ing Lord.

Their lips   are quick to sound   my praise, but in their hearts they hate.
Let   all   God's ser - vants trust   the LORD; in him we are   se - cure.
Our ev - ery deed, for good   or   ill, you sure - ly will re - ward.

Alternate tune: RESIGNATION *see 396*

For other settings of Ps. 62 see 370, 433

Words: David J. Diephouse, 1986, © 1987 Faith Alive Christian Resources
Music (THIRD MODE MELODY 8.6.8.6 D): Thomas Tallis, 1561, P.D.

How I Love You, Lord, My God

436

PSALM 18:1-6, 30-32

1 How I love you, Lord, my God, you, my rock and for - tress strong;
2 All God's prom - i - ses are sure. Who is God be - sides the Lord?

con - stant ref - uge, might - y shield— I will praise you in my song.
He is per - fect in his ways. Who the Rock ex - cept our God?

Snares of death en - tan - gled me; hell - ish tor - rents fright - ened me;
It is God who gives me strength; he en - a - bles me to stand

but you heard my des - perate cry, and your hand has set me free.
high a - bove the bat - tle - field, held up by his power - ful hand.

For another setting of Ps. 18 see 194

Words: Ada Roeper-Boulogne, 1985, © 1987 Faith Alive Chrsitian Resources
Music (ABERYSTWYTH 7.7.7.7 D): Joseph Parry (1841-1903); 1879, alt., P.D.

437

Day by Day

1 Day by day and with each pass-ing mo-ment, strength I
2 Ev-ery day the Lord him-self is near me, with a
3 Help me then in ev-ery trib-u-la-tion so to

find to meet my tri-als here; trust-ing in my Fa-ther's wise be-
spe-cial mer-cy for each hour; all my cares he glad-ly bears and
trust your prom-is-es, O Lord, that I lose not faith's sweet con-so-

stow-ment, I've no cause for wor-ry or for fear. He whose
cheers me, he whose name is Coun-sel-or and Power. The pro-
la-tion of-fered me with-in your ho-ly Word. Help me,

heart is kind be-yond all mea-sure gives un-to each
tec-tion of his child and trea-sure is a charge that
Lord, when toil and trou-ble meet-ing, e'er to take, as

Words: Carolina Sandell Berg (1865); tr. Andrew L. Skoog, 1931, alt. P.D.
Music (BLOTT EN DAG 10.9.10.9 D): Oscar Ahnfelt, 1872, P.D.

day what he deems best— lov-ing-ly, its part of pain and
on him-self he laid: "As your days, your strength shall be in
from a fa-ther's hand, one by one, the days, the mo-ments

plea-sure, min-gling toil with peace and rest.
mea-sure"— this the pledge to me he made.
fleet-ing, till I reach the prom-ised land.

Give to the Winds Your Fears 438

1 Give to the winds your fears; hope and be un-dis-mayed:
2 Why, heart, so heav-y still? Why, spir-it, so cast down?
3 Leave to God's sov-ereign sway to choose and to com-mand;
4 Let us in life and death, your stead-fast love de-clare,

God hears your sighs and counts your tears; God will lift up your head.
Bring ev-ery anx-ious thought to God, bid ev-ery fear be gone.
though won-dering, you will own God's way; how wise, how strong God's hand!
and pub-lish with our lat-est breath your love and guard-ian care.

To use with Psalm 109: Read Ps. 109:1-5, sing st. 1, read vv. 6-20, sing st. 2, read vv. 21-26, sing st. 3, read vv. 27-31, sing st. 4

For this music in a lower key see 632

Words: st. 1, 3, 4 Charles Wesley (1707-1788), alt., P.D.; st. 2 Martin Tel © 2011 Martin Tel, admin. Faith Alive Christian Resources
Music (GORTON 6.6.8.6): Ludwig van Beethoven, 1807, adapt., P.D.

439   I Love the Lord; He Heard My Cry

PSALM 116:1-2

1 I love the Lord; he heard my cry
2 I love the Lord; he heard my cry

and pit-ied ev - ery groan.
and chased my grief a - way.

Long as I live and trou-bles rise,
O let my heart no more des-pair

I'll has-ten to his throne.
while I have breath to pray.

For other settings of Ps. 116 see 152, 735, 819, 871

Words: Isaac Watts (1674-1748), P.D.
Music (I LOVE THE LORD; HE HEARD MY CRY 8.6.8.6): African American spiritual; harm. Richard Smallwood
  (b. 1948) © 1975 Century Oak Publishing Group / Richwood Music, admin. Conexion Media Group, Inc.;
  arr. Dave Maddux

He Leadeth Me

1 He lead-eth me: O bless-ed thought! O words with heaven-ly
2 Some-times mid scenes of deep-est gloom, some-times where E-den's
3 Lord, I would clasp thy hand in mine, nor ev-er mur-mur
4 And when my task on earth is done, when, by thy grace, the

com-fort fraught! What-e'er I do, wher-e'er I be, still 'tis God's
flow-ers bloom, by wa-ters calm, o'er trou-bled sea, still 'tis God's
nor re-pine; con-tent, what-ev-er lot I see, since 'tis my
vic-tory's won, e'en death's cold wave I will not flee, since God through

Refrain

hand that lead-eth me.
hand that lead-eth me.
God that lead-eth me.   He lead-eth me, he lead-eth me; by
Jor-dan lead eth me.

his own hand he lead-eth me: his faith-ful fol-lower

I would be, for by his hand he lead-eth me.

Words: Joseph H. Gilmore, 1862, P.D.
Music (AUGHTON/HE LEADETH ME 8.8.8.8 D): William B. Bradbury, 1864, P.D.

441 His Eye Is on the Sparrow

1 Why should I feel dis-cour-aged, why should the sha-dows
2 "Let not your heart be trou-bled," his ten-der word I
3 When-ev-er I am tempt-ed, when-ev-er clouds a-

come, why should my heart be lone-ly, and
hear, and rest-ing on his good-ness, I
rise; when songs give place to sigh-ing, when

long for heaven and home; when Je-sus is my
lose my doubts and fears; Though by the path he
hope with-in me dies, I draw the clos-er

por-tion? My con-stant Friend is he;
lead-eth, but one step I may see;
to him, from care he sets me free;

Words: Civilla D. Martin, P.D.
Music (SPARROW 7.6.7.6.7.6.7.7.7.7 refrain 7.6.8.7): Charles H. Gabriel; arr. Horace Clarence Boyer © 1982
Horace Clarence Boyer

442   Praise the Lord Who Heals

PSALM 147

1 Give thanks, for God is gracious.
2 The Lord consoles the grieving
3 Great is our God almighty;

For another setting of Ps. 147 see 549.

Words: Norman Agatep © 2010 Jesuit Communication Foundation, Inc.
Music (PRAISE THE LORD WHO HEALS 4.7.6.7 stanzas 7.6.7.6): Norman Agatep © 2010 Jesuit Communication Foundation, Inc.; arr. Joel Navarro © 2011 Joel Navarro, admin. Faith Alive Christian Resources

Sing out and lift your praise.
and heals their bit - ter pain.
God's wis - dom knows no bounds.

The Lord re - builds all na - tions
The stars in night sky shin - ing
The Lord sus - tains the low - ly

and gath - ers those a - stray.
the Lord calls each by name.
and casts the wick - ed out.

Optional concluding prayer

We worship you, O God,
builder, healer, counter of stars.
We sing praise to you,
O God, provider, delighter, protector of your people.
You give us life and joy through your Son.
By the power of your Spirit
may we never stop rejoicing in you. Amen.

443   My Life Flows On in Endless Song

1 My life flows on in end-less song; a-bove earth's lam-en-ta-tion,
2 Through all the tu-mult and the strife, I hear that mu-sic ring-ing.
3 What though my joys and com-forts die? The Lord my Sav-ior liv-eth.
4 The peace of Christ makes fresh my heart, a foun-tain ev-er spring-ing!

I catch the sweet, though far-off hymn that hails a new cre-a-tion.
It finds an ech-o in my soul. How can I keep from sing-ing?
What though the dark-ness gath-er round? Songs in the night he giv-eth.
All things are mine since I am his! How can I keep from sing-ing?

Refrain

No storm can shake my in-most calm while to that Rock I'm cling-ing.

Since Christ is Lord of heav-en and earth, how can I keep from sing-ing?

Words: Robert Lowry (1826-1899), P.D.
Music (HOW CAN I KEEP FROM SINGING 8.7.8.7 refrain 8.8.9.7): Robert Lowry, alt., P.D.

Nada te turbe/Nothing Can Trouble 444

Spanish Na - da te tur - be, na - da te_es - pan - te. Quien a Dios tie - ne
English Noth - ing can trou - ble, noth - ing can fright - en. Those who seek God shall

na - da le fal - ta. So - lo Dios bas - ta.
nev - er go want - ing. God a - lone fills us.

Words: The Community of Taizé © 1991 Ateliers et Presses de Taizé, Taizé Community, France, GIA Publica-
tions, Inc., exclusive North American agent
Music (NADA TE TURBE): Jacques Berthier (1923-1994) © 1991 Ateliers et Presses de Taizé, Taizé Community,
France, GIA Publications, Inc., exclusive North American agent

Stand, Oh, Stand Firm 445

Stand, oh, stand firm; stand, oh, stand firm;

stand, oh, stand firm and see what the Lord can do.

Words: traditional, P.D.
Music (STAND FIRM): origin unknown, Cameroon; arr. © 1990 Wild Goose Resource Group, Iona Community,
Scotland, GIA Publications, Inc., exclusive North American agent

446 We Cannot Measure How You Heal

1 We can-not meas-ure how you heal or an-swer
2 The pain that will not go a-way, the guilt that
3 So some have come who need your help and some have

ev-ery suf-ferer's prayer; yet we be-lieve your
clings from things long past, the fear of what the
come to make a-mends, as hands which shaped and

grace re-sponds where faith and doubt u-nite to care.
fu-ture holds, are pres-ent as if meant to last.
saved the world are pres-ent in the touch of friends.

Your hands, though blood-ied on the cross, sur-vive to
But pres-ent too is love, which tends the hurt we
Lord, let your Spir-it meet us here to mend the

Words: John L. Bell (b. 1949) © 1989 Wild Goose Resource Group, Iona Community, Scotland, GIA Publications, Inc., exclusive North American Agent
Music (YE BANKS AND BRAES 8.8.8.8 D): Scottish traditional; arr. Iona Community © 1989 Wild Goose Resource Group, Iona Community, Scotland, GIA Publications, Inc., exclusive North American Agent

hold and heal and warn, to car - ry all through
nev - er hoped to find, the pri - vate ag - o -
bod - y, mind, and soul, to dis - en - tan - gle

death to life and cra - dle chil - dren yet un - born.
nies in - side, the mem - o - ries that haunt the mind.
peace from pain, and make your bro - ken peo - ple whole.

A Prayer of Humility 447
PSALM 131

O LORD, my heart is not lifted up,
my eyes are not raised too high;
I do not occupy myself with things
too great and too marvelous for me.

Quiet

But I have calmed and quieted my soul,
like a weaned child with its mother;
my soul is like the weaned child that is with me.

Quiet

O Israel, hope in the LORD
from this time on and forevermore.

Quiet

Loving God,
even in times of turmoil,
give us grace to pray this Psalm.
When we are tempted
to speak out of arrogance,
help us learn the way of humility.
We cannot measure how you heal.
We cannot fathom the full depths of your love.
**Strengthened by your Spirit,
we place our hope and trust in you.
Amen.**

Consider using with 446.
For another setting of Ps. 131 see 335
Text: Psalm 131, NRSV

448   A Prayer: Our Times Are in Your Hands

Bless the LORD, O my soul,
and all that is within me,
bless his holy name.
Bless the LORD, O my soul,
and do not forget all his benefits.

Lord, remember us.
Our times are in your hands;
teach us to count our days.
Let your face shine upon us
and hold us in your steadfast love.
You note our laments;
you hold our tears in your bottle.
In you we trust and are not afraid.

For you know how we were made
and remember that we are dust.

Our days are like grass;
like flowers we bloom
and then fade away.
The wind blows and we are gone –
as though we had never been here.
But your steadfast love
is from everlasting to everlasting.
Your righteousness
extends to our children's children.

We bring before you those among us
whose lives are fading . . .

Lord, you know us completely.
You knit us together.
Our past, present, and future are in you.
Amen.

After the prayer, a soloist or the congregation may sing "When Memory Fades" 449.
Text: based on Psalm 103, 90, 56, 31, 139

449   When Memory Fades

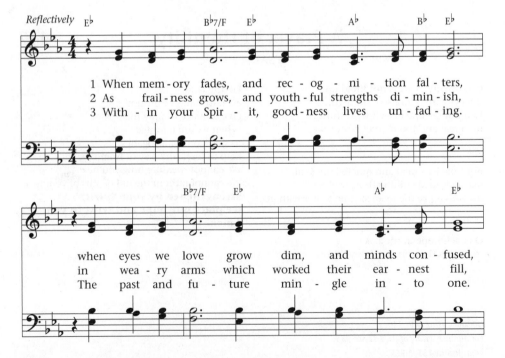

1 When mem-ory fades, and rec-og-ni-tion fal-ters,
2 As frail-ness grows, and youth-ful strengths di-min-ish,
3 With-in your Spir-it, good-ness lives un-fad-ing.

when eyes we love grow dim, and minds con-fused,
in wea-ry arms which worked their ear-nest fill,
The past and fu-ture min-gle in-to one.

For this music in a higher key see 685

speak to our souls of love that nev - er al - ters;
your ag - ing ser - vants la - bor now to fin - ish
All joys re - main, un - shad - owed light per - vad - ing.

speak to our hearts, by pain and fear a - bused.
their earth - ly tasks, as fits your mys - tery's will.
No val - ued deed will ev - er be un - done.

O God of life and heal - ing peace, em - power us
We grieve their wan - ing, yet re - joice, be - liev - ing,
Your mind en - folds all fi - nite acts and of - ferings.

with pa - tient cour - age, by your grace in - fused.
your arms, un - wea - ried, shall up - hold us still.
Held in your heart, our death - less life is won!

450 ## Neither Death nor Life

ROMANS 8:38-39

Nei-ther death nor life, nor an-gels, nor rul-ers, nor trials in the pres-ent, nor an-y trial to come; nei-ther height nor depth, nor all of cre-a-tion can ev-er sep-a-rate us from the love of God poured out in Christ Je-sus our Lord.

Words and Music (NEITHER DEATH): from Romans 8:38-39, Marty Haugen © 2001 GIA Publications, Inc.

When Peace like a River

451

1 When peace like a riv-er at-tend-eth my way, when
2 Though Sa-tan should buf-fet, though tri-als should come, let
3 My sin— oh, the bliss of this glo-ri-ous thought!— my
4 O Lord, haste the day when my faith shall be sight, the

sor-rows like sea bil-lows roll; what-ev-er my lot, thou hast taught
this blest as-sur-ance con-trol: that Christ has re-gard-ed my help-
sin, not in part, but the whole, is nailed to the cross, and I bear
clouds be rolled back as a scroll; the trump shall re-sound and the Lord

me to say, "It is well, it is well with my soul."
less es-tate, and has shed his own blood for my soul.
it no more; praise the Lord, praise the Lord, O my soul!
shall de-scend; e-ven so, it is well with my soul.

Refrain
It is well *it is*

well with my soul; *with my soul;* it is well, it is well with my soul.

Words: Horatio G. Spafford, 1873, P.D.
Music (VILLE DU HAVRE 11.8.11.9 refrain 6.9): Philip P. Bliss, 1876, P.D.

452 Pues si vivimos/When We Are Living

Unison

Spanish 1 Pues si vi - vi - mos pa - ra él vi - vi - mos
English 1 When we are liv - ing, it is in Christ Je - sus,
2 Through all our liv - ing, we our fruits must give.
3 'Mid times of sor - row and in times of pain,
4 A - cross this wide world, we shall al - ways find

y si mo - ri - mos pa - ra él mo - ri - mos.
and when we're dy - ing, it is in the Lord.
Good works of ser - vice and for of - fer - ing.
when sens - ing beau - ty or in love's em - brace,
those who are cry - ing with no peace of mind.

Sea que vi - va - mos o que mu - ra - mos,
Both in our liv - ing and in our dy - ing,
When we are giv - ing, or when re - ceiv - ing,
wheth - er we suf - fer, or sing re - joic - ing,
But when we help them, or when we feed them,

so - mos del Se - ñor, so - mos del Se - ñor.
we be - long to God, we be - long to God.

(continues)

Words: st. 1 Romans 14:8; traditional Mexican; st. 1 tr. Elise S. Eslinger © 1989 The United Methodist Publishing House, admin. The Copyright Company; sts. 2-4 Roberto Escamilla (b. 1931) © 1983 Abingdon Press; st. 2-4 tr. George Lockwood © 1989 The United Methodist Publishing House, admin. The Copyright Company
Music (SOMOS DEL SEÑOR): traditional Mexican

2 En esta vida, frutos hemos de dar
las obras buenas son para_ofrendar.
Ya sea que demos o que recibamos,
somos del Señor, somos del Señor.

3 En la tristeza y en el dolor,
en la belleza y en el amor,
sea que suframos o que gocemos
somos del Señor, somos del Señor.

4 En este mundo, hemos de_encontrar
gente que llora y sin consolar.
Sea que_ayudemos o que_alimentemos,
somos del Señor, somos del Señor.

How Sweet the Name of Jesus Sounds 453

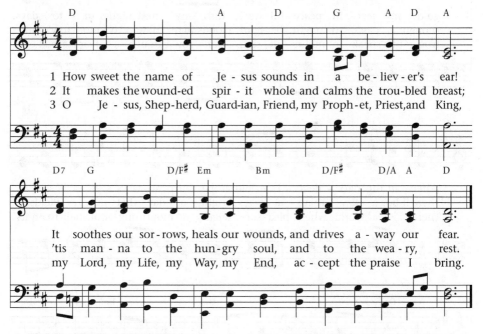

1 How sweet the name of Je - sus sounds in a be - liev - er's ear!
2 It makes the wound-ed spir - it whole and calms the trou-bled breast;
3 O Je - sus, Shep-herd, Guard-ian, Friend, my Proph-et, Priest, and King,

It soothes our sor - rows, heals our wounds, and drives a - way our fear.
'tis man - na to the hun-gry soul, and to the wea - ry, rest.
my Lord, my Life, my Way, my End, ac - cept the praise I bring.

4 How weak the effort of my heart,
how cold my warmest thought;
but when I see you as you are,
I'll praise you as I ought.

5 Till then I would your love proclaim
with every fleeting breath;
and may the music of your name
refresh my soul in death.

Words: John Newton, 1779, P.D.
Music (ST. PETER 8.6.8.6): Alexander R. Reinagle, 1836, P.D.

454 **Beams of Heaven**

hope, and soon from all life's grief and dan-ger I shall be free some-day.
night, and in its light the streets of glo-ry I shall be-hold some-day.
plains, and to that land of peace and glo-ry I want to go some-day.

Words: Charles A. Tindley (1851-1933), P.D.
Music (SOME DAY 7.7.7.7.8.8.9.6 refrain 8.8.9.7): Charles A. Tindley; harm. Dale Grotenhuis (1931-2012),
1985, © 1987 Faith Alive Christian Resources

I do not know how long 'twill be, nor what the fu-ture holds for me,

but this I know: if Je-sus leads me, I shall get home some-day.

Naming the Circumstances of Death and Dying Before God's Face 455

Every experience of death and dying is unique—in the circumstances surrounding the death and in the response of those who mourn. This prayer, which should be adapted for every circumstance, provides space for naming those situations, for asking for God's Spirit to heal in and through them, and for expressing deep trust in the promises of God's Word (e.g., Ps. 91).

God of all compassion,
to whom all hearts are open and all desires are known,
we gather today in the context of
[a long-expected death, an untimely death, a miscarriage, still birth, a violent death, a suicide, a death in military service, or other words appropriate to the occasion] . . .

So much of what we feel,
we can only haltingly put into words
the depths of our *[grief, pain, guilt, shame, or other words appropriate to the occasion]* . . .

Heal us we pray,
in the midst of our words and our silence.
Into our silence speak your Word,
so full of truth and grace.
Assure us that nothing in all creation
can separate us from your love for us
in Jesus Christ, our Lord. **Amen.**

Shepherd Me, O God

456

PSALM 23

For other settings of Ps. 23 see 368, 369, 732, 824

(stanza 5 on next page)

5 Sure - ly your kind - ness and mer - cy fol - low me all the

days of my life; I will dwell in the house of my

God for - ev - er - more.

Refrain Shep - herd me, O God, be - yond my wants, be - yond my fears, from

death in - to life.

O Love That Will Not Let Me Go

457

1 O love that will not let me go, I rest my wear-y
2 O light that fol-lowest all my way, I yield my flick-ering
3 O joy that seek-est me through pain, I can-not close my
4 O cross that lift-est up my head, I dare not ask to

soul in thee; I give thee back the life I owe, that
torch to thee; my heart re-stores its bor-rowed ray, that
heart to thee; I trace the rain-bow through the rain, and
fly from thee; I lay in dust life's glo-ry dead, and

in thine o - cean depths its flow may rich - er,
in thy sun - shine's blaze its day may bright - er,
feel the prom - ise is not vain that morn shall
from the ground there blos - soms red life that shall

ful - ler be.
fair - er be.
tear - less be.
end - less be.

Words: George Matheson, 1882, P.D.
Music (8.8.8.8.6): Christopher Miner © 1997 Christopher Miner Music

458 My Times Are in Your Hands

PSALM 31

Refrain

In you, Lord, I have taken refuge;
 let me never be put to shame;
 deliver me in your righteousness.
Turn your ear to me,
 come quickly to my rescue;
be my rock of refuge,
 a strong fortress to save me.
Since you are my rock and my fortress,
 for the sake of your name
 lead and guide me.

Keep me free from the trap
 that is set for me,
 for you are my refuge.
Into your hands I commit my spirit;
 deliver me, Lord, my faithful God.

Refrain

Be merciful to me, Lord, for I am in distress;
 my eyes grow weak with sorrow,
 my soul and body with grief.

(continues)

Words: AnnaMae Meyer Bush © 1982 AnnaMae Meyer Bush
Music (MARGARET 6.6.6.6): AnnaMae Meyer Bush © 1982 AnnaMae Meyer Bush; harm. Kathleen Hart
 Brumm (b. 1958) © 2000 Brummhart Publishing

My life is consumed by anguish
and my years by groaning;
my strength fails
because of my affliction,
and my bones grow weak.
Because of all my enemies,
I am the utter contempt of my neighbors
and an object of dread to my closest friends—
those who see me on the street flee from me.
I am forgotten as though I were dead;
I have become like broken pottery.

For I hear many whispering,
"Terror on every side!"
They conspire against me
and plot to take my life.

But I trust in you, Lord;
I say, "You are my God."
My times are in your hands;
deliver me from the hands of my enemies,
from those who pursue me.
Let your face shine on your servant;
save me in your unfailing love.

Refrain

How abundant are the good things
that you have stored up
for those who fear you,
that you bestow in the sight of all,
on those who take refuge in you.
In the shelter of your presence you hide them
from all human intrigues;
you keep them safe in your dwelling
from accusing tongues.
Praise be to the Lord,
for he showed me the wonders of his love
when I was in a city under siege.
In my alarm I said,
"I am cut off from your sight!"
Yet you heard my cry for mercy
when I called to you for help.

Love the Lord, all his faithful people!
The Lord preserves those who are true to him,
but the proud he pays back in full.
Be strong and take heart,
all you who hope in the Lord.

Refrain

Optional prayer in solidarity with the dying

God of all hope,
in life and in death, we belong to you.
As we gather before your face today,
we remember before you [name(s) of the dying].

Give *them* the grace to pray "into your hands I commit my spirit."
Give *them* the grace to pray "my times are in your hands."

By the power of your Holy Spirit,
let your face shine upon *them,*
and assure *them* that you
keep *them* safe in your dwelling.

By the power of your Holy Spirit,
teach us all to be strong and take heart,
as we hope in the Lord. Amen.

459 **Within the Shelter of the Lord**

PSALM 91

1 With - in the shel - ter of the Lord, at home in
2 Though bru - tal con - flicts scar the day, though name - less
3 God an - swers ev - ery cry for help; his love is

his un - fail - ing care, we trust in his e - ter - nal
per - ils fill the night, God's pres - ence calms our trou - bled
ours till jour - ney's end— how - ev - er long our lives may

strength to res - cue us from ev - ery snare: how
minds and puts our pri - mal fears to flight. When
be, on God's firm prom - ise we de - pend. Who

safe it is, this hid - ing - place be - neath his ev - er
sin per - sists and judg - ment falls, the true se - cur - i -
knows what dan - gers we are spared, since an - gels guard the

Words: Martin Leckebusch © 2006 Kevin Mayhew Ltd.
Music (YE BANKS AND BRAES 8.8.8.8 D): Scottish traditional; arr. Iona Community © 1989 Wild Goose
Resource Group, Iona Community, Scotland, GIA Publications, Inc., exclusive North American agent

last - ing wings; how strong a for - tress is our
ty is ours: pro - tect - ed by the Lord, we
way we take? And all who trust and love the

God, the Might - y One, the King of kings.
stand, be - yond the grasp of e - vil powers.
Lord he pledg - es nev - er to for - sake.

Our Eyes Are Turned

460

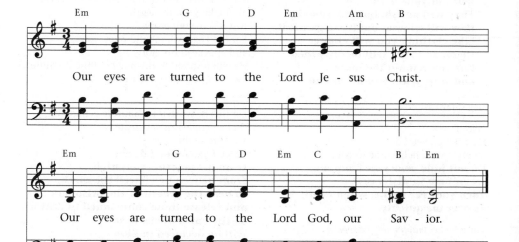

Our eyes are turned to the Lord Je - sus Christ.

Our eyes are turned to the Lord God, our Sav - ior.

Words and Music: The Community of Taizé and Jacques Berthier (1923-1994) © 1998 Ateliers et Presses de
Taizé, Taizé Community, France, GIA Publications, Inc., exclusive North American agent

461   A Litany for the Sick and Dying

PSALM 102

For use with "O Lord, Hear My Prayer" 462

Sing stanza 1

Voice 1:
Hear my prayer, LORD;
let my cry for help come to you.
Do not hide your face from me
when I am in distress.
Turn your ear to me; when I call,
answer me quickly.

Voice 2:
For my days vanish like smoke,
my bones burn like glowing embers.
My heart is blighted and withered like grass;
I forget to eat my food.

> *Optional: For those struck down or dying at*
> *a younger age:*
>
> *Voice 2:*
> In the course of my life he broke my
> strength; he cut short my days.
> So I said: "Do not take me away, my God,
> in the midst of my days;
> your years go on through all generations.
> **In the beginning you laid**
> **the foundation of the earth,**
> **and the heavens are the**
> **work of your hands.**
> **They will perish, but you remain;**
> **they will all wear out like a garment.**
> **Like clothing you will change**
> **them, and they will be discarded.**
> **But you remain the same,**
> **and your years will never end."**

Sing stanza 1

Voice 1:
Hear my prayer, LORD;
let my cry for help come to you.
Do not hide your face from me
when I am in distress.
Turn your ear to me; when I call,
answer me quickly.

This or other prayers may be spoken
Almighty God,
by your power Jesus Christ was raised
from death.
Watch over *[name]*.

Fill *his/her* eyes with your vision
to see, beyond human sight,
a home within your love,
where pain is gone
and frail flesh turns to glory.
Banish fear.
Brush tears away.
Let death be gentle as nightfall,
promising a day when songs of joy
shall make us glad
to be together with Jesus Christ,
who lives in triumph,
the Lord of life eternal. **Amen.**

After a period of silence, sing stanza 1

The psalm continues:

Voice 2:
My days are like the evening shadow;
I wither away like grass.
But you, LORD, sit enthroned forever;
your renown endures
through all generations.
You will arise
and have compassion on Zion,
for it is time to show favor to her;
the appointed time has come.

Voice 1:
The nations will fear the name of the LORD,
all the kings of the earth
will revere your glory.
For the LORD will rebuild Zion
and appear in his glory.
He will respond to the prayer of the destitute;
he will not despise their plea.

Voice 2:
Let this be written for a future generation,
that a people not yet created
may praise the LORD.
"The LORD looked down
from his sanctuary on high,
from heaven he viewed the earth,
to hear the groans of the prisoners
and release those condemned to death."
So the name of the LORD
will be declared in Zion
and his praise in Jerusalem
when the peoples and the kingdoms
assemble to worship the LORD.
Amen.

Sing stanza 2

O Lord, Hear My Prayer 462

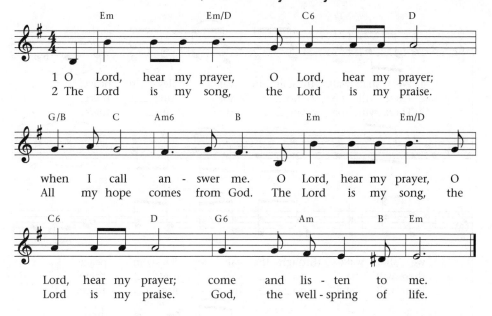

1 O Lord, hear my prayer, O Lord, hear my prayer;
2 The Lord is my song, the Lord is my praise.

when I call an - swer me. O Lord, hear my prayer, O
All my hope comes from God. The Lord is my song, the

Lord, hear my prayer; come and lis - ten to me.
Lord is my praise. God, the well - spring of life.

For four-part harmonization and accompaniment see 903

Words: Psalm 102:1-2; adapt. The Community of Taizé © 1991 Ateliers et Presses de Taizé, Taizé Community, France, GIA Publications, Inc., exclusive North American agent
Music (HEAR MY PRAYER 5.5.6 D): Jacques Berthier (1923-1994) © 1991 Ateliers et Presses de Taizé, Taizé Community, France, GIA Publications, Inc., exclusive North American agent

Affirmation: The Resurrection of the Body 463

How does "the resurrection of the body" comfort you?

**Not only will my soul
be taken immediately after this life
to Christ its head,
but also my very flesh will be
raised by the power of Christ,
reunited with my soul,
and made like Christ's glorious body.**

How does the promise of "life everlasting" comfort you?

**Even as I already now
experience in my heart
the beginning of eternal joy,
so after this life I will have
perfect blessedness such as
no eye has seen,
no ear has heard,
no human heart has ever imagined:
a blessedness in which to praise God forever.**

Text: Heidelberg Catechism Q&A 57-58

464   We Shall Walk Through the Valley in Peace

1 We shall walk through the val - ley in peace;
2 There will be no____ sor - row____ there;
3 There will be no____ dy - ing____ there;

we shall walk through the val - ley in peace.
there will be no____ sor - row____ there.
there will be no____ dy - ing____ there.

Refrain

If Je - sus him - self shall be our lead - er,

we shall walk through the val - ley in peace.

Chord symbols represent a simplified harmony.

Words: A. L. Hatter
Music (PEACEFUL VALLEY irregular): A. L. Hatter; arr. Joseph Joubert (b. 1958) © 2000 GIA Publications, Inc.

Precious Lord, Take My Hand

465

1 Pre-cious Lord, take my hand, lead me on, help me stand;
2 When my way grows drear, pre-cious Lord, lin-ger near;
3 When the dark-ness ap-pears and the night draws near,

I am tired, I am weak, I am worn; through the
when my life is al-most gone, hear my
when the day is past and gone, at the

storm, through the night, lead me on to the light;
cry, hear my call, hold my hand lest I fall;
riv-er I stand, guide my feet, hold my hand;

take my hand, pre-cious Lord, lead me home.

Words: Thomas A. Dorsey, 1938, © 1938, 1966, (ren.) Warner-Tamerlane Publishing Corp.
Music (PRECIOUS LORD irregular): George N. Allen, 1844; adapt. Thomas A. Dorsey, 1938, © 1938, 1966, (ren.) Warner-Tamerlane Publishing Corp, this arr. © 2012 Warner-Tamerlane Publishing Corp. Used by permission of Alfred Music Publishing Co., Inc.

466 Abide with Me

1 A - bide with me: fast falls the e - ven - tide; the dark - ness
2 Swift to its close ebbs out life's lit - tle day; earth's joys grow
3 I need thy pres - ence ev - ery pass-ing hour. What but thy

deep-ens; Lord, with me a - bide. When oth - er help-ers fail and
dim, its glo - ries pass a - way. Change and de - cay in all a -
grace can foil the tempt-er's power? Who like thy - self my guide and

com - forts flee, Help of the help - less, O a - bide with me.
round I see. O thou who chang-est not, a - bide with me.
stay can be? Through cloud and sun-shine, O a - bide with me.

4 I fear no foe with thee at hand to bless,
ills have no weight, and tears no bitterness.
Where is death's sting? Where, grave, thy victory?
I triumph still, if thou abide with me.

5 Hold thou thy cross before my closing eyes.
Shine through the gloom and point me to the skies.
Heaven's morning breaks and earth's vain shadows flee;
in life, in death, O Lord, abide with me.

Words: Henry F. Lyte, 1847, alt., P.D.
Music (EVENTIDE 10.10.10.10): William H. Monk, 1861, P.D.

O Christ, You Wept When Grief Was Raw   467

1 O Christ, you wept when grief was raw and felt for
2 The well-loved voice is si-lent now, and we have
3 We try to hold what is not here and fear for
4 In all our lone-li-ness and doubt, through what we

those who mourned their friend; come close to where we
much we meant to say; col-lect our lost and
what we do not know; O take our hands in
can-not re-al-ize, ad-dress us from your

would not be and hold us, numbed by this life's end.
wan-dering words and keep them till the end-less day.
yours, good Lord, and free us to let our friend go.
emp-ty tomb and tell us that life nev-er dies.

For a higher key see 871

Words: John L. Bell (b. 1949) and Graham Maule (b. 1958) © 1989, 1996 Wild Goose Resource Group, Iona
  Community, Scotland, GIA Publications, Inc., exclusive North American Agent
Music (ROCKINGHAM 8.8.8.8): *Second Supplement to Psalmody in Miniature,* ca. 1780; adapt. Edward Miller
  (1731-1807), 1790, P.D.

468   # I Will Rise

1 There's a peace I've come to know, though my
2 There's a day that's draw - ing near when this

heart and flesh may fail. There's an an - chor for my soul;
dark - ness breaks to light, and the sha - dows dis - ap - pear

I can say, "It is___ well." Je - sus has o - ver - come,
and my faith shall be my eyes.

Refrain

and the grave is o - ver - whelmed. The

vic-to-ry is won; he is ris-en from the dead.
And I will rise when he calls my name; no
more sor-row, no more pain. I will rise on ea-
-gles' wings, be-fore my God fall on my knees, and rise.
I will rise.

(continues)

469 # Swing Low, Sweet Chariot

Words and Music (SWING LOW 6.8.6.8 stanzas irregular): African American spiritual, P.D.

View the Present Through the Promise 470

1 View the pres-ent through the prom-ise, Christ will come a-gain.
2 Probe the pres-ent with the prom-ise, Christ will come a-gain.
3 Match the pres-ent to the prom-ise, Christ will come a-gain.

Trust de-spite the deep-ening dark-ness, Christ will come a-gain.
Let your dai-ly ac-tions wit-ness, Christ will come a-gain.
Make this hope your guid-ing prem-ise, Christ will come a-gain.

Lift the world a-bove its griev-ing through your watch-ing and be-liev-ing
Let your lov-ing and your giv-ing and your jus-tice and for-giv-ing
Pat-tern all your cal-cu-lat-ing and the world you are cre-a-ting

in the hope past hope's con-ceiv-ing: Christ will come a-gain.
be a sign to all the liv-ing: Christ will come a-gain.
to the ad-vent you are wait-ing: Christ will come a-gain.

Words: Thomas H. Troeger (b. 1945) © Oxford University Press Inc., 1986, assigned to Oxford University Press 2010, reproduced by permission
Music (FRANKLIN PARK 8.5.8.5.8.8.8.5): Roy Hopp (b. 1951) © 1997 Roy Hopp

471   Jesus Christ Is the Way

Words and Music (JESUS CHRIST IS THE WAY): Walter Hawkins © 1977 Bud John Music (BMI), admin.
EMICMIPublishing.com

472 O Morning Star, O Radiant Sun

1 O Morn - ing Star, O ra - diant Sun, when will our
2 Our lives are frail— a fleet - ing breath. We face our
3 O Sav - ior, rend the heav - ens wide; come down, come
4 There shall we all our prais - es bring ev - er to

hearts be - hold your dawn? O Sun, a - rise; with -
foe: the sting of death. Stretch out your hand, Lord,
down with might - y stride; un - lock the gates, the
you, our Sav - ior King; there shall we praise you

out your light we grope in gloom and dark of night.
hold us fast, un - til the storms of life are past.
doors break down; un - bar the way to heav - en's crown.
and a - dore for - ev - er and for - ev - er - more.

For use with Psalm 144: sing st. 1, read vv. 1-4, sing st. 2, read vv. 5-8, sing st. 3, read vv. 9-15, sing st. 4.

Words: st. 1, 3, 4, F. von Spee (1591-1635); tr. M. L. Seltz (1909-1967); st. 2 Martin Tel © 2011 Martin Tel, admin. Faith Alive Christian Resources
Music (O HEILAND, REISS DIE HIMMEL AUF 8.8.8.8): *Gesangbuch*, Augsburg, 1666; harm. Dale Grotenhuis (1931-2012), 1985, © 1987 Faith Alive Christian Resources

Come, You Thankful People, Come

473

1 Come, you thank-ful peo-ple, come, raise the song of har-vest home;
2 All the world is God's own field, fruit un-to his praise to yield;
3 For the Lord our God shall come and shall take his har-vest home;
4 E-ven so, Lord, quick-ly come to your fi-nal har-vest home;

all is safe-ly gath-ered in ere the win-ter storms be-gin;
wheat and weeds to-geth-er sown, un-to joy or sor-row grown:
he him-self in that great day all of-fense shall take a-way,
gath-er all your peo-ple in, free from sor-row, free from sin

God, our Mak-er, does pro-vide for our needs to be sup-plied;
first the blade and then the ear, then the full corn shall ap-pear;
give his an-gels charge at last in the fire the weeds to cast,
there, for-ev-er pu-ri-fied, in your pres-ence to a-bide;

come, with all his peo-ple come, raise the song of har-vest home.
Lord of har-vest, grant that we whole-some grain and pure may be.
but the fruit-ful ears to store in his gar-ner ev-er-more.
come, with all your an-gels come, raise the glo-rious har-vest home.

Words: Henry Alford, 1844, alt., P.D.
Music (ST. GEORGE'S WINDSOR 7.7.7.7 D): George J. Elvey, 1858, P.D.

474 **Sing to the King**

1 Sing to the King who is com - ing to reign.
2 For his re - turn - ing we watch and we pray;

Glo - ry to Je - sus, the Lamb that was slain.
we will be read - y the dawn of that day.

Life and sal - va - tion his em - pire shall bring, and
We'll join in sing - ing with all the re - deemed, 'cause

joy to the na - tions when Je - sus is King.
Sa - tan is van - quished and Je - sus is King.

Words and Music (SING TO THE KING): Billy Foote © 2003 worshiptogether.com Songs (ASCAP) / sixsteps Music (ASCAP), admin. EMICMGPublishing.com

475 When the King Shall Come Again

ISAIAH 35

1 When the King shall come a-gain, all his power re-veal-ing,
2 In the des-ert trees take root, fresh from his cre-a-tion;
3 Strength-en fee-ble hands and knees, faint-ing hearts be cheer-ful!
4 There God's high-way shall be seen where no roar-ing li-on,

splen-dor shall an-nounce his reign, life and joy and heal-ing;
plants and flowers and sweet-est fruit join the cel-e-bra-tion;
God, who comes for such as these, seeks and saves the fear-ful;
noth-ing e-vil or un-clean walks the road to Zi-on;

earth no long-er in de-cay, hope no more frus-tra-ted;
riv-ers spring up from the earth, bar-ren lands a-dorn-ing;
deaf ears, hear the si-lent tongues sing a-way their weep-ing;
ran-somed peo-ple, home-ward bound, all your prais-es voic-ing,

this is God's re-demp-tion day long-ing-ly a-wait-ed.
val-leys, this is your new birth; moun-tains greet the morn-ing!
blind eyes, see the life-less ones walk-ing, run-ning, leap-ing.
see your Lord with glo-ry crowned; share in his re-joic-ing!

Words: from Isaiah 35; Christopher Idle (b. 1938) © 1982 The Jubilate Group, admin. Hope Publishing Company
Music (GAUDEAMUS PARITER/AVE VIRGO VIRGINUM 7.6.7.6 D): Bohemian Brethren's *Gesangbuch*, 1544, P.D.

The King Shall Come When Morning Dawns 476

1 The King shall come when morn - ing dawns and
2 not, as of old, a lit - tle child, to
3 Oh, bright - er than the ris - ing morn when

light tri - um - phant breaks, when beau - ty gilds the
bear and fight and die, but crowned with glo - ry
Christ, vic - to - rious, rose and left the lone - some

east - ern hills and life to joy a - wakes
like the sun that lights the morn - ing sky.
place of death, de - spite the rage of foes—

4 oh, brighter than that glorious morn
shall dawn upon our race
the day when Christ in splendor comes
and we shall see his face.

5 The King shall come when morning dawns
and light and beauty brings.
Hail, Christ the Lord! Your people pray:
come quickly, King of kings.

For an alternate arrangement see 132

Words: Greek; tr. John Brownlie, 1907, alt., P.D.
Music (MORNING SONG 8.6.8.6): J. Wyeth's *Repository of Sacred Music,* 1813; harm. Jack Grotenhuis, 1983,
© 1987 Faith Alive Christian Resources

477   # Rejoice, Rejoice, Believers

1 Rejoice, rejoice, believers, and let your lights appear;
the evening is advancing, and darker night is near.
The Bridegroom is arising and soon is drawing nigh.
Up, pray and watch and wrestle; at midnight comes the cry.

2 The watchers on the mountain proclaim the Bridegroom near;
go forth as he approaches, with alleluias clear.
The marriage feast is waiting; the gates wide open stand.
Arise, O heirs of glory; the Bridegroom is at hand.

3 The saints, who here in patience their cross and sufferings bore,
shall live and reign forever when sorrow is no more.
Around the throne of glory the Lamb they shall behold;
in triumph cast before him their diadems of gold.

4 Our hope and expectation, O Jesus, now appear;
arise, O Sun so longed for, o'er this benighted sphere.
With hearts and hands uplifted, we plead, O Lord, to see
the day of earth's redemption that sets your people free!

Words: Laurentius Laurenti, 1700, tr. Sarah Borthwick Findlater, 1854, alt., *The Hymnal*, 1982, P.D.
Music (HAF TRONES LAMPA FÄRDIG 7.6.7.6 D): Swedish; arr. Henry V. Gerike (b. 1948) © 2006 Concordia
  Publishing House

Hark! A Thrilling Voice Is Sounding

478

1 Hark! A thrill-ing voice is sound-ing! "Christ is
2 Star-tled at the sol-emn warn-ing, from the
3 See, the Lamb so long ex-pect-ed comes with

near," we hear it say. "Cast a-way the
dark-ness we a-rise; Christ, our sun, all
par-don down from heaven. Let us haste, with

works of dark-ness, all you chil-dren of the day!"
ill dis-pel-ling, shines up-on the morn-ing skies.
tears of sor-row, one and all, to be for-given;

4 so when next he comes in glory
and the world is wrapped in fear,
he will shield us with his mercy
and with words of love draw near.

5 Honor, glory, might, dominion
to the Father and the Son,
with the everliving Spirit
while eternal ages run.

Optional readings
(1 Thess. 3:11-13; Phil. 3:20-21)

May the Lord make your love increase and
overflow for each other and for everyone else,
just as ours does for you.
May he strengthen your hearts
so that you will be blameless and holy
in the presence of our God and Father
when our Lord Jesus comes
with all his holy ones.

Our citizenship is in heaven.
And we eagerly await a Savior from there,
the Lord Jesus Christ,
**who, by the power that enables him
to bring everything under his control,
will transform our lowly bodies
so that they will be like his glorious
body.**

Words: Latin, ca. 6th c.; tr. *Hymns Ancient and Modern,* 1861, alt., P. D.
Music (MERTON 8.7.8.7): William H. Monk, 1850, P.D.

479 Lo! He Comes, with Clouds Descending

1 Lo! he comes, with clouds descending, once for
2 Now redemption, long expected, comes in
3 Those dear tokens of his passion still his
4 Yea, amen! let all adore thee, high on

our salvation slain; thousand thousand
solemn splendor near; all the saints this
dazzling body bears, cause of endless
thine eternal throne; Savior, take the

saints attending swell the triumph of his train:
world rejected thrill the trumpet sound to hear:
ex-ultation to his ransomed worshipers;
power and glory, claim the kingdom for thine own:

Alleluia! Alleluia! Alle-
Alleluia! Alleluia! Alle-
with what rapture, with what rapture, with what
O come quickly! O come quickly! O come

Words: Charles Wesley, 1758, P.D.
Music (HELMSLEY 8.7.8.7.4.4.4.7): attr. Augustine Arne; adapt. Thomas Olivers, 1763, P.D.

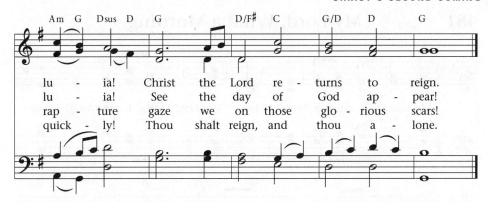

lu - ia! Christ the Lord re - turns to reign.
lu - ia! See the day of God ap - pear!
rap - ture gaze we on those glo - rious scars!
quick - ly! Thou shalt reign, and thou a - lone.

Optional readings (Rev. 1:4b-8)

Grace and peace to you
from him who is, and who was,
and who is to come,
and from the seven spirits before his throne,
and from Jesus Christ,
who is the faithful witness,
the firstborn from the dead,
and the ruler of the kings of the earth.
To him who loves us
and has freed us from our sins by his blood,
and has made us to be a kingdom and priests
to serve his God and Father—
to him be glory and power for ever and ever!
Amen.

"Look, he is coming with the clouds,"
and "every eye will see him,
even those who pierced him";
and all peoples on earth
"will mourn because of him."
So shall it be! Amen.

"I am the Alpha and the Omega,"
says the Lord God,
"who is, and who was,
and who is to come, the Almighty."
Amen and Amen!

Wait for the Lord   480

Em   C   Am6   B

Wait   for   the Lord,   whose day   is   near.

Em   D   G   Am7   B   Em

Wait   for   the Lord;   be strong,   take   heart!

To use with Psalm 37: sing the above, read vv. 1-5, sing, read vv. 6-9, sing, read vv. 10-11, 39-40, sing.

For another setting of Ps. 37 see 850

Words and Music (WAIT FOR THE LORD 8.8): Jacques Berthier, from *Songs and Prayers* from Taizé © 1991
Ateliers et Presses de Taizé, Taizé Community, admin. GIA Publications, Inc., exclusive North American agent

481 # My Lord, What a Morning

In the oral tradition this has been received as morning, mourning, or moaning.

Words: African American spiritual, P.D.
Music (WHAT A MORNING 8.8.7.7 refrain 6.6.7.7): African American spiritual; arr. Melva Costen © 1990
  Melva Costen

Soon and Very Soon

1,4 Soon and ver - y soon, we are going to see the King!
2 No more cry - ing there— we are going to see the King!
3 No more dy - ing there— we are going to see the King!

Soon and ver - y soon, we are going to see the King!
No more cry - ing there— we are going to see the King!
No more dy - ing there— we are going to see the King!

Soon and ver - y soon, we are going to see the King!
No more cry - ing there— we are going to see the King!
No more dy - ing there— we are going to see the King!

Hal - le - lu - jah! Hal - le - lu - jah! We're going to see the King!

Optional interlude and final ending

Hal - le - lu - jah! Hal - le - lu - jah!

Words and Music (SOON AND VERY SOON 12.12.12.14): Andraé Crouch (b. 1945) © 1976 Bud John Songs (ASCAP), Crouch Music (ASCAP), admin. EMICMGPublishing.com

483   # Come, We that Love the Lord

Words: Isaac Watts (1673-1748); ref. Robert Lowry (1826-1899), P.D.
Music (MARCHING TO ZION 6.6.8.8.6.6 refrain 6.8.8.8): Robert Lowry (1826-1899)

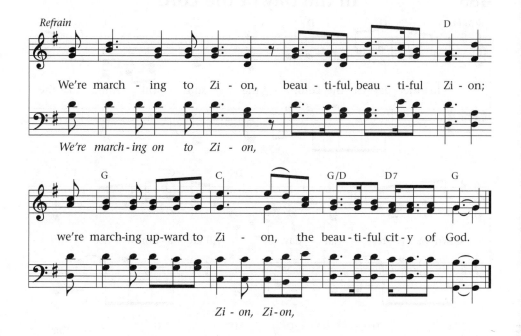

Refrain

We're march - ing to Zi - on, beau - ti-ful, beau - ti-ful Zi - on;

We're march - ing on to Zi - on,

we're march-ing up-ward to Zi - on, the beau - ti-ful cit - y of God.

Zi - on, Zi - on,

Affirmation: Come, Lord Jesus 484

We long for that day
when our bodies are raised,
the Lord wipes away our tears,
and we dwell forever
in the presence of God.
We will take our place in the new creation,
where there will be no more death
or mourning or crying or pain,
and the Lord will be our light.
Come, Lord Jesus, come.

On that day
we will see our Savior face to face,
sacrificed Lamb and triumphant King,
just and gracious.
He will set all things right,
judge evil, and condemn the wicked.
We face that day without fear,
for the Judge is our Savior,
whose shed blood declares us righteous.
We live confidently,
anticipating his coming,
offering him our daily lives—

our acts of kindness,
our loyalty, and our love—
knowing that he will weave
even our sins and sorrows
into his sovereign purpose.
Come, Lord Jesus, come.

With the whole creation
we join the song:
**"Worthy is the Lamb, who was slain,
to receive power and wealth
and wisdom and strength
and honor and glory and praise!"**
He has made us a kingdom of priests
to serve our God,
and we will reign on earth.
God will be all in all,
righteousness and peace will flourish,
everything will be made new,
and every eye will see at last
that our world belongs to God.
Hallelujah! Come, Lord Jesus!

Text: from stanzas 56, 57, 58, *Our World Belongs to God*

485   # In the Day of the Lord

Words: based on Isaiah 2, 25, 41; M.D. Ridge © 1992, 2006, M.D. Ridge, admin. by OCP Publications
Music (IN THE DAY OF THE LORD): M.D. Ridge © 1992, 2006, M.D. Ridge, admin. by OCP Publications;
arr. Randall DeBruyn (b. 1947) © 1992, 2006, M.D. Ridge, admin. by OCP Publications

day   will   all   be   free: free from   want,   free   from
moun - tain   of   the   Lord: they shall   walk   in   the
be   an   end   to   war: one   in   peace,   one   in
des -   ert   lands will   bloom.   Say   to   all,   "Do   not

fear, ____   free   to   live!   *free*   *to*   *live!*
light ____   of   the   Lord!   *of*   *the*   *Lord!*
love, ____   one   in   God!   *one*   *in*   *God!*
fear. Here   is   your   God!"   *is*   *your*   *God!"*

5 And on that day of Christ in glory,
   God will wipe away our tears,
   and the dead
       shall rise up from their graves!
   Refrain

6 O, give us eyes to see your glory,
   give us hearts to understand.
   Let our ears
       hear your voice 'til you come!
   Refrain

A New Heaven and Earth

486

REVELATION 21:1-4

Then I saw "a new heaven and a new earth,"
for the first heaven and the first earth had passed away,
and there was no longer any sea.
I saw the Holy City, the new Jerusalem,
coming down out of heaven from God,
prepared as a bride beautifully dressed for her husband.
And I heard a loud voice from the throne saying,
"Look! God's dwelling place is now among the people,
and he will dwell with them.

They will be his people,
and God himself will be with them and be their God.
'He will wipe every tear from their eyes.
There will be no more death'
 or mourning or crying or pain,
for the old order of things has passed away."
Alleluia! Amen. Come, Lord Jesus.

487 O Day of Peace

1 O day of peace that dim-ly shines through all our
2 Then shall the wolf dwell with the lamb, nor shall the

hopes and prayers and dreams, guide us to jus-tice, truth, and love, de-
fierce de-vour the small; as beasts and cat-tle calm-ly graze, a

liv-ered from our self-ish schemes. May swords of hate fall from our
lit-tle child shall lead them all. Then en-e-mies shall learn to

hands, our hearts from en-vy find re-lease, till by God's
love, all crea-tures find their true ac-cord; the hope of

grace our war-ring world shall see Christ's prom-ised reign of peace.
peace shall be ful-filled, for all the earth shall know the Lord.

Words: Carl P. Daw Jr (b. 1944) © 1982 Hope Publishing Company
Music (GRACE 8.8.8.8 D): Estelle White (b. 1925) © 1976 Kevin Mayhew Ltd.

Jerusalem the Golden

1 Je - ru - sa - lem the gold - en, de - scend - ing from a - bove,
2 They stand, those halls of Zi - on, all ju - bi - lant with song,
3 There is the throne of Da - vid, and there, from pain re - leased,
4 How love - ly is that cit - y, the home of God's e - lect!

the cit - y of God's pres - ence, the vi - sion of God's love—
so bright with man - y an an - gel and all the mar - tyr throng.
the shout of those who tri - umph, the song of those who feast.
How beau - ti - ful the coun - try that ea - ger hearts ex - pect!

I know not, oh, I know not what joys a - wait us there,
The Prince is ev - er in them, the day - light is se - rene;
And all who with their lead - er have con - quered in the fight,
O Christ, in mer - cy bring us to that e - ter - nal shore

what ra - dian - cy of glo - ry, what bliss be - yond com - pare!
the tree of life and heal - ing has leaves of rich - est green.
for - ev - er and for - ev - er are robed in pur - est white.
where Fa - ther, Son, and Spir - it are wor - shiped ev - er - more.

Words: Bernard of Cluny, 12th c.; tr. John M. Neale, 1858, alt., P.D.
Music (EWING 7.6.7.6 D): Alexander Ewing, 1853, P.D.

489 By the Sea of Crystal

REVELATION 4-5

1 By the sea of crys - tal saints in glo - ry stand,
2 Out of trib - u - la - tion, death, and Sa - tan's hand,
3 "Un - to God Al - might - y, sit - ting on the throne,

myr - i - ads in num - ber, drawn from ev - ery land.
they have been trans - lat - ed at the Lord's com - mand.
and the Lamb, vic - to - rious, be the praise a - lone."

Robed in white ap - par - el, washed in Je - sus' blood,
In their hands they're hold - ing palms of vic - to - ry.
God has wrought sal - va - tion; he did won - drous things.

they now reign in heav - en with the Lamb of God.
Hark! the ju - bilant cho - rus shouts tri - um - phant - ly:
Who shall not ex - tol thee, ho - ly King of kings!

Words: William Kuipers, 1933, based on Revelation 4-5, © 1976 Faith Alive Christian Resources
Music (CRYSTAL 6.5.6.5 D): John Vanderhoven, 1933, © 1976 Faith Alive Christian Resources

Here from All Nations

490

REVELATION 7:9-17

1 Here from all na - tions, all tongues, and all peo - ples,
2 These have come out of the great trib - u - la - tion;
3 Gone is their thirst and no more shall they hun - ger;

count - less the crowd but their voic - es are one.
now they may stand in the pres - ence of God,
God is their shel - ter, his power at their side.

Vast is the sight and ma - jes - tic their sing - ing:
serv - ing their Lord day and night in his tem - ple,
Sun shall not pain them, no burn - ing will tor - ture;

"God has the vic - tory: he reigns from the throne!"
ran - somed and cleansed by the Lamb's pre - cious blood.
Je - sus the Lamb is their shep - herd and guide.

4 He will go with them to clear living water
   flowing from springs
      which his mercy supplies.
   Gone is their grief,
      and their trials are over.
   God wipes away every tear from their eyes.

5 Blessing and glory and
      wisdom and power
   be to the Savior again and again.
   Might and thanksgiving
      and honor forever
   be to our God: Alleluia! Amen.

Words: from Revelation 7:9-17; Christopher Idle (1972) © 1973 The Jubilate Group, admin. Hope Publishing Company
Music (O QUANTA QUALIA 11.10.11.10): *Antiphoner,* Paris, 1681; harm. John B. Dykes (1823-1876), 1868, P.D.

491 Hallelujah, Salvation, and Glory

Part 1

Hal-le-lu - jah, sal - va-tion and glor-y, hon-or, and power un-to the

Lord our God. For the Lord our God is might - y. Yes, the

Lord our God is om-ni-po-tent. The Lord our God, he is won - der - ful.

Part 2

All prais - es be to the King of kings and the

Lord of Lords. He is won - der - ful!

Part 3

Hal - le - lu - jah, hal - le - lu - jah, hal-le-lu - jah, hal-le-

lu - jah, hal - le-lu - jah, hal - le - lu - jah, he is won - der-ful!

Accompaniment pattern to be repeated as desired

(*last time*)

Traditionally Part 1, 2, and 3 are each sung individually. Then they are layered starting with Part 1, and then adding Parts 2 and 3.

Words: from Rev. 19, Jeffrey LaValley © 1984 Candied Jamm Music/Savgos Music (BMI)
Music (HALLELUJAH, SALVATION, AND GLORY): Jeffrey La Valley Music © 1984 Candied Jamm Music/Savgos Music (BMI)

Worshiping the Triune God

Worshiping the Triune God

Come, Thou Almighty King

492

1 Come, thou al-might-y King, help us thy
2 Come, thou in-car-nate Word, gird on thy
3 Come, ho-ly Com-fort-er, thy sa-cred
4 To thee, great One in Three, e-ter-nal

name to sing; help us to praise.
might-y sword; scat-ter thy foes.
wit-ness bear in this glad hour.
prais-es be hence ev-er-more!

Fa-ther all-glo-ri-ous, o'er all vic-to-ri-ous,
Let thine al-might-y aid our sure de-fense be made,
Thou who al-might-y art, rule now in ev-ery heart,
Thy sov-ereign maj-es-ty may we in glo-ry see,

come and reign o-ver us, An-cient of Days.
our souls on thee be stayed; thy won-ders show.
and ne'er from us de-part, Spir-it of power.
and to e-ter-ni-ty love and a-dore.

Words: anonymous, 1757, alt., P.D.
Music (ITALIAN HYMN 6.6.4.6.6.6.4): Felice de Giardini, 1769, P.D.

493   Cantai ao Senhor/O Sing to the Lord

Portuguese 1 Can-tai ao Sen - hor um cân-ti-co no-vo. Can-
English 1 Oh, sing to the Lord, oh, sing God a new song. Oh,
2 Oh, shout to our God, who gave us the Spir-it. Oh,
3 For Je-sus is Lord! A-men! Al-le-lu-ia! For

tai ao Sen - hor um cân-ti-co no-vo. Can-
sing to the Lord, oh, sing God a new song. Oh,
shout to our God, who gave us the Spir-it. Oh,
Je-sus is Lord! A-men! Al-le-lu-ia! For

tai ao Sen-hor um cân-ti-co no-vo. Can-tai ao Sensing to the Lord, oh, sing God a new song. Oh, sing to our
shout to our God, who gave us the Spir-it. Oh, sing to our
Je-sus is Lord! A-men! Al-le-lu-ia! Oh, sing to our

hor; can - tai ao Sen - hor!
God, oh, sing to our God!
God, oh, sing to our God!
God, oh, sing to our God!

(continues)

Performance note: a tambourine or other percussive instrument can be used to keep the steady quarter note beat.
The left hand accompaniment can also be played as a quarter note pattern throughout.

Words: Brazilian (Portuguese) folk hymn based on Psalm 98; Sp. and Eng. tr. Gerhard M. Cartford (b. 1923)
Music (CANTAI AO SENHOR 5.6.5.6.5.6.5.5): Brazilian folk hymn; arr. Joel Navarro © 2012 Joel Navarro,
   admin. Faith Alive Christian Resources

Portuguese

2 É ele quem dá o Espirito Santo,
É ele quem dá o Espirito Santo,
É ele quem dá o Espirito Santo,
cantai ao Senhor, cantai ao Senhor!

3 Jesus é o Senhor! Amén, aleluia!
Jesus é o Senhor! Amén, aleluia!
Jesus é o Senhor! Amén, aleluia!
cantai ao Senhor, cantai ao Senhor!

Spanish

1 Cantad al Señor un cántico nuevo.
Cantad al Señor un cántico nuevo.
Cantad al Señor un cántico nuevo.
¡Cantad al Señor, cantad al Se-ñor!

2 Es él que nos da el_Espírtu Santo.
Es él que nos da el_Espírtu Santo.
Es él que nos da el_Espírtu Santo.
¡Cantad al Señor, cantad al Señor!

3 ¡Jesús es Señor! ¡Amén, aleluya!
¡Jesús es Señor! ¡Amén, aleluya!
¡Jesús es Señor! ¡Amén, aleluya!
¡Cantad al Señor, cantad al Señor!

A Greeting and Call to Worship   494

The grace of the Lord Jesus Christ be with you all.
And also with you!

Our help is in the name of the Lord,
the maker of heaven and earth.

OPENING PRAYER

Almighty God,
to whom all hearts are open
and all desires known,
and from whom no secrets are hid:
cleanse the thoughts of our hearts
by the inspiration of our Holy Spirit,
that we may perfectly love you,
and worthily magnify your holy name,
through Christ our Lord. Amen.

Or

God of grace,
whom saints and angels
delight to worship in heaven,
even as we gather before your face,
may your will be done on earth
as it is in heaven.
By the power of your Spirit,
help us to lift up our hearts in praise,
to receive your lavish gifts
stored up for us in Christ,
and to live as your faithful children
and witnesses,
through Jesus Christ, our Lord. Amen.

495 Come, All You People, Praise Our God

PSALM 66

1 Come, all you peo - ple, praise our God and tell his glo - rious
2 We come with of - ferings to God's house, and here we pay the
3 Come, lis - ten, all who fear the Lord, while I with grate - ful

works a - broad, who holds our souls in life;
sol - emn vows we ut - tered in dis - tress;
heart re - cord what God has done for me;

who nev - er lets our feet be moved and, though our faith has
to him our all we ded - i - cate, to him we whol - ly
I cried to him in deep dis - tress, and now his won - drous

of - ten proved, up - holds us in the strife.
con - se - crate the lives his mer - cies bless.
grace I bless, for he has set me free.

Chord symbols represent a simplified harmony.

For another setting of Ps. 66 see 496

Words: *Psalter,* 1912, P.D.
Music (ADOWA 8.8.6 D): Charles H. Gabriel, (1856-1932), P.D.

Uyai mose/Come, All You People

496

PSALM 66

For another setting of Ps. 66 see 495

Words: st. 1 Alexander Gondo (20th c., Zimbabwe), tr. I-to Loh (b. 1936) © 1986 World Council of Churches; st. 2-3 from *With One Voice*, 1995, © Augsburg Fortress
Music (UYAI MOSE 5.6.5.6.5.6.7): Alexander Gondo © 1986 World Council of Churches; arr. John L. Bell (b. 1949) © 1993 Wild Goose Resource Group, Iona Community, Scotland, GIA Publications, Inc., exclusive North American agent

497

Our Help

PSALM 124:8

Feel as a slow 2 beats per measure

1 Our help is in the name of the Lord,
(2 Our) help is in the name of the Lord,

who made the heavens, who made the earth.
who made the heavens, who made the earth.

A shel - ter from the cold and wear - ing storm,
The liv - ing hope that gives the blind - ed sight.

pro - tect - or of my heart, my home.
I rest up - on your strength and might.

For other settings of Ps. 124 see 498, 517

Words: Paul Thé © 2007 Votum Publishing, admin. Faith Alive Christian Resources
Music (OUR HELP): Paul Thé © 2007 Votum Publishing, admin. Faith Alive Christian Resources; arr. Eelco Vos,
alt. © 2011 Votum Publishing, admin. Faith Alive Christian Resources

You are the ev-er-last-ing glo-ry of the un-i-verse,

Refrain
and I have come to wor-ship, to sing,

to fall be-fore my King, to lift my hands

in praise. To you a-lone I raise my

voice in wor-ship. 2 Our

498 Our Help Is in the Name of God the LORD

PSALM 124

1 Our help is in the name of God the LORD; the one who
2 When e-vil seems to have the up-per hand, call on God's
3 Praise God the LORD who hears the cap-tives' prayer; like birds es-

made the heav-ens with a word; Cre - a - tor of the
name: the LORD, the great "I AM." When trou-bles rise and
cap - ing from the fowl-er's snare, we are set free; our

world, each liv - ing thing. Come, bless the LORD, lift up your
all a - round gives way, re - mem - ber God stays with us
prais - es now as - cend: "Blessed be the LORD: Cre - a - tor,

hearts and sing: "Our help is in the name of God the LORD."
night and day. Our help is in the name of God the LORD.
Sav - ior, Friend. Our help is in the name of God the LORD."

Chord symbols represent a simplified harmony.
For other settings of Ps. 124 see 497, 517

Words: Martin Tel © 2011 Martin Tel, admin. Faith Alive Christian Resources
Music (GENEVAN 124/OLD 124TH 10.10.10.10.10): *Genevan Psalter*, 1551, P.D.

The Earth, with All That Dwell Therein   499

PSALM 24

1 The earth, with all that dwell there - in, with all its
2 Oh, who shall stand be - fore the Lord on Zi - on's
3 Lo, such are they that seek the Lord, and blest by

wealth un - told, be - longs to God, who found - ed it up -
ho - ly hill? The clean of hand, the pure of heart, the
God they live; to them the Lord's pure right - eous ways the

on the seas of old, up - on the seas of old.
just who do God's will, the just who do God's will.
God of grace will give, the God of grace will give.

4 O everlasting doors, give way;
lift up your head, O gates!
For now, behold, to enter in,
the King of glory waits,
the King of glory waits.

5 Who is this glorious King that comes
to sit upon the throne?
All hail the Lord of Hosts, who is
our glorious King alone,
our glorious King alone.

For another setting of Ps. 24 see 144

Words: *Psalter*, 1912, alt., P.D.
Music (LOBT GOTT, IHR CHRISTEN 8.6.8.6.6): Nikolaus Herman (1480-1561), P.D.

500 LORD, Our Lord, Your Glorious Name

PSALM 8

1 LORD, our Lord, your glo - rious name all your won-drous works pro-claim;
2 In - fant voic - es chant your praise, tell-ing of your glo-rious ways;
3 Moon and stars in shin - ing height night-ly tell their Mak-er's might;
4 Who are we that we should share in your love and ten - der care—
5 With do - min-ion crowned, we stand o'er the crea - tures of your hand;

in the heavens with ra - diant signs ev - er-more your glo - ry shines.
weak-est means work out your will, might - y en - e - mies to still.
when I view the heavens a - far, then I know how small we are.
raised to an ex - alt - ed height, crowned with hon - or in your sight!
all to us sub - jec - tion yield, in the sea and air and field.

Refrain

How great your name! LORD, our Lord, in all the earth, how great your name! Yours the name of match - less worth, ex - cel - lent in all the earth. How great your name!

Words: *Psalter,* 1912, alt., P.D.
Music (EVENING PRAISE 7.7.7.7.4 refrain 7.4.7.7.4): William F. Sherwin (1826-1888), 1877, P.D.

Lord, Our Lord, Your Glorious Name 501

PSALM 8

1 LORD, our Lord, your glo - rious name all your
2 In - fant voic - es chant your praise, tell - ing
3 Moon and stars in shin - ing height night - ly
4 Who are we that we should share in your

won - drous works pro - claim; in the heavens with
of your glo - rious ways; weak - est means work
tell their Mak - er's might; when I view the
love and ten - der care— raised to an ex -

ra - diant signs ev - er - more your glo - ry shines.
out your will, might - y en - e - mies to still.
heavens a - far, then I know how small we are.
alt - ed height, crowned with hon - or in your sight!

5 With dominion crowned, we stand
o'er the creatures of your hand;
all to us subjection yield,
in the sea and air and field.

6 LORD, our Lord, your glorious name
all your wondrous works proclaim,
yours the name of matchless worth,
excellent in all the earth.

Chord symbols represent a simplified harmony.

Words: *Psalter*, 1912, alt., P.D.
Music (GOTT SEI DANK DURCH ALLE WELT 7.7.7.7): J. Freylinghausen's *Gesangbuch*, 1704, P.D.

502 O Give the LORD Wholehearted Praise

PSALM 111

1 O give the LORD whole-heart-ed praise. To him thanks-
2 His saints de-light to search and trace his might-y
3 God's won-drous deeds of faith-ful-ness his peo-ple
4 God's prom-ise shall for-ev-er stand; he cares for

giv-ing I will bring; with all his peo-ple
works and won-drous ways. Ma-jes-tic glo-ry,
ev-er keep in mind. His works of love and
those who trust his word. Up-on his saints his

I will raise my voice and of his glo-ry sing.
bound-less grace, and right-eous-ness his work dis-plays.
gra-cious-ness re-veal that God the LORD is kind.
might-y hand the wealth of na-tions has con-ferred.

5 His works are true and just indeed;
his precepts are forever sure.
In truth and righteousness decreed,
they shall forevermore endure.

6 By God's own hand redemption came;
his covenant sure no change can know.
Let all revere his holy name
in heaven above and earth below.

7 In reverence and in godly fear
we find the key to wisdom's ways;
the wise his holy name revere.
Through endless ages sound his praise!

For an alternate arrangement see 395

Words: *Psalter*, 1912, alt., P.D.
Music (GERMANY 8.8.8.8): W. Gardiner's *Sacred Melodies*, 1815, P.D.

As the Deer

503

PSALM 42:1

As the deer pants for the wa-ter, so my soul longs af-ter you; you a-lone are my heart's de-sire, and I long to wor-ship you. You a-lone are my strength, my shield; to you a-lone may my spir-it yield; you a-lone are my heart's de-sire, and I long to wor-ship you!

For other settings of Ps. 42 see 332, 504, 616

Words and Music (AS THE DEER 8.7.8.7.8.9.8.7): Martin Nystrom © 1984 Universal Music--Brentwood-Benson
  Publishing (ASCAP)

504 Como el ciervo/Like a Deer

PSALM 42:1, 2

For other settings of Ps. 72 see 332, 503, 616

Words: Juan Salinas; tr. Mary Louise Bringle (b. 1953), 2011
Music (LLÉNAME): Juan Salinas © 1991 CanZion Producciones; arr. Obed Valencia Lozada © 2001 Obed
   Valencia Lozada

da - me más, más de tu a - mor; yo
Give me more, more of your great love. I

ten - go sed só - lo de ti, llé - na - me, Se - ñor.
thirst for you, on - ly for you. Fill my heart, O Lord.

Out of Need and Out of Custom 505

The following text could be spoken by a single voice, responsorially as marked, or sung.

1 Out of need and out of custom **we have gathered here again.**
To the gathering we are bringing **love and laughter, grief and pain.**
Some believing, some rejoicing, **some afraid, and some in doubt;**
now we come our questions voicing, **we would search these matters out.**

2 We now come our masks displaying, **fearing that we shall be known,**
foolish games forever playing, **feeling meanwhile so alone.**
Let pretension's power be broken, **to be open let us dare;**
let the truth in love be spoken, **let us now the searching share.**

3 We have heard the glowing stories **of the things that God has done,**
of his power and his glory, **of his love in Christ, his Son.**
God of human transformation, **for your presence now we pray;**
lead us ever on the journey **as we gather here today.**

For music see 802 or another 8.7.8.7 D tune
Words: Ken Medema, 1972, © 1977 Word Music, a division of WORD, LLC

506

Better Is One Day

PSALM 84

For other settings of Ps. 84 see 46, 507

Words and Music (BETTER IS ONE DAY): Psalm 84 and 27:4; Matt Redman © 1995 Thankyou Music (PRS), admin. worldwide at EMICMGPublishing.com except Europe which is admin. by Kingswaysongs

(continues)

507 How Lovely Is Your Dwelling

PSALM 84

1 How love-ly is your dwell-ing, O Lord of hosts, to me;
2 Be-neath your care the spar-row finds place for peace-ful rest;
3 Blest they who love and serve you, whose joy and strength you are.

my soul is long-ing, faint-ing, the courts of God to see.
to keep her young in safe-ty the swal-low finds a nest.
For-ev-er they will praise you, your ways are in their heart.

The beau-ty of your dwell-ing will bring me joy a-new.
So, Lord, my King Al-might-y, your love will shel-ter me;
Though tried, their tears like show-ers shall fill the springs of peace,

My heart and flesh are cry-ing, O liv-ing God, for you.
be-neath your wings of mer-cy my dwell-ing place will be.
and all the way to Zi-on their strength shall still in-crease.

For other settings of Ps. 84 see 46, 506

Words: *Psalter*, 1912, alt., P.D.
Music (ST. EDITH 7.6.7.6 D): Justin H. Krecht, 1799, rev. Edward Husband, 1871, P.D.

I Rejoiced When I Heard Them Say

508

PSALM 122

1 I re-joiced when I heard them say: "Let us go to the house of God." And now our feet are stand-ing in your gates, O Je-ru-sa-lem!

2 Like a tem-ple of u-ni-ty is the cit-y, Je-ru-sa-lem. It is there all tribes will gath-er, all the tribes of the house of God.

3 It is faith-ful to Is-rael's law, there to praise the name of God. All the judg-ment seats of Da-vid were set down in Je-ru-sa-lem.

Refrain

Sha-lom, sha-lom, the peace of God be here. Sha-lom, sha-lom, God's jus-tice be ev-er near.

4 For the peace of all nations, pray:
for God's peace within your homes.
May God's lasting peace surround us;
may it dwell in Jerusalem. *Refrain*

5 For the love of my friends and kin
I will bless you with signs of peace.
For the love of God's own people
I will labor and pray for you. *Refrain*

For other settings of Ps. 122 see 66, 514

509 Come, Worship God

PSALM 95

1 Come, wor-ship God, who is wor-thy of hon-or;
en-ter God's pres-ence with thanks and a song!
You are the rock of your peo-ple's sal-va-tion,
to whom our ju-bi-lant prais-es be-long.

2 Ruled by your might are the heights of the moun-tains;
held in your hands are the depths of the earth.
Yours is the sea, yours the land, for you made them,
God a-bove all gods, who gave us our birth.

3 We are your peo-ple, the sheep of your pas-ture;
you are our Mak-er, and to you we pray.
Glad-ly we kneel in o-be-dience be-fore you;
great is the one whom we wor-ship this day!

4 Now let us lis-ten, for you speak a-mong us;
o-pen our hearts to re-ceive what you say.
Peace be to all who re-mem-ber your good-ness,
trust in your word, and re-joice in your way!

For other settings of Ps. 95 see 510, 512, 517

Words: Michael Perry © 1980 The Jubilate Group, admin. Hope Publishing Company
Music (O QUANTA QUALIA 11.10.11.10): *Antiphoner*, Paris, 1681; harm. John B. Dykes (1823-1876), 1868, P.D.

Come, Let Us Worship and Bow Down 510

PSALM 95:6-7

Come, let us wor-ship and bow down, let us kneel be-fore the
Lord, our God, our Mak - er. Mak - er. For he is our
God, and we are the peo-ple of his pas - ture, and the
sheep of his hand, just the sheep of his hand.

For other settings of Ps. 95 see 509, 512, 517

Words: Psalm 95:6-7
Music (COME, LET US WORSHIP): Dave Doherty © 1980 Universal Music--Brentwood-Benson Publishing
  (ASCAP); arr. © 1997 Universal Music--Brentwood-Benson Publishing

511 Amid the Thronging Worshipers

PSALM 22

1 A - mid the throng - ing wor - ship - ers the Lord, our God, I bless;
2 The bur - den of the sor - row - ful the Lord will not de - spise;
3 He feeds with good the hum - ble soul and sat - is - fies the meek,

be - fore his peo - ple gath - ered here his name will I con - fess.
he has not turned from those who mourn, he lis - tens to their cries.
and they shall live and praise the Lord who for his mer - cy seek.

Come, praise him, all who fear the Lord, the chil - dren of his grace;
His good - ness makes me join the throng where saints his praise pro - claim,
The ends of all the earth will hear, the na - tions seek the Lord;

with rev - erence sound his glo - ries forth and bow be - fore his face.
and there will I ful - fill my vows with those who fear his name.
they wor - ship him, the King of kings, in earth and heaven a - dored.

For other settings of Ps. 22 see 164, 165, 594

Words: *Psalter,* 1912, P.D.
Music (BOVINA 8.6.8.6 D): Laura A. Tate, 1912, P.D.

Now with Joyful Exultation

512

PSALM 95

1 Now with joy - ful ex - ul - ta - tion let us sing to God our praise;
2 For how great a God, and glo - rious, is the LORD of whom we sing;
3 To the LORD, such might re - veal - ing, let us come with rev - erence meet,
4 While he of - fers peace and par - don let us hear his voice to - day,

to the Rock of our sal - va - tion loud ho - san - nas let us raise.
o - ver i - dol gods vic - to - rious, great is he, our God and King.
and, be - fore our Mak - er kneel - ing, let us wor - ship at his feet.
lest, if we our hearts should hard - en, we should per - ish in the way—

Thank - ful trib - ute glad - ly bring - ing, let us come be - fore him now,
In his hand are earth's deep plac - es, al - so his are all the hills;
He is our own God who leads us, we the peo - ple of his care;
lest to us, so un - be - liev - ing, he in judg - ment should de - clare:

and, with psalms his prais - es sing - ing, joy - ful in his pres - ence bow.
his the sea whose bounds he trac - es, his the land his boun - ty fills.
with a shep - herd's hand he feeds us as his flock in pas - tures fair.
"You, so long my Spir - it griev - ing, nev - er in my rest will share."

For other settings of Ps. 95 see 509, 510, 517

Words: *Psalter*, 1912, alt., P.D.
Music (BEECHER 8.7.8.7 D): John Zundel, 1870, P.D.

513 It Is Good to Sing Your Praises

PSALM 92

1 It is good to sing your prais-es and to thank you,
2 You have filled my heart with glad-ness through the works your
3 But the good shall live be-fore you, plant-ed in your

O Most High, show-ing forth your lov-ing-kind-ness when the
hands have wrought; you have made my life vic-to-rious; great your
dwell-ing place, fruit-ful trees and ev-er ver-dant, nour-ished

morn-ing lights the sky. It is good when night is fall-ing
works and deep your thought. You, O Lord, on high ex-alt-ed,
by your bound-less grace. In his good-ness to the right-eous

of your faith-ful-ness to tell, while with sweet, me-
reign for-ev-er-more in might; all your en-e-
God his right-eous-ness dis-plays; God, my rock, my

Words: *Psalter,* 1912, P.D.
Music (ELLESDIE 8.7.8.7 D): J. Leavitt's *Christian Lyre,* 1831, P.D.

lo - dious prais - es songs of ad - o - ra - tion swell.
mies shall per - ish, sin be ban - ished from your sight.
strength and ref - uge, just and true are all your ways.

I Was Glad 514

PSALM 122:1

I was glad when they said to me, "Let us go to the house of the

Lord." I was glad, I was glad, I was glad.

If desired begin canon at this point.

Optional prayer

As we gather as your children, **we are glad!**
As we see our friends and neighbors, **we are glad!**
As we sing your praise, **we are glad!**
As we open your Word, **we are glad!**
As we feast at your table, **we are glad!**

(Add other phrases as appropriate.)

For other settings of Ps. 122 see 164, 66, 508

Words: from Psalm 122:1
Music (I WAS GLAD 8.9.8.9.3.3.3): M. Thomas Thangaraj, India © 1997 M. Thomas Thangaraj

515 Sing to the Lord, Sing His Praise

PSALM 96

1 Sing to the LORD, sing his praise, all you peo-ples; new be your song as new hon-ors you pay. Sing of his maj-es-ty, praise him for - ev - er, show his sal - va-tion from day to day.

2 Tell of his won-drous works, tell of his glo - ry till through the na - tions his name is re - vered. Praise and ex - alt him, for he is al-might-y; God o - ver all, let the LORD be feared.

3 Vain are the i - dols and gods of the na-tions; God made the heavens, and his glo - ry they tell. Splen - dor and maj-es - ty shine out be - fore him; glo - ry and strength in his tem - ple dwell.

4 Give un - to God Most High glo - ry and hon - or; come with your of - ferings and hum - bly draw near. Wor - ship the LORD in all beau - ty and splen-dor; trem - ble be - fore him with god - ly fear.

5 Say to the nations, "The LORD reigns forever."
Earth is established as he did decree.
Righteous and just is the King of the nations,
judging the peoples with equity.

6 Let heaven and earth be glad; oceans, be joyful;
forest and field, exultation express.
For God is coming, the judge of the nations,
coming to judge in his righteousness.

Words: *Psalter*, 1912, alt., P.D.
Music (WESLEY 11.10.11.9): Lowell Mason (1792-1872), 1830, P.D.

Bless the Lord, O My Soul

PSALM 103:1

516

Chord symbols represent a simplified harmony.

Words: Andraé Crouch, 1973, © 1973 Bud John Songs, admin. EMICMGPublishing.com
Music (BLESS THE LORD): Andraé Crouch (b. 1945), 1973; arr. Richard Smallwood (b. 1948) © 1973 Bud John
  Songs, Inc., admin. EMICMGPublishing.com

517   Our Approach to God

PSALM 124:8; 95:6-7; PHILIPPIANS 1:2

Our help is in the name of the Lord,
who made heaven and earth.
Amen.

O come, let us worship and bow down,
let us kneel before the Lord, our Maker!
For he is our God,
and we are the people of his pasture
and the sheep of his hand.

Grace to you and peace from God our Father
and the Lord Jesus Christ.
Amen.

For other settings of Ps. 124 see 497, 498; Ps. 95 see 509, 510, 512
Text: Psalm 124:8, Psalm 95:6-7, Phil. 1:2 NRSV

518   Praise the LORD! Sing Hallelujah

PSALM 146

1 Praise the LORD! Sing hal - le - lu - jah! Come, our great Re -
2 Hap - py are the ones pro - fess - ing Ja - cob's God to
3 Food he dai - ly gives the hun - gry, sets the mourn-ing
4 Praise the LORD! Sing hal - le - lu - jah! Come, our great Re -

deem - er praise. I will sing the glo - rious prais - es of my
be their aid. They are blest whose hope of bless - ing on the
pris - oner free, rais - es those bowed down with an - guish, makes the
deem - er praise. I will sing the glo - rious prais - es of my

Words: *Psalter*, 1887, alt., P.D.
Music (RIPLEY 8.7.8.7 D): Lowell Mason (1792-1872), 1839, P.D.

God through all my days. Put no con - fi - dence in princ - es,
LORD their God is stayed. Heaven and earth the LORD cre - at - ed,
sight - less eyes to see. God our Sav - ior loves the right-eous,
God through all my days. O - ver all God reigns for - ev - er;

nor on hu - man help de - pend. They shall die, to dust re -
seas and all that they con - tain. He de - liv - ers from op -
and the strang - er he be - friends, helps the or - phan and the
through all a - ges he is King. Un - to him, your God, O

turn - ing; all their thoughts and plans shall end.
pres - sion; right - eous - ness he will main - tain.
wid - ow, judg - ment on the wick - ed sends.
Zi - on, joy - ful hal - le - lu - jahs sing.

Optional prayer

Blessed are you, Lord our God.
You uphold the cause of the oppressed.
You give food to the hungry.
You lift up those who are bowed down.
You set prisoners free.

[Add other phrases as appropriate.]

Blessed are those whose help is in your name.
Blessed are those who put their trust in you.
Amen.

519 God, We Sing Your Glorious Praises

1 God, we sing your glo - rious prais - es as we tell your
2 We re - mem - ber, God, your cov - enant, which ex - tends from
3 Fueled by pow - er from your Spir - it, we com - mit our -
4 Lord, we of - fer you our wor - ship as we cel - e -

awe - some deeds; you have fash - ioned all cre - a - tion,
heaven to earth; how Christ's death and res - ur - rec - tion
selves a - new to be faith - ful to your gos - pel
brate your grace which you show - er on your peo - ple

and you meet each crea - ture's needs. We re - joice in
con - quers sin, re - news our birth. Thank you for this
in the dai - ly work we do. We will shout your
gath - ered here and ev - ery - place. Blessed by wa - ter,

how your peo - ple tast - ed your great faith - ful - ness;
gos - pel mes - sage, which in - spires your church to preach
glo - rious prais - es, tel - ling all who have not heard;
Word, and ta - ble, we, your church, now pledge to share

Alternate tune NETTLETON *see 521*
Words: Bert Polman © 2006 Faith Alive Christian Resources
Music (BLAENWERN 8.7.8.7 D): William P. Rowlands (1860-1937), P.D.

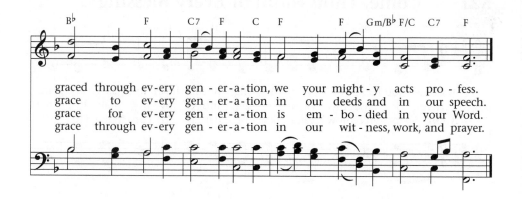

graced through ev-ery gen-er-a-tion, we your might-y acts pro-fess.
grace to ev-ery gen-er-a-tion in our deeds and in our speech.
grace for ev-ery gen-er-a-tion is em-bo-died in your Word.
grace through ev-ery gen-er-a-tion in our wit-ness, work, and prayer.

Jesu, tawa pano/Jesus, We Are Here   520

Shona   Je-su, ta-wa pa-no; Je-su, ta-wa pa-no;
English   Je-sus, we are here;__ Je-sus, we are here;__
Spanish   He me_a-quí, Je-sús;__ he me_a-quí, Je-sús;__

Je-su, ta-wa pa-no; ta-wa pa-no mu zi-ta ren-yu.
Je-sus, we are here;__ we are here_____ for_____ you.
he me_a-quí, Je-sús;__ he-me_a-quí, por tu gra-cia, Je-sús.

Other stanzas may be added:
Father, we are here . . .
Spirit, we are here . . .

Words: Patrick Matsikenyiri (20th c. Zimbabwe); Sp. tr. Pedro P. Pirón (b. 20th c) © 1990, 1996 General Board of Global Ministries t/a GBGMusik
Music (JESU, TAWA PANO): Patrick Matsikenyiri (20th c. Zimbabwe) © 1990, 1996 General Board of Global Ministries t/a GBGMusik

521   Come, Thou Fount of Every Blessing

1 Come, thou Fount of ev-ery bless-ing, tune my heart to sing thy grace;
2 Here I raise my *Eb-en - e - zer; hith-er by thy help I've come;
3 Oh, to grace how great a debt - or dai - ly I'm con-strained to be!

streams of mer - cy, nev - er ceas - ing, call for songs of loud-est praise.
and I hope, by thy good plea-sure, safe - ly to ar - rive at home.
Let that grace now like a fet - ter, bind my wan-dering heart to thee:

Teach me some me - lo-dious son - net, sung by flam-ing tongues a - bove.
Je - sus sought me when a stran - ger, wan-dering from the fold of God;
prone to wan - der, Lord, I feel it, prone to leave the God I love;

Praise the mount—I'm fixed up - on it—mount of God's un-chang-ing love.
he, to res - cue me from dan-ger, in - ter-posed his pre-cious blood.
here's my heart, oh, take and seal it; seal it for thy courts a - bove.

* *"Then Samuel took a stone . . . called its name Ebenezer, saying, 'Thus far the Lord has helped us'"* (1 Sam. 7:12)

Words: Robert Robinson, 1758, alt., P.D.
Music (NETTLETON 8.7.8.7 D): J. Wyeth's *Repository of Sacred Music*, Part II, 1813, P.D.

Dios está aquí/God Is Here Today

Dios es-tá a-quí, tan
God is here to-day; as

cier-to co-mo_el ai - re que res-pi - ro, tan
cer - tain___ as the air I breathe,_____ as

cier-to co-mo la ma - ña - na se le - van - ta, tan
cer - tain___ as the morn-ing sun that ris - es, as

cier-to co-mo que le can - to_y me pue-de o - ír.
cer - tain___ when I sing you'll___ hear___ my song.

Words: from Mexico; tr. C. Michael Hawn, 1998, © 1999 Choristers Guild
Music (DIOS ESTÁ AQUÍ): from Mexico; arr. C. Michael Hawn and Arturo González, 1999, © 1999 Choristers
   Guild

523   # Creator Spirit, by Whose Aid

1 Cre - a - tor Spir - it, by whose aid the world's foun - da - tions
2 O source of un - cre - a - ted light, the Fa - ther's prom - ised
3 Plen - teous of grace, de - scend from high, rich in thy seven - fold

first were laid, come, vis - it ev - ery pi - ous mind; come,
Par - a - clete, thrice ho - ly fount, thrice ho - ly fire, our
en - er - gy; make us e - ter - nal truths re - ceive and

pour thy joys on hu - man - kind; from sin and sor - row
hearts with heav - enly love in - spire; come, and thy sa - cred
prac - tice all that we be - lieve; give us thy - self that

set us free and make thy tem - ples worth - y thee.
unc - tion bring to sac - ti - fy us while we sing.
we may see the Fa - ther and the Son by thee.

Words: Latin hymn, *Veni Creator Spiritus*, 9th c.; para. John Dryden, 1693, P.D.
Music (MELITA 8.8.8.8.8.8): John B. Dykes (1823-1876), 1861, P.D.

Lord Jesus Christ, Be Present Now

Optional opening of worship (based on Ps. 124:8, 118:24, 51:15)

Our help is in the name of the Lord,
who made heaven and earth.

This is the day the Lord has made,
Let us rejoice and be glad in it.

O Lord, open our lips,
And our mouths shall declare your praise.

1 Lord Je - sus Christ, be pres - ent now; our hearts in
2 Un - seal our lips to sing your praise in end - less
3 Then shall we join the hosts that cry, "O ho - ly,
4 All glo - ry to the Fa - ther, Son, and Ho - ly

true de - vo - tion bow. Your Spir - it send with
hymns through all our days; in - crease our faith and
ho - ly, Lord Most High!" And in the light of
Spir - it, Three in One! To you, O bless - ed

light di - vine, and let your truth with - in us shine.
light our minds; and set us free from doubt that binds.
that blest place we then shall see you face to face.
Trin - i - ty, be praise through - out e - ter - ni - ty!

Words: attr. Wilhelm II (1598-1662); tr. Catherine Winkworth (1827-1878), alt., P.D.
Music (HERR JESU CHRIST, DICH ZU UNS WEND 8.8.8.8): *Cantionale Germanicum*, Gochsheim, 1628, P.D.

525   For Your Gift of God the Spirit

1 For your gift of God the Spir - it, power to make our
2 He who in cre - a - tion's dawn - ing brood - ed on the
3 He, him - self the liv - ing Au - thor, wakes to life the

lives a - new, pledge of life and hope of glo - ry,
life - less deep, still a - cross our na - ture's dark - ness
sa - cred Word, reads with us its ho - ly pa - ges

Sav - ior, we would wor - ship you. Crown - ing gift of
moves to wake our souls from sleep, moves to stir, to
and re - veals our ris - en Lord. He it is who

res - ur - rec - tion sent from your as - cend - ed throne,
draw, to quick - en, thrusts us through with sense of sin;
works with - in us teach - ing reb - el hearts to pray,

Words: Margaret Clarkson, 1959, © 1960 Hope Publishing Company
Music (FOR YOUR GIFT 8.7.8.7 D): Darwin Jordan © Darwin Jordan Music; arr. Marcus Hong, 2011, © Darwin
   Jordan Music

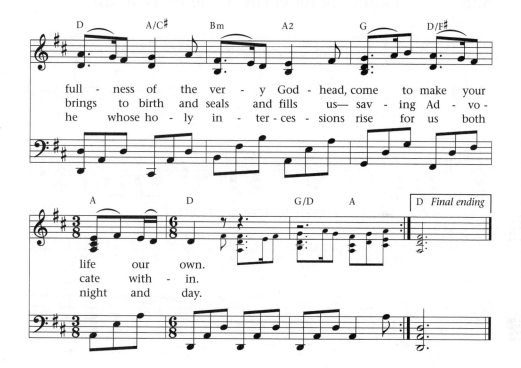

full - ness of the ver - y God - head, come to make your
brings to birth and seals and fills us— sav - ing Ad - vo -
he whose ho - ly in - ter - ces - sions rise for us both

life our own.
cate with - in.
night and day.

4 He, the mighty God, indwells us;
his to strengthen, help, empower;
his to overcome the tempter,
ours to call in danger's hour.
In his strength we dare to battle
all the raging hosts of sin,
and by him alone we conquer
foes without and foes within.

5 Father, grant your Holy Spirit
in our hearts may rule today,
grieved not, quenched not, but unhindered,
work in us his sovereign way.
Fill us with your holy fullness,
God the Father, Spirit, Son;
in us, through us, then forever,
shall your perfect will be done.

526   Come, Now Is the Time to Worship

527 Come Away from Rush and Hurry

1 Come a - way from rush and hur - ry to the
2 In the pas - tures of God's good - ness we lie
3 Come, then, chil - dren, with your bur - dens— life's con -

still - ness of God's peace; from our vain am - bi - tion's wor - ry,
down to rest our soul. From the wa - ters of God's mer - cy
fu - sions, fears, and pain. Leave them at the cross of Je - sus,

come to Christ to find re - lease. Come a - way from
we drink deep - ly, are made whole. At the ta - ble
take in - stead his king - dom's reign. Bring your thirsts, for

noise and clam - or, life's de - mands and fren - zied pace; come to
of God's pres - ence all the saints are rich - ly fed. With the
he will quench them—he a - lone will sat - is - fy. All our

Words: Marva J. Dawn © 1999 Marva J. Dawn, from A "Royal" Waste of Time: The Splendor of Worshiping God and Being Church for the World, W. B. Eerdmans
Music (PROMISE 8.7.8.7 D): Natalie Sleeth © 1986 and this arr. © 2011 Hope Publishing Company

join the peo - ple gath - ered here to seek and find God's grace.
oil of God's a - noint - ing in - to ser - vice we are led.
long - ings find at - tain - ment when to self we glad - ly die.

Come and Fill Our Hearts 528

Come and fill our hearts with your peace. You a - lone, O Lord, are ho - ly.

Come and fill our hearts with your peace. Al - le - lu - ia!

Optional prayer

Jesus, our Lord.
Jesus, our Savior.
Help us to set aside all that cannot bring us peace.
Help us to turn away from self-concern.
Help us to turn toward you in trust.
Amen.

Consider singing the refrain and praying this prayer several times in alternation.

529   # Gather Us In

1 Here in this place the new light is stream-ing, now is the dark-ness
2 We are the young, our lives are a mys - tery, we are the old who
3 Here we will take the wine and the wa - ter, here we will take the
4 Not in the dark of build-ings con - fin - ing, not in some heav - en,

van - ished a - way; see in this space our fears and our
yearn for your face; we have been sung through - out all of
bread of new birth, here you shall call your sons and your
light years a - way— here in this place the new light is

dream-ings brought here to you in the light of this day.
his - tory, called to be light to the whole hu-man race.
daugh-ters, call us a - new to be salt for the earth.
shin - ing, now is the king-dom, and now is the day.

Gath-er us in, the lost and for - sak - en,
Gath-er us in, the rich and the haugh-ty,
Give us to drink the wine of com - pas - sion,
Gath-er us in and hold us for - ev - er,

gath - er us in, the blind and the lame;
gath - er us in, the proud and the strong;
give us to eat the bread that is you;
gath - er us in and make us your own;

call to us now, and we shall a - wak - en, we shall a -
give us a heart, so meek and so low - ly, give us the
nour-ish us well, and teach us to fash-ion lives that are
gath - er us in, all peo-ples to - geth - er, fire____ of

rise at the sound of our name.
cour-age to en - ter the song.
ho - ly and hearts that are true.
love in our flesh and our bone.

Optional prayer (based on Eph. 4:12-13)

Triune God,
Father, Son, and Holy Spirit,
you have adopted us as your children,
you lavish your grace upon us at Word and table.
May all we do here equip us for ministry,
build us up as the body of Christ,
strengthen our unity in faith,
deepen our knowledge of Jesus, our Lord,
and help us to grow into maturity as your children,
reflecting the full stature of Christ.
Amen.

530   Welcome Into this Place

Optional readings (from 2 Cor. 4:7; Ps. 22:3)

But we have this treasure in jars of clay
to show that this all-surpassing power
is from God and not from us.

You are enthroned as the Holy One;
you are the one Israel praises.

God, You Call Us to This Place

531

1 God, you call us to this place, where we know your love and grace.
2 Now as-sem-bled in Christ's name, all your mer-cies to pro-claim—
3 In the wa-ter we were born of the Spir-it in the Son.

Here your hos-pi-tal-i-ty makes of us one fam-i-ly,
in the hear-ing of your word, in our prayer through Christ the Lord,
Now a priest-ly, roy-al race rich in ev-ery gift of grace—

makes our rich di-ver-si-ty rich-er still in u-ni-ty,
in the min-is-tries we share, learn-ing how to serve with care—
called, for-giv-en, loved, and freed, for the world we in-ter-cede:

makes our man-y voic-es one, joined in praise with Christ your Son.
in the Spir-it let us be one in faith and u-ni-ty.
gath-er in-to u-ni-ty all the hu-man fam-i-ly.

For an alternate arrangement see 546

Words: Delores Dufner (b. 1939) © 1993 The Sisters of St. Benedict, admin. OCP Publications
Music (SALZBURG 7.7.7.7 D): Jakob Hintze (1622-1702); harm. after Johann S. Bach (1685-1750), P.D.

532

Be Still, for the Presence

1 Be still, for the pres-ence of the Lord, the Ho - ly One, is here.
2 Be still, for the glo - ry of the Lord is shin-ing all a - round.
3 Be still, for the pow - er of the Lord is mov-ing in this place.

Come, bow be - fore him now, with rev - er - ence and fear.
He burns with ho - ly fire; with splen-dor he is crowned.
He comes to cleanse and heal, to min - is - ter his grace.

In him no sin is found; we stand on ho - ly ground.
How awe-some is the sight, our rad-iant King of light!
No work too hard for him; in faith re - ceive from him.

Be still, for the pres-ence of the Lord, the Ho - ly One, is here.
Be still, for the glo - ry of the Lord is shin-ing all a - round.
Be still, for the pow - er of the Lord is mov-ing in this place.

Words and Music (BE STILL, FOR THE PRESENCE): David Evans (b. 1957) © 1986 Thankyou Music (PRS), admin. worldwide at EMICMGPublishing.com except Europe which is admin. by Kingswaysongs

I Come with Joy

533

1 I come with joy, a child of God, for-
   giv - en, loved, and free, the life of Je - sus
   to re - call, in love laid down for me.

2 I come with Chris - tians far and near to
   find, as all are fed, the new com - mu - ni -
   ty of love in Christ's com - mu - nion bread.

3 As Christ breaks bread and bids us share, each
   proud di - vi - sion ends. The love that made us,
   makes us one, and strang - ers now are friends.

4 The Spir - it of the ri - sen Christ, un -
   seen, but ev - er near, is in such friend - ship
   bet - ter known, a - live a - mong us here.

5 A cloud of loving witnesses
   surrounds us while we sing
   as all the saints, forgiven, loved,
   immortal praises bring.

6 Together met, together bound
   by all that God has done,
   we'll go with joy, to give the world
   the love that makes us one.

Words: Brian Wren, 1970, © 1971, rev. 1995 Hope Publishing Company
Music (LAND OF REST 8.6.8.6): American folk melody; harm. Annabel Morris Buchanan (1889-1983),
   1938, P.D.

534

All Who Hunger, Gather Gladly

Unison

1 All who hun-ger, gath-er glad-ly; ho-ly man-na is our bread.
2 All who hun-ger, nev-er stran-gers; seek-er, be a wel-come guest.
3 All who hun-ger, sing to-geth-er, Je-sus Christ is liv-ing bread.

Come from wil-der-ness and wan-dering. Here in truth we will be fed.
Come from rest-less-ness and roam-ing. Here in joy we keep the feast.
Come from lon-li-ness and long-ing. Here in peace we have been led.

You that yearn for days of full-ness, all a-round us is our food.
We that once were lost and scat-tered in com-mu-nion's love have stood.
Blest are those who from this ta-ble live their days in grat-i-tude.

Taste and see the grace e-ter-nal. Taste and see that God is good.
Taste and see the grace e-ter-nal. Taste and see that God is good.
Taste and see the grace e-ter-nal. Taste and see that God is good.

For an alternate arrangement see 766

Words: Sylvia G. Dunstan (1955-1993) © 1991 GIA Publications, Inc.
Music (HOLY MANNA 8.7.8.7 D): W. Moore, *Columbian Harmony*, 1825; harm. Norman E. Johnson, 1973,
© 1973 Covenant Publications

The Lord Be with You

535

Leader G   C/G   G *All*   C/G

1 *The Lord be with you.* And al - so with you. The
2 *Lord, o - pen our lips,* and we'll sing your praise. O

G   D/F#   Em   Em/D   A/C#   C2

Lord of heav-en and earth be wor-shiped in this place. The
Lord, your un - fail-ing love and mer - cy will en - dure as

A   C2   C/E   F   C/E   D

cov - e - nant of grace____ be re - newed. The
fresh and bright and sure as morn-ing sun. We

Am7   Dsus   D   C/G   G   C/G *Last time* G

Lord____ be with you.
bless you, Three in One!

Words: Ron Rienstra © 1999 Ron Rienstra
Music (DOMINUS VOBISCUM irregular): Ron Rienstra © 1999 Ron Rienstra; arr. Greg Scheer © 2008
  Ron Rienstra

536 The Trumpets Sound, the Angels Sing

1 The trum-pets sound, the an - gels sing, the feast is
2 Ta - bles are lad - en with good things; oh, taste the
3 The hun - gry heart he sat - is - fies, of - fers the

read - y to be - gin. The gates of heaven are o -
peace and joy he brings. He'll fill you up with love
poor his par - a - dise. Now hear all heaven and earth

- pen wide, and Je - sus wel - comes you in - side.
di - vine; he'll turn your wa - ter in - to wine.
ap - plaud the a - maz - ing good - ness of the Lord.

Refrain

Sing with thank - ful - ness songs of pure de - light.

Come and re - vel in heav - en's love and light.

Take your place at the ta - ble of the King.

The feast is read - y to be - gin;

the feast is read - y to be - gin.

Last time / Optional interlude

537 Open the Eyes of My Heart

Optional reading (Eph. 1:17-19)

I keep asking that the God of our Lord Jesus Christ,
the glorious Father,
may give you the Spirit of wisdom and revelation,
so that you may know him better.
I pray that the eyes of your heart may be enlightened
in order that you may know the hope to which he has called you,
the riches of his glorious inheritance in his holy people,
and his incomparably great power for us who believe.

538   Holy, Holy, Holy! Lord God Almighty

1 Holy, holy, holy! Lord_____ God Almight - y!
2 Holy, holy, holy! All the saints a - dore thee,
3 Ho - ly, holy, ho - ly! Though the dark-ness hide thee,
4 Ho - ly, holy, ho - ly! Lord_____ God Al - might - y!

Ear - ly in the morn - ing our song shall rise to thee;
cast - ing down their gold - en crowns a - round the glass - y sea;
though the eye made blind by sin thy glo - ry may not see,
All thy works shall praise thy name, in earth and sky and sea;

ho - ly, holy, ho - ly! mer - ci - ful and might - y,
cher - u - bim and ser - a - phim fall - ing down be - fore thee,
on - ly thou art ho - ly; there is none be - side thee,
ho - ly, holy, ho - ly! mer - ci - ful and might - y,

Words: Reginald Heber, 1827, alt., P.D.
Music (NICAEA 11.12.12.10): John B. Dykes, 1861; desc. David McK. Williams (1887-1978), P.D.

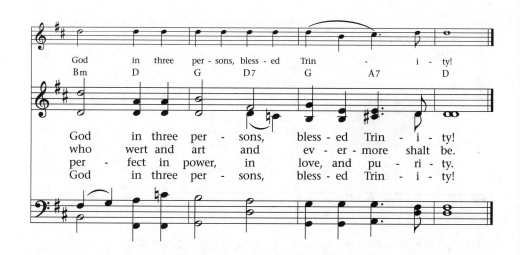

God in three per - sons, bless - ed Trin - i - ty!

| Bm | D | G | D7 | G | A7 | D |

God in three per - sons, bless - ed Trin - i - ty!
who wert and art and ev - er - more shalt be.
per - fect in power, in love, and pu - ri - ty.
God in three per - sons, bless - ed Trin - i - ty!

A Call to Worship and Greeting   539

PSALM 34:3; 9:1-2; REVELATION 1:4-5

O magnify the LORD with me.
Let us exalt God's name together!

We will give thanks to you, O LORD, with our whole heart;
we will tell of all your wonderful deeds.
We will be glad and exult in you;
we will sing praise to your name, O Most High.

Grace to you and peace from him who is
and who was and who is to come,
and from the seven spirits who are before his throne,
and from Jesus Christ, the faithful witness,
the firstborn of the dead,
and the ruler of the kings of the earth.
Amen.

Continue with the singing of "Holy, Holy, Holy! Lord God Almighty" or another appropriate song.

Text: from Ps. 34:3, Ps. 9:1-2, Rev. 1:4b-5, NRSV

540 ## Holy God, We Praise Your Name

Chord symbols represent a simplified harmony.

Words: *Te Deum*, 4th c.; vers. Ignaz Franz, ca. 1774; tr. Clarence A. Walworth, 1853, alt., P.D.
Music (GROSSER GOTT 7.8.7.8.7.7): *Katholisches Gesangbuch*, Vienna, 1774; desc. Emily R. Brink, 1986,

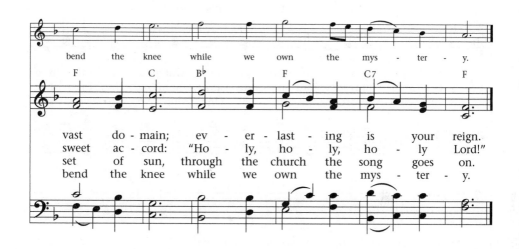

bend   the   knee   while   we   own   the   mys - ter - y.

vast	do - main;	ev - er - last - ing	is	your	reign.
sweet	ac - cord:	"Ho - ly, ho - ly, ho - ly			Lord!"
set	of sun,	through the church the song		goes	on.
bend	the knee	while we own the	mys	- ter -	y.

We Praise You, O God (Te Deum)   541

We praise you, O God;
we acclaim you as Lord;
all creation worships you,
the Father everlasting.
To you all angels and all the heavenly powers cry aloud;
the cherubim and seraphim, sing in endless praise:
> **Holy, holy, holy Lord, God of power and might,**
> **heaven and earth are full of your glory.**

The glorious company of apostles, praise you.
The noble fellowship of prophets, praise you.
The white-robed army of martyrs, praise you.
Throughout the world the holy church acclaims you:
> **Father, of majesty unbounded;**
> **your true and only Son, worthy of all praise;**
> **the Holy Spirit, advocate and guide.**

You, Christ, are the King of glory,
the eternal Son of the Father.
When you took our flesh to set us free,
you humbly chose the virgin's womb.
You overcame the sting of death
and opened the kingdom of heaven to all believers.
You are seated at God's right hand in glory.
We believe that you will come to be our judge.

Come, then, Lord, and help your people,
bought with the price of your own blood,
and bring us with your saints
to glory everlasting. Amen.

Text: 4th c. Christian hymn, P.D.

542 ## All Glory Be to God on High

1 All glo-ry be to God on high, and peace on earth from
2 O Lamb of God, Lord Je-sus Christ, whom God the Fa-ther
3 You on-ly are the Ho-ly One who came for our sal-

heav-en, and God's good-will un-fail-ing-ly be to his
gave us, who for the world was sac-ri-ficed up-on the
va-tion, and on-ly you are God's true Son who was be-

peo-ple giv-en. Al-might-y God, you are our King: we
cross to save us, at God's right hand you in-ter-cede for
fore cre-a-tion. You on-ly, Christ, as Lord we own, and

wor-ship you, our thanks we bring, we praise you for your glo-ry.
those who for your mer-cy plead; re-ceive the prayer we of-fer.
with the Spir-it you a-lone share in the Fa-ther's glo-ry.

Chord symbols represent a simplified harmony.

Words: Latin, *Gloria in excelsis Deo,* 4th c.; vers. Nikolaus Decius, 1525; tr. F. Bland Tucker, 1977, alt. © 1985
The Church Pension Fund
Music (ALLEIN GOTT IN DER HÖH' SEI EHR 8.7.8.7.8.8.7): attr. Nikolaus Decius, 1539, P.D.

Now Thank We All Our God

543

1 Now thank we all our God with heart and hands and voic - es,
2 O may this boun - teous God through all our life be near us,
3 All praise and thanks to God the Fa - ther now be giv - en,

who won - drous things has done, in whom his world re - joic - es;
with ev - er joy - ful hearts and bless - ed peace to cheer us,
the Son and Spir - it blest, who reign in high - est heav - en—

who from our moth - ers' arms has blessed us on our way
to keep us in his grace, and guide us when per - plexed,
the one e - ter - nal God, whom earth and heaven a - dore;

with count - less gifts of love, and still is ours to - day.
and free us from all ills in this world and the next.
for thus it was, is now, and shall be ev - er - more.

Chord symbols represent a simplified harmony.

Words: Martin Rinkart, 1636; tr. Catherine Winkworth, 1863, alt., P.D.
Music (NUN DANKET 6.7.6.7.6.6.6.6): Johann Crüger, 1647; harm. based on Felix Mendelssohn's *Lobgesang*,
   Opus 52, 1840, P.D.

544 Cantemos al Señor/O Sing unto the Lord

Spanish 1 Can-te-mos al Se-ñor un him-no de_a - le - grí - a,
2 Can-te-mos al Se-ñor un him-no de_a - la - ban-za
English 1 O sing un-to the Lord a hymn of cel - e - bra-tion;
2 O sing un-to the Lord a hymn of joy and prais-ing;

un cán - ti - co de_a-mor al na - cer el nue-vo dí - a.
que_ex-pre - se nues-tro_a - mor, nues-tra fe y nues-tra_es-pe - ran-za.
O sing a hymn of love, ev-ery day a new cre - a - tion.
a song that shares our love, our___ faith and hope-ful wait-ing.

Él hi - zo_el cie-lo,_el mar, el sol y las es - tre-llas
En to - da la crea-ción a - bun-da su gran-de-za;
God made the sky and sea, the sun and stars of heav-en
Cre - a - tion shouts to all that God is grand and glo-rious;

y_en e - llos vio bon-dad, pues sus o-bras e - ran be - llas.
a - sí nues-tro can - tar va_a-nun-cian-do su be - lle - za.
and saw that they were good; all cre - a - tion sings in splen-dor!
and so we sing our song to the God of grace and beau-ty.

Words: Carlos Rosas (b. 1939) © 1976 Resource Publications, Inc.; tr. C. Michael Hawn (b. 1948) © 1999
Choristers Guild
Music (ROSAS 6.7.6.8 D refrain 4.4.6.4): Carlos Rosas © 1976 Resource Publications, Inc; arr. Raquel Martinez
© 1983 the United Methodist Publishing House, admin. The Copyright Company

Optional prayer

For the gift of creation, **we praise you!**
For the stars and planets, **we praise you!**
For the sun and moon, **we praise you!**
For the mountains and seas, **we praise you!**
For the trees and plants, **we praise you!**
For the birds and animals, **we praise you!**
For boys and girls, **we praise you!**
For women and men, **we praise you!**
For work and rest, **we praise you!**

(Add other phrases as appropriate, and conclude with the refrain.)

545 Praise Is Your Right, O God, in Zion

PSALM 65

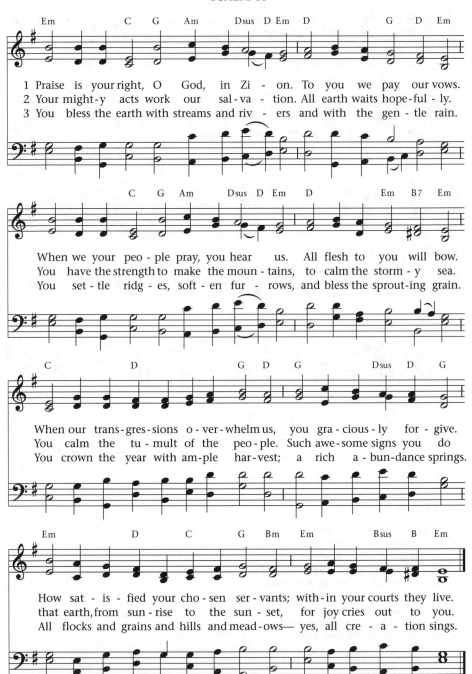

1 Praise is your right, O God, in Zi - on. To you we pay our vows.
2 Your might-y acts work our sal-va - tion. All earth waits hope-ful-ly.
3 You bless the earth with streams and riv - ers and with the gen - tle rain.

When we your peo - ple pray, you hear us. All flesh to you will bow.
You have the strength to make the moun - tains, to calm the storm - y sea.
You set - tle ridg - es, soft - en fur - rows, and bless the sprout-ing grain.

When our trans-gres-sions o - ver-whelm us, you gra - cious-ly for - give.
You calm the tu - mult of the peo - ple. Such awe-some signs you do
You crown the year with am-ple har-vest; a rich a - bun-dance springs.

How sat - is - fied your cho - sen ser - vants; with-in your courts they live.
that earth, from sun - rise to the sun - set, for joy cries out to you.
All flocks and grains and hills and mead-ows— yes, all cre - a - tion sings.

Chord symbols represent a simplified harmony.

For other settings of Ps. 65 see 388, 398

Words: Stanley Wiersma (1930-1986), 1980, © 1987 Faith Alive Christian Resources
Music (GENEVAN 65 | 9.6.9.6 D): *Genevan Psalter*, 1543; harm. Dale Grotenhuis (1931-2012), 1985, © 1987
Faith Alive Christian Resources

Robed in Majesty

PSALM 93

1 Robed in maj-es-ty, he reigns, sov-ereign from e-ter-ni-ty;
2 Surg-ing seas and pound-ing waves: might-ier is the Lord than these;

praise the Lord, the God of strength, robed in awe-some maj-es-ty.
might-ier than the break-er's roar, might-ier than those surg-ing seas.

Firm and sure the world will stand: here the Mak-er's power is shown—
Ho-li-ness a-dorns his house; age on age will hear his law;

yet, pre-dat-ing e-ven time, firm-er, sur-er stands his throne.
praise the Lord, whose reign up-holds ho-li-ness for-ev-er-more.

For an alternate arrangement see 104, 531, 832

Words: Martin Leckebusch © 2003 Kevin Mayhew Ltd.
Music (SALZBURG 7.7.7.7 D): Jakob Hintze (1622-1702); harm. after Johann S. Bach (1685-1750), adapt., P.D.

547 Sing, Sing a New Song to the Lord God

PSALM 98

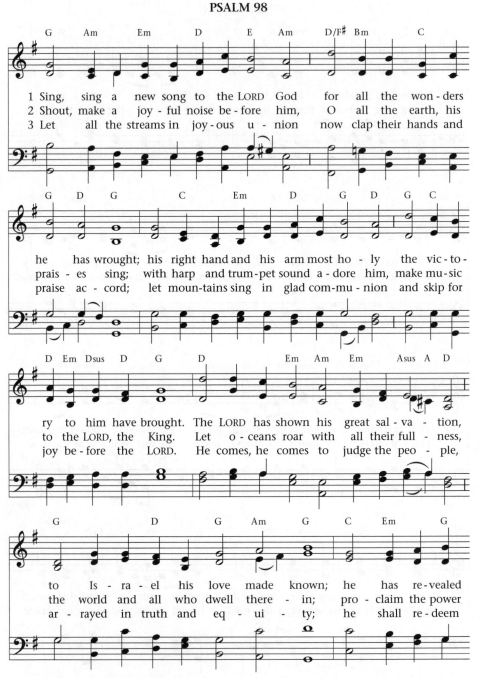

Chord symbols represent a simplified harmony.

For an alternate arrangement see 196.

For another setting of Ps. 98 see 92

Words: Dewey Westra, 1931; rev. *Psalter Hymnal*, 1987, © 1987 Faith Alive Christian Resources
Music (GENEVAN 98/118/RENDEZ À DIEU 9.8.9.8 D): *Genevan Psalter*, 1551; harm. Dale Grotenhuis
  (1931-2012), 1985, © 1987 Faith Alive Christian Resources

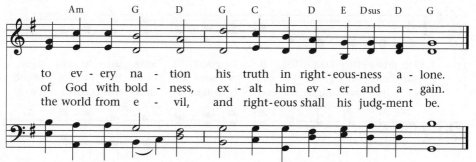

to ev - ery na - tion his truth in right-eous-ness a - lone.
of God with bold - ness, ex - alt him ev - er and a - gain.
the world from e - vil, and right-eous shall his judg-ment be.

My God, How Wonderful You Are   548

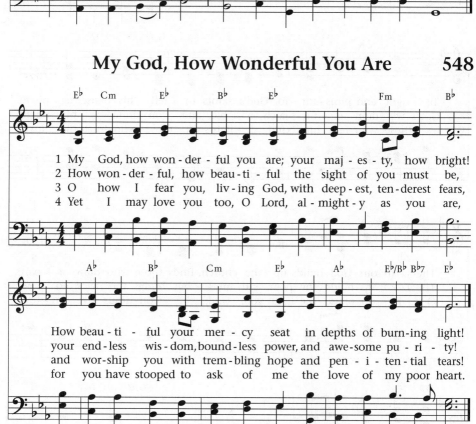

1 My God, how won - der - ful you are; your maj - es - ty, how bright!
2 How won - der - ful, how beau - ti - ful the sight of you must be,
3 O how I fear you, liv - ing God, with deep - est, ten - derest fears,
4 Yet I may love you too, O Lord, al - might - y as you are,

How beau - ti - ful your mer - cy seat in depths of burn - ing light!
your end - less wis - dom, bound - less power, and awe - some pu - ri - ty!
and wor - ship you with trem - bling hope and pen - i - ten - tial tears!
for you have stooped to ask of me the love of my poor heart.

5 No earthly father loves like you,
   no mother half so mild
   bears and forbears as you have done
   with me, your sinful child.

6 Father of Jesus, Love divine,
   great King upon your throne,
   what joy to see you as you are
   and worship you alone!

Chord symbols represent a simplified harmony.
Words: Frederick W. Faber, 1849, alt., P.D.
Music (ST. ETHELDREDA 8.6.8.6): Thomas Turton, 1860, P.D.

549   **O Praise the LORD, for It Is Good**

PSALM 147

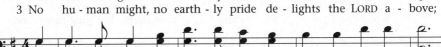

1 O praise the LORD, for it is good to sing un - to our God;
2 Our Lord is great: he calls by name and counts the stars of night;
3 No hu - man might, no earth - ly pride de - lights the LORD a - bove;

'tis right and pleas - ant for God's saints to tell his praise a - broad.
God's wis - dom is un - search - a - ble, and won - drous is his might.
in those who fear him God de - lights, in those who trust his love.

The LORD our God builds up the church, finds those who draw a - part;
The LORD up - holds the poor and meek but brings the wick - ed low;
O Zi - on, praise the LORD your God, his won - drous love con - fess;

God binds their wounds and gent - ly leads; he heals the bro - ken heart.
sing praise to God who sends the rain, whose care the cat - tle know.
God is your glo - ry and your strength, he will your chil - dren bless.

For another setting of Ps. 147 see 442

Words: *Psalter,* 1912, alt.
Music (MINERVA 8.6.8.6 D): John H. Stockton, 1874, P.D.

Nyanyikanlah/Hallelujah!
Sing Praise to Your Creator PSALM 148

Indonesian Nya-nyi-kan-lah nya-nyi-an ba-ru ba-gi Al-lah,

English 1 Hal-le-lu-jah! Sing praise to your Cre-a-tor, sun, moon,
2 Praise the LORD, all moun-tains and o-ceans, roll-ing thun-der
3 Give to God all glo-ry and hon-or. From the depths to

Pen-cip-ta ca-kra-wa-la. Se-ga-la se-ra-

and stars and an-gels a-bove. Praise the LORD, whose word es-
and wind and storm clouds on high. Praise the LORD your Mak-er,
the heights let prais-es re-sound to the LORD, the source of

fim ke-ru-bim, pu-ji-lah Di-a be-sar-kan-

tab-lished the heav-ens, who up-holds all his works in
all liv-ing crea-tures, all the beasts in the fields and
strength and sal-va-tion for all peo-ple on whom his

lah Na-ma-Nya. Ber-so-rak so-rai ba-gi Ra-ja-mu!

his sov-ereign love. God reigns on high, let the heav-ens re-joice!
birds in the sky. Both young and old, come and join in the song!
fa-vor is found. Praise God, you saints he has claimed for his own!

Oh!
*Sing only when repeating

For other settings of Ps. 148 see 6, 555

Words: Indonesian, Tilly Lubis © 2009 Yamuger, Indonesian Institute for Sacred Music; English vers. David
Diephouse © 2009 Faith Alive Christian Resources
Music (NYANYIKANLAH): traditional Batak melody, Toba, Indonesia; arr. H.A. Pandopo © 1999 H. A. Pandopo

551　All Creatures of Our God and King

Chord symbols represent a simplified harmony.

For an alternate arrangement see 208, 317, 847

Words: Francis of Assisi, 1225; tr. William H. Draper, c. 1910, alt., P.D.
Music (LASST UNS ERFREUEN 8.8.8.8.8.8.6.4.4.4): *Auserlesen Catholische Geistliche Kirchengesänge*, Cologne,
  1623; adapt. and harm. Ralph Vaughan Williams (1872-1958), 1906, P.D.

4 Earth ever fertile, day by day
bring forth your blessings on our way;
alleluia, alleluia!
All flowers and fruits that in you grow,
let them his glory also show:
O praise him, O praise him,
alleluia, alleluia, alleluia!

5 All you who are of tender heart,
forgiving others, take your part;
alleluia, alleluia!
All you who pain and sorrow bear,
praise God and on him cast your care:
O praise him, O praise him,
alleluia, alleluia, alleluia!

6 Let all things their Creator bless,
and worship him in humbleness,
alleluia, alleluia!
Praise, praise the Father, praise the Son,
and praise the Spirit, Three in One:
O praise him, O praise him,
alleluia, alleluia, alleluia!

Alleluia

552

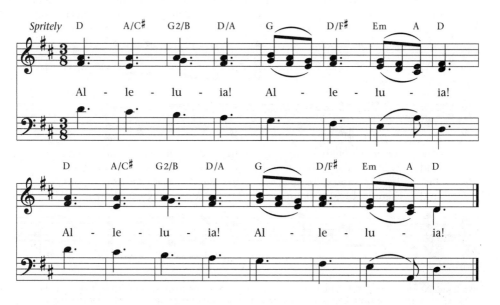

Words: traditional
Music (ALLELUIA DUNCAN): Norah Duncan IV © 1987 GIA Publications, Inc.

553 How Great Thou Art

1 O Lord, my God, when I in awe-some won-der
2 When through the woods and for-est glades I wan-der,
3 But when I think that God, his Son not spar-ing,
4 When Christ shall come, with shout of ac-cla-ma-tion,

con-sid-er all the works thy hand hath made,
I hear the birds sing sweet-ly in the trees;
sent him to die, I scarce can take it in,
and take me home, what joy shall fill my heart!

I see the stars, I hear the roll-ing thun-der,
when I look down from loft-y moun-tain gran-deur
that on the cross, my bur-den glad-ly bear-ing,
Then I shall bow in hum-ble ad-o-ra-tion

thy power through-out the u-ni-verse dis-played;
and hear the brook and feel the gen-tle breeze;
he bled and died to take a-way my sin;
and there pro-claim, "My God, how great thou art!"

Words and Music (HOW GREAT THOU ART 11.10.11.10 refrain 10.8.10.8): Stuart K. Hine, 1949, © 1949, 1953, The Stuart Hine Trust, USA print rights admin. Hope Publishing Company. All other USA rights admin. by EMICMGPublishing.com

Refrain

Then sings my soul, my Sav-ior God, to thee: how great thou art,

how great thou art! Then sings my soul, my Sav-ior God, to thee:

how great thou art, how great thou art!

We Gather in Your Presence 554

We gather in your presence,
King of the Universe,
to acclaim your great salvation.
You have done marvelous things.
You rescued your people from sin and death,
through the mighty work of Jesus, your Son.
You send missionaries to the ends of the earth.
You raise up prophets to witness to justice.
You reveal your righteousness to the nations.
Send forth your Spirit, Lord;
renew the face of the earth.

The whole earth rejoices.
Waves crash over waves in echoes of praise.
Rivers proclaim your goodness
as they cascade against their beds.
Mountains, standing together as a chorus,
declare your faithfulness.
Wind whispering through the leaves
make music to you.

Creatures of all shapes and sizes
join in the song.
Into this glorious harmony
send forth your Spirit, Lord;
renew the face of the earth.

We too raise our voices, Almighty God.
With all the earth, we shout for joy.
We burst into jubilant song
for the marvelous things you have done.
For your faithfulness, for your love,
for your salvation,
for the promise of your return in glory,
we make music to you, our Lord and King.
While we wait for your coming,
send forth your Spirit, Lord;
renew the face of the earth. Amen.

Text: based on Psalm 98 and Psalm 104:30, from *The Worship Sourcebook* 2nd edition, Faith Alive Christian Resources, 2013, © Creative Commons Attribution-NonCommercial-ShareAlike

555 Let All Creation's Wonders

PSALM 148

Unison

1 Let all cre - a - tion's won - ders and count - less an - gel hordes
2 From far be - neath the o - ceans let joy - ful songs a - rise,
3 So let us lift our voic - es for all that we are worth

u - nite in cease - less wor - ship to praise the Lord of lords:
while hail and wind and light - ning toss psalms a - cross the skies.
to God whose time - less splen - dor sur - pass - es heaven and earth:

he spoke, and formed the cos - mos; he set the stars in place;
You beasts of farm and jun - gle, let na - ture's hymn be heard;
in love he chose and called us, a peo - ple of his own,

his voice de - fines the con - tours of in - ter - stel - lar space—
tell out your mak - er's great - ness, each in - sect, ev - ery bird;
and gave to us a Sav - ior to make his mer - cy known.

For other settings of Ps. 148 see 6, 550

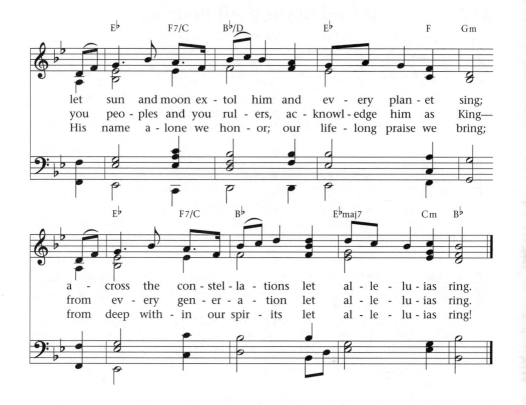

let   sun   and moon ex - tol   him   and   ev - ery   plan - et   sing;
you   peo - ples and you rul - ers,   ac - knowl - edge   him   as   King—
His   name   a - lone we hon - or;   our   life - long praise we   bring;

a - cross the   con - stel - la - tions let   al - le - lu - ias   ring.
from   ev - ery   gen - er - a - tion   let   al - le - lu - ias   ring.
from   deep with - in   our spir - its   let   al - le - lu - ias   ring!

A Song of Creation (Benedicite) 556

All you works of the Lord: **bless the Lord.**
Angels and all heavenly hosts: **bless the Lord.**
Sun, moon, and stars: **bless the Lord.**
Rain and dew, wind and cloud: **bless the Lord.**
Fire and ice, summer and winter: **bless the Lord.**
Night and day, light and darkness: **bless the Lord.**
Mountains and hills, all that grows in the ground: **bless the Lord.**
Rivers and seas, all that has life in the water: **bless the Lord.**
Birds of the air, wild beasts, and tame animals: **bless the Lord.**
People on earth, you servants of the Lord: **bless the Lord.**
Give thanks to the Lord for he is good, **for his mercy endures forever.**

557   O God Beyond All Praising

1 O God be-yond all prais-ing, we wor-ship you to-day
2 The flower of earth-ly splen-dor in time must sure-ly die,
3 Then hear, O gra-cious Sav-ior, ac-cept the love we bring,

and sing the love a-maz-ing that songs can-not re-pay;
its fra-gile bloom sur-ren-der to you, the Lord most high;
that we who know your fa-vor may serve you as our King;

for we can on-ly won-der at__ ev-ery gift you send,
but hid-den from all na-ture the e-ter-nal seed is sown—
and wheth-er our to-mor-rows be__ filled with good or ill,

at bless-ings with-out num-ber and mer-cies with-out end.
though small in mor-tal sta-ture, to hea-ven's gar-den grown:
we'll tri-umph through our sor-rows and rise to bless you still:

We lift our hearts be-fore you and wait up-on your Word,
for Christ, your gift from heav-en, from death has set us free,
to mar-vel at your beau-ty and glo-ry in your ways,

we hon-or and a-dore you, our great and might-y Lord.
and we through him are giv-en the fi-nal vic-to-ry.
and make a joy-ful du-ty our sac-ri-fice of praise.

For accompaniment see 555

Words: Michael Perry (1942-1996) © 1982, 1987 The Jubilate Group, admin. Hope Publishing Company
Music (THAXTED 7.6.7.6 triple): Gustav Holst (1874-1934), 1921, P.D.

O Praise God's Name Together

PSALM 135

558

1 O praise God's name to-geth - er, you ser - vants of the LORD;
2 O LORD, no mind can mea - sure the great-ness of your might;
3 For you, LORD of cre - a - tion, con - trol your vast do - main;
4 False gods may rise be - fore us, their van - i - ty dis - play;

O LORD, for all your fa - vor to us, you are a - dored!
you gave the earth its or - bit and set the stars to flight.
you speak, and na - tions trem - ble; in ho - ly peace you reign.
but as the hands that made them, they too shall fade a - way.

With - in your ho - ly tem - ple, be - fore your sa - cred throne,
The clouds you raised in heav - en give to the fields their rain;
When kings en - slave your cho - sen, your might un - bars the door;
Your name, O God Al - might - y, en - dures for end - less days;

the cho - sen heirs of Ja - cob pro - claim you God a - lone!
your word lifts waves from o - ceans and moun-tains from the plain.
and ty - rants, once in pow - er, now kneel be - fore the poor.
and new - born gen - er - a - tions u - nite to sing your praise.

Chord symbols represent a simplified harmony.

Words: Michael Morgan © 2011 Michael Morgan, admin. Faith Alive Christian Resources
Music (AURELIA 7.6.7.6 D): Samuel S. Wesley, 1864, P.D.

559 **Ten Thousand Reasons**

Words and Music: Jonas Myrin and Matt Redman © 2011 Shout! Publishing, sixsteps Music, Said and Done Music and Thankyou Music (PRS), admin. in the United States and Canada at EMICMGPUBLISHING.com, sixsteps Music and Said and Done Music admin. at EMICMGPUBLISHING.com, Thankyou Music admin. worldwide at EMICMGPUBLISHING.com excluding Europe which is admin. at Kingswaysongs

ᶅ it's time to sing your___ song a-gain.
name___ is___ great, and your heart is kind.
end___ draws___ near, and my time has come;

Whatever may
For all___ your
ᶅ still,___ my

pass,___ and what-ev-er lies be-fore me,
good-ness, I will keep___ on___ sing-ing—
soul will sing your praise___ un - end-ing—

let me be
ten thou-sand
ten thou-sand

To Refrain

sing - ing when the eve-ning comes.
rea - sons for my heart to find.
years and then for - ev - er - more!

Coda

wor-ship your ho - ly name,

wor-ship your ho - ly name.

560   We Praise You, O God

1 We praise you, O God, our Re - deem - er, Cre - a - tor;
2 We wor - ship you, God of our fa - thers and moth - ers;
3 With voic - es u - nit - ed our prais - es we of - fer;

in grate - ful de - vo - tion our trib - ute we bring.
through life's storm and tem - pest our guide you have been.
our songs of thanks - giv - ing to you we now raise.

We lay it be - fore you, we kneel and a - dore you;
When per - ils o'er - take us, you nev - er for - sake us.
Your strong arm will guide us, our God is be - side us.

we bless your ho - ly name, glad prais - es we sing.
And with your help, O Lord, our bat - tles we win.
To you, our great Re - deem - er, for - e'er be praise!

Chord symbols represent a simplifed harmony.

Words: Julia C. Cory, 1902, alt., P.D.
Music (KREMSER 12.11.12.11): A. Valerius, *Nederlandtsch Gedenckclanck,* 1626, P.D.

I Will Extol You, O My God

561

PSALM 145

1 I will ex - tol you, O my God, and praise you, O my King;
2 Each gen - er - a - tion to the next shall tes - ti - mo - ny bear,
3 Your might-y acts and glo - rious deeds we shall with awe con - fess.

yes, ev - ery day and ev - er - more your prais - es I will sing.
and to your praise, from age to age, your won - drous acts de - clare.
Your good - ness we will cel - e - brate and sing your right - eous - ness.

Great is the LORD, our might - y God, and great - ly to be praised;
Up - on your glo - rious maj - es - ty and hon - or I will dwell,
Most gra - cious and com - pas - sion - ate is God, who reigns a - bove;

his great - ness is un - search - a - ble, a - bove all glo - ry raised.
and all your grand and glo - rious works and great - ness I will tell.
his wrath is ev - er slow to rise, un - bound - ed is his love.

For other settings of Ps. 145 see 37, 562

Words: *Psalter,* 1912, alt., P.D.
Music (GERARD/NOEL 8.6.8.6 D): English; adapt. Arthur S. Sullivan, 1874, P.D.

562

We Will Extol You, God and King

PSALM 145

For other settings of Ps. 145 see 37, 561

Words and Music (SCARECROW 8.7.8.7 refrain 10.9.10.10): Greg Scheer © 2006 Faith Alive Christian Resources

Optional call to worship (from Ps. 78:3-7)

We will not hide things we have heard and known, stories our ancestors have told.
We will tell the next generation.
We will recount the praiseworthy deeds and power of the Lord,
so that children yet unborn will know them and tell them to their children,
so that they will set their hope in God and obey God's commands.

563 Praise Ye the Lord, Hallelujah

PSALM 150

For other settings of Ps. 150 see 7, 952

Words and Music (CLEVELAND irregular): J. Jefferson Cleveland (1937-1986) © 1981 Abingdon Press, admin. The Copyright Company

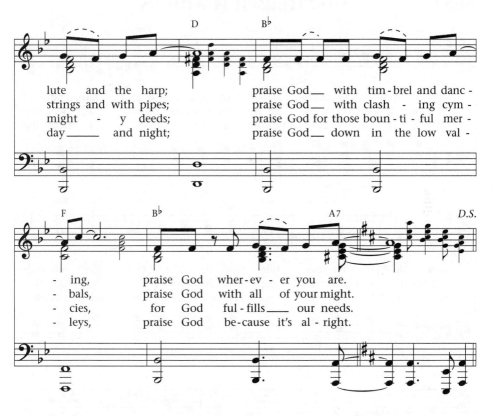

lute and the harp; praise God with tim-brel and danc-
strings and with pipes; praise God with clash - ing cym-
might - y deeds; praise God for those boun - ti - ful mer-
day and night; praise God down in the low val-

- ing, praise God wher-ev - er you are.
- bals, praise God with all of your might.
- cies, for God ful - fills our needs.
- leys, praise God be-cause it's al - right.

Alleluia, Alleluia 564

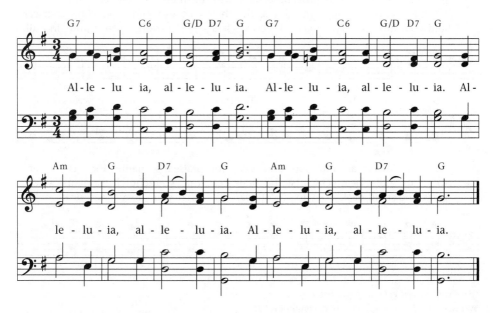

Al-le-lu - ia, al-le-lu - ia. Al-le-lu - ia, al-le-lu - ia. Al-

le-lu - ia, al-le-lu - ia. Al-le-lu - ia, al-le-lu - ia.

Words and Music (ALLELUIA SOUTH AFRICA): South African traditional

565 God Himself Is with Us

1 God him-self is with us; let us now a - dore him, and with
2 God him-self is with us; hear the harps re - sound - ing! See the
3 Fount of ev - ery bless - ing, pur - i - fy my spir - it, trust - ing

awe ap - pear be - fore him. God is in his tem - ple; all with -
crowds the throne sur - round - ing! "Ho - ly, ho - ly, ho - ly," hear the
on - ly in your mer - it. Like the ho - ly an - gels who be -

in keep si - lence, pros - trate lie with deep-est rev - erence. Him a - lone
hymn as-cend - ing, an - gels, saints, their voic - es blend - ing! Bow your ear
hold your glo - ry, may I cease - less - ly a - dore you, and in all,

do we own as our God and Sav - ior; praise his name for - ev - er.
to us here; hear, O Christ, the prais - es that your church now rais - es.
great and small, seek to do most near - ly what you love so dear - ly.

Chord symbols represent a simplified harmony.

Words: Gerhardt Tersteegen (1729); tr. composite, P.D.
Music (ARNSBERG/WUNDERBARER KÖNIG 6.6.8.6.6.8.6.6.6): Joachim Neander, 1680, P.D.

Give Praise to Our God

566

PSALM 149

1 Give praise to our God and sing a new song,
2 With tim-brel and harp and joy-ful ac-claim,
3 In glo-ry ex-ult, you saints of the Word;
4 For this is God's word: the saints shall not fail,

a-mid all the saints God's prais-es pro-long;
with glad-ness and mirth, we praise your great name;
with songs in the night high prais-es ac-cord;
but o-ver the earth the hum-ble pre-vail;

a song to your Mak-er and Rul-er now raise,
for now in your peo-ple your plea-sure you seek,
go forth in God's ser-vice, be strong in God's might
all rul-ers and na-tions shall yield to their sway.

all chil-dren of Zi-on, re-joice and give praise.
with robes of sal-va-tion a-dorn-ing the meek.
to con-quer all e-vil and stand for the right.
To God give the glo-ry; sing prais-es for aye.

Chord symbols represent a simplified harmony.

Words: *Psalter,* 1912, alt. 1995, P.D.
Music (LAUDATE DOMINUM 10.10.11.11): C. Parry H. Hubert, 1894, P.D.

567

Here I Am to Worship

1 Light of the world, you stepped down in-to dark-ness, o - pened my
2 King of all days, oh so high - ly ex - al - ted, glo - rious in

eyes, let me see. Beau - ty that made this_ heart_ a - dore you,
heav-en a - bove. Hum - bly you came to the earth you cre-a-ted,

hope of a life spent with you.
all for love's sake be - came poor.

Refrain

Here I am to

wor - ship; here I am to bow down; here I am to say that you're my God.

You're al - to - geth - er love - ly, al - to - geth - er wor - thy, al - to - geth - er

Words and Music (HERE I AM TO WORSHIP): Tim Hughes; acc. Ed Bolduc © 2001 Thankyou Music, admin.
EMICMGPublishing.com (excl. Europe which is admin. by Kingswaysongs)

568 I Will Sing of My Redeemer

1 I will sing of my Re-deem-er and his won-drous love to me;
2 I will tell the won-drous sto - ry, how my lost es - tate to save,
3 I will praise my dear Re-deem-er, his tri - umph-ant power I'll tell,
4 I will sing of my Re-deem-er and his heaven-ly love to me;

on the cru - el cross he suf - fered, from the curse to set me free.
in his bound-less love and mer - cy he the ran - som free - ly gave.
how the vic - to - ry he give - th o - ver sin and death and hell.
he from death to life has brought me, Son of God, with him to be.

Refrain

Sing, oh, sing of my Re - deem - er, with his
Sing, oh, sing of my Re-deem - er, sing, oh, sing of my Re-deem-er, with his

blood he pur - chased me;
blood he pur - chased me, with his blood he pur - chased me;

Words: Philip P. Bliss, 1878, P.D.
Music (MY REDEEMER 8.7.8.7 refrain 8.7.8.7): James McGranahan (1840-1907); rev. 1956, P.D.

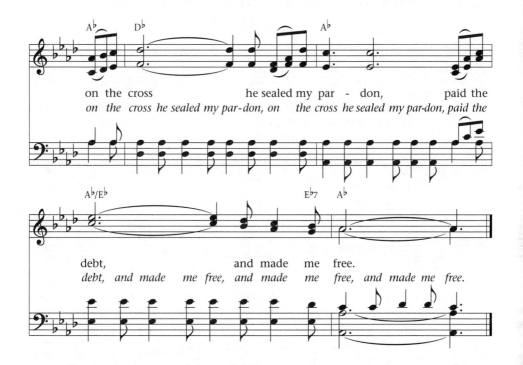

on the cross   he sealed my par - don,   paid the
on the cross he sealed my par-don, on   the cross he sealed my par-don, paid the

debt,   and made   me   free.
debt,   and made   me free,   and made   me   free,   and made me free.

Affirmation: The Benefits of Christ's Death and Resurrection   569

What further benefit do we receive
from Christ's sacrifice and death on the cross?

**By Christ's power
our old selves are crucified,
put to death, and buried with him,
so that the evil desires of the flesh
may no longer rule us,
but that instead we may offer ourselves
as a sacrifice of gratitude to him.**

How does Christ's resurrection benefit us?

**First, by his resurrection he has overcome death,
so that he might make us share in the righteousness
he obtained for us by his death.**

**Second, by his power we too
are already raised to a new life.**

**Third, Christ's resurrection
is a sure pledge to us of our blessed resurrection.**

Text: Heidelberg Catechism Q&A 43, 45

570   From All That Dwell Below the Skies

PSALM 117

1 From all that dwell be - low the skies   let the Cre - a - tor's praise a -
2 In ev - ery land be - gin the song,   to ev - ery land the strains be -
3 E - ter - nal are thy mer - cies, Lord;   e - ter - nal truth at - tends thy

rise: Al - le - lu - ia! Al - le - lu - ia! Let the Re - deem - er's
long: Al - le - lu - ia! Al - le - lu - ia! In cheer - ful sound all
word: Al - le - lu - ia! Al - le - lu - ia! Thy praise shall sound from

name be sung through ev - ery land, in ev - ery tongue.
voic - es raise and fill the world with joy - ful praise. Al - le - lu - ia!
shore to shore, till suns shall rise and set no more.

Al - le - lu - ia! Al - le - lu - ia, al - le - lu - ia, al - le - lu - ia!

Chord symbols represent a simplifed harmony.

For an alternate arrangement see 208, 317, 847

For other settings of Ps. 117 see 279, 588, 589, 591

Words: Isaac Watts (1674-1748), 1719, P.D.
Music (LASST UNS ERFREUEN 8.8.4.4.8.8 with alleluias): *Auserlesen Catholische Geistliche Kirchengesänge*,
  Cologne, 1623; adapt. and harm. Ralph Vaughan Williams, 1906, P.D.

Praise, My Soul, the King of Heaven 571

PSALM 103

1 Praise, my soul, the King of heav - en; to his feet your trib-ute bring.
2 Praise him for his grace and fa - vor to his peo-ple in dis-tress.
3 Fa - ther-like he tends and spares us; well our fee-ble frame he knows.

Ran - somed, healed, re - stored, for - giv - en, ev - er-more his prais-es sing.
Praise him, still the same as ev - er, slow to chide, and swift to bless.
In his hand he gent - ly bears us, res-cues us from all our foes.

Al - le - lu - ia, al - le - lu - ia! Praise the ev - er - last-ing King!
Al - le - lu - ia, al - le - lu - ia! Glo - rious in his faith-ful - ness!
Al - le - lu - ia, al - le - lu - ia! Wide - ly yet his mer - cy flows!

4 Frail as summer's flower we flourish,
blows the wind and it is gone;
but while mortals rise and perish
God endures unchanging on.
Alleluia, alleluia!
Praise the High, Eternal One.

5 Angels, help us to adore him;
you behold him face to face.
Sun and moon, bow down before him,
dwellers all in time and space.
Alleluia, alleluia!
Praise with us the God of grace!

For other settings of Ps. 103 see 516, 671, 672, 836

Words: Henry F. Lyte, 1834, alt., P.D.
Music (LAUDA ANIMA 8.7.8.7.8.7): John Goss, 1869, P.D.

572 Sing Praise to God Who Reigns Above

1 Sing praise to God who reigns a - bove, the God of all cre -
2 What God's al-might-y power has made, in mer - cy he is
3 The Lord is nev - er far a - way, but through all grief dis -
4 We sought the Lord in our dis-tress; O God, in mer - cy
5 Let all who name Christ's ho - ly name give God the praise and

a - tion, the God of power, the God of love, the God of
keep - ing; by morn-ing glow or eve - ning shade his eye is
> tress - ing, an ev - er pres - ent help and stay, our peace, and
hear us. Our Sav - ior saw our help - less - ness and came with
glo - ry. Let all who know his power pro - claim a - loud the

our sal - va - tion. My soul with com - fort rich he fills, and
nev - er sleep - ing. And where he rules in king - ly might, there
> joy, and bless - ing; as with a mo-ther's ten - der hand, God
peace to cheer us. For this we thank and praise the Lord, who
won - drous sto - ry. Cast ev - er - y i - dol from its throne; the

ev - ery grief he gent-ly stills: to God all praise and glo - ry!
all is just and all is right: to God all praise and glo - ry!
> gent-ly leads the cho-sen band: to God all praise and glo - ry!
is by one and all a - dored: to God all praise and glo - ry!
Lord is God, and he a - lone: to God all praise and glo - ry!

Words: Johann J. Schütz, 1675; tr. Frances Cox, 1864, alt., P.D.
Music (MIT FREUDEN ZART 8.7.8.7.8.8.7): Bohemian Brethren's *Kirchengesänge*, 1566; harm. Heinrich Rei-
mann, 1895, P.D.

Not unto Us, O Lord of Heaven

573

PSALM 115

1 Not un-to us, O Lord of heaven, but un-to you be glo-ry given. In love and truth you do ful-fill the coun-sels of your sov-ereign will; though na-tions fail your power to own, yet you still reign, and you a-lone.

2 The i-dol gods of hea-then lands are but the work of hu-man hands; they can-not see, they can-not speak, their ears are deaf, their hands are weak; like them shall be all those who hold to gods of sil-ver and of gold.

3 So let us trust in God a-lone, the Lord whose grace and power are known; and our com-plete al-le-giance yield to God who is our help and shield. Join, heaven and earth, in sweet ac-cord; sing "Hal-le-lu-jah, praise the Lord!"

Chord symbols represent a simplified harmony.

For an alternate arrangement see 919

Words: *Psalter*, 1912, alt., P.D.
Music (VATER UNSER 8.8.8.8.8.8): V. Schumann's *Geistliche Lieder*, 1539; arr. Alfred V. Fedak (1953) © 2011
  Alfred V. Fedak, admin. Faith Alive Christian Resources

574   How Great Is Our God

1 The splen-dor of the King, clothed in maj-es-ty;
2 From age to age he stands, and time is in his hands;

let all the earth re-joice, let all the earth re-joice.
be-gin-ning and the end, be-gin-ning and the end.

He wraps him-self in light, and
The god-head, three in one,

dark-ness tries to hide, and trem-bles at his voice,
Fa-ther, Spir-it, Son, the li-on and the lamb,

Words and Music (HOW GREAT IS OUR GOD): Chris Tomlin, Jesse Reeves and Ed Cash © 2004
worshiptogether.com songs/SixSteps Music (ASCAP), admin. EMI CMG Publishing/Alletrop Music (BMI)

575   Praise to the Lord, the Almighty

Chord symbols represent a simplifed harmony.

Words: Joachim Neander, 1680; tr. Catherine Winkworth, 1863, alt., P.D.
Music (LOBE DEN HERREN 14.14.4.7.8): *Ernewerten Gesangbuch, Stralsund,* 1665; desc. Craig S. Lang
  (1891-1971) © Novello and Co., Ltd, admin. G. Schirmer, Inc.

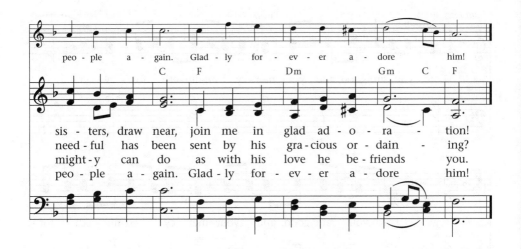

peo - ple a - gain. Glad - ly for - ev - er a - dore him!

| C | F | | Dm | | Gm | C | F |

sis - ters, draw near, join me in glad ad - o - ra - tion!
need - ful has been sent by his gra - cious or - dain - ing?
might - y can do as with his love he be - friends you.
peo - ple a - gain. Glad - ly for - ev - er a - dore him!

Bless the Lord, Bless the Lord 576

Leader 1 You chil - dren, F C7 F you chil - dren, Gm C you chil - dren.

All Bless the Lord, bless the Lord,

F C7 Dm Gm F/C C7 F 2 To - geth - er,

bless the Lord, there is no oth - er God.

Ad lib call by leader
3 My sisters . . .
4 My brothers . . .
5 You elders . . .

Words and Music (BLESS THE LORD, BLESS THE LORD): Kenyan traditional, P.D.

577 You Are Good

Words and Music (YOU ARE GOOD): Israel Houghton © 2001 Integrity's Praise! Music (BMI), admin.
EMICMGPublishing.com; arr. Denise Miersma © 2012 EMICMGPublishing.com

578 **Forever**

Optional prayer (based on Ps. 90:1-2)

Holy God, by your Holy Spirit,
open our minds and hearts
to the immensity of your glory.
Teach us what it means to confess:
"Before the mountains were born,
before you formed the world which you so love,
from everlasting to everlasting you are God."
From everlasting to everlasting, you are God.
Truly, you are our dwelling place through all generations. Amen.

579 Immortal, Invisible, God Only Wise

1 Im - mor - tal, in - vis - i - ble, God on - ly wise,
2 Un - rest - ing, un - hast - ing, and si - lent as light,
3 To all, life thou giv - est, to both great and small;
4 Thou reign - est in glo - ry, thou rul - est in light,

in light in - ac - ces - si - ble hid from our eyes,
nor want - ing, nor wast - ing, thou rul - est in might;
in all life thou liv - est, the true life of all;
thine an - gels a - dore thee, all veil - ing their sight;

most bless - ed, most glo - rious, the An - cient of Days,
thy jus - tice like moun - tains high soar - ing a - bove,
we blos - som and flour - ish like leaves on the tree,
all praise we would ren - der; O help us to see

al - might - y, vic - to - rious, thy great name we praise.
thy clouds which are foun - tains of good - ness and love.
then with - er and per - ish, but naught chang - eth thee.
'tis on - ly the splen - dor of light hid - eth thee!

Words: Walter C. Smith, 1867, alt., P.D.
Music (ST. DENIO 11.11.11.11): Welsh, in J. Roberts' *Caniadau y Cyssegr*, 1839, P.D.

Our God

1 Wa - ter you turned in - to wine,   o - pened the eyes
2 In - to the dark - ness you shine;   out of the ash-

of the blind;   there's no one like you,
- es we rise.   There's no one like you,

none like   you.
none like   you.

(continues)

581   Joyful, Joyful, We Adore Thee

1 Joy - ful, joy - ful, we a - dore thee, God of glo - ry, Lord of love;
2 All thy works with joy sur - round thee, earth and heaven re - flect thy rays;
3 Thou art giv - ing and for - giv - ing, ev - er bless - ing, ev - er blest,

hearts un - fold like flowers be - fore thee, open - ing to the sun a - bove.
stars and an - gels sing a - round thee, cen - ter of un - bro - ken praise.
well - spring of the joy of liv - ing, o - cean depth of hap - py rest!

Melt the clouds of sin and sad - ness, drive the gloom of doubt a - way;
Field and for - est, vale and moun - tain, flower - y mead - ow, flash - ing sea,
Thou our Fa - ther, Christ, our broth - er, all who live in love are thine;

giv - er of im - mor - tal glad - ness, fill us with the light of day!
chant - ing bird and flow - ing foun - tain call us to re - joice in thee.
teach us how to love each oth - er, lift us to the joy di - vine.

Words: Henry Van Dyke (1852-1933), P.D.
Music (HYMN TO JOY 8.7.8.7 D): Ludwig van Beethoven (1770-1827), 1824, adapt. Edward Hodges
  (1796-1867), alt., P.D.

You Servants of God, Your Master Proclaim 582

1 You ser-vants of God, your Mas-ter pro-claim,
2 God rules in the height, al-might-y to save;
3 "Sal-va-tion to God, who sits on the throne!"
4 Then let us a-dore and give him his right:

and pub-lish a-broad his won-der-ful name;
though hid from our sight, his pres-ence we have;
let all cry a-loud, and hon-or the Son;
all glo-ry and power, all wis-dom and might,

the name all-vic-to-rious of Je-sus ex-tol;
the great con-gre-ga-tion his tri-umph shall sing,
the prais-es of Je-sus the an-gels pro-claim,
all hon-or and bless-ing—with an-gels a-bove—

his king-dom is glo-ri-ous and rules o-ver all.
as-crib-ing sal-va-tion to Je-sus, our King.
fall down on their fac-es and wor-ship the Lamb.
and thanks nev-er ceas-ing for in-fi-nite love.

Chord symbols represent a simplified harmony.

Words: Charles Wesley, 1744, alt., P.D.
Music (HANOVER 10.10.11.11): arr. William Croft, 1708, P.D.

583   O Love of God, How Strong and True

1 O love of God, how strong and true,
2 O heaven - ly love, how pre - cious still in days of
3 O wide - em - brac - ing, won - drous love! We read you
4 We read you in the flowers, the trees, the fresh - ness

and yet ev - er new, un - com - pre - hend - ed
wea - ri - ness and ill, in nights of pain and
in the sky a - bove, we read you in the
of the fra - grant breeze, the song of birds up -

and un - bought, be - yond all knowl - edge and all thought.
help - less - ness, to heal, to com - fort, and to bless.
earth be - low, in seas that swell and streams that flow.
on the wing, the joy of sum - mer and of spring.

5 We read you best in him who came
to bear for us the cross of shame,
sent by the Father from on high,
our life to live, our death to die.

6 We read your power to bless and save
even in the darkness of the grave;
still more in resurrection light
we read the fullness of your might.

7 O love of God, our shield and stay
through all the perils of our way;
eternal love, in you we rest,
forever safe, forever blest.

Chord symbols represent a simplified harmony.

Words: Horatius Bonar, 1861, P.D.
Music (WAREHAM 8.8.8.8): William Knapp, 1738, P.D.; harm. Emily R. Brink (b. 1940) © 1994 Faith Alive
  Christian Resources

Je louerai l'Eternel/
Praise, I Will Praise You, Lord

French 1 Je loue-rai l'E-ter-nel de tout mon coeur,
English 1 Praise, I will praise you, Lord, with all my heart.
2 Love, I will love you, Lord, with all my heart.
3 Serve, I will serve you, Lord, with all my heart.

je ra-con-te-rai tou-tes___ tes mer-veilles, je chan-te-rai ton nom.
O God, I will tell the won-ders of your ways and glo-ri-fy your name.

Je loue-rai l'E-ter-nel de tout mon coeur,
Praise, I will praise you, Lord, with all my heart.
Love, I will love you, Lord, with all my heart.
Serve, I will serve you, Lord, with all my heart.

je fe-rai de toi le su-jet de ma joie. Al-le-lu-ia!
In you I will find the source of all my joy. Al-le-lu-ia!

Words: based on Psalm 9:1-2, Claude Frayssé © 1976 Claude Frayssé; tr. Kenneth I. Morse © 1989 The Hymnal
Project, used by permission of Brethren Press
Music (JE LOUERAI L'ETERNAL 6.4.11.6.6.4.11.4): Claude Frayssé © 1976 Claude Frayssé

585 With Grateful Heart My Thanks I Bring

PSALM 138

1 With grate-ful heart my thanks I bring; be-fore the "gods" your praise I sing.
2 I cried to you, and you did save; your word of grace new cour-age gave.
3 O LORD, en-throned in glo-ry bright, you reign a-lone in heaven-ly height;
4 You will stretch forth your might-y arm to save me when my foes a-larm.

I wor-ship in your ho-ly place and praise you for your
The kings of earth shall thank you, LORD, for they have heard your
the proud in vain your fa-vor seek, but you have mer-cy
The work you have for me be-gun shall by your grace be

truth and grace; for truth and grace to-geth-er shine in
won-drous word; yes, they shall come with songs of praise for
for the meek. Through trou-ble though my path-way be, you
ful-ly done. Your love for-ev-er will en-dure: your

your most ho-ly Word di-vine, in your most ho-ly Word di-vine.
great and glo-rious are your ways, for great and glo-rious are your ways.
will re-vive and strength-en me, you will re-vive and strength-en me.
mer-cy, LORD, is ev-er sure; your mer-cy, LORD, is ev-er sure.

For another setting of Ps. 138 see 323

Words: *Psalter,* 1912, alt., P.D.
Music (SOLID ROCK 8.8.8.8.8.8.8.8): William B. Bradbury, 1863, P.D.

I Greet Thee, Who My Sure Redeemer Art 586

1 I greet thee, who my sure Re-deem-er art, my on-ly
trust and Sav-ior of my heart, who pain didst un-der-go for
my poor sake; I pray thee from our hearts all cares to take.

2 Thou art the King of mer-cy and of grace, reign-ing om-
nip-o-tent in ev-ery place: so come, O King, and our whole
be-ing sway; shine on us with the light of thy pure day.

3 Thou art the life by which a-lone we live, and all our
sub-stance and our strength re-ceive; sus-tain us by thy faith and
by thy power, and give us strength in ev-ery try-ing hour.

4 Thou hast the true and perfect gentleness,
no harshness hast thou and no bitterness:
O grant to us the grace we find in thee,
that we may dwell in perfect unity.

5 Our hope is in no other save in thee;
our faith is built upon thy promise free;
Lord, give us peace, and make us calm and sure,
that in thy strength we evermore endure.

Chord symbols represent a simplified harmony.

Words: anonymous, French, 1545; tr. Elizabeth Lee Smith 1868, P.D.
Music (TOULON 10.10.10.10): *Genevan Psalter,* 1551; adapt. from GENEVAN 124, P.D.

587 Praise Him! Jesus, Blessed Savior

Bān-bîn ah/Let All Nations Praise the Lord 588
PSALM 117

For other settings of Ps. 117 see 279, 570, 589, 591

Words: Psalm 117, tr. Hsiang-chi Chang and I-to Loh (b. 1936), alt. © 1990 Christian Conference of Asia,
  admin. GIA Publications, Inc.
Music (O-LÓ 7.7.7.7): Hsiang-chi Chang and I-to Loh © 1990, 2000 and arr. I-to Loh (b. 1936) © 2011
  Christian Conference of Asia, admin. GIA Publications, Inc.

Psalm 117 589

Praise the LORD, all you nations;
  extol him, all you peoples.
For great is his love toward us,
  and the faithfulness of the LORD, endures forever.

Praise the LORD.

For other settings of Ps. 117 see 279, 570, 588, 591

590   Oh, for a Thousand Tongues to Sing

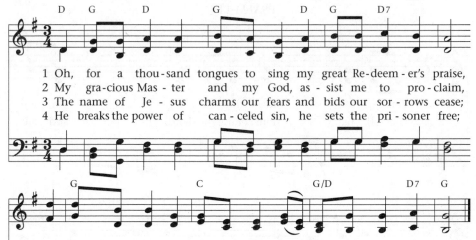

1 Oh, for a thou-sand tongues to sing my great Re-deem-er's praise,
2 My gra-cious Mas - ter and my God, as - sist me to pro-claim,
3 The name of Je - sus charms our fears and bids our sor - rows cease;
4 He breaks the power of can-celed sin, he sets the pri-soner free;

the glo - ries of my God and King, the tri-umphs of his grace!
to spread through all the earth a - broad the hon-ors of your name.
'tis mu - sic in the sin-ner's ears, 'tis life and health and peace.
his blood can make the foul-est clean; his blood a - vailed for me.

5 He speaks, and, listening to his voice,
  new life the dead receive;
  the mournful, broken hearts rejoice;
  the humble poor believe.

6 Look unto him, your Savior own,
  O fallen human race!
  Look and be saved through faith alone,
  be justified by grace!

7 Hear him, you deaf; you voiceless ones,
  your loosened tongues employ;
  you blind, behold your Savior come;
  and leap, you lame, for joy!

8 To God all glory, praise, and love
  be now and ever given
  by saints below and saints above,
  the church in earth and heaven.

French
1 Seigneur, que n'aije mille voix
  pour chanter tes louanges.
  Et faire monter jusqu' aux anges
  les glories de ta croix!

Spanish
1 Mil voces para celebrar
  a mi Libertador,
  las glorias de su majestad,
  los triunfos de su amor.

Korean
1 만 입이 내게 있으면
  그 입 다 가지고
  내 구주 주신 은총을
  늘 찬송하겠네

Japanese
1 すべての人々
  ほめたたえよ、
  御神の栄光
  恵みの勝利。

Mandarin
1 但愿万口欢声高唱，
  颂扬救主我王，
  赞美我神恩爱深长，
  并他莫大荣光。

Words: English Charles Wesley, 1739, alt., P.D.; French Ruben Sailens, (d. 1942) © Ruben Sailens; Spanish Federico J. Pagura © 1989 The United Methodist Publishing House, admin. The Copyright Company; Korean Eunae Chung © 2012 Faith Alive Christian Resources; Japanese Reita Yazawa © 2012 Faith Alive Christian Resources; Mandarin Phoebe H'fe © 2012 Faith Alive Christian Resources
Music (AZMON 8.6.8.6): Carl G. Gläser, 1828; adapt. and arr. Lowell Mason, 1839, P.D.

Laudate Dominum/Sing, Praise, and Bless the Lord PSALM 117:1

591

Latin Lau - da - te Do - mi - num, lau - da - te Do - mi - num
English Sing, praise, and bless the Lord. Sing, praise, and bless the Lord,

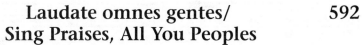

om - nes, gen - tes! al - le - lu - ia! al - le - lu - ia!
peo - ples! na - tions! Al - le - lu - ia! Al - le - lu - ia!

For other settings of Ps. 117 see 279, 570, 588, 589

Words and Music (LAUDATE DOMINUM 6.6.2.2.4): The Community of Taizé, Jacques Berthier (1923-1994)
© 1991 Ateliers et Presses de Taizé, Taizé Community, France, GIA Publications, Inc.,
exclusive North American agent

Laudate omnes gentes/ Sing Praises, All You Peoples

592

Latin Lau - da - te om - nes gen - tes, lau - da - te Do - mi - num!
English Sing prai - ses, all you peo - ples, sing prai - ses to the Lord!

Lau - da - te om - nes gen - tes, lau - da - te Do - mi - num.
Sing prai - ses, all you peo - ples, sing prai - ses to the Lord.

Words and Music (LAUDATE OMNES GENTES): Psalm 117:1 The Community of Taizé © 1991 Ateliers et
Presses de Taizé, Taizé Community, France, GIA Publications, Inc., exclusive North American agent

593 Lord Most High

Words and Music (LORD MOST HIGH): Don Harris (b. 1959) and Gary Sadler (b. 1954); arr. Gregg DeMey (b. 1972), alt. © 1996 Integrity's Hosanna! Music (ASCAP), admin. EMICMGPublishing.com

To be played only if returning to beginning.

594 The Ends of All the Earth Shall Hear

PSALM 22:27-31

1 The ends of all the earth shall hear and turn un-to the
2 His is the king-dom, his of right; he rules the na-tions
3 Both rich and poor, both bond and free shall wor-ship him on
4 The Lord's un-fail-ing right-eous-ness all gen-er-a-tions

Lord in fear; all kin-dreds of the earth shall own
by his might. All earth to him her hom-age brings,
bend-ed knee, and chil-dren's chil-dren shall pro-claim
shall con-fess; from age to age they shall be taught

Refrain

and wor-ship him as God a-lone.
the Lord of lords, the King of kings.
the glo-rious hon-or of his name. All earth to him
what won-drous works the Lord has wrought.

her hom-age brings, the Lord of lords, the King of kings.

For other settings of Ps. 22 see 164, 165, 511

Words: *Psalter*, 1912, P.D.
Music (VISION 8.8.8.8 refrain 8.8): William H. Doane (1832-1915), P.D.

Santo, santo, santo, mi corazón/
Holy, Holy, Holy, My Heart

595

Spanish ¡San - to, san - to, san - to, mi co - ra - zón te a - do - ra!

English Ho - ly, ho - ly, ho - ly, my heart, my heart a - dores you!

Dutch Hei - lig, hei - lig, hei - lig, mijn hart brengt U de e - re!

French Dieu saint, Dieu saint, Dieu saint, mon coeur, mon coeur t'a - do - re.

Mi co - ra - zón te sa - be de - cir: san - to e - res Se - ñor.

My heart pours out my praise to you; you are ho - ly, Lord.

Van har - te loof ik U - we Naam; hei - lig bent U, Heer.

Mon coeur le dit, mon coeur s'en ré - jouit: tu es saint, mon Dieu.

Optional prayer

To you, O holy God, all creation sings, **"Santo. Holy. Heilig."**
All the earth sings: **"Santo. Holy. Heilig."**
All of heaven sings: **"Santo. Holy. Heilig."**
The church universal sings: **"Santo. Holy. Heilig."**
All our women and girls sing: **"Santo. Holy. Heilig."**
All our men our boys sing: **"Santo. Holy. Heilig."**
As we join our voices with all creation,
help us to sense the breadth of your immense glory,
the wonder of your love,
the beauty of your holiness. Amen.

Adapt the refrain to include additional languages represented in your community.

Words: Spanish traditional; English tr. *Sing! A New Creation* (2001); Dutch tr. Robert DeMoor (b. 1950);
Fr. tr. Otto Selles (b. 1964)
Music (ARGENTINE SANTO 6.7.8.5): Spanish traditional; arr. Jorge Lockward © 2000 Jorge Lockward

596   Santo, santo, santo/Holy, Holy, Holy

Optional acclamation

Con los ángeles y los arcángeles
y con todos los coros celestiales,
cantamos sin cesar
el himno de tu gloria:

We sing our hymn
with all the angels and archangels
and the entire company of heaven
who praise and magnify your glorious name,
forever praising you and saying:

Refrain

Spanish San -to, san -to, san - to, san - to, san-to, san - to_es nues-tro Dios,
English Ho - ly, ho - ly, ho - ly, ho - ly, ho-ly, ho - ly, is our God,

Se - ñor de to-da la tie - rra. San -to, san - to_es nues-tro Dios.
God the Lord of earth and hea - ven. Ho - ly, ho - ly is our God.

San - to, san - to, san - to, san - to, san-to, san - to_es nues - tro Dios,
Ho - ly, ho - ly, ho - ly, ho - ly, ho-ly, ho - ly, is our God,

Words and Music (SANTO, SANTO, SANTO): Guillermo Cuéllar (b. 1955), from the *Misa popular salvadoreña;*
tr. Linda McCrae (b. 20th c.) © 1988 GIA Publications, Inc.

Se - ñor de to-da la hi-to - ria. San-to, san - to es nues-tro Dios.
God the Lord of all of his-to-ry. Ho-ly, ho - ly is our God.

1 Que a - com - pa - ña a nues - tro pue - blo, que
2 Ben - di - tos los que en su nom - bre el
1 Who ac - com - pan - ies our peo - ple, who
2 Bless - ed those who in the Lord's name an -

vi - ve en nues - tras lu - chas, del u - ni - ver - so en -
e - van - ge - lio a - nun - cian, la bue - na y gran no -
lives with - in our strug - gles, of all the earth and
nounce the ho - ly gos - pel, pro - claim - ing the good

te - ro el ú - ni - co Se - ñor.
ti - cia de la li - be - ra - ción.
hea - ven the one and on - ly Lord.
news that our lib - er - a - tion comes.

597

Holy Is the Lord

Words and Music (GIGLIO): Chris Tomlin and Louie Giglio © 2003 worshiptogether.com Songs/sixsteps
Music, admin. EMICMGPublishing.com

598

You are Holy

Words and Music (YOU ARE HOLY): Marc Imboden and Tammi Rhoton © 1994 Imboden Music/Martha Jo Music, both admin. by Music Services, Inc.

(continues)

Come, Christians, Join to Sing

599

1 Come, Chris-tians, join to sing, al - le - lu - ia, a - men!
2 Come, lift your hearts on high; al - le - lu - ia, a - men!
3 Praise yet our Christ a - gain; al - le - lu - ia, a - men!

Loud praise to Christ our King; al - le - lu - ia, a - men!
Let prais - es fill the sky; al - le - lu - ia, a - men!
Life shall not end the strain; al - le - lu - ia, a - men!

Let all with heart and voice be - fore his throne re - joice;
Christ is our guide and friend; to us he'll con - de - scend;
On heav - en's bliss - ful shore his good - ness we'll a - dore,

praise is his gra - cious choice: al - le - lu - ia, a - men!
his love shall ne - ver end; al - le - lu - ia, a - men!
sing - ing for - ev - er - more, al - le - lu - ia, a - men!

Words: Christian Henry Bateman, 1843, P.D.
Music (MADRID 6.6.6.6 D): Spanish folk melody; arr. Benjamin Carr, 1824; harm. David Evans (1874-1948)
from *Revised Church Hymnary*, 1927, reproduced by permission of Oxford University Press

600 Yesu azali awa/Jesus Christ Is with Us

Words: Congolese folk hymn; English tr. Emily R. Brink, © 2006 Faith Alive Christian Resources; Dutch tr. Elly Zuiderveld-Nieman; Korean tr. Eunae Chung © 2012 Faith Alive Christian Resources; Taiwanese Mei-hui Lai © 2012 Faith Alive Christian Resources
Music (YESU AZALI AWA): Congolese folk hymn, traditional, P.D.

Al - le - lu - ia, al - le - lu - ia, al - le - lu - ia, na Ye - su.
Hal - le - lu - jah, hal - le - lu - jah, hal - le - lu - jah, he is here.

Hal - le

Ngala

2 Biso tokomona ye *(3x)*, na lola. *Repeat*
  Alleluia *(3x)*, na lola. *Repeat*

3 Biso tokosepela (3x), na lola. *Repeat*
  Alleluia *(3x)*, na lola. *Repeat*

4 Biso tokokutana *(3x)*, na Yesu. *Repeat*
  Alleluia *(3x)*, na Yesu. *Repeat*

5 Biso tokolingana *(3x)*, na lola. *Repeat*
  Alleluia *(3x)*, na lola. *Repeat*

Dutch

1 Jezus Christus is bij ons *(3x)*,
  hij is hier. *Repeat*
  Halleluja *(3x)*, hij is hier. *Repeat*

Korean

1 예수 우리와 함께 *(2x)*
  예수 우리와 함께 이 곳에 (반복)
  할렐루야 *(3x)*, 이 곳에 (반복)

English

2 We will see him on his throne *(3x)*,
  on his throne. *Repeat*
  Hallelujah *(3x)*, on his throne. *Repeat*

3 We'll bring praises to him *(3x)*,
  on his throne. *Repeat*
  Hallelujah *(3x)*, on his throne. *Repeat*

4 There'll be joy evermore *(3x)*,
  with the Lord. *Repeat*
  Hallelujah *(3x)*, with the Lord. *Repeat*

5 For his love makes us one *(3x)*,
  with the Lord. *Repeat*
  Hallelujah *(3x)*, with the Lord. *Repeat*

Taiwanese

1 Jaso Quito kah lahn dee day *(3x)*,
  ee dee chay! *Repeat*
  Hallelujah *(3x)*, ee dee chay! *Repeat*

601 All Hail the Power of Jesus' Name

Optional acclamation (Rev. 1:5b)

To him who loves us and has freed us
from our sins by his blood,
and has made us to be a
kingdom and priests
to serve his God and Father—
**to him be glory and power
for ever and ever! Amen.**

Chord symbols represent a simplified harmony.

Words: st. 1-3 Edward Perronet, 1780, alt., st. 4 John Rippon, 1787, alt., P.D.
Music (CORONATION 8.6.8.6.8.6): Oliver Holden, 1793, P.D.

Jesus Is Our King

Refrain / **Unison**

Al - le - lu - ia! Al - le - lu - ia! O - pen-ing our hearts to him, sing-ing

al - le - lu - ia! Al - le - lu - ia! Je - sus is our King!

Harmony

1 Cre - ate in us, __ O God, a hum - ble heart that sets us free to pro-
2 We bear the name __ of Christ. Jus - ti - fied, we meet with him. His __
3 Let kin-dred voic - es join, hon - or - ing the Lamb of God, who __
4 Pour out your Spir-it on us, em-power-ing us to live as one, to __

To Refrain

claim the won-drous maj - es - ty of our Fa - ther in heaven. __
words and pres-ence calm our fear, re - veal - ing God, our Fa-ther, here.
teach - es us by bread and wine the __ mys - tery of his bod - y.
car - ry your re - deem - ing love to a world en-slaved by sin. __

Words: Sherrell Prebble and Howard Clark © 1978 Celebration
Music (POST GREEN 8.9.8.5 stanzas irregular): Sherrell Prebble © 1978 Celebration

603
Shout to the Lord

604 To God Be the Glory

1 To God be the glo - ry, great things he has done; so loved he the
2 O per - fect re - demp - tion, the pur - chase of blood, to ev - ery be -
3 Great things he has taught us, great things he has done, and great our re -

world that he gave us his Son, who yield - ed his life an a -
liev - er the prom - ise of God; the vil - est of - fend - er who
joic - ing through Je - sus the Son; but pur - er and high - er and

tone - ment for sin, and o - pened the life - gate that all may go in.
tru - ly be - lieves, that mo - ment from Je - sus a par - don re - ceives.
great - er will be our won - der, our *trans - port, when Je - sus we see.

Refrain

Praise the Lord, praise the Lord; let the earth hear his voice! Praise the Lord,

*ecstatic joy

Words: Fanny J. Crosby, 1875, alt., P.D.
Music (TO GOD BE THE GLORY 11.11.11.11 refrain 6.6.6.6.11.11): William H. Doane, 1875, P.D.

praise the Lord; let the peo-ple re-joice! O come to the Fa-ther through

Je-sus the Son, and give him the glo-ry; great things he has done.

Digno es Jesús/Worthy Is Christ   605

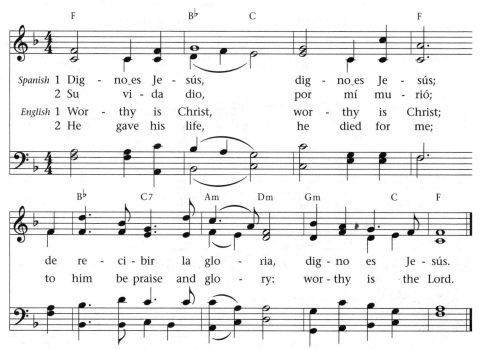

Spanish 1 Dig - no_es Je - sús, dig - no_es Je - sús;
2 Su vi - da dio, por mí mu - rió;

English 1 Wor - thy is Christ, wor - thy is Christ;
2 He gave his life, he died for me;

de re - ci - bir la glo - ria, dig - no es Je - sús.
to him be praise and glo - ry: wor - thy is the Lord.

Words and Music (DIGNO ES JESÚS): traditional Spanish, P.D.

606

In the Sanctuary

With a driving rhythm

1 We lift our hands in the sanc - tu - ar - y,

we lift our hands to give you the glo - ry;

we lift our hands to give you the praise,

and we will praise you for the rest of our days; yes,

we will praise you for the rest of our days.

Words and Music (IN THE SANCTUARY): Kurt Carr © 2008 KCartunes (BMI), Lilly Mack Publishing (BMI), admin. EMICMGPublishing; arr. Faith Alive Christian Resources © 2012 KCartunes (BMI), Lilly Mack Publishing (BMI), admin. EMICMGPublishing

Additional stanzas
2 We clap our hands in the sanctuary . . .
3 We sing our song in the sanctuary . . .
4 Hallelujah in the sanctuary . . .

607 Beautiful One

1 Won - der - ful, so won - der - ful is your un - fail - ing love; your
2 Pow - er - ful, so pow - er - ful, your glo - ry fills the skies, your

cross has spo - ken mer - cy o - ver me. No
might - y works dis - played for all to see. The

eye has seen, no ear has heard, no heart could ful - ly know how
beau - ty of your maj - es - ty a - wakes my heart to sing. How

glo - ri - ous, how beau - ti - ful you are.
mar - ve - lous, how won - der - ful you are.

Refrain

Beau - ti - ful
One, I love; Beau - ti - ful One, I a - dore. Beau - ti - ful One, my

608 Salvation Belongs to Our God

1 Salvation belongs to our God, who sits upon the throne, ——— and to the Lamb.

(2 And) we, the redeemed, shall be strong in purpose and unity, declaring aloud:

Praise and glory, wisdom and thanks, honor and power and strength

Refrain be to our God forever and ever, be to our God forever and ever. Amen.

2 And

Shukuru, Yesu/Thanking You, Jesus

Swahili   Asanti, asanti, Yesu
Bari (Sudanese dialect)   Tinati, tinati, Yesu
Luganda   Webale, webale, Yesu
Arabic   نشـكر نشـكر يسـوع

Words: Sudanese worship chorus © 2007 East Africa Annual Conference, admin. General Board of Global
Ministries t/a GBGMusik; Arabic tr. Maged Dakdouk and Anne Zaki © 2012 East Africa Annual Conference,
admin. General Board of Global Ministries t/a GBGMusik
Music (SHUKURU, YESU): arr. Greg Scheer © 2007 Greg Scheer, admin. General Board of Global Ministries
t/a GBG Musik

610 Lord, I Lift Your Name on High

Lord, I lift your name on high;

Lord, I love to sing your prais - es.

I'm so glad you're in my life;

I'm so glad you came to save us.

You came from heav - en to earth to show the

Words and Music (LORD, I LIFT YOUR NAME ON HIGH 7.8.7.8.10.10.7.7.7): Rick Founds (b. 1954) © 1989 Maranatha Praise, Inc., admin. Music Services

way, from the earth to the cross, my debt to

pay, from the cross to the grave, from the grave to the

sky. Lord, I lift your name on high!

Optional readings (1 Tim. 3:16; Heb. 1:1-3)

He appeared in the flesh,
was vindicated by the Spirit,
was seen by angels,
was preached among the nations,
was believed on in the world,
was taken up in glory.
Alleluia! Amen.

In the past God spoke to our ancestors
through the prophets
at many times and in various ways,
but in these last days
he has spoken to us by his Son,
whom he appointed heir of all things,
and through whom also he made the universe.
The Son is the radiance of God's glory
and the exact representation of his being,
sustaining all things by his powerful word.
After he had provided purification for sins,
he sat down at the right hand
of the Majesty in heaven.

611 Mighty to Save

Words and Music (MIGHTY TO SAVE): Ben Fielding, Reuben Morgan, arr. Jay Rouse © 2006 Hillsong
Publishing (APRA), admin. in the US and Canada at EMICMGPublishing.com

the hope of na‑tions.
Now I sur‑ren‑der, yes, I sur‑ren‑der.

Refrain

Sav‑ior, he can move the moun‑tains; my God is might‑y to save, he is

might‑y to save. For‑ev‑er au‑thor of sal‑va‑tion, he rose and

(continues)

612 LORD, Who May Dwell Within Your House

PSALM 15

1 LORD, who may dwell with - in your house or
2 Who have no guile up - on their tongues nor
3 Who do no wrong, but keep their word and

on your ho - ly hill? Those who do good and
harm their neigh - bor's life, but hon - or those who
seek no bribe or gain; all those who do such

speak the truth, whose lives are blame - less still;
fear the LORD and turn a - way from strife;
things shall live and safe from harm re - main.

Optional prayer

Holy God, we come to you
not as those who have obtained
righteousness on our own,
but as your dearly loved children,
clothed in the righteousness of Jesus Christ.

**How we marvel at your love for us.
How grateful we are
for the beauty of your holiness.**

**How astonished we are
that you call us to be saints,
your holy people.**

**By the power of your Spirit,
help us receive these gifts with joy
and embrace our calling in Christ. Amen.**

For a descant see 732

For another setting of Ps. 15 see 854

Words: Christopher L. Webber © 1986 Christopher L. Webber
Music (CRIMOND 8.6.8.6): Jessie Seymour Irvine, 1872; harm. David Grant, 1872, P.D.

Come to the Savior Now

613

1 Come to the Sav-ior now, he gent-ly calls to you;
2 Come to the Sav-ior now, all who have wan-dered far;
3 Come to the Sav-ior now, he of-fers all to you,
4 Come to the Sav-ior, all, what-e'er your bur-dens be;

in true re-pen-tance bow, let him your heart re-new.
re-new your sol-emn vow, for his by right you are;
and on his mer-its you can plead for life a-new.
hear now his lov-ing call, "Cast all your care on me."

Christ came that you may know sal-va-tion, peace, and love,
come like poor, wan-dering sheep re-turn-ing to his fold;
No vain ex-cus-es frame, re-spond to Christ to-day!
Come, and for ev-ery grief, in Je-sus you will find

true joy on earth be-low, a home in heaven a-bove.
his arm will safe-ly keep, his love will ne'er grow cold.
None who to Je-sus came were ev-er sent a-way.
a sure and safe re-lief, a lov-ing friend and kind.

Words: John M. Wigner, 1871, alt., P.D.
Music (INVITATION 6.6.6.6 D): Frederick C. Maker, 1895, P.D.

614 ## Come, You Disconsolate

1 Come, you dis-con-so-late, wher-e'er you lan-guish;
come to the mer-cy seat, fer-vent-ly kneel.
Here bring your wound-ed hearts, here tell your an-guish;
earth has no sor-rows that heaven can-not heal.

2 Joy of the des-o-late, light of the stray-ing,
hope of the pen-i-tent, fade-less and pure!
Here speaks the Com-fort-er, in mer-cy say-ing,
"Earth has no sor-rows that heaven can-not cure."

3 Here see the bread of life; see wa-ters flow-ing
forth from the throne of God, pure from a-bove.
Come to the feast pre-pared; come, ev-er know-ing
earth has no sor-rows but heaven can re-move.

Words: st. 1-2 Thomas Moore, 1824; st. 1-2 rev. and st. 3, Thomas Hastings, 1832, P.D.
Music (CONSOLATOR 11.10.11.10): arr. from Samuel Webbe, 1792, P.D.

Softly and Tenderly Jesus Is Calling

615

1 Soft - ly and ten-der - ly Je - sus is call - ing, call - ing for
2 Why should we tar - ry when Je - sus is plead - ing, plead - ing for
3 Oh! For the won-der - ful love he has prom-ised, prom-ised for

you and for me; see, on the por - tals he's
you and for me? Why should we lin - ger and
you and for me; though we have sinned he has

wait - ing and watch-ing, watch-ing for you and for me.
heed not his mer - cies, mer - cies for you and for me?
mer - cy and par - don, par - don for you and for me.

Refrain

Come home, come home, you who are wear - y, come home;
Come home, come home,

ear-nest-ly, ten-der - ly, Je - sus is call-ing, call-ing, O sin - ner, come home!

Words: Will L. Thompson (1847-1909), P.D.
Music (THOMPSON 11.7.11.7 refrain 4.7.11.7): Will L. Thompson (1847-1909), P.D.

616

As a Deer in Want of Water

PSALM 42 AND 43

1 As a deer in want of wa - ter, so I long for you, O LORD.
2 Bit - ter tears of lam - en - ta - tion are my food by night and day.
Refrain O my soul, why are you griev - ing, why dis - qui - et - ed in me?

All my heart and be - ing fal - ter, thirst - ing for your liv - ing word.
In my deep hu - mil - i - a - tion "Where is now your God?" they say.
Put your hope in God, be - liev - ing he will still your ref - uge be.

When shall I be - hold your face? When shall I re - ceive your grace?
When my sor - rows weigh on me, then I bring to mem - o - ry
I a - gain shall praise his grace for the com - fort of his face;

When shall I, your prais - es voic - ing, come be - fore you with re - joic - ing? *To st.2*
how with throngs I would as - sem - ble, shout - ing prais - es in your tem - ple. *To Ref.*
he will show his help and fa - vor, for he is my God and Sav - ior.

Chord symbols represent a simplified harmony.

For other settings of Ps. 42 see 332, 503, 504; Ps. 43 see 332

Words: *Psalter Hymnal*, 1987, © 1987 Faith Alive Christian Resources
Music (FREU DICH SEHR/GENEVAN 42 | 8.7.8.7.7.7.8.8): Louis Bourgeois (ca. 1510-1561), 1551; harm. Johann
Crüger (1598-1662), 1658, P.D.

(continues)

3 From the land beyond the Jordan
in my grief I think of you;
from the foothills of Mount Hermon
I will still remember you.
As the waters plunge and leap,
stormy troubles o'er me sweep.
Day and night God's song is with me
as a prayer to him who loves me.
To stanza 4

4 I will say to God, my fortress,
"Why have you forgotten me?
Why must I proceed in sadness,
hounded by the enemy?"
Their rebukes and scoffing words
pierce my bones like pointed swords,
as they say with proud defiance,
"Where is God, your firm reliance?"
Refrain

Psalm 43

5 Vindicate me, God, my Father,
come and plead my urgent cause,
for my enemies forever
threaten me and flout your laws.
I am safe with you alone;
why do you reject your own?
LORD, I need your help and blessing;
keep me safe from this oppressing.
To stanza 6

6 Send your light and truth to lead me:
send them forth to be my guide.
To your mountain let them bring me,
to the place where you reside.
Then, O God, I will come near
and before your throne appear,
to my Savior praises bringing
with the harp and joyful singing.
Refrain

Spirit Divine, Inspire Our Prayer 617

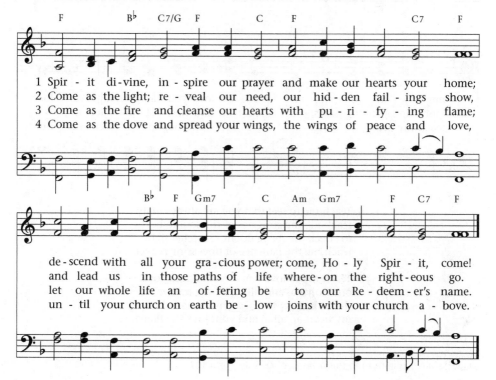

1 Spir - it di-vine, in - spire our prayer and make our hearts your home;
2 Come as the light; re - veal our need, our hid - den fail - ings show,
3 Come as the fire and cleanse our hearts with pu - ri - fy - ing flame;
4 Come as the dove and spread your wings, the wings of peace and love,

de - scend with all your gra - cious power; come, Ho - ly Spir - it, come!
and lead us in those paths of life where-on the right-eous go.
let our whole life an of - fering be to our Re - deem - er's name.
un - til your church on earth be - low joins with your church a - bove.

Words: Andrew Reed, 1829, alt., P.D.
Music (GRÄFENBERG 8.6.8.6): Johann Crüger, 1647, P.D.

618 Spirit of God, Who Dwells Within My Heart

1 Spir-it of God, who dwells with-in my heart, wean it from
2 I ask no dream, no proph-et, ec-sta-sies, no sud-den
3 Did you not bid us love you, God and King, love you with

sin, through all its puls-es move. Stoop to my weak-ness,
rend-ing of the veil of clay, no an-gel vis-i-
all our heart and strength and mind? I see the cross—there

might-y as you are, and make me love you as I ought to love.
tant, no open-ing skies; but take the dim-ness of my soul a-way.
teach my heart to cling. O let me seek you, and O let me find!

4 Teach me to feel that you are always nigh;
teach me the struggles of the soul to bear,
to check the rising doubt, the rebel sigh;
teach me the patience of unceasing prayer.

5 Teach me to love you as your angels love,
one holy passion filling all my frame;
the fullness of the heaven-descended Dove;
my heart an altar, and your love the flame.

Words: George Croly, 1867, alt., P.D.
Music (MORECAMBE 10.10.10.10): Frederick C. Atkinson, 1870, P.D.

Tama ngakau marie/
Son of God, Whose Heart Is Peace

Maori 1 Ta - ma nga - kau ma - ri - e, ta - ma
English 1 Son of God, whose heart is peace, Son of
2 Take a - way our sin - ful - ness, e - vil
3 Warm our hearts to love you, Lord, you who

a t'A - tu - a, te - nei to - nu
God, most ho - ly, to your pres - ence
that im - pri - sons us, free us from what
died to save___ us, gath - er us with -

ma - tou, a - ro - hai - na mai.
we have come; give us now your love.
trou - bles us, give our souls re - lease.
in your arms, Je - sus, on this day.

Maori

2 Murua ra nga hara:
wetekina mai,
enei here kino,
whakararu nei.

3 Homai he aroha
mou i mate nei
tenei ra, e lhu
takina i koe.

Words: traditional New Zealand; para. Shirley Murray © 1990, 2000 Christian Conference of Asia, admin. GIA Publications, Inc.
Music (TAMA NGAKAU MARIE): Maori traditional melody, New Zealand, P.D.

620

Good to Me

621

Give Me a Clean Heart

PSALM 51

Give me a clean heart so I may serve thee.

Lord, fix my heart so that I may be used by thee.

For I'm not wor - thy of all these bless - ings.

Give me a clean heart, Lord, and I'll fol-low thee.

For other settings of Ps. 51 see 622, 623

622

God, Be Merciful to Me

PSALM 51:1-9

1 God, be mer-ci-ful to me, / on your grace I / rest my plea; / Wash me, make me pure with-in; / cleanse, O cleanse me from my sin.

2 My trans-gres-sions I con-fess; / grief and guilt my / soul op-press. / I have sinned a-gainst your grace / and pro-voked you to your face.

3 I am e-vil, born in sin; / you de-sire / truth with-in. / Make me pure, your mer-cy show; / wash me whit-er than the snow.

4 Let my con-trite heart re-joice / and in glad-ness / hear your voice; / from my sins, O hide your face, / blot them out in bound-less grace.

Refrain (last time repeat)

God, be mer-ci-ful to me, on your grace I rest my plea.

D.C. for stanzas — *Fine*

For stanzas in the same meter based on additional portions of Psalm 51, see 623 st. 2-5

Words: *Psalter*, 1912, alt., P.D.
Music (GOD, BE MERCIFUL 7.7.7.7.7.7.7.7): Christopher Miner © 1998 Christopher Miner Music; arr. Eelco Vos
© 2011 Christopher Miner Music

God, Be Merciful to Me

623

PSALM 51:1-2, 10-19

1 God, be mer-ci-ful to me; on your grace I rest my plea.
2 Gra-cious God, my heart re-new; make my spir-it right and true.
3 So shall sin-ners be re-stored and re-turn to you, their Lord;

My trans-gres-sions I con-fess; grief and guilt my soul op-press.
In your pres-ence let me stay; by your Spir-it show the way.
Sav-ior, all my guilt re-move, and my tongue shall sing your love;

Wash me, make me pure with-in; cleanse, O cleanse me from my sin.
Your sal-va-tion's joy im-part, stead-fast make my will-ing heart.
touch my si-lent lips, O Lord, and my mouth shall praise ac-cord.

4 Not the formal sacrifice has acceptance in your eyes;
broken hearts are in your sight more than sacrificial rite;
contrite spirit, pleading cries, you, O God, will not despise.

5 Prosper Zion in your grace and her broken walls replace:
then our righteous sacrifice shall delight your holy eyes;
free-will offerings, gladly made, on your altar shall be laid.

For stanzas in the same meter based on additional portions of Ps.51, see 622 st. 2-4

This music in an alternate key see 354

Words: *Psalter,* 1912, alt., P.D.
Music (REDHEAD 76 7.7.7.7.7.7): Richard Redhead, 1853, P.D.

624 Not What My Hands Have Done

1 Not what my hands have done can save my guilt-y soul;
2 Your voice a-lone, O Lord, can speak to me of grace;
3 I praise the Christ of God; I rest on love di-vine;

not what my toil-ing flesh has borne can make my spir-it whole.
your power a-lone, O Son of God, can all my sin e-rase.
and with un-fal-tering lip and heart I call this Sav-ior mine.

Not what I feel or do can give me peace with God;
No oth-er work but yours, no oth-er blood will do;
My Lord has saved my life and free-ly par-don gives;

not all my prayers and sighs and tears can bear my aw-ful load.
no strength but that which is di-vine can bear me safe-ly through.
I love be-cause he first loved me, I live be-cause he lives.

Words: Horatius Bonar, 1861, alt., P.D.
Music (LEOMINSTER 6.6.8.6 D): George William Martin, 1862, P.D.

Lord, to You My Soul Is Lifted

PSALM 25

625

1 LORD, to you my soul is lift-ed. Let me nev-er be a-shamed
2 LORD of cov-e-nant and good-ness, par-don and cor-rect my sin.
3 Turn to me in grace and mer-cy, as I suf-fer all a-lone.

that I trust in you to keep me though I seem to wait in vain.
They who wor-ship you and fear you choose the paths you choose for them.
Take a-way my sin and sad-ness, all the trou-ble I have known.

LORD, re-mem-ber all your love; in your ho-ly will in-struct me.
They and all their fam-i-ly shall pos-sess the earth for-ev-er.
May my fierce and spite-ful foes not suc-ceed to harm and curse me.

LORD, do not re-mem-ber sins of those youn-ger years be-hind me.
You, O LORD, will be their friend. From the snare you will de-liv-er.
In your faith-ful-ness I hope. On your peo-ple, LORD, have mer-cy.

Chord symbols represent a simplified harmony.

For another setting of Ps. 25 see 354

Words: Stanley Wiersma (1930-1986), 1980, © 1987 Faith Alive Christian Resources
Music (GENEVAN 25 | 8.7.8.7.7.8.7.8): Louis Bourgeois, 1551; harm. Howard Slenk, 1985, © 1987 Faith Alive Christian Resources

626 Cast Down, O God, the Idols

1 Cast down, O God, the i-dols that hold us in their power,
the emp-ty gods we wor-ship when dark-ness has its hour.
We bow to oth-er mas-ters and by their prom-ise live.
Re-deem our way-ward pas-sions; our re-bel wills for-give.

2 In vain we search for mean-ing where tran-sient joys a-bound,
and seek the soul's con-tent-ment where peace can-not be found.
We wan-der, lost and home-less, in end-less, aim-less quest,
our hearts for-ev-er rest-less, un-til in you they rest.

3 O God, we have our be-ing in you and you a-lone.
Re-call us from our wan-derings; re-claim us as your own.
Re-store in us the im-age re-vealed in Christ, your Word,
till heart and will pay hom-age to him, our God and Lord.

Words: Herman G. Stuempfle (1923-2007) © 1997 GIA Publications, Inc.
Music (RUTHERFORD 7.6.7.6 D): Chrétien Urhan, 1834; arr. Edward F. Rimbault, 1867, P.D.

Just as I Am, Without One Plea 627

1 Just as I am, with-out one plea, but that thy blood was
2 Just as I am, though tossed a-bout with man-y a con-flict,
3 Just as I am, thou wilt re-ceive, wilt wel-come, par-don,
4 Just as I am, thy love un-known has bro-ken ev-ery

shed for me, and that thou bidd'st me come to thee,
man-y a doubt, fight-ings and fears with-in, with-out,
cleanse, re-lieve; be-cause thy prom-ise I be-lieve,
bar-rier down; now to be thine, yea, thine a-lone,

O Lamb of God, I come, I come.

Optional prayer

Loving God, I come to you in the name of Jesus.
Sensing that you loved me before I could ever love you,
I come to you as a sinner who needs your forgiveness.
Trusting in your power,
I long to turn away from all that keeps me from you.
With your family in all times and places,
I believe that salvation—
for me, for others, for creation itself—
comes through Jesus Christ.
**Thank you for this indescribable gift.
Amen.**

Words: Charlotte Elliott, 1836, P.D.
Music (WOODWORTH 8.8.8.8): William B. Bradbury, 1849, P.D.

628

Give Us Clean Hands

Words and Music (GIVE US CLEAN HANDS): Charlie Hall © 2000 Worshiptogether.com Songs (ASCAP)/Six
Steps Music (ASCAP), admin. EMICMGPublishing.com

give us pure hearts; let us not lift our souls to an-

oth - er. O God, let us be a gen - er - a - tion that seeks,

that seeks your face, O God of Ja - cob. O God, let us be

a gen - er - a - tion that seeks, that seeks your face,

D.C. for optional repeat *Fine*

O God of Ja - cob.

629 Ishworo/Father in Heaven, Have Mercy

Words: traditional
Music (ISHWORO): Unknown; arr. Geoff Weaver © 1995 The Jubilate Group, admin. Hope Publishing Company

O Christ, the Lamb of God

When accompanying male voices, keyboard may play treble clef one octave lower.

Words: *Agnus Dei,* based on John 1:29, P.D.
Music (CHRISTE, DU LAMM GOTTES): *Kirchenordnung,* Braunschweig, 1528; harm. Dale Grotenhuis
  (1931-2012), 1984, © 1987 Faith Alive Christian Resources

631 **Holy God**

Words: traditional Orthodox liturgy, P.D.
Music (AGIOS, O THEOS 7.6.7.6): traditional Orthodox liturgy; harm. Alfred V. Fedak (b. 1953) © 2000 Alfred
   V. Fedak

632 **Remember Not, O God**

PSALM 79

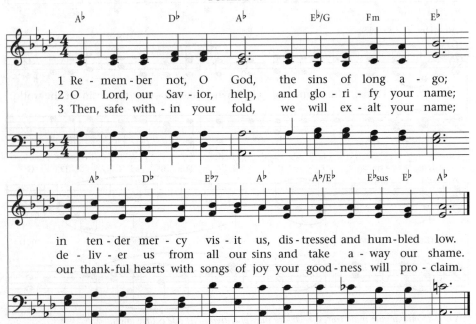

1 Re - mem - ber not, O God, the sins of long a - go;
2 O Lord, our Sav - ior, help, and glo - ri - fy your name;
3 Then, safe with - in your fold, we will ex - alt your name;

in ten - der mer - cy vis - it us, dis - tressed and hum - bled low.
de - liv - er us from all our sins and take a - way our shame.
our thank - ful hearts with songs of joy your good - ness will pro - claim.

To use with Psalm 79: read Ps. 79:1-7; sing st. 1; read Ps. 79:8-10; sing st. 2; read Ps. 79:11-13; sing st. 3.

This music in a higher key see 438.

Words: *Psalter*, 1912, P.D.
Music (GORTON 6.6.8.6): Ludwig van Beethoven, 1807, adapt., P.D.

Kyrie/Lord, Have Mercy 633

Ky - ri - e. Ky - ri - e. Lord, have mer - cy. Lord, have mer - cy.

Chris - te. Chris - te. Christ, have mer - cy. Christ, have mer - cy.

Ky - ri - e. Ky - ri - e. Lord, have mer - cy. Lord, have mer - cy.

Ky - ri - e, Ky - ri - e, e - le - i - son. e - le - i - son.

Words and Music (KYRIE BRUMM): Kathleen Hart Brumm (b. 1958) © 1992 Brummhart Publishing

A Prayer for God's Mercy (Trisagion) 634

English: Holy God, Holy and mighty, Holy Immortal One, have mercy upon us.

Spanish: Santo Dios, Santo Poderoso, Santo Inmortal, ten piedad de nosotros.

French: Saint Dieu, Saint Fort, Saint Immortel, aie pitié de nous.

Japanese: 聖なる神, 聖なる勇毅, 聖なる常生の者や、我等を憐れめよ。

Greek: Ἅγιος ὁ Θεός, Ἅγιος ἰσχυρός, Ἅγιος ἀθάνατος, ἐλέησον ἡμᾶς

Dutch: Heilige God, Heilige en machtige, Heilige Onsterfelijke, ontferm U over ons.

German: Heiliger Gott, Heiliger Starker, Heiliger Unsterblicher, erbarme dich unser.

Text: *Trisagion*, by St. John of Damascus, from early Eastern liturgies, P.D.

635 Kyrie Eleison/Lord, Have Mercy

Greek Ky - ri - e   e - lei - son.   Ky - ri - e   e - lei - son.
English Lord,____ have mer - cy.   Lord,____ have mer - cy.

Ky - ri - e   e - lei - - - son.
Lord,____ have mer - - - cy.

Words: early Greek Liturgy, P.D.
Music (KYRIE RUSSIA): Russian Orthodox Liturgy, P.D.

636 A Prayer of Confession and Assurance of Pardon

Gracious God,
**our sins are too heavy to carry,
too real to hide, and too deep to undo.
Forgive what our lips tremble to name,
what our hearts can no longer bear,
and what has become for us a
consuming fire of judgment.
Set us free from a past
that we cannot change;
open us to a future in
which we can be changed;
and grant us grace
to grow more and more
in your likeness and image;
through Jesus Christ, the light
of the world.**

All sing "Kyrie Eleison" see 633, 635, 637, 639

This saying is sure and worthy
of full acceptance:
Christ Jesus came into the world to save sinners.
He bore our sins in his body on the cross,
so that free from sins,
we might live for righteousness.
By his wounds we are healed.
Alleuia! Amen.

All sing a hymn or psalm of praise.

Prayer: *Book of Worship,* United Church of Christ © 1986, 2002 United Church of Christ
Text: from 1 Tim. 1:15; 1 Pet. 2:24

Kyrie Eleison/Lord, Have Mercy 637

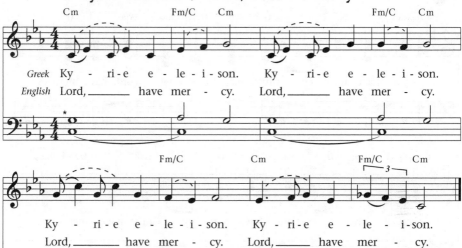

Greek Ky - ri-e e - le - i - son. Ky - ri-e e - le - i - son.
English Lord,_____ have mer - cy. Lord,_____ have mer - cy.

Ky - ri-e e - le - i - son. Ky - ri-e e - le - i - son.
Lord,_____ have mer - cy. Lord,_____ have mer - cy.

Lower voices may hum.

Words: early Greek Liturgy, P.D.
Music (KYRIE GHANA): Ghana, Dinah Reindorf (b. 1938) © 1987 Dinah Reindorf; arr. Faith Alive Christian
Resources © 2001 Dinah Reindorf

Forgive Our Sins as We Forgive 638

1 "For - give our sins as we for - give," you taught us, Lord, to pray;
2 How can your par - don reach and bless the un - for - giv - ing heart
3 In blaz - ing light your cross re - veals the truth we dim - ly knew:
4 Lord, cleanse the depths with - in our souls and bid re - sent-ment cease;

but you a - lone can grant us grace to live the words we say.
that broods on wrongs and will not let old bit - ter - ness de - part?
that triv - ial debts are owed to us, how great our debt to you!
then bound to all in bonds of love, our lives will spread your peace.

Chord symbols represent a simplified harmony.

Words: Rosamond E. Herklots (1905-1987), reproduced by permission of Oxford University Press
Music (ST. ETHELDREDA 8.6.8.6): Thomas Turton, 1860, P.D.

639 Lord, Have Mercy

Lord, have mer - cy. Christ, have mer - cy. Lord, have mer - cy
on me. Lord, have mer - cy. Christ, have mer - cy.
Lord, have mer - cy on me. me.

Words and Music (LORD, HAVE MERCY 4.4.6 D): Steve Merkel © 2000 Integrity's Hosanna! Music (ASAP) admin. EMICMGPublishing.com

640 A Prayer of Confession

Merciful God,
we confess that we have sinned against you
in thought, word, and deed,
by what we have done
and by what we have left undone.
We have not loved you
with our whole heart and mind and strength.
We have not loved our neighbors as ourselves.
In your mercy forgive what we have been,
help us amend what we are,
and direct what we shall be,
so that we may delight in your will
and walk in your ways,
to the glory of your holy name.
Through Christ, our Lord. Amen.

Text: from *The Book of Common Prayer*

Eternal Spirit, God of Truth

1 E - ter - nal Spi - it, God of truth, our con - trite hearts in - spire;
2 Sub - due the power of ev - ery sin and make our hearts your throne,

ig - nite a flame of heaven - ly love and feed the pure de - sire.
that we in sin - gle - ness of heart may wor - ship God a - lone.

O come to sooth the sor - rowing mind with guilt and fear op - pressed;
Then with our spir - its wit - ness bear, O Spir - it of our God,

O come to bid the dy - ing live and give the wea - ry rest.
that we are chil - dren of the Lord, re - deemed through Christ's own blood.

Chord symbols represent a simplifed harmony.

Words: Thomas Cotterill, 1810, alt., P.D.
Music (FOREST GREEN 8.6.8.6 D): English folk tune; adapt. and harm. Ralph Vaughan Williams (1892-1958), 1906, P.D.

642 Perdón, Señor/Forgive Us, Lord

Spanish 1 Per - dón, Se - ñor. Por tan - tas in - jus - ti - cias,
2 Per - dón, Se - ñor. Es - ta - mos en pri - sio - nes,

English 1 For - give us, Lord. For all the world's in - jus - tice,
2 For - give us, Lord. We're shack - led by our ha - bits,

Per - dón, Se - ñor. Por tan - ta_in-di - fe - ren - cia, Per - dón, Se - ñor.
Per - dón, Se - ñor. Es - cla - vos del pe - ca - do, Per - dón, Se - ñor.

For - give us, Lord. For all of our in - dif - ference, For - give us, Lord.
For - give us, Lord. We're chained to dis - o - be - dience, For - give us, Lord.

Spanish solista
3 Al perdonar a otros, . . .
  De_acuerdo_a tu promesa, . . .

4 Libera hoy tu pueblo, . . .
  Que pueda hoy servirte, . . .

English solo or choir
3 As we forgive each other, . . .
  According to your promise, . . .

4 Deliver us from evil, . . .
  For joyful service free us, . . .

Optional response of Assurance (Ezek. 36:25-26)

I will sprinkle clean water upon you,
and you shall be clean from all your uncleannesses,
and from all your idols I will cleanse you.
A new heart I will give you,
and a new spirit I will put within you;
and I will remove from your body the heart of stone
and give you a heart of flesh.

*Following this assurance, consider responding by singing the words "Gloria_a Dios"/"Glory to God,"
"Jesu christo"/"Jesus Christ," "te bendecimos"/"we bless you," "te_adoramamos"/"we praise you, Lord,"
or "te glorificamos" /"we glorify you," to the first two measures of music.*

Text: Ezekiel 36:25-26, NRSV
Words and Music (CONFESSION): Jorge Lockward (b. 1965); English tr. Raquel M. Martinez © 1996, 2000
  Abingdon Press, admin. The Copyright Company

Plaintive Is the Song I Sing

643

PSALM 7

1 Plain-tive is the song I sing, woe-ful the la-ment I bring;
2 My pur-su-ers take de-light in their mal-ice and their spite.
3 Try me, put me to the test: If I ev-er have op-pressed

all my an-guish I lay bare: God, my Sav-ior, hear my prayer.
They ac-cuse me with-out cause, held as in a li-on's claws.
those who taunt me and de-ride, then they might be jus-ti-fied.

4 Seated on your lofty throne,
summon all the lands, each one;
hold high court, lay motives bare,
give just judgment, firm but fair,

5 leading to a different way,
where revenge no more holds sway,
and where Christ will set us free,
free to build community.

A. Optional prayer of lament in circumstances of injustice

Loving God,
we pray these ancient words
in the middle of our own despair…
We long for the justice and peace,
righteousness and mercy
that only you can provide.
**Free us from revenge,
and teach us to trust in you,
through Jesus, our Lord. Amen.**

B. Optional prayer of lament in solidarity with others who experience injustice

Almighty and loving God,
We pray these ancient words
in solidarity with those in our world
who suffer from injustice…
Encourage us in our ministry
of prayer on their behalf,
and strengthen them with courage and patience.

**Send your Spirit to bring about
the fullness of your coming kingdom,
in which justice and peace will embrace.
Through Jesus Christ, our Lord. Amen.**

*C. Optional prayer for use with Psalm 7
in conjunction with biblical narratives
about injustice (e.g. 2 Sam. 16)*

Almighty God,
as we open your Word today
and sense the struggles and foibles
of your ancient people,
teach us by your Spirit what it means
to walk in the way of righteousness.
As we pray these ancient words
help us be faithful and honor you even as
we face our own struggles and challenges.
**May your kingdom come
in all its fullness,
through Jesus Christ, our Lord. Amen.**

Words: Norman J. Goreham © 2010 Norman J. Goreham, admin. Faith Alive Christian Resources
Music (NUN KOMM DER HEIDEN HEILAND 7.7.7.7): *Enchiridia*, Erfurt, 1524; harm. Seth Calvisius, 1594, P.D.

644

Lying Lips

PSALM 12

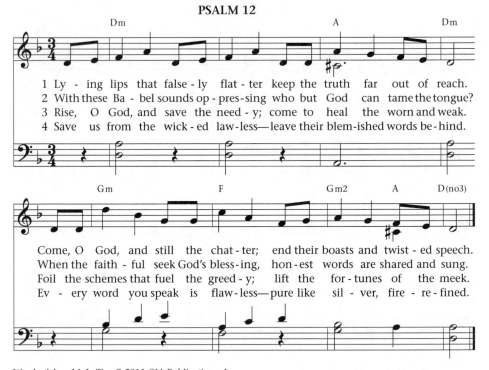

1 Ly - ing lips that false - ly flat - ter keep the truth far out of reach.
2 With these Ba - bel sounds op - pres-sing who but God can tame the tongue?
3 Rise, O God, and save the need - y; come to heal the worn and weak.
4 Save us from the wick - ed law-less—leave their blem-ished words be-hind.

Come, O God, and still the chat - ter; end their boasts and twist - ed speech.
When the faith - ful seek God's bless-ing, hon - est words are shared and sung.
Foil the schemes that fuel the greed - y; lift the for - tunes of the meek.
Ev - ery word you speak is flaw-less—pure like sil - ver, fire - re - fined.

Words: Adam M. L. Tice © 2011 GIA Publications, Inc.
Music (CAPTIVITY/KAS DZIEDAJA 8.7.8.7): Latvian melody; harm. Geoffrey Laycock (b. 1927), P.D.

645 Litany for the Slandered PSALM 35/JAMES 3:9-10

Refrain: repeat paragraph as indicated
With the tongue we praise
our Lord and Father,
and with it we curse human beings,
who have been made in God's likeness.
Out of the same mouth come
praise and cursing.
My brothers and sisters,
this should not be.
May my tongue proclaim
your righteousness,
your praises all day long.

Contend, Lord, with those who contend with me; arise and come to my aid. Say to me, "I am your salvation." Ruthless witnesses come forward; they question me on things I know nothing about. They repay me evil for good and leave me like one bereaved. They slandered me without ceasing. How long, Lord, will you look on?

Refrain

Lord, you have seen this; do not be silent. Do not be far from me, Lord. Awake, and rise to my defense! Contend for me, my God and Lord. Vindicate me in your righteousness, Lord my God; do not let them gloat over me. May those who delight in my vindication shout for joy and gladness; may they always say, "The Lord be exalted, who delights in the well-being of his servant." My tongue will proclaim your righteousness, your praises all day long.

Refrain

The litany continues with this prayer and/or the singing of "O God, My Faithful God," as found on the next page.

Loving and faithful God, giver of every good and perfect gift, you know our thoughts before they are formed and our words before they are spoken. Save us from our inclination to think, act, or speak in crude, demeaning, or vengeful ways, and heal the wounds made by the carelessness of others.
By the power of your redeeming Spirit,
fill our lives with wisdom and grace
so that we may speak truthfully, live
peacefully, and bring glory and
honor to your name. Amen.

O God, My Faithful God

646

1 O God, my faith-ful God, true foun-tain ev-er flow-ing,
2 Give me the strength to do with read-y heart and will-ing
3 Keep me from say-ing words that lat-er need re-call-ing;
4 When dan-gers gath-er round, O keep me calm and fear-less;

with-out whom noth-ing is, all per-fect gifts be-stow-ing:
what-ev-er you com-mand, my call-ing here ful-fill-ing.
guard me lest i-dle speech may from my lips be fall-ing;
help me to bear the cross when life seems dark and cheer-less.

give me a health-y frame, and may I have with-in
Help me do what I should in all that comes my way;
but when with-in my place I must and ought to speak,
Help me, as you have taught, to love both great and small,

a con-science free from blame, a soul un-stained by sin.
I know that you are good, you bless those who o-bey.
then to my words give grace lest I of-fend the weak.
to speak the truth in love, to live at peace with all.

Chord symbols represent a simplified harmony.

Words: Johann Heermann, 1630, tr. Catherine Winkworth, 1863, alt., P.D.
Music (DARMSTADT 6.7.6.7.6.6.6.6): Ahawuerus Fritsch, 1679; harm. Johann S. Bach (1675-1750),
Cantata 45, P.D.

647 Come, Sing to God with All Your Heart

PSALM 9

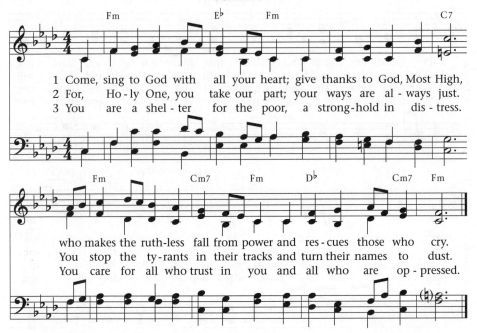

1 Come, sing to God with all your heart; give thanks to God, Most High,
2 For, Ho-ly One, you take our part; your ways are al-ways just.
3 You are a shel-ter for the poor, a strong-hold in dis-tress.

who makes the ruth-less fall from power and res-cues those who cry.
You stop the ty-rants in their tracks and turn their names to dust.
You care for all who trust in you and all who are op-pressed.

4 The violent move in vicious stealth
to dig their victims' grave.
Come, snare them in the nets they cast.
Come, mighty God, and save!

5 Rise up, O God; our blood cries out.
Bring justice! Raise your hand!
Then we will tell how you have saved.
Your praise will fill the land.

Chord symbols represent a simplified harmony. For an alternate arrangement see 132

Words: Ruth Duck © 2011 GIA Publications, Inc.
Music (MORNING SONG 8.6.8.6): J. Wyeth, *Repository of Sacred Music,* 1813, P.D.; harm. Jack Grotenuis, 1983,
© 1987 Faith Alive Christian Resources

648 Why Stand So Far Away, My God

PSALM 10

1 Why stand so far away, my God?
Why hide in times of need?
The proud, unbridled, chase the poor,
and curse you in their greed.

2 Why do you hide when, full of lies,
they murder and betray?
They wait to pounce upon the weak
as lions stalk their prey.

3 The weak are crushed and fall to earth;
the wicked strut and preen.
Why in these cruel, chaotic times
cannot your face be seen?

4 In ages past you heard the voice
of those the proud oppress.
Remember those who suffer now,
who cry in deep distress.

5 Arise, O God, and lift your hand;
bring justice to the poor.
Come, help us stop the flow of blood!
Let terror reign no more!

For music see 647
Words: Ruth Duck © 1992 GIA Publications, Inc.

I Call to You, My Rock

649

PSALM 28

1 I call to you, my Rock: Lord, hear my ear-nest prayer—
2 May I be spared the fate of those who cling to sin,
3 But you have heard my prayer; in you I will be strong:

if you ig-nore my plea, how can I not de-spair?
whose friend-ly words be-lie mal-i-cious thoughts with-in—
since I re-ly on you, my heart is filled with song.

As I reach out, make this the place of fresh en-coun-ters
would ru-in not be my re-ward if I should dis-re-
Yes, Lord, I sing to you, my Rock: e-ter-nal Shep-herd,

with your grace, of fresh en-coun-ters with your grace.
gard you, Lord, if I should dis-re-gard you, Lord?
guard your flock, e-ter-nal Shep-herd, guard your flock.

For an alternate arrangement see 148

Words: Martin Leckebusch © 2002, 2011 Kevin Mayhew Ltd
Music (RHOSYMEDRE 6.6.6.6.8.8 with repeat): John D. Edwards, ca. 1840, P.D.

650 O When Will We See Justice Done

PSALMS 58-61

(Ps. 58) 1 O when will we see jus-tice done? When will the right-eous win?
(Ps. 59) 2 De-li-ver me, O God my strength, from those who lie in wait,
(Ps. 60) 3 O God, have you re-ject-ed us, or do you on-ly sleep?

O speed the day when we can say, "God judg-es hu-man sin!"
from en-e-mies who prowl and plot, whose on-ly law is hate.
Give vic-tory with your might-y hand, your prom-is-es to keep.

The ven-om of the wick-ed's lies de-stroys all in their path.
But you, O Lord, could come and save, de-flat-ing their false pride,
For you have caused our land to quake; no step now seems se-cure.

Their fangs are bared; no one is spared, and to our cries they're deaf.
and show the earth your right-eous worth as in your love we hide.
We stag-ger in our suf-fer-ing; our faith seems less than sure.

(continues)

For an alternate arrangement see 10

Words: from Psalms 58-61, Carol Bechtel © 2011 Carol Bechtel, admin. Faith Alive Christian Resources
Music (KINGSFOLD 8.6.8.6 D refrain 4.11.11.6): traditional English; adapt. Ralph Vaughan Williams
(1872-1958), 1906, P.D.

Refrain (Ps. 61)

God, hear my cry! To you I call e-ven when my heart is faint.

To your strong tower lead me in power, and keep me ev-er safe.

By the Babylonian Rivers 651
PSALM 137

1 By the Bab-y-lo-nian riv-ers we sat down in grief and wept;
2 There our cap-tors in de-ri-sion did re-quire of us a song;
3 How shall we sing the Lord's song in a strange and bit-ter land;

hung our harps up-on the wil-low, mourned for Zi-on when we slept.
so we sat with star-ing vi-sion, and the days were hard and long.
can our voic-es veil the sor-row? Lord God, hold your ho-ly band.

Words: Ewald Bash, 1964, © 1964 American Lutheran Church, admin. Augsburg Fortress
Music (KAS DZIEDAJA 8.7.8.7): Latvian melody, P.D.; arr. Greg Scheer © 2011 Greg Scheer

652

I Lift My Eyes Up

PSALMS 121

I lift my eyes up to the moun-tains;
where does my help come from?
My help comes from you, Mak-er of heav-en,
Cre-a-tor of the earth.
Oh, how I need you, Lord. You are my on-ly hope;

Fine

For another setting of Ps. 121 see 331

you're my on - ly prayer.

So I will wait for you to come and res - cue me.

D.C. al Fine

Come and give me life.

A Prayer: Confession of Idolatry 653

Almighty and loving God,
**we confess
that we put our trust in other gods.
We honor these gods
alongside of you and in place of you.
By the Holy Spirit's power,
help us to know you,
the only true God,
as you have revealed
yourself in your Word,
to trust in you alone,
to look to you for every good thing,
humbly and patiently,
and to love, fear, and honor you
with all our hearts.
In Jesus' name. Amen.**

Text: adapted from Heidelberg Catechism Q&A 94, 95

654

Do Not Keep Silent, O God

PSALM 83

Sing angrily. Keep the half-note pulse steady from the refrain to the stanzas.

Out of the Depths I Cry to You on High   655

PSALM 130

1 Out of the depths I cry to you on high; Lord, hear my call.
2 I wait for God, I trust his ho-ly word; he hears my sighs.
3 Hope in the Lord: un-fail-ing is his love; in him con-fide.

Bend down your ear and lis-ten to my sigh, for-giv-ing all.
My soul still waits and looks un-to the Lord; my prayers a-rise.
Mer-cy and full re-demp-tion from a-bove he does pro-vide.

If you should mark our sins, who then could stand?
I look for him to drive a-way my night—
From sin and e-vil, might-y though they seem,

But grace and mer-cy dwell at your right hand.
yes, more than those who watch for morn-ing light.
his arm al-might-y will his saints re-deem.

Words: *Psalter*, 1912, alt., P.D.
Music (SANDON 10.4.10.4.10.10): Charles H. Purday, 1860, P.D.

656 Deliver Me from Evil

PSALM 140

1 De - liv - er me from e - vil; de - fend me, LORD, from wrong.
2 O LORD, I have con - fessed you to be my God a - lone.
3 Let their own e - vil strike them and cause their o - ver - throw,

The vi - o - lent have gath - ered, with poi - son on their tongue.
Now hear my cry for mer - cy and make your pow - er known.
so that the poor see jus - tice when e - vil is brought low.

From those who plot to hurt me or catch me in their snare,
O sov - ereign LORD and Sav - ior, my ar - mor in the strife,
The right - eous will sing prais - es, pro - claim your name and grace;

pro - tect me, LORD, and keep me safe - guard - ed in your care.
let not the wick - ed tri - umph who wish to take my life.
the up - right will live safe - ly with - in your sure em - brace.

For an alternate arrangement see 168.

Words: *Psalter,* 1912; rev. Bert Witvoet, 1985, © 1987 Faith Alive Christian Resources
Music (HERZLICH TUT MICH VERLANGEN 7.6.7.6 D): Hans Leo Hassler, 1601, arr. Alfred V. Fedak © 2012
  Alfred V. Fedak, admin. Faith Alive Christian Resources

Hear My Cry and Supplication

657

PSALM 142

1 Hear my cry and sup-pli-ca-tion; LORD, I pour out my com-plaint. Heed my tale of trib-u-la-tion; lead the way when I am faint.

2 When my path is filled with dan-gers, no one comes to res-cue me. When I am en-snared by strang-ers, no one comes to set me free.

3 LORD, I am op-pressed and low-ly; I de-pend up-on your care. Save me now, O God most ho-ly; hear me in my deep de-spair.

4 When you lead me from this pris-on, right-eous friends will gath-er round. When from depths I have a-ris-en, I will make your praise re-sound.

Optional refrain or final stanza
I will arise and go to Jesus;
he will embrace me in his arms;
in the arms of my dear Savior,
oh, there are ten thousand charms.

Words: Clarence P. Walhout, 1982, © 1987 Faith Alive Christian Resources; opt. ref. American, 17th c., P.D.
Music (ARISE/RESTORATION 8.7.8.7): W. Walker's *Southern Harmony*, 1835; harm. Charles H. Webb (b. 1933), P.D.

658   Bring Peace to Earth Again

1 Where ar - mies scourge the coun-try-side, and peo - ple flee in
2 Where an - ger fes - ters in the heart, and strikes with cru - el
3 Where homes are torn by bit - ter strife, and love dis-solves in
4 O God, whose heart com-pas-sion-ate bears ev - ery hu - man

fear; where si - rens scream through flam - ing nights, and
hand; where vio - lence stalks the trou - bled streets, and
blame; where walls you meant for shel - tering care hide
pain, re - deem this vio - lent, wound - ing world till

death is ev - er near:
ter - ror haunts the land:
deeds of hurt and shame:
gen - tle - ness shall reign.

O God of mer - cy,

hear our prayer: bring peace to earth a - gain!

Chord symbols represent a simplified harmony.

Words: Herman G. Stuempfle Jr (1923 - 2007) © 1996 World Library Publications
Music (PACE MIO DIO 8.6.8.6.8.6): Perry Nelson (b. 1955) © 1996 World Library Publications

Nearer, Still Nearer

659

1 Near - er, still near - er, close to thy heart, draw me, my
2 Near - er, still near - er, noth - ing I bring, naught as an
3 Near - er, still near - er, Lord, to be thine, sin with its
4 Near - er, still near - er, while life shall last, till safe in

Sav - ior, so pre - cious thou art. Fold me, O fold me
of - fering to Je - sus, my King— on - ly my sin - ful,
fol - lies I glad - ly re - sign, all of its pleas - ures,
glo - ry my an - chor is cast; through end - less ag - es,

close to thy breast; shel - ter me safe in that ha - ven of
now con - trite heart; grant me the cleans - ing thy blood doth im -
pomp and its pride; give me but Je - sus, my Lord cru - ci -
ev - er to be near - er, my Sav - ior, still near - er to

rest, shel - ter me safe in that ha - ven of rest.
part, grant me the cleans - ing thy blood doth im - part.
fied, give me but Je - sus, my Lord cru - ci - fied.
thee, near - er, my Sav - ior, still near - er to thee.

Words and Music (STILL NEARER 9.10.9.10.10): Leila N. Morris (1862-1929), P.D.

660 Jesus, Draw Me Ever Nearer

1 Je - sus, draw me ev - er near - er as I la - bor
2 Je - sus guide me through the tem - pest; keep my spir - it
3 Let the trea - sures of the tri - al form with - in me

through the storm. You have called me to this
staid and sure. When the mid - night meets the
as I go, and at the end of this long

pass - age, and I'll fol - low though I'm worn.
morn - ing, let me love you ev - en more.
pass - age let me leave them at your throne.

Refrain

May this jour - ney bring a bless - ing; may I

rise on wings of faith; and at the end of my heart's

test - ing with your like - ness let me wake.

Just a Closer Walk with Thee 661

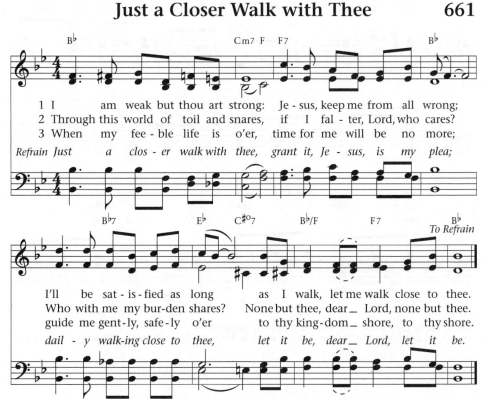

1 I am weak but thou art strong: Je - sus, keep me from all wrong;
2 Through this world of toil and snares, if I fal - ter, Lord, who cares?
3 When my fee - ble life is o'er, time for me will be no more;
Refrain Just a clos - er walk with thee, grant it, Je - sus, is my plea;

I'll be sat - is - fied as long as I walk, let me walk close to thee.
Who with me my bur - den shares? None but thee, dear Lord, none but thee.
guide me gent - ly, safe - ly o'er to thy king - dom shore, to thy shore.
dail - y walk - ing close to thee, let it be, dear Lord, let it be.

Words and Music (CLOSER WALK): Anonymous, P.D.

662 In an Age of Twisted Values

1 In an age of twist-ed val-ues we have lost the truth we need. In so-phis-ti-ca-ted lan-guage we have jus-ti-fied our greed.

2 We have built dis-crim-i-na-tion on our prej-u-dice and fear. Ha-tred swift-ly turns to cru-el-ty if we hold re-sent-ments dear.

3 When our fam-i-lies are bro-ken, when our homes are full of strife, when our chil-dren are be-wil-dered, when they lose their way in life,

4 We who hear your word so of-ten choose so rare-ly to o-bey. Turn us from our will-ful blind-ness; give us truth to light our way.

Words: Martin E. Leckebusch (b. 1962) © 1995 Kevin Mayhew Ltd.
Music (CHURCH UNITED 8.7.8.7 D): Alfred V. Fedak (b. 1953), 1988, © 1989 Selah Publishing Company, Inc.

By our strug - gle for pos - ses - sions we have robbed the
For com - mu - ni - ties di - vid - ed by the walls of
when we fail to give the ag - ed all the care we
In the pow - er of your Spir - it come to cleanse us,

poor and weak. Hear our cry and heal our na-tion;
class and race, hear our cry and heal our na-tion;
know they need, hear our cry and heal our na-tion;
make us new; hear our cry and heal our na-tion

your for - give - ness, Lord we seek.
show us, Lord, your love and grace.
help us show more love, we plead.
till our na - tion hon - ors you.

663 Pelas dores deste mundo/For the Troubles

Portuguese 1 Pe - las do - res des - te mun - do, ó Se - nhor,
(2 Teus ou -) vi - dos se in - cli - nem ao cla - mor

English 1 For the trou-bles and the suf-ferings of the world,
(2 Lend an) ear___ to the ris - ing cry for help

im - plo - ra - mos pi - e - da - de. A
des - ta gen - te o - pri - mi - da. A -
God, we call up - on your mer - cy: the
from op - pressed and hope - less peo - ple. Come!

um só tem-po ge-me_a cri - a - ção. 2 Teus ou -
pres - sa - te com tu - a sal - va ção.
whole cre - a-tion's la - bor - ing in pain! 2 Lend an
Has - ten your sal - va - tion, heal-ing love!

A tu - a paz, ben - di - ta e_ir - ma-
O teu po - der sus - ten - te_o tes - te-
We pray for peace, the bless - ed peace that
We pray for power, the power that will sus-

na - da co'a jus - ti - ça a - bra - ce_o mun - do_in-
mu - nho do teu po - vo. Teu Rei - no ve - nha_a
comes from mak - ing jus - tice, to cov - er and em-
tain your peo - ple's wit - ness un - til your king - dom

tei - ro. Tem com-pai - xão!
brace us. Have mer - cy, Lord!
nos! Ky - ri - e_e - le - i - son!
comes, Ky - ri - e_e - le - i - son!

664 I Need Your Help, O Lord My God

PSALM 55

These two stanzas can provide an introduction and conclusion for the reading of Psalm 35.

Chord symbols represent a simplifed harmony.

Alternate tune: THIRD MODE MELODY *see 435*

Words: st. 1 Helen Otte (b. 1931), 1984, © 1987 Faith Alive Christian Resources; st. 2 Martin Tel © 2011 Faith
  Alive Christian Resources
Music (RESTING PLACE 8.6.8.6 D): Henry Vander Werp (1846-1918), 1911, P.D.

I Heard the Voice of Jesus Say

665

1 I heard the voice of Jesus say,
  "Come unto me and rest;
  lay down, O weary one, lay down
  your head upon my breast."
  I came to Jesus as I was,
  so weary, worn, and sad;
  I found in him a resting place,
  and he has made me glad.

2 I heard the voice of Jesus say,
  "Behold, I freely give
  the living water; thirsty one,
  stoop down and drink and live."
  I came to Jesus, and I drank
  of that life-giving stream;
  my thirst was quenched, my soul revived,
  and now I live in him.

3 I heard the voice of Jesus say,
  "I am this dark world's light;
  look unto me; your morn shall rise
  and all your day be bright."
  I looked to Jesus, and I found
  in him my star, my sun;
  and in that light of life I'll walk
  till traveling days are done.

For music see 664
Words: Horatius Bonar, 1846, P.D.

I Will Give You Rest

666

MATTHEW 11:28-29

"I will give you rest for your wear-y soul.
If you on-ly come to me, I will make you whole."

Words (based on Matt. 11:28-29) and Music (REST 5.5.7.5): Barbara Boertje (b. 1959) © 1996 Barbara Boertje

667 Christ, Whose Glory Fills the Skies

1 Christ, whose glo - ry fills the skies, Christ, the true and on - ly Light,
2 Dark and cheer - less is the morn un - ac - com - pa - nied by thee;
3 Vis - it, then, this soul of mine, pierce the gloom of sin and grief;

Sun of Right-eous - ness, a - rise, tri-umph o'er the shade of night;
joy - less is the day's re - turn till thy mer - cy's beams I see,
fill me, Ra - dian - cy di - vine, scat - ter all my un - be - lief;

Day - spring from on high, be near; Day - star, in my heart ap - pear.
till they in - ward light im - part, glad my eyes and warm my heart.
more and more thy - self dis - play, shin - ing to the per - fect day!

Optional assurance (2 Cor. 4:6-7)

For it is the God who said,
"Let light shine out of darkness,"
who has shone in our hearts
to give the light of the knowledge
of the glory of God in the
face of Jesus Christ.

But we have this treasure in clay jars,
so that it may be made clear
that this extraordinary
power belongs to God
and does not come from us.

Words: Charles Wesley, 1740, P.D.
Music (LUX PRIMA 7.7.7.7.7.7): Charles F. Gounod (1818-1893), 1872, P.D.

I Worship You, O Lord

668

PSALM 30

1 I wor-ship you, O LORD, for you have raised me up;
2 Sing prais-es to the LORD, all those who know his name;
3 I said, "I am so strong, I nev-er shall be moved";

I cried to you for help, and you re-stored my life.
for while his wrath is brief, his fa-vor knows no end.
but you, LORD, shook my life— my heart was in dis-tress.

You brought me back from death and saved me from the grave.
Though tears flow for a night, the morn-ing brings new joy.
I cried out for your help and plead-ed for your grace:

4 "What good am I when dead,
   while lying in the grave?
   Can dust recount your love,
   the grave proclaim your praise?
   O hear me, gracious LORD,
   in mercy be my aid!"

5 My mourning you have turned
   to dancing and to joy;
   my sadness you dispelled
   as gladness filled my soul.
   And so I'll sing your praise,
   my God, through all my days.

Words: st. 1-3, 5: James E. Seddon © 1973 The Jubilate Group, admin. Hope Publishing Company; st. 4 Calvin Seerveld © 1982 Calvin Seerveld
Music (BISHOP TUCKER 6.6.6.6.6.6): Norman L. Warren © 1990 The Jubilate Group, admin. Hope Publishing Company

669 How Blest Are They Whose Trespass

PSALM 32

1 How blest are they whose tres - pass has free - ly been for - given,
2 While I kept guilt - y si - lence, my strength was spent with grief:
3 So let the god - ly seek you in times when you are near;
*4 "I gra - cious - ly will teach you the way that you should go,
5 The sor - rows of the wick - ed in - crease from year to year,

whose sins are whol - ly cov - ered be - fore the sight of heaven.
your hand was heav - y on me; my soul found no re - lief.
no whelm - ing floods shall reach them or cause their hearts to fear.
and, with my eye up - on you, help you my coun - sel know.
but those who trust the LORD God know love in - stead of fear.

Blest they to whom the LORD God does not im - pute their sin,
But when I owned my tres - pass and did not hide my sin,
O LORD, you are my ref - uge, you are my hid - ing place,
Then do not be un - ru - ly or slow to un - der - stand;
Then in the LORD be joy - ful, in song lift up your voice;

who have a guile - less spir - it, whose heart is true with - in.
then you for - gave my guilt, LORD, re - stored my life with - in.
and you sur - round me al - ways with songs of sav - ing grace.
be not per - verse, but will - ing to heed my wise com - mand."
be glad in God, you right - eous: re - joice, O saints, re - joice!

*Stanza 4 may be sung by a solo voice.

For another setting of Ps. 32 see 412

Words: Psalter, 1912, alt., P.D.
Music (RUTHERFORD 7.6.7.6 D): Chrétien Urhan, 1834; arr. Edward F. Rimbault, 1867, P.D.

I Waited Patiently for God

670

PSALM 40

1 I wait-ed pa-tient-ly for God, for God
2 God raised me from a mir-y pit, from mud
3 And on my lips a song was put, a new
4 Great won-ders you have done, O Lord, all pur-

to hear my prayer; and God bent down to
and sink-ing sand, and set my feet up-
song to the Lord. Man-y will mar-vel
posed for our good. Un-a-ble ev-ery

where I sank and lis-tened to me there.
on a rock where I can firm-ly stand.
o-pen-eyed and put their trust in God.
one to name, I bow in grat-i-tude.

For an alternate arrangement see 691

671 The Lord Is Compassionate and Gracious
PSALM 103:8-13, 17-18

The Lord is compassionate and gracious,
slow to anger, abounding in love.
He will not always accuse,
nor will he harbor his anger forever;
he does not treat us as our sins deserve
or repay us according to our iniquities.
For as high as the heavens are above the earth,
so great is his love for those who fear him;
as far as the east is from the west,
so far has he removed our transgressions from us.
As a father has compassion on his children,
so the Lord has compassion on those who fear him;

From everlasting to everlasting
the Lord's love is with those who fear him,
and his righteousness with their children's children—
with those who keep his covenant
and remember to obey his precepts.

For other settings of Ps. 103 see 516, 571, 672, 836

672 O Come, My Soul, Sing Praise to God
PSALM 103

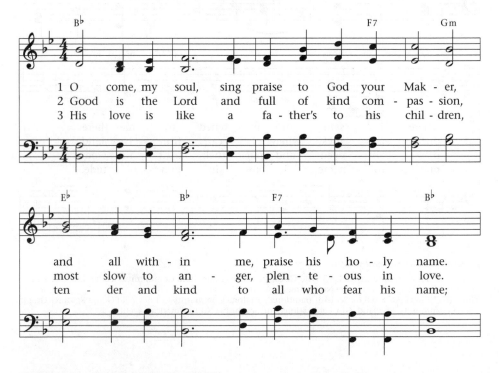

1 O come, my soul, sing praise to God your Mak - er,
2 Good is the Lord and full of kind com - pas - sion,
3 His love is like a fa - ther's to his chil - dren,

and all with - in me, praise his ho - ly name.
most slow to an - ger, plen - te - ous in love.
ten - der and kind to all who fear his name;

For other settings of Ps. 103 see 516, 571, 671, 836
Words: *Psalter,* 1912, alt., P.D.
Music (TIDINGS 11.10.11.10 refrain 5.4.11): James Walch, 1875, P.D.

Sing praise to God, for-get not all his mer-cies;
Rich is his grace to all who hum-bly seek him,
for well he knows our weak-ness and our frail-ty;

his par-doning grace and sav-ing love pro-claim.
bound-less and end-less as the heavens a-bove.
he knows that we are dust, he knows our frame.

Refrain
Praise him, you an-gels, won-drous in might;

praise him, you ser-vants who in his will de-light.

4 We fade and die like <u>flowers</u> that grow in beauty,
like tender grass that soon will disappear;
but evermore the love of God is changeless,
still shown to those who look to him in fear. *Refrain*

5 High in the <u>heavens</u> his throne is fixed forever;
his kingdom rules o'er all from pole to pole.
Praise to the Lord through all his wide dominion;
forever praise his holy name, my soul. *Refrain*

673   How Precious Is Your Unfailing Love

PSALM 36

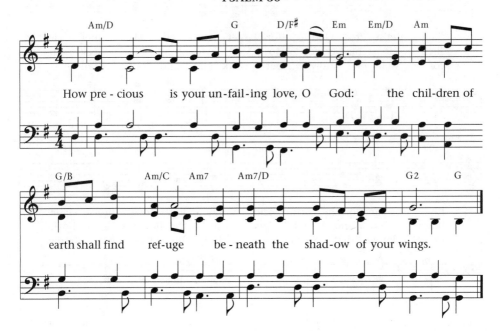

Refrain

I have a message from God in my heart
concerning the sinfulness of the wicked:
There is no fear of God
before their eyes.

In their own eyes they flatter themselves
too much to detect or hate their sin.
The words of their mouths
are wicked and deceitful;
they fail to act wisely or do good.
Even on their beds they plot evil;
they commit themselves to a sinful course
and do not reject what is wrong.

Refrain

Your love, LORD, reaches to the heavens,
your faithfulness to the skies.
Your righteousness
is like the highest mountains,
your justice like the great deep.
You, LORD, preserve
both people and animals.

How priceless is your unfailing love,
O God!
People take refuge
in the shadow of your wings.
They feast on the abundance
of your house;
you give them drink
from your river of delights.
For with you is the fountain of life;
in your light we see light.

Refrain

Continue your love to those who know you,
your righteousness to the upright in heart.
May the foot of the proud not come against me,
nor the hand of the wicked drive me away.
See how the evildoers lie fallen—
thrown down, not able to rise!

Refrain

Words and Music (YOUR UNFAILING LOVE 11.9.8): David Lee © 2010 David Lee

As Moses Raised the Serpent Up

674

JOHN 3:14-17

Words: from John 3:14-17; vers. Marie J. Post, 1985, © 1987 Faith Alive Christian Resources
Music (O WALY WALY 8.8.8.8): English folk melody; arr. and desc. Emily R. Brink (b. 1940) © 2001 Faith Alive
  Christian Resources

675   By Grace We Have Been Saved

Eph. 2:8 1 By grace we have been saved through faith and not by
Rom. 3:23 2 For all have sinned and fal - len short. God's plan not
Rom. 5:8 3 God gave to earth a per - fect love through Je - sus

keep - ing law. God's saints be - lieved by
one o - beyed. Christ has for all ful -
on the cross. While we were foes, Christ

what they heard and not by what they saw.
filled the law. Be - lieve, con - fess, be saved.
died for us. We gained by God's own loss.

Refrain

Oh, how I love Je - sus! Oh, how I love Je - sus!

*Left hand may be played an octave lower throughout.

Words: sts. Rusty Edwards, ref. Frederick Whitfield © 1996 Selah Publishing Company
Music (OH, HOW I LOVE JESUS 8.6.8.6 refrain 6.6.6.6): North American traditional; arr. Sean Ivory © 2008
  Faith Alive Christian Resources

Rom. 6:23 4 We know the wage of sin is death; thank God, we shall revive.
For just as Jesus rose again, we too are made alive. *Refrain*

Rom. 5:1 5 Set free, we now have peace with God. Salvation is secured.
How beautiful the feet of those who share this gospel word. *Refrain*

Oh, How I Love Jesus   676

1 There is a name I love to hear, I love to sing its worth;
it sounds like music in my ear, the sweetest name on earth. *Refrain*

Refrain
Oh, how I love Jesus! Oh, how I love Jesus!
Oh, how I love Jesus, because he first loved me.

2 It tells me of a Savior's love, who died to set me free;
it tells me of his precious blood, the sinner's perfect plea. *Refrain*

3 It tells of one whose loving heart can feel my deepest woe;
who in each sorrow bears a part that none can bear below. *Refrain*

For music see 675
Words: Frederick Whitfield, 1855, P.D.

677 For the Glories of God's Grace

2 CORINTHIANS 5:18-21

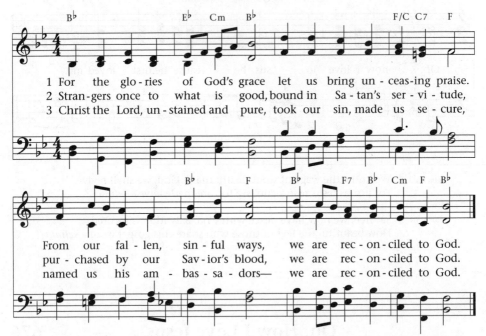

1 For the glo-ries of God's grace let us bring un-ceas-ing praise.
2 Stran-gers once to what is good, bound in Sa-tan's ser-vi-tude,
3 Christ the Lord, un-stained and pure, took our sin, made us se-cure,

From our fal-len, sin-ful ways, we are rec-on-ciled to God.
pur-chased by our Sav-ior's blood, we are rec-on-ciled to God.
named us his am-bas-sa-dors— we are rec-on-ciled to God.

4 Sinless and immortal, he
paid our debt on Calvary.
Raised from slaves to royalty,
we are reconciled to God.

5 God's good news of love we bring
to the lost and wandering.
Come, believe, rejoice, and sing:
we are reconciled to God.

Words: based on 2 Corinthians 5:18-21; vers. Marie J. Post, 1985, © 1987 Faith Alive Christian Resources
Music (MONKLAND 7.7.7.7): J. Freylinghausen's *Geistreiches Gesangbuch,* 1704; adapt. John Antes, ca. 1800;
arr. John Wilkes, 1861, P.D.

678 Affirmation: The Forgiveness of Sins

What do you believe concerning "the forgiveness of sins"?

I believe that God,
because of Christ's satisfaction,
will no longer remember
any of my sins
or my sinful nature
which I need to struggle against all my life.

Rather, by grace
God grants me the righteousness of Christ
to free me forever from judgment.

Text: Heidelberg Catechism Q&A 56

For Freedom Christ Has Set Us Free 679

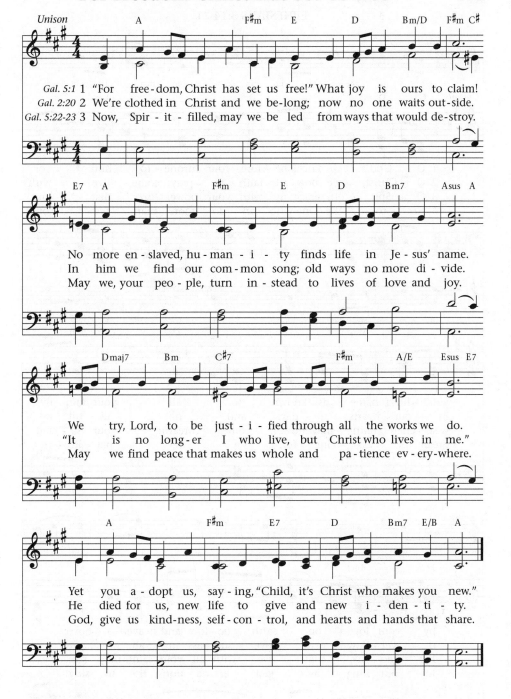

Gal. 5:1 1 "For free-dom, Christ has set us free!" What joy is ours to claim!
Gal. 2:20 2 We're clothed in Christ and we be-long; now no one waits out-side.
Gal. 5:22-23 3 Now, Spir-it-filled, may we be led from ways that would de-stroy.

No more en-slaved, hu-man-i-ty finds life in Je-sus' name.
In him we find our com-mon song; old ways no more di-vide.
May we, your peo-ple, turn in-stead to lives of love and joy.

We try, Lord, to be just-i-fied through all the works we do.
"It is no long-er I who live, but Christ who lives in me."
May we find peace that makes us whole and pa-tience ev-ery-where.

Yet you a-dopt us, say-ing, "Child, it's Christ who makes you new."
He died for us, new life to give and new i-den-ti-ty.
God, give us kind-ness, self-con-trol, and hearts and hands that share.

For an alternate arrangement see 22, 145, 356, 726

Words: Sylvia Dunstan (1955-1993) © 1991 GIA Publications, Inc.
Music (ELLACOMBE 8.6.8.6 D): *Gesangbuch der Herzogl,* Hofkapelle, Würtemberg, 1784; arr. Kenneth Bos
© 2008 Faith Alive Christian Resources

680 O God, We Kneel Before Your Throne

EPHESIANS 3:14-21

Descant

4 Now to the One who can do more than we could dream

Unison

1 O God, we kneel be - fore your throne to hon - or
2 O Christ, we bow in faith to pray: come, live with -
3 O Spir - it, grace us with your power so that our
4 Now to the One who can do more than we could

of ask - ing for, e - ter - nal glo - ry

you whose name is known to all your fam - ily
in our hearts to - day, and fill us till we
weak - ened faith may flower; come, breathe your sa - cred
dream of ask - ing for, e - ter - nal glo - ry

to our King as gen - er - a - tions sing:

by your love on earth be - low and heaven a - bove:
o - ver - flow with love sur - pass - ing all we know.
har - mo - ny, that we with all your saints may see:
to our King as gen - er - a - tions rise to sing:

Words: Ruth van Baak Griffioen © 2002 GIA Publications, Inc.
Music (KNOLLCREST FARM 8.8.8.8 refrain 8.5): Roy Hopp © 2002 GIA Publications, Inc.

Optional acclamation (Eph. 1:17-23)

I pray that the God of our Lord Jesus Christ,
the Father of glory,
may give you a spirit of wisdom
and revelation as you come to know him,
so that, with the eyes of your
heart enlightened,
you may know what is the hope
to which he has called you,
what are the riches of his glorious
inheritance among the saints,
and what is the immeasurable greatness
of his power for us who believe,
according to the working of his great power.

**God put this power to work in Christ
when he raised him from the dead
and seated him at his right hand
in the heavenly places,
far above all rule and authority
and power and dominion,
and above every name that is named,
not only in this age
but also in the age to come.**

And he has put all things under his feet
and has made him the head
over all things for the church,
which is his body,
the fullness of him who fills all in all.

681   A Great High Priest

HEBREWS 4:14-16

Therefore, since we have a great high priest
who has ascended into heaven, Jesus the Son of God,
let us hold firmly to the faith we profess.
For we do not have a high priest
who is unable to empathize with our weaknesses,
but we have one who has been tempted in every way,
just as we are—yet he did not sin.

Let us then approach God's throne of grace with confidence,
so that we may receive mercy
and find grace to help us in our time of need.

682   Before the Throne of God Above

1 Be - fore the throne of God a - bove   I have a
2 When Sa - tan tempts me to de - spair   and tells me
3 Be - hold him there! The ris - en Lamb,   my per - fect,

strong and per - fect plea,   a great High Priest whose name is
of the guilt with - in,   up - ward I look and see him
spot - less right - eous - ness;   the great un - change - a - ble "I

Words: Charitie Lees DeCheney Bancroft (1841-1923), P.D.
Music (BEFORE THE THRONE 8.8.8.8 D with repeat): Vikki Cook, 1997, © 1997 Soveriegn Grace Worship,
  admin. EMICMGPublishing.com

Love, who ev - er lives and pleads for me. My name is
there who made an end of all my sin. Be - cause the
AM," the King of glo - ry and of grace! One with him -

grav - en on his hands, my name is writ - ten on his
sin - less Sav - ior died, my sin - ful soul is count - ed
self I can - not die, my soul is pur - chased by his

heart; I know that while in heaven he stands no tongue can
free; for God the Just is sat - is - fied to look on
blood; my life is hid with Christ on high, with Christ, my

bid me thence de - part, no tongue can bid me thence de - part.
him and par - don me, to look on him and par - don me.
Sav - ior and my God, with Christ, my Sav - ior and my God.

683 How Great Is the Love of the Father

1 JOHN 3:1-3

1 How great is the love of the Fa - ther, the love he has
2 The world with-out God does not know us be - cause it did
3 What we are to be in the fu - ture as yet has not

shown to us— so great that he calls us his chil - dren, and
not know Christ. Lord, help us to be pure and spot - less, for
been made known, but when Christ re -turns, we shall see him, and

chil - dren of God we are, and chil-dren of God we are!
chil - dren of God we are, for chil-dren of God we are.
then we shall be like him, and then we shall be like him.

Words: I John 3:1-3; vers. Edna W. Sikkema, 1986, © 1987 Faith Alive Christian Resources
Music (ANNO DOMINI 9.7.9.7 with repeat): James C. Ward, 1985, © 1987 James Ward Music

There in God's Garden

684

REVELATION 22

1 There in God's gar-den stands the Tree of Wis-dom, whose leaves hold
2 Its name is Je-sus, name that says, "Our Sav-ior!" There on its
3 Thorns not its own are tan-gled in its fo-liage; our greed has
4 See how its branch-es reach to us in wel-come; hear what the

forth the heal-ing of the na-tions: Tree of all know-ledge,
branch-es see the scars of suf-fering; see where the ten-drils
starved it, our des-pite has choked it. Yet, look! It lives! Its
Voice says, "Come to me, ye wear-y! Give me your sick-ness,

Tree of all com-pas-sion, Tree of all beau-ty.
of our hu-man self-hood feed on its life-blood.
grief has not de-stroyed it, nor fire con-sumed it.
give me all your sor-row; I will give bless-ing."

5 This is my ending, this my resurrection;
into your hands, Lord, I commit my spirit.
This have I searched for; now I can possess it.
This ground is holy.

6 All heaven is singing, "Thanks to Christ whose Passion
offers in mercy healing, strength, and pardon.
Peoples and nations, take it, take it freely!"
Amen! My Master!

Words: Király Imre von Pécselyi (ca. 1590-1641); tr. Erik Routley (1917-1982) © 1976 Hinshaw Music, Inc.
Music (SHADES MOUNTAIN 11.11.11.5): K. Lee Scott (b.1950) © 1987 Birnamwood Publications, a div. of
MorningStar Music Publishers, Inc.

685 I Sought the Lord, and Afterward I Knew

1 I sought the Lord, and af-ter-ward I knew
2 Thou didst reach forth thy hand and mine en-fold;
3 I find, I walk, I love; but, oh, the whole

he moved my soul to seek him, seek-ing me;
I walked and sank not on the storm-vexed sea;
of love is but my an-swer, Lord, to thee!

it was not I that found, O Sav-ior true;
'twas not so much that I on thee took hold,
For thou wert long be-fore-hand with my soul;

no, I was found, was found of thee.
as thou, dear Lord, took hold on me.
al-ways, al-ways thou lov-edst me.

For this music in a lower key see 449

Words: anonymous, 1878, P.D.
Music (FINLANDIA 11.10.11.10.11.10): Jean Sibelius (1865-1957), P.D. in the U.S. and Canada, © Breitkopf &
   Härtel in other territories of the world

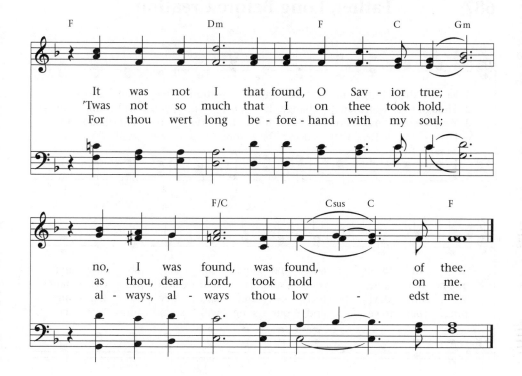

It was not I that found, O Sav - ior true;
'Twas not so much that I on thee took hold,
For thou wert long be - fore - hand with my soul;

no, I was found, was found, of thee.
as thou, dear Lord, took hold on me.
al - ways, al - ways thou lov - edst me.

A Prayer of Praise 686

All glorious God, we give you thanks:
in your Son, Jesus Christ,
you have given us every spiritual blessing
in the heavenly realms.

You chose us, before the world was made,
to be your holy people, without fault in your sight.
You adopted us as your children in Christ.
You have set us free by his blood;
you have forgiven our sins.
You have made known to us your secret purpose,
to bring heaven and earth into unity in Christ.
You have given us your Holy Spirit,
the seal and pledge of our inheritance.

**All praise and glory be yours, O God,
for the richness of your grace,
for the splendor of your gifts,
for the wonder of your love.
Amen.**

Text: based on Ephesians 1:3-18, Desmund Tutu, P.D.

687 Father, Long Before Creation

1 Fa - ther, long be - fore cre - a - tion you had cho - sen
2 Though the world may change its fash - ion, you will still re -
3 Your com - pas - sion is our sto - ry, is our boast - ing
4 Lov - ing Fa - ther, now be - fore you we shall ev - er

us in love, and that love so deep, so mov - ing,
main the same; your com - pas - sion and your cov - enant
all the day; mer - cy free and nev - er fail - ing
sing your grace, and our song will sound for - ev - er

draws us close to Christ a - bove. Still it
through all a - ges will re - main. Your own
moves our will, di - rects our way. God so
when we see you face to face, giv - ing

keeps us firm - ly fixed in Christ a - lone.
chil - dren shall for - ev - er praise your name.
loved us that he gave his on - ly Son.
glo - ry to the Lamb up - on the throne.

Words: Chinese, ca. 1951; tr. Francis P. Jones, 1953, alt., P.D.
Music (CORONAE 8.7.8.7.4.7): William H. Monk, 1871, P.D.

How Vast the Benefits Divine

688

1 How vast the ben-e-fits di-vine which we in Christ pos-sess!
2 To you, O Christ, a-lone is due all glo-ry and re-nown;
3 With-in the arms of sov-ereign love we ev-er shall re-main;

We are re-deemed from sin and shame, and called to ho-li-ness.
no mer-it of our own we claim, nor rob you of your crown.
nor shall the rage of earth or hell make God's sure coun-sel vain.

'Tis not for works that we have done—these all to him we owe;
You were our on-ly sur-e-ty in God's re-demp-tion plan;
Each one of all the cho-sen race shall sure-ly heaven at-tain;

but he of his e-lect-ing love sal-va-tion does be-stow.
in you his grace was giv-en us be-fore the world be-gan.
here they will share a-bound-ing grace, and there with Je-sus reign.

Words: Augustus M. Toplady, 1774, alt., P.D.
Music (BETHLEHEM 8.6.8.6 D): Gottfried W. Fink, 1842, P.D.

689   There's a Wideness in God's Mercy

1 There's a wide - ness in God's mer - cy, like the wide-ness of the sea;
2 For the love of God is broad-er than the mea-sures of the mind;

there's a kind-ness in God's jus - tice, which is more than lib - er - ty.
and the heart of the e - ter - nal is most won - der - ful - ly kind.

There is no place where earth's sor - rows are more felt than up in heaven;
Make our love, O God, more faith-ful, let us take you at your word,

there is no place where earth's fail-ings have such kind - ly judg - ment
and our lives will be thanks - giv - ing for the good-ness of the

given.
Lord.

Words: Frederick Faber, adapt. Gregg DeMey © 2008 Re:Create Music, admin. Faith Alive Christian Resources
Music (CIVILITY 8.7.8.7 D): Gregg DeMey © 2008 Re:Create Music, admin. Faith Alive Christian Resources

I Know Not Why God's Wondrous Grace 690

1 I know not why God's won-drous grace to me he has made known,
2 I know not how this sav - ing faith to me he did im - part,
3 I know not how the Spir - it moves, con-vin-cing us of sin,
4 I know not what of good or ill may be re-served for me,

nor why, un-wor-thy, Christ in love re - deemed me for his own.
nor how be - liev-ing in his Word wrought peace with - in my heart.
re - veal-ing Je - sus through the Word, cre - a - ting faith in him.
of wea - ry ways or gold - en days, be - fore his face I see.

Refrain

But "I know whom I have be - liev-ed, and am per - suad-ed that he is a-ble

to keep that which I've com - mit-ted un-to him a-gainst that day."

Words: based on 2 Timothy 1:12, Daniel W. Whittle, 1883; P.D.
Music (EL NATHAN 8.6.8.6 refrain 9.10.8.7): James McGranahan, 1883, P.D.

691 **Amazing Grace**

1 A - maz - ing grace— how sweet the sound— that
2 'Twas grace that taught my heart to fear, and
3 The Lord has prom - ised good to me, his

saved a wretch like me! I once was lost, but
grace my fears re - lieved; how pre - cious did that
word my hope se - cures; he will my shield and

now am found, was blind, but now I see.
grace ap - pear the hour I first be - lieved!
por - tion be as long as life en - dures.

4 Through many dangers, toils, and snares
I have already come;
'tis grace hath brought me safe thus far,
and grace will lead me home.

5 When we've been there ten thousand years,
bright shining as the sun,
we've no less days to sing God's praise
than when we'd first begun.

For an alternate arrangement see 670

Words: st. 1-4 John Newton, 1779, st. 5 *A Collection of Sacred Ballads,* 1790, P.D.
Music (NEW BRITAIN 8.6.8.6): *Virginia Harmony,* 1831; adapt. and harm. Edwin O. Excell, 1900, P.D.

Amazing Grace Chant

*drum beat

Words and Music (AMAZING GRACE CHANT): Stanley Jim; arr. Gail De Young and Robert Ippel © 2012
Stanley Jim , admin. Faith Alive Christian Resources

693 Amazing Grace (My Chains Are Gone)

Refrain

My chains are gone, I've been set free; my God, my
Sav-ior has ran-somed me. And like a flood, his mer-cy
rains un-end-ing love, a-maz-ing grace.

To stanzas

3 The
5 When

694   Assurance: No Condemnation in Christ

ROMANS 8:1, 11, 14-16

There is therefore now no condemnation
for those who are in Christ Jesus.

If the Spirit of him who raised
Jesus from the dead dwells in you,
he who raised Christ from the dead
will give life to your mortal bodies
also through his Spirit that dwells in you.

For all who are led by the Spirit of God
are children of God.
For you did not receive a spirit of slavery
to fall back into fear,
but you have received a spirit of adoption.
When we cry, "Abba! Father!"
it is the very Spirit bearing witness with our spirit
that we are children of God.
Alleluia! Amen.

Text: Romans 8:1, 11, 14-16, NRSV

695   And Can It Be

1 And can it be that I should gain an in - terest in the
2 He left his Fa - ther's throne a - bove— so free, so in - fi -
3 Long my im - pris - oned spir - it lay fast bound in sin and
4 No con - dem - na - tion now I dread, for Christ, and all in

Sav - ior's blood? Died he for me, who caused his pain— for
nite his grace— emp - tied him - self of all but love, and
na - ture's night. Your sun - rise turned that night to day; I
him, is mine! A - live in him, my liv - ing Head, and

Words: Charles Wesley, 1738, alt., P.D.
Music (SAGINA 8.8.8.8 D): Thomas Campbell, 1825, P.D.

me, who caused his bit - ter death? A - maz - ing love! How
bled for Ad - am's help - less race! What mer - cy this, im -
woke— the dun - geon flamed with light! My chains fell off, your
clothed in right - eous - ness di - vine, bold I ap - proach the e -

can it be that you, my Lord, should die for me?
mense and free, for, O my God, it found out me!
voice I knew; I rose, went out, and fol - lowed you.
ter - nal throne and claim the crown, through Christ, my own.

Refrain

A - maz - ing love! How can it
A - maz - ing love! How

be that you, my Lord, should die for me?
can it be that you, my Lord,

696 Marvelous Grace

1 Mar - vel - ous grace of our lov - ing Lord, grace that ex -
2 Dark is the stain that we can - not hide, what can a -
3 Mar - vel - ous, in - fi - nite, match - less grace, free - ly be -

ceeds our sin and our guilt, yon - der on Cal - va - ry's
vail to wash it a - way! Look! there is flow - ing a
stowed on all who be - lieve: you that are long - ing to

mount out - poured, there where the blood of the Lamb was spilt.
crim - son tide; whit - er than snow you may be to - day.
see his face, will you this mo - ment his grace re - ceive?

Refrain

Grace, grace, God's grace,
Mar - vel - ous grace, in - fi - nite grace,
grace that will

Words: Julia H. Johnston, P.D.
Music (MOODY 9.9.9.9 refrain 4.9.4.9): Daniel B. Towner, P.D.

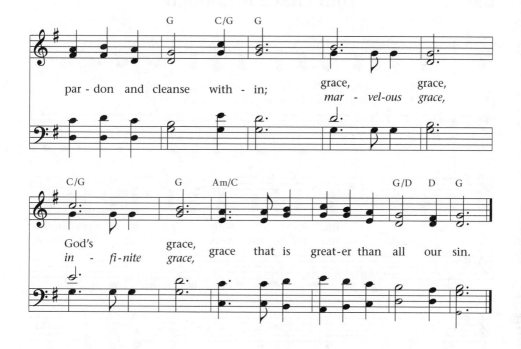

par - don and cleanse with - in; grace, grace,
mar - vel-ous grace,

God's grace, grace that is great-er than all our sin.
in - fi-nite grace,

Affirmation: Righteous Before God 697

How are you righteous before God?

**Only by true faith in Jesus Christ.
Even though my conscience accuses me
of having grievously sinned against all God's commandments,
of never having kept any of them,
and of still being inclined toward all evil,
nevertheless,
without any merit of my own,
out of sheer grace,
God grants and credits to me
the perfect satisfaction, righteousness, and holiness of Christ,
as if I had never sinned nor been a sinner,
and as if I had been as perfectly obedient
as Christ was obedient for me.
All I need to do
is accept this gift with a believing heart.**

Text: Heidelberg Catechism Q&A 60

698 **Your Grace Is Enough**

1 Great is your faith - ful - ness, O God.
2 Great is your love and jus - tice, God.

You wres - tle with the sin - ner's heart.
You use the weak to lead the strong.

You lead us by
You lead us in

still wa - ters in - to mer - cy,
the song of your sal - va - tion,

and noth - ing can keep us a - part.
and all your peo - ple sing a - long.

(continues)

Like a River Glorious

1 Like a riv-er glo-rious is God's per-fect peace, o-ver all vic-
2 Hid-den in the hol-low of his might-y hand, where no harm can

to-rious in its bright in-crease: per-fect, yet still flow-ing
fol-low, in his strength we stand. We may trust him ful-ly

full-er ev-ery day; per-fect, yet still grow-ing deep-er all the way.
all for us to do; those who trust him whol-ly find him whol-ly true.

Refrain

Trust-ing in the Fa-ther, hearts are ful-ly blest,

find-ing, as he prom-ised, per-fect peace and rest.

Words: Frances R. Havergal, 1878, alt., P.D.
Music (WYE VALLEY 6.5.6.5 D refrain 6.5.6.5): James Mountain, 1876, P.D.

700   Your Mercy Flows

Words and Music (YOUR MERCY FLOWS 11.10.11.10.5.6.7.9): Wes Sutton (b. 1955) © 1988 Sovereign Lifestyle Music, Ltd.

Assurance: Who Is a God Like You   701
MICAH 7:18-20

Who is a God like you, pardoning iniquity
and passing over the transgression
of the remnant of your possession?
He does not retain his anger forever,
because he delights in showing clemency.
He will again have compassion upon us;
he will tread our iniquities under foot.
You will cast all our sins
into the depths of the sea.
You will show faithfulness to Jacob
and unswerving loyalty to Abraham,
as you have sworn to our ancestors
from the days of old.

Text: Micah 7:18-20 NRSV

702   # Depth of Mercy

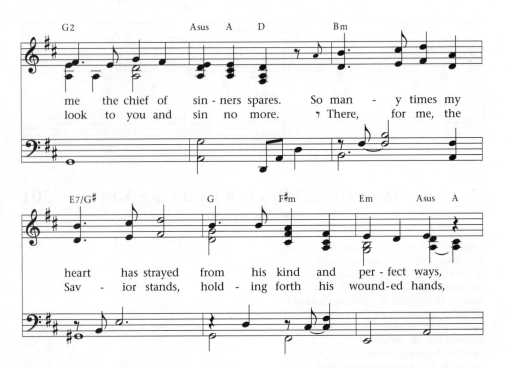

1 Depth of mer - cy! Can there be   mer - cy reach - ing
2 Give me grace, Lord, let me own   all the wrongs that

ev - en me? God, the just, his wrath for - bears,
I have done. Let me now my sins de - plore,

me the chief of sin - ners spares. So man - y times my
look to you and sin no more. There, for me, the

heart has strayed from his kind and per - fect ways,
Sav - ior stands, hold - ing forth his wound-ed hands,

mak - ing clear my des - perate need for his blood poured
scars which ev - er cry for me; once con - demned but

out for me.
now set free.

Assurance: Surely He Took Up Our Pain   703
ISAIAH 53:4-6

Surely he took up our pain
and bore our suffering,
yet we considered him punished by God,
stricken by him, and afflicted.
But he was pierced for our transgressions,
he was crushed for our iniquities;
the punishment that brought us peace was on him,
and by his wounds we are healed.
We all, like sheep, have gone astray,
each of us has turned to our own way;
and the LORD has laid on him
the iniquity of us all.

Text: Isaiah 53:4-6,NRSV

704 The Blood That Jesus Sheds for Me

1 The blood that Je - sus shed for me
2 It soothes my doubts and calms my fears,

'way back on Cal - va - ry, the blood that gives me strength from
and it dries all my tears; the blood that gives me strength from

day to day— it will nev - er lose its power.
day to day— it will nev - er lose its power.

Refrain

It reach - es to the high - est moun - tain.

It flows to the low - est val - ley.

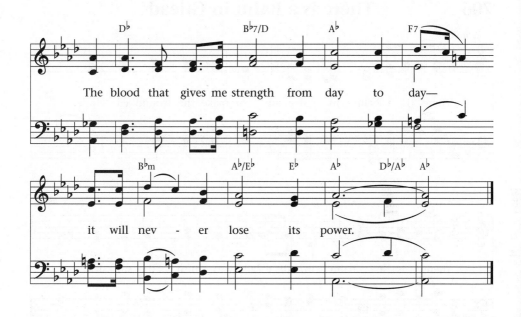

The blood that gives me strength from day to day—
it will nev - er lose its power.

Affirmation: Washed with Christ's Blood and Spirit

705

How does holy baptism remind and assure you
that Christ's one sacrifice on the cross
benefits you personally?

In this way:
Christ instituted this outward washing
and with it promised that,
as surely as water washes away
the dirt from the body,
so certainly his blood and his Spirit
wash away my soul's impurity,
that is, all my sins.

What does it mean to be washed with Christ's blood and Spirit?

To be washed with Christ's blood means
that God, by grace, has forgiven our sins
because of Christ's blood
poured out for us in his sacrifice on the cross.

To be washed with Christ's Spirit means
that the Holy Spirit has renewed
and sanctified us to be members of Christ,
so that more and more
we become dead to sin
and live holy and blameless lives.

Text: Heidelberg Catechism Q&A 69, 70

706 There Is a Balm in Gilead

Refrain
F
C7
There is a balm in Gil-e-ad to make the wound-ed whole,
F
F/C
C7
F Fine
there is a balm in Gil-e-ad to heal the sin-sick soul.
B♭
F
C
1 Some-times I feel dis-cour-aged and__ think my work's in vain,
2 If you can-not preach like Pe-ter, if you can-not pray like Paul,
To Refrain
F
B♭
F/c
C7
Dm B♭
but__ then the Ho-ly Spir-it re-vives my soul a-gain.
you can tell the love of Je-sus and say, "He died for all."

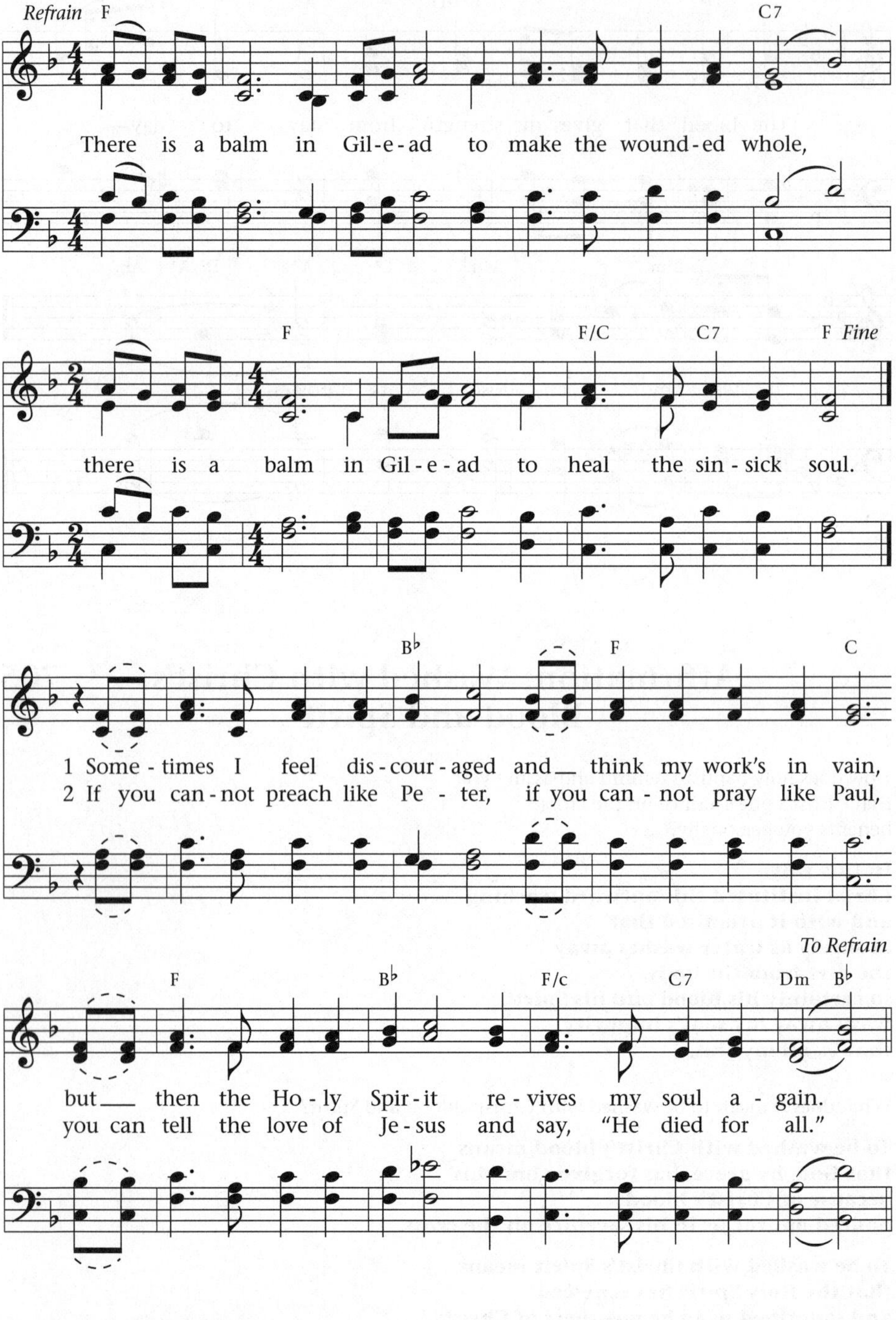

Chord symbols represent a simplified harmony.

Words and Music (BALM IN GILEAD 8.6.8.6 stanzas irregular): African American spiritual, P.D.

Goodness Is Stronger than Evil

Words: from *An African Prayer Book,* Desmond Tutu © 1996 Desmond Tutu, admin. Lynn C. Franklin
   Assoc., Ltd.
Music (GOODNESS IS STRONGER 7.6.7.6.4.4.5): John L. Bell © 1996 Wild Goose Resource Group, Iona
   Community, Scotland, GIA Publications, Inc., exclusive North American agent

708

Kwake Yesu nasimama/
Here on Jesus Christ I Will Stand

Refrain *Swahili* Kwa - ke Ye - su na - si - ma - ma, ndi - ye
English Here on Je - sus Christ I will stand. He's the

Stanzas
1 There's no oth - er place I can hide till the
2 It is not the work of my hands that has
3 When my days on this earth are done, and I

mwam - ba ni sa - la - ma. Ndi - ye mwam - ba ni sa - la -
sol - id rock of my life. He's the sol - id rock of my

storm that rag - es sub - sides. My voice cries to God from the
washed a - way all my sins. I'm re - deemed, and all of my
stand at God's ho - ly throne, my heart will not have an - y

ma, ndi - ye mwam - ba ni sa - la - ma.
life. He's the sol - id rock of my life.

flood, and I'm saved be - cause of his blood. *To Refrain*
days, Je - sus Christ will be my heart's praise. *To Refrain*
fear; in Christ's right - eous - ness I am here. *To Refrain*

Last time

Words and Music (KWAKE YESU): traditional Kenyan © 2007 East Africa Annual Conference, admin. General Board of Global Ministries t/a GBGMusik; adapt. and arr. Greg Scheer © 2007 Greg Scheer, admin. General Board of Global Ministries t/a GBGMusik

Jesus Loves Me

1 Je - sus loves me! This I know, for the Bi - ble tells me so.
2 Je - sus loves me— he who died heav - en's gate to o - pen wide.
3 Je - sus loves me, this I know, as he loved so long a - go,

Lit - tle ones to him be - long; they are weak, but he is strong.
He will wash a - way my sin, let his lit - tle child come in.
tak - ing chil - dren on his knee, say - ing, "Let them come to me."

Refrain

Yes, Je - sus loves me! Yes, Je - sus loves me!

Yes, Je - sus loves me! The Bi - ble tells me so.

Words: st. 1-2 Anna B. Warner, 1859, st. 3 David R. McGuire, 1971, P.D.
Music (JESUS LOVES ME 7.7.7.7 refrain 5.5.5.6): William B. Bradbury, 1861, P.D.

710 Glory, Glory, Hallelujah

1 Glo - ry, glo - ry, hal - le - lu - jah!
2 I feel bet - ter, so much bet - ter,
3 Feel like shout - in' hal - le - lu - jah!

since I laid my bur - dens down.
since I laid my bur - dens down!
since I laid my bur - dens down!

Glo - ry, glo - ry, hal - le - lu - jah!
I feel bet - ter, so much bet - ter,
Feel like shout - in' hal - le - lu - jah!

since I laid my bur - dens down.
since I laid my bur - dens down!
since I laid my bur - dens down!

4 Friends don't treat me like they used to . . .
5 I'm goin' home to live with Jesus . . .

Words: African American spiritual, P.D.
Music (GLORY 15.15): African American spiritual; arr. Nolan Williams Jr (b. 1969) © 2000 GIA Publications, Inc.

The Lord Is God, the One and True God   711

Optional prayer

Lord our God,
your Word is a light for our path.
Even as we sing,
imprint the words of your commands on our hearts,
and teach us to walk in step with your Spirit.

 [sing 3 stanzas]

We receive these commands as your gift to us.
We long for your Spirit to guide us on this path.
Through Jesus we pray. **Amen.**

1 The Lord is God, the one and true God, be - yond all
2 Fa - ther and moth - er we will hon - or; all hu - man
3 Truth - ful in speech, our rep - u - ta - tion; by self - less -

we can think or see. God's name a - mong us shall be
life will we be - friend. All whom we love will find us
ness shall we be known. Un - end - ing love we pledge all

ho - ly. God's Sab - bath rest shall make us free.
faith - ful; our neigh - bor's goods will we de - fend.
peo - ple, our high - est love for God a - lone.

Chord symbols represent a simplified harmony.

Words: The Ten Commandments; para. Daniel J. Meeter (b. 1953) © 1980 Daniel J. Meeter
Music (COMMANDMENTS 9.8.9.8): *Genevan Psalter,* 1547; harm. Claude Goudimel (ca. 1505-1572), P.D.

712 Happy Is the One

PSALM 1

1 Hap - py ___ is the one who does not take bad ad -
2 Hap - py ___ is the one who takes de - light in the
3 Such a ___ one as this is like a tree by the
4 Not so the wick - ed's fate; for they, like chaff which the
5 Nor will ___ sin - ners walk a - mong the as - sem - bly of

vice for a guide, nor walks the path on which sin - ners have
law of the LORD, and med - i - tates on it both day and
>nour - ish - ing streams, which yields its fruit when the sea - son is
wind blows a - way, will nev - er stand and be con - fi -
God's own ___ folk; for wick - ed ways are all doomed by the

trod, nor sits where the cyn - ics mock.
night, and pros - pers in ev - ery way.
>right and bears leaves that nev - er fade.
dent on God's great ___ judg - ment day.
Lord who bless - es the hon - est path.

For another setting of Ps. 1 see 714

Words: The Iona Community © 1993 Wild Goose Resource Group, Iona Community, Scotland,
 GIA Publications, Inc., exclusive North American agent
Music (BENEDICTUS PRIMUS 5.10.10.6): The Iona Community © 1993 Wild Goose Resource Group,
 Iona Community, Scotland, GIA Publications, Inc., exclusive North American agent

What Does the Lord Require of You

MICAH 6:8

713

May be sung as a canon

Words and Music (MOON irregular): Jim Strathdee; adapt. Linda White © 1986 Desert Flower Music

714

The One Is Blest

PSALM 1

1 The one is blest who, fear - ing God, walks not where sin - ners meet,
2 How blest the one who in God's law finds good - ness and de - light,
3 That one is nour-ished like a tree set by the riv - er's side;

who does not stand with wick - ed ones, and shuns the scorn - ers' seat.
and med - i - tates up - on that law with glad-ness day and night.
its leaf is green, its fruit is sure: the works of such a - bide.

4 The wicked, like the driven chaff,
are swept from off the land;
they shall not gather with the just,
nor at the judgment stand.

5 The LORD will guard the righteous well,
their way to God is known;
the way of sinners, far from God,
shall surely be o'erthrown.

For another setting of Ps. 1 see 712

Words: *Psalter*, 1912, alt. 1985, P.D.
Music (WINCHESTER OLD 8.6.8.6): attr. George Kirbye, 1592, P.D.

715 **Litany: The Ten Commandments 1**

DEUTERONOMY 5:6-21, EXODUS 20:1-17

I am the Lord your God,
who brought you out of Egypt,
out of the land of slavery.
You shall have no other gods before me.
I sincerely acknowledge
the only true God,
trust him alone,
look to him for every good thing,
humbly and patiently,
and love him, fear him,
and honor him with all my heart.
In short, I will give up anything rather
than go against God's will in any way.

You shall not make for yourself an idol
in the form of anything in heaven above
or on the earth beneath
or in the waters below.

I will in no way make any image of God
nor worship him in any other way
than he has commanded in his Word.

You shall not misuse the name
of the Lord your God,
for the Lord will not hold anyone
guiltless who misuses his name.
I will use the holy name of God
only with reverence and awe,
so that I may properly confess him,
pray to him, and praise him
in everything I do and say.

Remember the Sabbath day by keeping it holy.
I will regularly attend
the assembly of God's people
to learn what God's Word teaches,

(continues)

to participate in the sacraments,
to pray to God publicly,
and to bring Christian offerings
for the poor.
Every day of my life
I will rest from my evil ways,
let the Lord work in me
through his Spirit,
and so begin already in this life
the eternal Sabbath.

Honor your father and your mother.
I will honor, love, and be loyal
to my father and mother
and all those in authority over me.
I will obey and submit to them,
as is proper,
when they correct and punish me;
and I will be patient with their failings—
for through them God chooses to rule us.

You shall not murder.
I will not belittle, insult, hate,
or kill my neighbor-
not by my thoughts, my words,
my look or gesture,
and certainly not by actual deeds—
and I will not be party to this in others;
rather, I will put away
all desire for revenge.

I will not harm
or recklessly endanger myself either.

You shall not commit adultery.
God condemns all unchastity.
I therefore thoroughly detest it
and will live a decent and chaste life.

You shall not steal.
I will do whatever I can
for my neighbor's good,
treating others as I would like them
to treat me,
and I will work faithfully
so that
I may share with those in need.

You shall not give false testimony
against your neighbor.
I will love the truth, speak it candidly,
and openly acknowledge it.
And I will do what I can to guard
and advance my neighbor's good name.

You shall not covet anything that belongs to
your neighbor.
With all my heart I will always hate sin
and take pleasure in whatever is right.

For alternate versions of the Ten Commandments see 718, 722

Text: based on Heidelberg Catechism Q&A's 92, 94, 96, 99, 103-105, 108, 111-113; Deuteronomy 5:6-21,
   Exodus 20:1-17

Love God with All Your Soul and Strength 716

Love God with all your soul and strength, with all your heart and mind.

And love your neigh-bor as your-self; be faith-ful, just, and kind.

Chord symbols represent a simplified harmony.

Words: Deuteronomy 6:5; Leviticus 19:18; vers. Isaac Watts, 1715, P.D.
Music (FARRANT 8.6.8.6): English, 16th c.; adapt. Edward Hodges, ca. 1835, P.D.

717

Sing a Psalm of Joy

PSALM 81

1 Sing a psalm of joy! Shout in cel - e - bra - tion.
2 Sound the fes - tal horn, your thanks - giv - ing voic - ing.
(The exhortation of the LORD may be read here (Ps. 81:6-16), or a reading of the Law.)
*3 Tune our hearts to praise; turn our ears to hear you.

Let the tam - bou - rine and the trum - pet bring
Praise the LORD your God, as he did com - mand
Then in thank - ful - ness may we walk your way

prais - es to our King for his great sal - va - tion.
when from E - gypt's land you came forth re - joic - ing.
and from day to day hon - or and a - dore you.

*To sing the entire psalm, skip stanza 3 and continue with the optional stanzas 4-8.

4 When in need you cried,
  I was near and saved you.
  From the cloud I spoke,
  answered your request—
  Meribah the test—
  I did not forsake you.

5 O my people, hear;
  when I call you, listen.
  Choose no foreign god—
  listen to my plea.
  Have no god but me;
  come and be forgiven.

(continues)

Chord symbols represent a simplified harmony.

Words: Marie J. Post, 1984, © 1987 Faith Alive Christian Resources, st. 3 Martin Tel © 2011 Martin Tel, admin.
Faith Alive Christian Resources
Music (GENEVAN 81 | 5.6.5.5.5.6): *Genevan Psalter,* 1562; harm. Dale Grotenhuis (1931-2012), 1985, © 1987
Faith Alive Christian Resources

Optional stanzas for use when the exhortation or a reading of the Law is not spoken.

6 I, the LORD your God,
　　brought you out of Egypt.
　　I removed your yoke,
　　all your needs supplied.
　　Open your mouth wide:
　　surely I will fill it.

7 Oh, that Israel
　　would but hear my pleading!
　　Oh, that they would turn,
　　walk upon my path;
　　I would pour my wrath
　　on their foes unheeding.

8 With the finest wheat
　　I, your LORD, would feed you.
　　Honey from the rock
　　I would gladly give
　　that you all might live.
　　Hear me, O my people.

Litany: The Ten Commandments 2　　718
EXODUS 20:1-17

Hear the Word of the Lord:
"I am the LORD your God; who brought you out of Egypt, out of the land of slavery.
You shall have no other gods before me.
You shall not make for yourself an image in the form of anything
in heaven above or on the earth beneath or in the water below.
You shall not bow down to them or worship them.
You shall not misuse the name of the LORD your God.
Remember the Sabbath day by keeping it holy.
Honor your father and your mother.
You shall not murder.
You shall not commit adultery.
You shall not steal.
You shall not give false testimony against your neighbor.
You shall not covet anything that belongs to your neighbor.

With God's grace and the support of each other as part of Christ's body we promise:
I will love the Lord, our God, with all my heart, soul, and mind,
and my neighbor as myself.

May the God of peace,
who through the blood of the eternal covenant
brought back from the dead our Lord Jesus,
that great Shepherd of the sheep,
equip you with everything good for doing his will,
and may he work in us what is pleasing to him,
through Jesus Christ, to whom be glory forever and ever. **Amen.**

For alternate versions of the Ten Commandments see 715, 722
Text: based on Exodus 20:1-17, Matthew 22:37-40, Hebrews 13:20-21, NIV

719 God's Glory Fills the Heavens

PSALM 19

1 God's glo - ry fills the heavens with hymns;
2 God's per - fect law re - vives the soul;
3 God's ser - vant may I ev - er be:

the domed sky bears the Mak - er's mark.
its pre - cepts make the sim - ple wise.
this world my joy, that word my guide.

New prais - es sound from day to day
Its just com - mands re - joice the heart;
O cleanse me, LORD, from se - cret sin;

and ech - o through the know - ing dark.
its truth gives light un - to the eyes.
de - liv - er me from self - ish pride.

For another setting of Ps. 19 see 3

Words: Carl P. Daw Jr (b. 1944) © 1989 Hope Publishing Company
Music (CREATION 8.8.8.8 D): Franz J. Haydn (1732-1809), 1798, P.D.

720 How Shall the Young Direct Their Way

PSALM 119:9-16

1 How shall the young di - rect their way? What light shall
2 Sin - cere - ly I have sought you, Lord; O let me
3 O bless - ed Lord, teach me your law, your right-eous
4 Up - on your pre - cepts and your ways my heart will

be their per - fect guide? Your word, O Lord, will
not from you de - part; to know your will and
judg - ments I de - clare; your tes - ti - mo - nies
med - i - tate with awe; your word shall be my

safe - ly lead if in its wis - dom they con - fide.
keep from sin, your word I cher - ish in my heart.
make me glad, for they are wealth be - yond com - pare.
chief de - light, and I will not for - get your law.

For other settings of Ps. 119 see 721, 758, 759, 760

Words: Psalm 119:9-16; *Psalter*, 1912, P.D.
Music (ST. CRISPIN 8.8.8.8): George J. Elvey, 1862, P.D.

Teach Me, O LORD, Your Way of Truth   721

PSALM 119:33-40

1 Teach me, O LORD, your way of truth,
and from it I will not depart.
That I may steadfastly obey,
give me an understanding heart.

2 In your commandments make me walk,
for in your law my joy shall be.
Give me a heart that loves your will,
from discontent and envy free.

3 Turn heart and eye from vanities,
preserve my life within your way.
Confirm to me your holy word
promised to those who fear your name.

4 LORD, turn away disgrace and dread.
Your righteous judgments I confess.
To know your word is my desire.
Revive me in your righteousness.

For music see 720
For other settings of Ps. 119 see 720, 758, 759, 760
Words: Psalm 119:33-40; *Psalter*, 1912, P.D.

Litany: The Ten Commandments 3   722

DEUTERONOMY 5:6-21, EXODUS 20:1-17

You shall have no other gods before me.
For from him and through him
and to him are all things.
To him be the glory forever!

You shall not make for yourself an idol.
In Christ we have redemption,
the forgiveness of sins.
He is the image of the invisible God,
the firstborn over all creation.

You shall not misuse the name
of the Lord your God,
for the Lord will not hold anyone guiltless
who misuses his name.
Let us continually offer to God
a sacrifice of praise—
the fruit of lips that confess his name.

Remember the Sabbath day by keeping it holy.
Six days you shall labor and do all your work,
but the seventh day is a Sabbath
to the Lord your God.
Let the Word of Christ
dwell in you richly
as you teach and admonish
one another with all wisdom,
and as you sing psalms, hymns,
and spiritual songs
with gratitude in your hearts to God.

Honor your father and your mother,
so that you may live long in the land
the Lord your God is giving you.

Children, obey your parents
in everything,
for this pleases the Lord.

You shall not murder.
Be kind and compassionate
to one another,
forgiving each other,
just as in Christ God forgave you.

You shall not commit adultery.
You are not your own;
you were bought at a price.
Therefore honor God
with your body.

You shall not steal.
Those who have been stealing
must steal no longer,
but must work,
doing something useful with their hands,
so that they may have something
to share with those in need.

You shall not give false testimony
against your neighbor.
Instead, speaking the truth in love,
we will in all things grow up into him
who is the Head, that is, Christ.

You shall not covet your neighbor's house
or anything that belongs to your neighbor.
I have learned to be content whatever
the circumstances.

For alternate versions of the Ten Commandments see 715, 718

Text: Responsive Reading of the Law from the Epistles, *Psalter Hymnal* 1987; Deuteronomy 5:6-21, Exodus 20:1-17

723

Deep Within

Words: from Jeremiah 31:33, Ezekiel 36:26, Joel 2:12; David Haas © 1987 GIA Publications, Inc.
Music (DEEP WITHIN refrain 8.7.8.5.6 stanzas irregular): David Haas © 1987 GIA Publications, Inc.

be my own, and I will be your God.

Stanzas Fmaj9   C/E

1 I will give you a new heart, a new spir - it with-
2 ‡ Seek___ my face, and__ see___ your
3 Re - turn___ to me, with__ all___ your

Am7   G/B   C   Dsus   D *To Refrain*

in you, for I will be your strength.
God, for I will be your hope.
heart, and I will bring you back.

Coda G

God.

C/E   D   G

724

You Shall Love the Lord

1 You shall love the Lord your God with all your
(2 You shall) love the Lord your God with all your
(3 You shall) love the Lord your God with all your

heart, with all your heart. You shall love the Lord your
soul, with all your soul. You shall love the Lord your
mind, with all your mind. You shall love the Lord your

God with all your heart, soul, and mind.
God with all your heart, soul, and
God with all your heart, soul, and

2 You shall mind. You shall

love your neigh - bor as you love your -

self. You shall love the Lord your God with all your

heart, soul, and mind. 3 You shall

Charge: A Living Sacrifice 725

ROMANS 12:1-3

Therefore, I urge you, brothers and sisters, in view of God's mercy,
 to offer your bodies as a living sacrifice, holy and pleasing to God
—this is your true and proper worship.
Do not conform to the pattern of this world,
but be transformed by the renewing of your mind.
Then you will be able to test and approve what God's will is
—his good, pleasing and perfect will.
For by the grace given me I say to every one of you:
Do not think of yourself more highly than you ought,
but rather think of yourself with sober judgment,
in accordance with the faith God has distributed to each of you.

726 The Lord is King, Enthroned in Might

PSALM 99

1 The LORD is king, en-throned in might on wings of cher-u-bim;
2 Of old to priests and proph-ets known with trem-bling, fear and awe,
3 O mag-ni-fy the God of grace who hears his peo-ple's cry,

he reigns in hol-i-ness and light, bow down to wor-ship him!
he gave his peo-ple, set in stone, his stat-utes and his law.
and come with songs be-fore his face, ex-alt his name on high!

Be-yond all maj-es-ty and praise his ho-ly name con-fess:
By those who called up-on his name the voice of God was heard,
To see at last, by grace re-stored from sin and all its stains,

the king of ev-er-last-ing days, who rules in right-eous-ness.
his pres-ence shown in cloud and flame when they o-beyed his word.
the ho-ly moun-tain of the Lord where God in glo-ry reigns.

For an alternate arrangement see 679. This music in a lower key see 22, 145, 356

Words: Timothy Dudley-Smith (b. 1926) © 2007 Hope Publishing Company
Music (ELLACOMBE 8.6.8.6 D): *Gesangbuch der Herzogl, Hofkapelle, Würtemberg*, 1784, P.D.

Christian Hearts in Love United

727

1 Chris - tian hearts in love u - nit - ed: search to know God's ho - ly will.
2 Grant, Lord, that with your di - rec-tion, "Love each oth - er" we com-ply.
3 Come, then, liv - ing church of Je - sus, cov - e - nant with him a - new.

Let his love, in us ig - nit - ed, more and more our spir-its fill.
Help us live in true af - fec - tion, your love to ex - em pli - fy.
Un - to him who con - quered for us may we pledge our ser-vice true.

Christ the head, and we his mem - bers—we re - flect the light he is.
Let our mu - tual love be glow - ing bright-ly so that all may view
May our lives re - flect the bright-ness of God's love in Je - sus shown.

Christ the mas - ter, we dis - ci - ples—he is ours, and we are his.
that we, as on one stem grow-ing, liv - ing branch-es are in you.
To the world we then bear wit - ness: we be - long to God a - lone.

Chord symbols represent a simplified harmony.

Words: Nicolaus L. von Zinzendorf, 1723, tr. composite, P.D.
Music (O DU LIEBE MEINER LIEBE 8.7.8.7 D): *Moravian Chorale Book* manuscript, *Herrnhut*, 1735, P.D.

728

People of the Lord

PSALM 78

1 Peo - ple of the Lord, lis - ten to my voice.
2 Tell of God's great deeds. Teach his lov - ing law
3 Tell the news till each gen - er - a - tion knows.
4 May we trust in God, rest in his strong hand,

Hear the an - cient words. Once a - gain re - joice!
that faith's pre - cious seed in each heart may grow.
They, in turn, will teach those yet to be born.
live in his strong love, fol - low his com - mands.

Refrain

What we have heard, what we have known, let our tongues tell our sons and

daugh - ters the won - ders of our liv - ing God, that they may

Words: Greg Scheer © 2010 Greg Scheer
Music (JENNY VAN TSCHEGG 5.5.5.5.8.9.8.9): Greg Scheer © 2010 Greg Scheer

join us in the cho - rus.

Let This Be My Supreme Desire 729

PSALM 26

1 Let this be my su - preme de - sire, my ob - ject and my prayer,
2 To lead a blame - less life, O Lord, to trust you with - out fear,
3 To walk be - fore you in the truth, to shun all e - vil ways,
4 Let this be my su - preme de - sire, my ob - ject and my prayer,

un - til I stand be - fore your throne to glo - ri - fy you there:
to bring my hum - ble heart to you and know your love is near:
to come in - to your house to pray and shout a - loud your praise:
un - til I stand be - fore your throne to glo - ri - fy you there!

Chord symbols represent a simplified harmony.

Words: Michael Perry © 1989 The Jubilate Group, admin. Hope Publishing Company
Music (WINCHESTER OLD 8.6.8.6): attr. George Kirbye, 1592, P.D.

730 I Want to Walk as a Child of the Light

1 I want to walk as a child of the light;
  I want to follow Jesus. God set the stars to give
  light to the world; the star of my life is Jesus.

2 I want to see the brightness of God;
  I want to look at Jesus. Clear Sun of righteousness,
  shine on my path, and show me the way to the Father.

3 I'm looking for the coming of Christ;
  I want to be with Jesus. When we have run with
  patience the race, we shall know the joy of Jesus.

Refrain
In him there is no darkness at all; the night and the

Chord symbols represent a simplified harmony.

Words and Music (HOUSTON 10.7.10.8 refrain 9.9.11.7): Kathleen Thomerson (b. 1934) © 1970, 1975
Celebration

day are both a - like. The Lamb is the light of the

cit - y of God; shine in my heart, Lord Je - sus.

Affirmation: Why We Do Good Works 731

Since we have been delivered from our misery by grace through Christ
without any merit of our own, why then should we do good works?

**Because Christ, having redeemed us by his blood,
is also restoring us by his Spirit into his image,
so that with our whole lives
we may show that we are thankful to God
for his benefits,
so that he may be praised through us,
so that we may be assured of our faith by its fruits,
and so that by our godly living
our neighbors may be won over to Christ.**

Text: Heidelberg Catechism Q&A 86

732 The LORD, My Shepherd, Rules My Life
PSALM 23

5 Your good - ness and your gra - cious love pur -
1 The LORD, my shep - herd, rules my life and
2 The LORD re - vives my fail - ing strength, he
3 Though in a val - ley dark as death, no

sue me all my days; your house, O LORD, shall
gives me all I need; he leads me by re -
makes my joy com - plete; and in right paths, for
e - vil makes me fear; your shep - herd's staff pro -

be my home— your name, my end - less praise.
fresh - ing streams; in pas - tures green I feed.
his name's sake, he guides my fal - tering feet.
tects my way, for you are with me there.

4 While all my enemies look on,
you spread a royal feast;
you fill my cup, anoint my head,
and treat me as your guest.

5 Your goodness and your gracious love
pursue me all my days;
your house, O LORD, shall be my home—
your name, my endless praise.

For other settings of Ps. 23 see 368, 369, 456, 824

Words: Christopher Idle © 1982 The Jubilate Group, admin. Hope Publishing Company
Music (CRIMOND 8.6.8.6): Jessie Seymour Irvine, 1872; harm. David Grant, 1872; desc. W. Baird Ross
(1871-1950), P.D.

Humbly in Your Sight

733

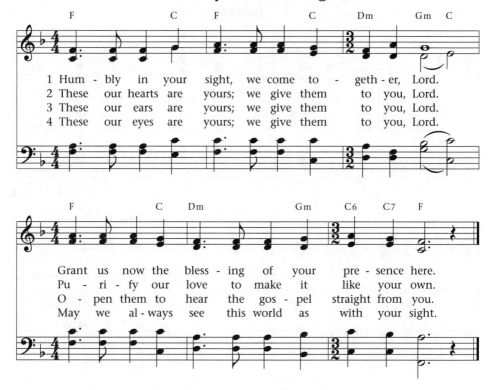

1 Hum - bly in your sight, we come to - geth - er, Lord.
2 These our hearts are yours; we give them to you, Lord.
3 These our ears are yours; we give them to you, Lord.
4 These our eyes are yours; we give them to you, Lord.

Grant us now the bless - ing of your pre - sence here.
Pu - ri - fy our love to make it like your own.
O - pen them to hear the gos - pel straight from you.
May we al - ways see this world as with your sight.

5 These our hands are yours;
we give them to you, Lord.
Give them strength and skill
to work and build for you.

6 These our tongues are yours;
we give them to you, Lord.
May we speak your healing words
of light and truth.

7 These our feet are yours;
we give them to you, Lord.
May we always walk the path
of light with you.

8 Our whole selves are yours;
we give them to you, Lord.
Take us now and keep us
safe forevermore.

9 Praise the Father,
praise the Spirit,
praise the Son;
praise to God forevermore
the Three in One.

Words and Music (HUMBLY IN YOUR SIGHT 5.6.11): from Malawi, Tom Colvin © 1967 Hope Publishing Company; arr. Geoff Weaver © 1967 Hope Publishing Company

734

My Heart Is Firmly Fixed

PSALM 108

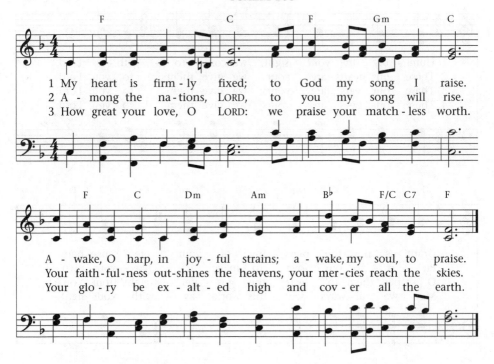

1 My heart is firm-ly fixed; to God my song I raise.
2 A-mong the na-tions, LORD, to you my song will rise.
3 How great your love, O LORD: we praise your match-less worth.

A-wake, O harp, in joy-ful strains; a-wake, my soul, to praise.
Your faith-ful-ness out-shines the heavens, your mer-cies reach the skies.
Your glo-ry be ex-alt-ed high and cov-er all the earth.

4 Stretch forth your mighty hand
in answer to our prayer,
and let your own beloved ones
your great salvation share.

5 God speaks: "All lands are mine,
to serve me and obey;
my people and their foes will serve
my glory day by day."

6 O who will lead us on
in triumph on this day?
LORD, why do you reject your own
and turn your face away?

7 An army's help is vain;
to God for help we plead.
With God we shall do valiantly;
with God we shall succeed.

Optional prayer of dedication

Lord God,
we receive with joy your lavish gifts to us:
    forgiveness from sin,
    adoption as your children,
    your Word, a light on our path.
    your Holy Spirit, our teacher and comforter.

[Add other phrases as appropriate]

With hearts overflowing with gratitude, we dedicate ourselves to you.
**We long for our lives to be a song of praise to you, our gracious Lord.
Amen.**

Chord symbols represent a simplified harmony.

Words: Psalter, 1912; rev. *Psalter Hymnal*, 1987, © 1987 Faith Alive Christian Resources
Music (ST. THOMAS 6.6.8.6): Aaron Williams, 1763; harm. Lowell Mason (1792-1872), P.D.

I Love You, LORD, For You Have Heard My Voice 735

PSALM 116

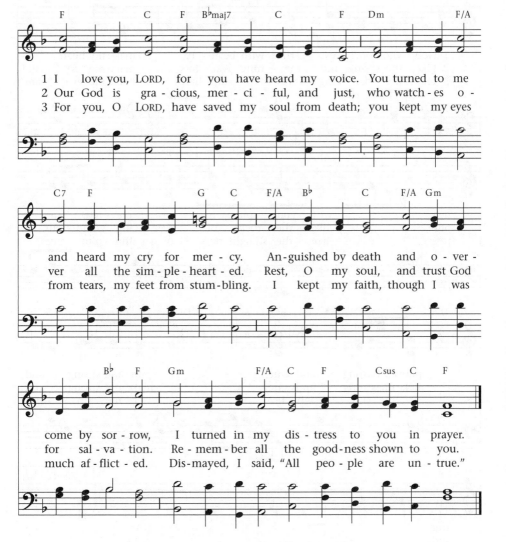

1 I love you, LORD, for you have heard my voice. You turned to me
2 Our God is gra - cious, mer - ci - ful, and just, who watch - es o -
3 For you, O LORD, have saved my soul from death; you kept my eyes

and heard my cry for mer - cy. An - guished by death and o - ver -
ver all the sim - ple - heart - ed. Rest, O my soul, and trust God
from tears, my feet from stum - bling. I kept my faith, though I was

come by sor - row, I turned in my dis - tress to you in prayer.
for sal - va - tion. Re - mem - ber all the good - ness shown to you.
much af - flict - ed. Dis - mayed, I said, "All peo - ple are un - true."

4 How can I pay you, LORD, for all your gifts?
   I will lift up the cup of full salvation.
   I will fulfill my vows to you, my Savior.
   With all your saints, I'll call upon your name.

5 Precious to you the dying of your saints.
   I am your faithful servant, freed from bondage.
   I'll pay my vows and, with your people, thank you.
   Come to God's house, O people; praise the LORD!

Chord symbols represent a simplified harmony.

Words: Helen Otte, 1980, alt. © 1987 Faith Alive Christian Resources
Music (GENEVAN 116 | 10.11.11.10): *Genevan Psalter,* 1562; harm. Seymour Swets, 1954, P.D.

736 God, Who Touches Earth With Beauty

1 God, who touch-es earth with beau-ty, make my heart a-
2 Like the springs and run-ning wa-ters, make me crys-tal
3 Like the dan-cing waves in sun-light, make me glad and

new; with your spir-it re-cre-ate me,
pure, like the rocks of tow-er-ing grand-eur,
free; like the straight-ness of the pine trees,

pure and strong and true; pure and strong and
make me strong and sure; make me strong and
let me up-right be; let me up-right

true.
sure.
be.

4 Like the arching of the heavens,
lift my thoughts above;
turn my dreams to noble action,
ministries of love; ministries of love.

5 God, who touches earth with beauty,
make my heart anew;
keep me ever, by your Spirit,
pure and strong and true;
pure and strong and true.

Words: Mary Susanne Edgar (1889-1973), 1925, © Estate of Mary Susanne Edgar
Music (LUDINGTON 8.5.8.5 with repeat): Gregg DeMey © 2008 Re:Create Music, admin. Faith Alive Christian Resources

Have Thine Own Way, Lord

737

1 Have thine own way, Lord! Have thine own way!
2 Have thine own way, Lord! Have thine own way!
3 Have thine own way, Lord! Have thine own way!
4 Have thine own way, Lord! Have thine own way!

Thou art the pot - ter, I am the clay.
Search me and try me, Mas - ter, to - day.
Wound - ed and wea - ry, help me, I pray.
Hold o'er my be - ing ab - so - lute sway.

Mold me and make me af - ter thy will,
O - pen mine eyes, my sin show me now,
Pow - er, all pow - er, sure - ly is thine.
Fill with thy Spir - it till all shall see

while I am wait - ing, yield - ed and still.
as in thy pres - ence hum - bly I bow.
Touch me and heal me, Sav - ior di - vine.
Christ on - ly, al - ways, liv - ing in me.

Words: Adelaide A. Pollard, 1901, P.D.
Music (ADELAIDE 9.9.9.9): George C. Stebbins, 1907, P.D.

738 Jesus, All for Jesus

Je - sus, all for Je - sus, all I am and have and ev - er hope to be.

All of my am - bi-tions, hopes, and plans— I sur - ren - der these in - to your hands. For it's

739 I Surrender All

1 All to Je-sus I sur-ren-der, all to him I free-ly give;
2 All to Je-sus I sur-ren-der, make me, Sav-ior, whol-ly thine;
3 All to Je-sus I sur-ren-der, Lord, I give my-self to thee;

I will ev-er love and trust him, in his pres-ence dai-ly live.
let me feel thy Ho-ly Spir-it, tru-ly know that thou art mine.
fill me with thy love and pow-er, let thy bless-ing fall on me.

Refrain

I sur-ren-der all, I sur-ren-der all;

I sur-ren-der all, I sur-ren-der all.

all to thee, my bless-ed Sav-ior, I sur-ren-der all.

Words: Judson W. VanDeVenter, P.D.
Music (SURRENDER 8.7.8.7 refrain 5.5.8.5): Winfield S. Weeden, P.D.

Here I Am

Here I am, Lord, here I am.
I come to do your will.

For use with Psalm 40: Sing refrain, read vv 1-3, refrain, vv 4-8, refrain, vv 9-11, refrain, vv 12-17, refrain.

Words: © 1969, 1981, 1997, International Commission on English in the Liturgy Corporation
Music (HERE I AM 4.3.6): Rory Cooney © 1971, 1991 OCP Publications

Take, O Take Me as I Am

Take, O take me as I am; sum-mon out what I shall be;
set your seal up-on my heart and live in me.

Words and Music (TAKE ME AS I AM 7.7.7.4): John L. Bell (b. 1949) © 1995 Wild Goose Resource Group, Iona
Community, Scotland, GIA Publications, Inc., exclusive North American agent

742   Will You Come and Follow Me

Words: The Iona Community © 1987 Wild Goose Resource Group, Iona Community, Scotland,
GIA Publications, Inc., exclusive North American agent
Music (KELVINGROVE 7.6.7.6.7.7.7.6): Scottish traditional; arr. John L. Bell © 1987 Wild Goose Resource
Group, Iona Community, Scotland, GIA Publications, Inc., exclusive North American agent

O God, You Are My God

743

Words and Music (STEP BY STEP 6.7.6.7.8.9.7.10): David Strasser, Rich Mullins © 1991 BMG Songs, Inc./Kid Brothers of St. Frank Publishing, admin. BMG Songs, Inc./Music Services

744

In Great Thanksgiving

1 In great thanks-giv-ing, O Love Di-vine, who from our
2 In ce-le-bra-tion of power be-stowed, we who were
3 In ded-i-ca-tion we give our lives, to heed your
4 In ex-al-ta-tion of Christ, our Lord, who for the

sor-row re-deemed us all, cleansed of re-gret-ting, re-lieved of
sin-ners are fol-lowers bold, for-giv-ing ene-mies we sing your
bid-ding to seek the lost, to all the hun-gry bring food for
faith-ful true life en-sured, we laud him Sav-ior, we teach his

fear, we come re-joic-ing for new life here.
praise, with ju-bi-la-tion love's ban-ner raise.
feasts, to fear-bound peo-ple strength for life's tests.
way of peace with jus-tice, hope for to-day.

For an alternate arrangement see 807

Words: Melchizedek M. Solis, Philippines © 2000 Christian Conference of Asia, admin. GIA Publications, Inc.
Music (MALATE 9.9.9.9): Mutya Lopez Solis, Philippines © 1990, 2000 Christian Conference of Asia, admin.
GIA Publications, Inc.; arr. Greg Scheer © 2009 Christian Conference of Asia, admin. GIA Publications, Inc.

Dwell in Me, O Blessed Spirit

745

1 Dwell in me, O bless-ed Spir - it! How I need your help di - vine!
2 Grant to me your sa - cred pres-ence; then my faith will ne'er de - cline.

In the way of life e - ter - nal, keep, O keep this heart of mine.
Com - fort me and help me on - ward; fill with love this heart of mine.

Refrain

Dwell in me, O bless - ed Spir - it, gra - cious Teach - er, Friend di - vine!

For the king - dom work that calls me, O pre - pare this heart of mine.

Words: Martha J. Lankton, 1899, alt., P.D.
Music (DWELL IN ME 8.7.8.7 D): Georgia G. Berky, 1899, P.D.

746 Holy Spirit, Living Breath of God

1 Ho - ly Spir - it, liv - ing Breath of God, breathe new
2 Ho - ly Spir - it, come a - bide with - in, may your
3 Ho - ly Spir - it, from cre - a - tion's birth, giv - ing

life in - to my will - ing soul.
joy be seen in all I do.
life to all that God has made,

Bring the pres - ence of the ris - en Lord to re -
Love e - nough to cov - er ev - er - y sin, in each
show your pow - er once a - gain on earth, cause your

new my heart and make me whole.
thought and deed and at - ti - tude.
church to hun - ger for your ways.

Words and Music (HOLY SPIRIT, LIVING BREATH 9.9.9.9 D): Keith Getty and Stuart Townend © 2006
Thankyou Music (PRS), admin. worldwide at EMICMGPublishing.com (excl. Europe admin. Kingswaysongs)

Cause your Word to come a - live in me;
Kind - ness to the great - est and the least,
Let the fra - grance of our prayers a - rise;

give me faith for what I can - not see; give me pas - sion for your
gen - tle - ness that sows the path of peace. Turn my striv - ing in - to
lead us on the road of sa - cri - fice, that in u - ni - ty the

pur - i - ty; Ho - ly Spir - it, breathe new life in
works of grace; Breath of God, show Christ in all I
face of Christ may be clear for all the world to

me.
do.
see.

747 Breathe on Me, Breath of God

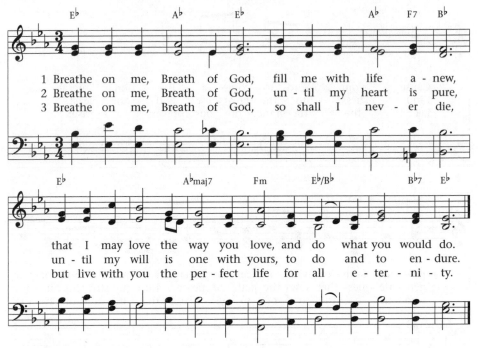

1 Breathe on me, Breath of God, fill me with life a-new,
2 Breathe on me, Breath of God, un-til my heart is pure,
3 Breathe on me, Breath of God, so shall I nev-er die,

that I may love the way you love, and do what you would do.
un-til my will is one with yours, to do and to en-dure.
but live with you the per-fect life for all e-ter-ni-ty.

For this music in a higher key see 291

Words: Edwin Hatch, 1878, alt., P.D.
Music (TRENTHAM 6.6.8.6): Robert Jackson (1840-1914), 1878, P.D.

748 Lord, to Whom Shall We Go

JOHN 6:68

Lord, to whom shall we go? Yours are the words of e-ter-nal life.

Words: John 6:68
Music (TO WHOM SHALL WE GO 7.9): The Iona Community © 1987, 1995 Wild Goose Resource Group,
  Iona Community, Scotland, GIA Publications, Inc., exclusive North American agent

Spirit of the Living God

749

1 Spir - it of the liv - ing God, fall a - fresh on me;
2 Spir - it of the liv - ing God, move a - mong us all;

Spir - it of the liv - ing God, fall a - fresh on me.
make us one in heart and mind, make us one in love;

Melt me, mold me, fill me, use me.
hum - ble, car - ing, self - less, shar - ing.

Spir - it of the liv - ing God, fall a - fresh on me.
Spir - it of the liv - ing God, fill our lives with love.

750   The Word Will Accomplish Its Purpose
ISAIAH 55:10-11

As the rain and the snow
come down from heaven,
and do not return to it
without watering the earth
and making it bud and flourish,
so that it yields seed for the sower and bread

for the eater,
so is my word that goes out from my mouth:
It will not return to me empty,
but will accomplish what I desire
and achieve the purpose
for which I sent it.

751   Open Your Ears, O Faithful People

1 O-pen your ears, O faith-ful peo-ple, o-pen your
2 They who have ears to hear the mes-sage, they who have
3 What we have heard we'll teach our chil-dren; may they have

ears and hear God's Word. O-pen your hearts, O
ears, now let them hear. They who would learn the
ears to hear God's Word. Let us through ev-ery

roy-al priest-hood, God has come to you.
way of wis-dom, let them hear God's Word.
gen-er-a-tion make God's won-ders known.

Words: Hasidic traditional; tr. Willard F. Jabusch © 1966, 1982 Willard F. Jabusch, admin. OCP Publications;
st. 3, Psalm 78:4, vers. Martin Tel © 2011 Martin Tel, admin. Faith Alive Christian Resources
Music (YISRAEL V'ORAITA 9.8.9.5 refrain 8.4.8.4): Hasidic traditional; arr. *Evangelical Lutheran Worship* © 2006
Augsburg Fortress

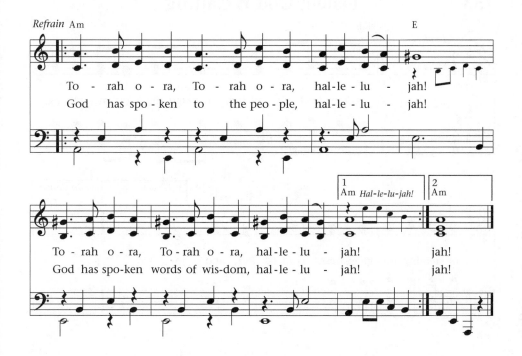

Refrain

To - rah o - ra, To - rah o - ra, hal-le-lu - jah!
God has spo-ken to the peo - ple, hal-le-lu - jah!

To - rah o - ra, To - rah o - ra, hal-le-lu - jah! jah!
God has spo-ken words of wis-dom, hal-le-lu - jah! jah!

Dawk'yah towgyah/   752
Take the Saving Word of God

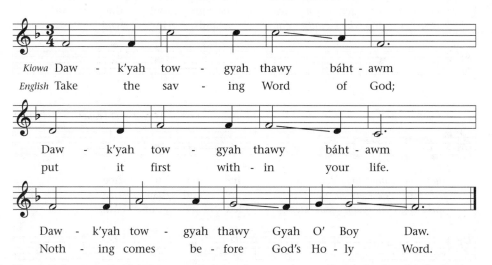

Kiowa	Daw - k'yah tow - gyah thawy				báht - awm		
English	Take	the	sav - ing	Word	of	God;	

Daw - k'yah tow - gyah thawy báht - awm
put it first with - in your life.

Daw - k'yah tow - gyah thawy Gyah O' Boy Daw.
Noth - ing comes be - fore God's Ho - ly Word.

*To support the congregational singing you may include an instrumental or sung drone on F to be re-articulated at the beginning of each phrase.

Words: Pawltay (Kiowa); English vers. John Thornburg, Eng. vers. © 2008 General Board of Global Ministries
t/a GBGMusik
Music (DAWK'YAH TOWGYAH): Unknown (Kiowa); transcr. Carlton R. Young from the CD *With Our Voices*,
transcr. © 2008 General Board of Global Ministries t/a GBGMusik

753   Listen, God Is Calling

Words: Tanzanian traditional; tr. Howard S. Olson (1922 - 2010) © 1979 Lutheran Theological College, Makumira, Tanzania
Music (NENO LAKE MUNGU 6.4.6.4 refrain 6.6.6.4): Tanzanian traditional; arr. C. Michael Hawn (b. 1948) © 2001 C. Michael Hawn

Lord, Speak to Me that I May Speak

754

1 Lord, speak to me that I may speak in liv - ing
2 O lead me, Lord, that I may lead the wan - dering
3 O teach me, Lord, that I may teach the pre - cious

ech - oes of your tone. As you have sought, so
and the wa - vering feet. O feed me, Lord, that
truths which you im - part. And wing my words that

let me seek your err - ing chil - dren, lost and lone.
I may feed your hun - gry ones with man - na sweet.
they may reach the hid - den depths of man - y a heart.

4 O fill me with your fullness, Lord,
  until my very heart o'erflows
  in kindling thought and glowing word,
  your love to tell, your praise to show.

5 O use me, Lord, use even me,
  just as you will, and when, and where
  until your blessed face I see,
  your rest, your joy, your glory share.

Chord symbols represent a simplified harmony.

Words: France R. Havergal, 1872, alt., P.D.
Music (CANONBURY 8.8.8.8): Robert A. Schumann, 1839, from *Nachtstücke,* Op. 23, No. 4, P.D.

755 Speak, O Lord

1 Speak, O Lord, as we come to you to re-ceive the food
2 Teach us, Lord, full o-be-di-ence, ho-ly rev-er-ence,
3 Speak, O Lord, and re-new our minds; help us grasp the heights

of your ho-ly Word. Take your truth, plant it
true hu-mil-i-ty. Test our thoughts and our
of your plans for us. Truths un-changed from the

deep in us; shape and fash-ion us in your like-ness—
at-ti-tudes in the ra-di-ance of your pur-i-ty.
dawn of time that will ech-o down through e-ter-ni-ty.

that the light of Christ might be seen to-day in our
Cause our faith to rise; cause our eyes to see your ma-
And by grace we'll stand on your prom-is-es, and by

Words and Music (SPEAK, O LORD 8.10.8.10.10.10.8.9): Keith Getty, Stuart Townend © 2006 Thankyou Music, admin. worldwide at EMICMGPublishing.com (excl. Europe admin. by Kingswaysongs)

acts of love and our deeds of faith. Speak, O Lord, and ful-
jes - tic love and au - thor - i - ty. Words of power that can
faith we'll walk as you walk with us. Speak, O Lord, till your

fill in us all your pur - pos - es for your
nev - er fail; let their truth pre - vail o - ver
church is built, and the earth is filled with your

glo - ry.
un - be-lief.
glo - ry.

A Prayer: Make Us Hungry for Your Word   756

Gracious God,
we do not live by bread alone,
but by every word that comes from your mouth.
Make us hungry for your Word,
that it may nourish us today
in the ways of eternal life.
Through Jesus Christ, the bread of heaven. Amen.

Text: Source unknown, P.D.

757   # O Word of God Incarnate

1 O Word of God in-car-nate, O Wis-dom from on high,
2 The church from you, dear Mas-ter, re-ceived this gift di-vine;
3 O make your church, dear Sav-ior, a lamp of bur-nished gold

O Truth un-changed, un-chang-ing, O Light of our dark sky:
and still the light is lift-ed o'er all the earth to shine.
to bear be-fore the na-tions your true light as of old.

we praise you for the ra-diance that from the Scrip-ture's page,
It is the chart and com-pass that all life's voy-age through,
O teach your wan-dering pil-grims by this their path to trace

a lan-tern to our foot-steps, shines on from age to age.
mid mists and rocks and quick-sands, still guides, O Christ, to you.
till, clouds and dark-ness end-ed, we see you face to face.

Chord symbols represent a simplified harmony.

Words: William W. How, 1867, alt., P.D.
Music (MUNICH 7.6.7.6 D): *Neu-vermehrtes Gesangbuch*, Meiningen, 1693; adapt. and harm. Felix Mendelssohn, 1847, P.D.

Order My Steps

PSALM 119:9-16

Refrain

How can a young person stay
on the path of purity?
By living according to your word.
I seek you with all my heart;
**do not let me stray
from your commands.**
I have hidden your word in my heart
that I might not sin against you.
Praise be to you, LORD;
teach me your decrees.

Refrain

With my lips I recount
**all the laws that come
from your mouth.**
I rejoice in following your statutes
as one rejoices in great riches.
I meditate on your precepts
and consider your ways.
I delight in your decrees;
I will not neglect your word.

Refrain

For other settings of Ps. 119 see 720, 721, 759, 760

Text: Psalm 119:9-16, NRSV
Words: Glenn Burleigh © 1991 Glenn Burleigh, Burleigh Inspirations Music
Music (IN YOUR WORD 9.7.9.7.8): Glenn Burleigh © 1991 Glenn Burleigh, Burleigh Inspirations Music

759 Your Word Sheds Light upon My Path

PSALM 119:105-112

1 Your word sheds light up - on my path;
2 In my dis - tress I plead with you;
3 When dan - ger brings me close to death,
4 Your pre - cepts are my her - i - tage;

a shin - ing light, it guides my feet.
send help ac - cord - ing to your word.
your law stays with me night and day.
they make my heart and soul re - joice.

Your right - eous judg - ments to ob - serve,
Ac - cept my sac - ri - fice of praise
The wick - ed lay a snare for me,
To keep your stat - utes faith - ful - ly

my sol - emn vow I now re - peat.
and make me know your judg - ments, LORD.
yet from your truth I will not stray.
shall ev - er be my will - ing choice.

For other settings of Ps. 119 see 720, 721, 758, 760

Words: Psalm 119:105-112; *Psalter*, 1912, P.D.
Music (FEDERAL STREET 8.8.8.8): Henry K. Oliver, 1832, P.D.

O Let My Supplicating Cry 760

PSALM 119:169-176

1 O let my supplicating cry
by you, my gracious LORD, be heard.
Give wisdom and deliver me
according to your faithful word.

2 Instructed in your holy law,
to praise your word I lift my voice.
Come, LORD, and be my present help,
for your commandments are my choice.

3 For your salvation I have longed,
my joy is in your law, O LORD.
Now, let me live, your praise to sing;
sustain me by your holy word.

4 Your servant, like a wandering sheep,
has lost the path and gone astray.
Restore my soul and lead me home,
for your commands I would obey.

For music see 759
For other settings of Ps. 119 see 720, 721, 758, 759
Words: Psalm 119:169-176; *Psalter*, 1912, P.D.

I Will Hide Your Word Inside My Heart 761

1 I will hide your word in-side my heart so that
2 Come and pour your grace in-to my heart so that

it may guide me. Like a shin-ing light, let it
it may fill me with the pre-cious things that your

burn so bright; I will fol - low you.
Spir - it brings; I will live in you.

Words and Music (I WILL HIDE 9.6.10.5): Paul Field © 2003 Daybreak Music; arr. Greg Scheer © 2008 Faith Alive Christian Resources

762   # Ancient Words

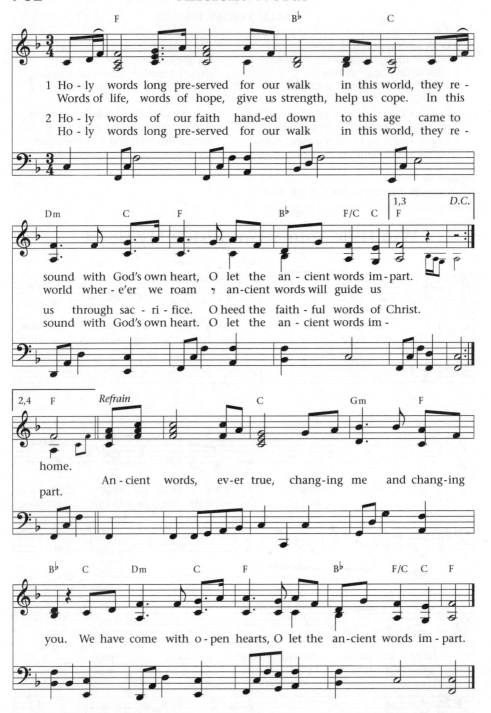

1 Ho - ly words long pre-served for our walk   in this world, they re -
Words of life, words of hope, give us strength, help us cope.   In this

2 Ho - ly words of our faith hand-ed down   to this age   came to
Ho - ly words long pre-served for our walk   in this world, they re -

sound with God's own heart, O let the an - cient words im - part.
world wher - e'er we roam ᾿ an-cient words will guide us
us through sac - ri - fice. O heed the faith - ful words of Christ.
sound with God's own heart. O let the an - cient words im -

home.
part.

An - cient words, ev - er true, chang-ing me and chang-ing

you. We have come with o - pen hearts, O let the an-cient words im - part.

Words and Music (ANCIENT WORDS 7.6.7.8 D refrain 6.7.7.8): Lynn DeShazo © 2001 Integrity's Hosanna!
Music, (ASCAP), admin. EMICMGPublishing.com

Blessed Jesus, at Your Word

1 Bless - ed Je - sus, at your word we are gath - ered
2 All our knowl - edge, sense, and sight lie in deep - est
3 Glo - rious Lord, your - self im - part; Light of Light, from

all to hear you. Let our hearts and souls be stirred
dark - ness shroud - ed, till your Spir - it breaks our night
God pro - ceed - ing, o - pen lips and ears and heart;

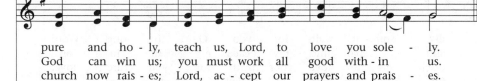

now to seek and love and fear you. By your gos - pel
with your beams of truth un - cloud - ed. You a - lone to
help us by your Spir - it's lead - ing. Hear the cry your

pure and ho - ly, teach us, Lord, to love you sole - ly.
God can win us; you must work all good with - in us.
church now rais - es; Lord, ac - cept our prayers and prais - es.

Words: Tobias Clausnitzer, 1663; tr. Catherine Winkworth, 1858, alt., P.D.
Music (LIEBSTER JESU 7.8.7.8.8.8): Johann R. Ahle, 1664, P.D.

764 **Break Now the Bread of Life**

1 Break now the bread of life, dear Lord, to me,
2 Bless your own word of truth, dear Lord, to me,
3 You are the bread of life, dear Lord, to me,
4 O send your Spir - it now, dear Lord, to me,

as once you broke the loaves be - side the sea.
as when you blessed the bread by Gal - i - lee.
your ho - ly Word the truth that res - cues me.
that he may touch my eyes and make me see.

Be - yond the sa - cred page I seek you, Lord;
Then shall all bond - age cease, all fet - ters fall;
Give me to eat and live with you a - bove;
Show me the truth made plain with - in your Word,

my spir - it waits for you, O liv - ing Word.
and I shall find my peace, my All in all!
teach me to love your truth, for you are love.
for in your book re - vealed I see you, Lord.

Words: st. 1-2 Mary A. Lathbury, 1877, alt., P.D.; st. 3-4 Alexander Groves (1842-1909), P.D.
Music (BREAD OF LIFE 6.4.6.4 D): William F. Sherwin, 1877, P.D.

God of the Word

Out of the bab-ble that sur-rounds us, out of the cha-os that's with-in, where can we go to find our mean-ing? Is there a place we can be-gin? God of the Word, now let the Word be spo-ken. Word of our God, come vis-it us with grace. Rise like a fra-grance, like a chord of mu-sic, fill-ing all this ho-ly place.

Words and Music (SAN FRANCISCO 9.8.9.8.10.10.11.7): Ken Medema (b. 1943) © 1993 Ken Medema Music/
Brier Patch Music

766   Lord, We Hear Your Word with Gladness

1 Lord, we hear your Word with glad-ness: you have spo-ken—we re-joice:
2 May we hear with un-der-stand-ing, by your Spir-it taught and led.
3 You have spo-ken; yours the full-ness, ours the wealth of this, your Word.

words of love and life and free-dom—help us make their truth our choice!
May the springs of all our be-ing by your liv-ing Word be fed.
Debt-ors, then, as liv-ing let-ters, we must make your gos-pel heard!

Now in ho-ly cel-e-bra-tion for your Word we wor-ship you;
May our hearts ac-cept with meek-ness all the grace your light makes known.
By your Spir-it's power trans-form us; shed your sav-ing light a-broad

spo-ken, writ-ten, known in Je-sus, ours to-day to prove a-new.
May o-be-dience mark our foot-steps till we make each word our own.
till our lives by love in ac-tion show our world the truth of God!

For alternate arrangement see 927

Words: Margaret Clarkson (b. 1915) © 1987 Hope Publishing Company
Music (HOLY MANNA 8.7.8.7 D): W. Moore, *Columbian Harmony*, 1825, P.D.

御言葉をください/Send Your Word, O Lord   767

Japanese 1 御言葉を ください 降り注
English 1 Send your Word, O LORD, like the rain, fall-ing down up-
2 Send your Word, O LORD, like the wind, blow-ing down up-
3 Send your Word, O LORD, like the dew, com-ing gent-ly

ぐ雨のように恵みの主よ。
on all the earth. Send your Word. We seek your end-less grace,
on all the earth. Send your Word. We seek your won-drous power,
down all the hills. Send your Word. We seek your end-less love,

飢えと渇きにあえぎ苦しみ、
with souls that hun-ger and thirst, sor-row-ful-ly a-go-nize.
pure-ness that re-jects all sins, though they will per-sist and cling.
for life that suf-fers in strife, with ad-ver-si-ties and hurts,

闇路さすらう命のために。
We would all be lost in dark if with-out your guid-ing light.
Bring us to com-plete vic-tory; set us all now free in-deed.
send your heal-ing power of love; we a-wait your brand-new world.

Japanese

2 御言葉をください、
吹く風のように強く
救いの主よ。からみつく罪、
根こそぎされて、命新たに
芽生えるために。

3 御言葉をください、
草に置く露のように、
命の主よ。人と人との、
心かよわず、乱れ争う
世界のために。

Words: Yasuchige Imakoma, Japan; para. Nobuaki Hanaoka © 1990 JNCC; tr. Nobuaki Hanaoka © 1983 The United Methodist Publishing House, admin. The Copyright Company
Music (MIKOTOBA): Shōzō Koyama, Japan; arr. Martin Tel © 2012 Martin Tel, admin. Faith Alive Christian Resources

768

Halle, Halle, Halle

Words: Caribbean traditional
Music (HALLE): Caribbean; arr. John Bell (b. 1949) and Graham Maule (b. 1958) © 1990 Wild Goose Resource Group, Iona Community, Scotland, GIA Publications, Inc., exclusive North American agent

Keep What You Have Believed

769

2 TIMOTHY 3:14-17

Words: 2 Timothy 3:14-17; para. Emily Brink © 2008 Faith Alive Christian Resources
Music (DIADEMATA 6.6.8.6 D): George J. Elvey, 1868, P.D.

770 In Christ Alone

1 In Christ a - lone my hope is found; he is my
2 In Christ a - lone, who took on flesh— full - ness of
3 There in the ground his bod - y lay, light of the
4 No guilt in life, no fear in death, this is the

light, my strength, my song— this cor - ner - stone, this sol - id
God in help - less babe!— this gift of love and right-eous-
world by dark - ness slain; then, burst-ing forth in glo - rious
power of Christ in me; from life's first cry to fin - al

ground, firm through the fierc - est drought and storm. What heights of
ness, scorned by the ones he came to save. 'Til on the
day, up from the grave he rose a - gain! And as he
breath, Je - sus com - mands my des - ti - ny. No power of

love, what depths of peace, when fears are stilled, when striv-ings
cross as Je - sus died, the wrath of God was sat - is -
stands in vic - to - ry, sin's curse has lost its grip on
hell, no hu - man plan, can ev - er pluck me from his

Words and Music (IN CHRIST ALONE 8.8.8.8 D): Keith Getty and Stuart Townend © 2002 Thankyou Music (PRS), admin. worldwide at EMICMGPublishing.com (excl. Europe admin. by Kingswaysongs)

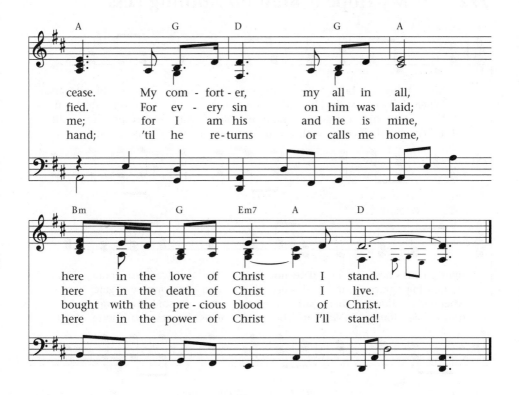

			cease.	My com - fort - er,	my all in all,
			fied.	For ev - ery sin	on him was laid;
			me;	for I am his	and he is mine,
			hand;	'til he re-turns	or calls me home,

	here	in the love of Christ	I stand.
	here	in the death of Christ	I live.
	bought	with the pre - cious blood	of Christ.
	here	in the power of Christ	I'll stand!

The Nicene Creed 1   771

We believe in one God,
the Father, the almighty,
maker of heaven and earth,
of all that is, seen and unseen.

We believe in one Lord, Jesus Christ,
the only Son of God,
eternally begotten of the Father,
God from God,
Light from Light,
true God from true God,
begotten, not made;
of one Being with the Father;
through him all things were made.
For us and for our salvation
he came down from heaven,
was incarnate of the Holy Spirit
and the Virgin Mary,
and became truly human.
For our sake he was crucified
for us under Pontius Pilate;
he suffered death and was buried.

On the third day he rose again,
in accordance with the Scriptures;
he ascended into heaven
and is seated at the right hand of the Father.
He will come again with glory
to judge the living and the dead,
and his kingdom will have no end.

And we believe in the Holy Spirit,
the Lord, the giver of life,
who proceeds from the Father and the Son*,
and with the Father and the Son
is worshiped and glorified,
who has spoken through the prophets.
We believe in one holy catholic
and apostolic Church.
We acknowledge one baptism
for the forgiveness of sins.
We look for the resurrection of the dead,
and the life of the world to come. Amen.

*and the Son was not originally part of this creed
For an alternate version of this creed see 806

772 My Hope Is Built on Nothing Less

1 My hope is built on noth-ing less than Je - sus' blood and
2 When dark-ness veils his love - ly face, I rest on his un -
3 His oath, his cov - e - nant, his blood sup - port me in the
4 When he shall come with trum-pet sound, O may I then in

right - eous - ness; I dare not trust the sweet-est frame, but
chang - ing grace; in ev - ery high and storm - y gale, my
whelm-ing flood; when all a-round my soul gives way, he
him be found, dressed in his right - eous - ness a - lone, fault -

whol-ly lean on Je - sus' name.
an - chor holds with - in the veil.
then is all my hope and stay. On Christ, the sol - id rock, I stand; all
less to stand be - fore the throne.

oth-er ground is sink-ing sand, all oth-er ground is sink-ing sand.

Words: Edward Mote (1797-1874), P.D.
Music (SOLID ROCK 8.8.8.8 refrain 8.8.8): William B. Bradbury (1816-1868), P.D.

O Lord, You Are My Light

PSALM 27

773

1 O LORD, you are my light and my sal-va-tion near:
2 My one re-quest has been and still this prayer I raise;
3 When trou-bles round me swell, when fears and dan-gers throng,
4 Up-lift-ed on a rock a-bove my foes a-round,

then who will cause me fright or fill my heart with fear?
that I may live with-in God's house for all my days.
se-cure-ly I will dwell in his pa-vil-ion strong.
a-mid the bat-tle shock my song shall still re-sound.

While God my strength, my life sus-tains, se-cure from fear
God's glo-rious beau-ty to ad-mire, and in his tem-
With-in the shel-ter of God's tent he hides me till
Then joy-ful of-fer-ings I will bring; the LORD God's praise

my soul re-mains, se-cure from fear my soul re-mains.
ple to in-quire, and in his tem-ple to in-quire.
the storm is spent, he hides me till the storm is spent.
my heart shall sing, the LORD God's praise my heart shall sing.

For an alternate arrangement see 148

For other settings of Ps. 27 see 431, 774, 885

Words: st. 1 *Psalter*, 1887; st. 2-4 *Psalter*, 1912; alt., P.D.
Music (RHOSYMEDRE 6.6.6.6.8.8 with repeat): John D. Edwards, ca. 1840, P.D.

774 El Señor es mi luz/The Lord Is My Light

PSALM 27

Refrain

Spanish El Se-ñor es mi luz y mi sal-va-ción. El Se-ñor es la de-
English The Lord is my light, my help and sal-va-tion. The Lord is the

fen-sa de mi vi-da. Si_el Se-ñor es mi luz, ¿a
strong-hold of my life. If the Lord is my light, what

quién te-me-ré? ¿Quién me_ha-rá tem-blar? *Fine*
then shall I dread? Whom shall I fear?

Stanza 1

1 U-na co-sa pi-do_al Se-ñor: ha-bi-tar por
1 One re-quest, Lord, I make of you: to a-bide in

siem-pre_en su ca-sa, go-zar de la dul-zu-ra del Se-
your house for-ev-er, to re-flect up-on your beau-ty with de-

For other settings of Ps. 29 see 431, 773, 885

Words: Psalm 27 © 1970 Comision Episcopal Española de Liturgia; tr. Mary Louise Bringle, 2011
Music (EL SEÑOR ES MI LUZ): Father Alberto Taulé; arr. Gerhard Cartford © 1982 Fr. Alberto Taulé,
  admin. OCP Publications

ñor   con - tem - plan - do   su   tem - plo   san - to.
light   and   to   in - quire   with - in   your   tem - ple.

Stanza 2

2 No me es - con - das tu ros - tro,   Se - ñor;   bus - ca - ré   to - do el
2 Turn your face not a - way from   me, Lord,   for your face   is the

dí - a   tu   ros - tro.   Si   mi   pa - dre y mi   ma - dre me a - ban -
light   that   I   long for.   If   my   fa - ther or moth - er   should for -

do - nan,   el   Se - ñor   me a - bra - za - rá.
sake me,   still you hold   me   in your care.

Stanza 3

3 Oh   Se - ñor, en - sé - ña - me el ca - mi - no;   guí - a - me   por la
3 Teach me, Lord, the way that   I should fol - low;   guide my steps   in the

sen - da   ver - da - de - ra.   Go - za - ré   de la   dul -
way   of   truth   and   good - ness.   I   shall tell___   of   your

zu - ra del Se - ñor   en   la   tie - rra   de la   vi - da.
bless - ings all my days   through the lands___   of the   liv - ing.

775

Across the Lands

1 You're the Word of God the Fa-ther from be-fore the world be-
2 Yet you left the gaze of an-gels, came to seek and save the
3 With a shout you rose vic-tor-ious, wrest-ing vic-tory from the

gan; ev-ery star and ev-ery pla-net has been fas-hioned
lost and ex-changed the joy of heav-en for the an-guish
grave, and as-cend-ed in-to heav-en, lead-ing cap-tives

by your hand. All cre-a-tion holds to-geth-er by the
of a cross. With a prayer you fed the hun-gry, with a
in your way. Now you stand be-fore the Fa-ther, in-ter-

pow-er of your voice. Let the skies de-clare your
word you calmed the sea; yet how sil-ent-ly you
ced-ing for your own; from each tribe and tongue and

Words and Music (ACROSS THE LANDS 8.7.8.7 D refrain 8.7.11): Keith Getty and Stuart Townend © 2002
Thankyou Music (PRS), admin. worldwide at EMICMGPublishing.com except Europe which is admin. by
Kingswaysongs

776 A Mighty Fortress Is Our God

Words: based on Psalm 46, Martin Luther, 1529; tr. Frederick H. Hedge, 1852, P.D.
Music (EIN FESTE BURG 8.7.8.7.6.6.6.6.7): Martin Luther, 1529, alt.; harm. Johann S. Bach (1685-1750), P.D.

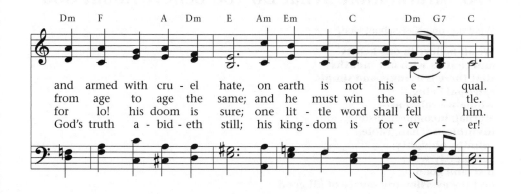

and armed with cru - el hate, on earth is not his e - qual.
from age to age the same; and he must win the bat - tle.
for lo! his doom is sure; one lit - tle word shall fell him.
God's truth a - bid - eth still; his king - dom is for - ev - er!

God Is So Good

777

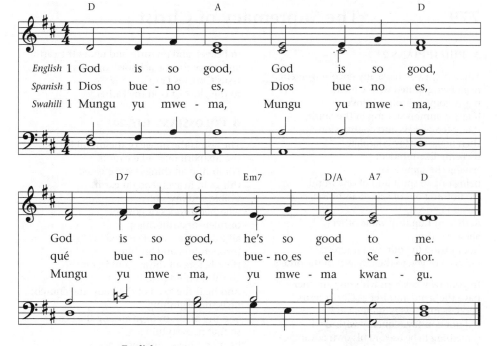

English 1 God is so good, God is so good,
Spanish 1 Dios bue - no es, Dios bue - no es,
Swahili 1 Mungu yu mwe - ma, Mungu yu mwe - ma,

God is so good, he's so good to me.
qué bue - no es, bue - no es el Se - ñor.
Mungu yu mwe - ma, yu mwe - ma kwan - gu.

English
2 He cares for me, *(3x)* . . . he's so good to me.
3 God answers prayer, *(3x)* . . . he's so good to me.
4 I praise his name, *(3x)* . . . he's so good to me.

Portugese
1 Deus é tão bom, *(3x)* . . . É tão bom pra mim.

Lugandan
1 Katonda Mulungi, *(3x)* . . . Katonda wange.

Words and Music (GOD IS SO GOOD): traditional, P.D.

778 Affirmation: What Do You Believe About God

What do you believe about God?

**We all believe in our hearts
and confess with our mouths
that there is a single and simple
spiritual being,
whom we call God—
eternal, incomprehensible,
invisible, unchangeable,
infinite, almighty;
completely wise,
just, and good,
and the overflowing source of all good.**

Text: based on Belgic Confession, Art. 1

779 The Supremacy of Christ

A. PHILIPPIANS 2

Therefore if you have any encouragement
from being united with Christ,
if any comfort from his love,
if any common sharing in the Spirit,
if any tenderness and compassion,
then make my joy complete
by being like-minded,
having the same love,
being one in spirit and of one mind.
Do nothing out of selfish ambition
or vain conceit.
Rather, in humility value others
above yourselves,
not looking to your own interests
but each of you to the interests of the others.

In your relationships with one another,
have the same mindset as Christ Jesus:
Who, being in very nature God,
did not consider equality with God
something to be used to his own advantage;
rather, he made himself nothing
by taking the very nature of a servant,
being made in human likeness.
And being found in appearance as a man,
he humbled himself
by becoming obedient to death—
even death on a cross!
Therefore God exalted him to the highest place
and gave him the name
that is above every name,
that at the name of Jesus every knee
should bow,
in heaven and on earth and under the earth,
and every tongue acknowledge that
Jesus Christ is Lord,
to the glory of God the Father.

B. COLOSSIANS 1:15-20

The Son is the image of the invisible God,
the firstborn over all creation.
For in him all things were created:
things in heaven and on earth,
visible and invisible,
whether thrones or powers
or rulers or authorities;
all things have been created
through him and for him.
He is before all things, and in him
all things hold together.
And he is the head of the body, the church;
he is the beginning
and the firstborn from among the dead,
so that in everything
he might have the supremacy.
For God was pleased to have all
his fullness dwell in him,
and through him to reconcile
to himself all things,
whether things on earth
or things in heaven,
by making peace
through his blood,
shed on the cross.

I Love You, Lord, Today

1 I love you. I love you. I love you, Lord, to-day,
2 My heart, __ my mind, __ my soul be-long to you.

be-cause you care for me in such a spe-cial way.
You paid the price for me way back on Cal - va - ry.

Refrain

And, yes, I praise you. I lift you up. I mag-ni-fy your name.

That's why my heart is filled with praise.

Words and Music (I LOVE YOU, LORD, TODAY irregular): William F. Hubbard © 1985 Chinwah Songs

781

My Only Comfort

1 My on-ly com-fort, now, al-ways, in both my life and death,
2 He ful-ly paid for all my sins with his own pre-cious blood
3 Since I be-long to him a-lone, Christ, through the Spir-it gives

is know-ing I am not my own; I be-long to Je-sus Christ.
and through his death has set me free from Sa-tan's ty-ran-ny.
as-sur-ance of e-ter-nal life, and so I live for him.

My bo-dy and soul be-long to him in life, in death, al-ways.
With-out my heaven-ly Fa-ther's will, not a sin-gle hair can fall.
My on-ly com-fort, now, al-ways, in both my life and death,

He is my faith-ful Sav-ior, Friend; Je-sus Christ, my Lord and King.
In fact, all things must work for good, for my sal-va-tion.
is know-ing I am not my own; I be-long to Je-sus Christ.

Chord symbols represent a simplified harmony.

Words: Zacharius Ursinus and Caspar Olevianus, 1563; Heidelberg Catechism Q&A 1; vers. Marlene Veen-
stra, 2003, alt. © 2004 Faith Alive Christian Resources
Music (RESIGNATION 8.6.8.6 D): W. Walker's *Southern Harmony*, 1835; harm. Dale Grotenhuis (1931-2012)
© 1990 Dale Grotenhuis

In God the Father I Believe

782

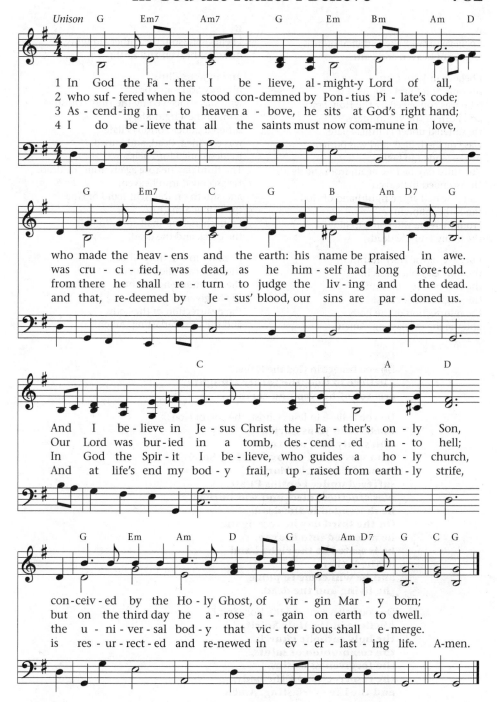

Words: Apostles' Creed; vers. Frank De Vries, 1969, © 1975 Faith Alive Christian Resources
Music (CREEDAL SONG 8.6.8.6 D): Frank De Vries, 1972; harm. Bert Polman, 1975, © 1975 Faith Alive
Christian Resources

783   The Apostles' Creed

A

I believe in God, the Father almighty,
creator of heaven and earth.

I believe in Jesus Christ,
his only Son, our Lord,
who was conceived by the Holy Spirit
and born of the virgin Mary.
He suffered under Pontius Pilate,
was crucified, died, and was buried;
he descended to hell.
The third day he rose again from the dead.
He ascended to heaven
and is seated at the right hand of God
the Father almighty.
From there he will come to judge
the living and the dead.

I believe in the Holy Spirit,
the holy catholic church,
the communion of saints,
the forgiveness of sins,
the resurrection of the body,
and the life everlasting. Amen.

B

I believe in God, the Father almighty,
maker of heaven and earth;

And in Jesus Christ,
his only Son, our Lord;
who was conceived by the Holy Ghost,
born of the Virgin Mary,
suffered under Pontius Pilate,
was crucified, dead, and buried.
He descended into hell.
The third day he rose again from the dead.
He ascended into heaven,
and sitteth on the right hand of God
the Father almighty.
From thence he shall come to judge
the quick and the dead.

I believe in the Holy Ghost,
the holy catholic Church,
the communion of saints,
the forgiveness of sins,
the resurrection of the body,
and the life everlasting. Amen.

C

Do you believe in God the Father?
I believe in God, the Father almighty,
creator of heaven and earth.

Do you believe in Jesus Christ, the Son of God?
I believe in Jesus Christ,
God's only Son, our Lord.
who was conceived by the Holy Spirit,
born of the virgin Mary.
suffered under Pontius Pilate,
was crucified, died, and was buried;
he descended to the dead.
On the third day he rose again;
he ascended into heaven,
he is seated at the right hand
of the Father,
and he will come to judge
the living and the dead.

Do you believe in God the Holy Spirit?
I believe in the Holy Spirit,
the holy catholic church,
the communion of saints,
the forgiveness of sins,
the resurrection of the body,
and the life everlasting. Amen

Text A: tr. from the 4th century Latin text, © 1988 Faith Alive Christian Resources
Text B: tr. from the 4th century Latin text, RCA traditional version
Text C: taken from the Order for the Sacrament of Baptism, *Worship the Lord, the Liturgy of the Reformed Church in America* © 2005 Reformed Church Press

The Sacrament of Baptism 1 784

PREPARATION

Scripture Reading: Matt. 28:18-20, along with one or more of the following: Eph. 4:4-6; Gal. 3:27-28, Rom. 6:3-4; John 1:12-13; Gen. 17:7; Gal. 3:29; and/or Acts 2:39

Baptism is the sign and seal of God's promises
to this covenant people.
In baptism God promises by grace alone:
to forgive our sins;
to adopt us into the Body of Christ,
the Church;
to send the Holy Spirit daily
to renew and cleanse us;
and to resurrect us to eternal life.

This promise is made visible
in the water of baptism.

Water may be poured into the font at this time.

Water cleanses; purifies; refreshes; sustains:
Jesus Christ is living water.

Through baptism Christ calls us
to new obedience:
to love and trust God completely;
to forsake the evil of the world;
and to live a new and holy life.

Yet, when we fall into sin,
we must not despair of God's mercy,
nor continue in sin,
for baptism is the sign and seal
of God's eternal covenant of grace with us.

An elder or pastor presents the adult candidates or the parents of children for baptism.

PROFESSION OF FAITH

Beloved of God,
you stand before us
[having brought *this child/these children*]
to receive the sacrament of baptism.
I ask you, therefore,
before God and Christ's church
to reject evil,
to profess your faith in Christ Jesus,
and to confess the faith of the church.

Do you renounce sin and the power of evil
in your life and in the world?
I renounce them.

Who is your Lord and Savior?
Jesus Christ is my Lord and Savior.

At the baptism of adults:
Will you be a faithful member
of this congregation,
and through worship and service
seek to advance God's purposes
here and throughout the world?
I will, and I ask God to help me.

At the baptism of infants or young children:
Do you promise
to instruct *this child/these children*
in the truth of God's word,
in the way of salvation through Jesus Christ;
to pray for *them*, to teach *them* to pray;
and to train *them* in Christ's way
by your example,
through worship, and
in the nurture of the church?
I do, and I ask God to help me.

Continue by addressing the congregation:
Do you promise to love,
encourage, and support
these brothers and sisters
by teaching the gospel of God's love,
by being an example of Christian faith and
character, and
by giving the strong support of God's family
in fellowship, prayer, and service?
We do.

The congregation and the candidates (or their parents) join in affirming the faith in the words of the Apostles' Creed. See 783

PRAYER OF THANKSGIVING

The Lord be with you.
And also with you.
Let us give thanks to the Lord our God.
**It is right to give our
thanks and praise.**

We give you thanks,
O holy and gracious God,
for the gift of water.
In the beginning of creation
your Spirit moved over the waters.
In the waters of the flood you destroyed evil.
You led the children of Israel through the sea
into the freedom of the promised land.
In the river Jordan, John baptized our Lord
and your Spirit anointed him.

(continues)

Text: taken from the Order for the Sacrament of Baptism, *Worship the Lord, the Liturgy of the Reformed Church in America* © 2005 Reformed Church Press

By his death and resurrection
Jesus Christ, the Living Water,
frees us from sin and death and opens the way
to life everlasting.

We thank you, O God, for the gift of baptism.
In this water you confirm to us
that we are buried with Christ in his death,
raised to share in his resurrection,
and are being renewed by the Holy Spirit.

Pour out on us your Holy Spirit,
so that those here baptized
may be washed clean
and receive new life.
To you be all honor and glory,
dominion and power,
now and forever,
through Jesus Christ our Lord.
Amen.

*The celebration continues with water baptism,
the declaration and prayer.*

WELCOME AND BLESSING

Welcome our new *brothers* and *sisters* in
Christ.

**Joyfully we receive you
into the body of Christ.
Join with us as we give
witness in the world to the good news,
for we are all one in Christ Jesus.
Alleluia.**

The Lord bless you and keep you;
the Lord make his face to shine upon you,
and be gracious to you;
the Lord lift up his countenance upon you,
and give you peace. **Amen.** *(Num. 6:24-26)*

785   You Have Put on Christ

You have put on Christ; in him we have been bap-tized.

Al - le - lu - ia! Al - le - lu - ia!

Accompaniment pattern, repeat as needed

Words: from Galatians 3:27 © 1969 International Committee on English in the Liturgy, Inc., ICEL
Music (BAPTIZED IN CHRIST): from *Music for the Rite of Funerals and Rite of Baptism for Children*, International
  Committee on English in the Liturgy, Inc., ICEL

The Sacrament of Baptism 2

The celebration begins with scriptural texts about the institution, promises, meaning, and significance of baptism (Matt. 28:18-20), followed by a prayer of preparation:

Father in heaven, we pray that you will never destroy us in our sin as with the flood,
but save us as you saved believing Noah and his family,
and spare us as you spared the Israelites who walked safely through the sea.

We pray that Christ, who went down into the Jordan and came up to receive the Spirit,
who sank deep into death and was raised up Lord of life,
will always keep us and our little ones in the grip of his hand.

We pray, O holy Father, that your Spirit will separate us from sin
and openly mark us with a faith that can stand the light of day and endure the dark of night.
Prepare us now, O Lord, to respond with glad hope to your promises
so that we, and all entrusted to our care,
may drink deeply from the well of living water.
We pray in the name of Jesus Christ our Lord. Amen!

The celebration continues with vows spoken by the candidates for baptism or their parents, followed by the vow of the congregation as follows:

Baptism of Adults
Do you, the people of the Lord, promise to receive *[names]* into your fellowship
as member(s) of the body of Christ,
and do you promise to encourage them in the Christian faith
and help them in doing the work of the Lord?
We do, God helping us.

Baptism of Children
Do you, the people of the Lord, promise to receive *this child/these children* in love,
pray for *them*, help instruct *them* in the faith, and encourage
and sustain *them* in the fellowship of believers?
We do, God helping us

The celebration continues with the baptism, words of welcome and blessing, and songs of praise, followed by one of these concluding prayers:

Baptism of Adults
Our Father in heaven, we thank you for Jesus Christ, for the new life given in him,
and for the one faith, one hope, and one baptism
which your people have shared through the ages.
We rejoice that *[names] are* now one with your church
and that we may receive *them* as member(s) of this congregation.
Guide *them* in the Christian way and sustain us all
in the fellowship and service of our Lord. Amen.

Baptism of Children
Lord our God, forever faithful to your promise,
we thank you for assuring us again that you will forgive us
and receive us as children in Christ.
Grant wisdom and love to the parent(s) and to us all
as we carry out the vows we have just made.
We pray that you will guide our little ones throughout their lives.
Enable them to respond in faith to the gospel.
Fill them with your Spirit and make their lives fruitful.
Give them strength to endure trials.
And when Christ returns, let them celebrate with all the people of God
your greatness and goodness forever in the joy of your new creation. Amen.

Text: adapt. from the Service for Baptism of the Christian Reformed Church of North America

787 Affirmation: For You Jesus Christ Came

For you Jesus Christ came into the World;
for you he died and for you he conquered death;
all this he did for you, little one,
though you know nothing of it as yet.
We love because God first loved us.

Text: from baptism liturgy, French Reformed Church

788 Take Me to the Water

1 Take me to the wa - ter, take me to the wa - ter,
2 None — but the right - eous, none — but the right - eous,
3 I — love — Je - sus, I — love — Je - sus,
4 He's — my — Sav - ior, he's — my — Sav - ior,

take me to the wa - ter to be bap - tized.
none — but the right - eous — shall see God.
I — love — Je - sus, oh, yes, I do.
he's — my — Sav - ior, oh, yes, he is.

Words: African American spiritual, P.D.
Music (TAKE ME TO THE WATER irregular): African American spiritual; arr. Valeria A. Foster © 2000 GIA
Publications, Inc.

789 Baptized into Christ Jesus

ROMANS 6:3-4

Don't you know that all of us
who were baptized into Christ Jesus
were baptized into his death?
**We were buried with him
through baptism into death in order that,
just as Christ was raised from the dead
through the glory of the Father,
we too may live a new life.**

Baptized in Water

1 Bap-tized in wa - ter, sealed by the Spir - it, cleansed by the blood of Christ, our King; heirs of sal - va - tion, trust-ing his prom - ise, faith - ful-ly now God's praise we sing.

2 Bap-tized in wa - ter, sealed by the Spir - it, dead in the tomb with Christ, our King; one with his ris - ing, freed and for - giv - en, thank - ful-ly now God's praise we sing.

3 Bap-tized in wa - ter, sealed by the Spir - it, marked with the sign of Christ, our King; born of one Fa - ther, we are his chil - dren, joy - ful-ly now God's praise we sing.

Words: Michael Saward, 1981, © 1982 The Jubilate Group, admin. Hope Publishing Company
Music (BUNESSAN 5.5.8 D): Gaelic; harm. Dale Grotenhuis (1931-2012), 1985, © 1987 Faith Alive Christian Resources

A Trustworthy Saying

TITUS 3:4-8

When the kindness and love of God our Savior appeared,
he saved us,
not because of righteous things we had done,
but because of his mercy.
He saved us through the washing of rebirth
and renewal by the Holy Spirit
whom he poured out on us generously through Jesus Christ our Savior,
so that, having been justified by his grace,
we might become heirs having the hope of eternal life.
This is a trustworthy saying.

792 **Through the Red Sea**

1 Through the Red Sea brought at last, al - le - lu - ia!
2 Like the cloud that ov - er - head, al - le - lu - ia!
3 In that cloud and in that sea, al - le - lu - ia!

E - gypt's chains be - hind we cast, al - le - lu - ia!
Through the bil - lows Is - rael led, al - le - lu - ia!
Bur - ied and bap - tized were we, al - le - lu - ia!

Deep and wide flows the tide sev - ering us from
By his tomb Christ makes room, souls re - stor - ing
Earth - ly night brought us light, which is ours e -

bond - age past, al - le - lu - ia!
from the dead, al - le - lu - ia!
ter - nal - ly, al - le - lu - ia!

Chord symbols represent a simplified harmony.

Words: Ronald A. Knox (1888-1957), P.D.
Music (STRAF MICH NICHT 7.4.7.4.6.7.4): *Straf mich nicht,* melody from *Hundert Arien,* 1694, P.D.

Loving Spirit

1 Lov - ing Spir - it, lov - ing Spir - it, you have cho - sen
2 Like a moth - er, you en - fold me, hold my life with -
3 Like a fa - ther, you pro - tect me, teach me the dis -
4 Friend and lov - er, in your close - ness I am known and
5 Lov - ing Spir - it, lov - ing Spir - it, you have cho - sen

me to be. You have drawn me to your
in your own, feed me with your ver - y
cern - ing eye, hoist me up up - on your
held and blessed. In your prom - ise is my
me to be. You have drawn me to your

won - der, you have set your sign on me.
bod - y, form me of your flesh and bone.
shoul - der, let me see the world from high.
com - fort; in your pres - ence I may rest.
won - der, you have set your sign on me.

May also be accompanied with soft instruments or humming voices sustaining the pitches B and F#.

Words: Shirley Erena Murray (b. 1931) © 1987 The Hymn Society, admin. Hope Publishing Company
Music (CHHUN-BIN 8.7.8.7): I-to Loh (b. 1936) © I-to Loh

794 O Blessed Spring

Words: Susan Palo Cherwien (b. 1953) © 1993 Susan Palo Cherwien, admin. Augsburg Fortress
Music (BERGLUND 8.8.8.8): Robert Buckley Farlee (b. 1950) © 1993 Robert Buckley Farlee, admin. Augsburg
  Fortress

We Know that Christ Is Raised

1 We know that Christ is raised and dies no more.
2 We share by wa - ter in his sav - ing death.
3 The Fa - ther's splen - dor clothes the Son with life.
4 A new cre - a - tion comes to life and grows

Em - braced by death, he broke its fear - ful hold, and our de -
Re - born, we share with him an Eas - ter life as liv - ing
The Spir - it's pow - er shakes the church of God. Bap - tized, we
as Christ's new bod - y takes on flesh and blood. The un - i -

spair he turned to blaz - ing joy. Al - le - lu - ia!
mem - bers of a liv - ing Christ. Al - le - lu - ia!
live with God, the Three in One. Al - le - lu - ia!
verse, re - stored and whole, will sing: Al - le - lu - ia!

Accompaniment for final stanza

Words: John B. Geyer, 1967, alt., © 1969 John B. Geyer
Music (ENGELBERG 10.10.10 with alleluia): Charles Villiers Stanford (1852-1924), P.D.

796 Oh, the Deep, Deep Love of Jesus

1 Oh, the deep, deep love of Je - sus, vast, un -
2 Oh, the deep, deep love of Je - sus— spread his
3 Oh, the deep, deep love of Je - sus, love of

mea - sured, bound - less, free! Roll - ing as a
praise from shore to shore! How he loves us,
ev - ery love the best! 'Tis an o - cean

might - y o - cean in its full - ness o - ver me!
ev - er loves us, chang-es nev - er, nev - er - more!
vast of bless - ing, 'tis a ha - ven sweet of rest!

Un - der - neath me, all a - round me, is the cur - rent
How he watch - es o'er his loved ones, died to call them
Oh, the deep, deep love of Je - sus— 'tis a heaven of

Chord symbols represent a simplified harmony. For an alternate key see 922

Words: Samuel Trevor Francis, ca. 1890, alt., P.D.
Music (EBENEZER 8.7.8.7 D): Thomas J. Williams (1869-1944), 1890, P.D.

of thy love— lead-ing on-ward, lead-ing home-ward,
all his own; how for them he's in - ter - ced - ing,
heavens to me; and it lifts me up to glo - ry,

to thy glo - rious rest a - bove!
watch - ing o'er them from the throne!
for it lifts me up to thee!

Sing! A New Creation   797

1 Sing! A new creation calls us: God's Son, firstborn from the dead,
makes the drowning which befalls us into cleansing birth instead.
Singing water, wild with wonder, washing, more than what it seems,
baptizes and drags us under, lifts us as our Christ redeems.

2 Sing anew! Creation flowers as the Spirit draws us near,
safe from storming earth-bound powers on this ark, though tossed by fear.
Sing as family, filled, forgiven, fed by joyous tablegrace.
Baptized, we receive God's leaven, rising in our time and place.

3 Sing, a new creation growing lifetrees by the Father's stream.
Go and teach, send justice flowing, quench dry souls, compose a dream.
Sing amens, alive and agile, answering God's creating song.
Baptize peoples, parched and fragile, in the Name that makes us strong.

For music see 796

Words: James Hart Brumm (b. 1962) © 2000 Wayne Leupold Editions, Inc.

798 Todos los que han sido bautizados/ All Who Have Been Baptized

Words: Fernando Rodríguez © 1989 OCP Publications; adapt. Emily Brink, 2008, © OCP Publications
Music (TODOS LOS QUE HAN SIDO BAUTIZADOS 10.12.12 stanzas 7.8.8.7): Fernando Rodríguez © 1989
OCP Publications; arr. De.J. Hylton

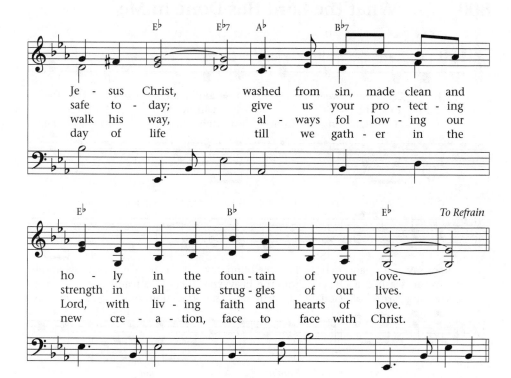

Je - sus	Christ,	washed	from	sin,	made	clean	and
safe	to - day;	give	us	your	pro - tect -	ing
walk	his way,	al - ways	fol - low - ing	our
day	of life	till	we	gath - er	in	the

ho - ly	in	the	foun - tain	of	your	love.
strength in	all	the	strug - gles	of	our	lives.
Lord,	with	liv - ing	faith and	hearts	of	love.
new	cre - a - tion,	face to	face with	Christ.

To Refrain

Spanish

1 Hemos sido bautizados
en tu nombre, buen Señor,
y lavados del pecado
en la fuente de tu_amor.
Refrain

2 Pueblo tuyo todos somos,
danos hoy tu protección.
Danos fuerza en la lucha,
danos vida, Buen Pastor.
Refrain

3 Que, salvados por la sangre
de Jesús el Salvador,
siempre sigamos sus pasos
con fe viva y con amor.
Refrain

4 Que_el Espíritu Divino
nos dirija_y dé sostén
en la lucha por la vida
y nos guíe_hasta_el Edén.
Refrain

A Prayer at Baptisms 799

Gracious God,
we thank you that you cleanse
and renew *these* your children
through grace alone.
Bless and strengthen *them* daily
with the gift of your Holy Spirit;
unfold to *them* the riches of your love,
deepening *their* faith,
keeping *them* from the power of evil,
and enabling *them* to live a holy
and blameless life until your kingdom comes. **Amen.**

Text: from the RCA Order for the Sacrament of Baptism

800 What the Lord Has Done in Me

Words and Music (WHAT THE LORD HAS DONE): Reuben Morgan © 1998 Hillsong Music Publishing (APRA), admin. in the US and Canada EMICMGPublishing.com

O God, Great Father, Lord and King 801

1 O God, great Fa - ther, Lord and King, our chil - dren
2 Your cov - enant bless - ing did of old our par - ents
3 Look down up - on us while we pray and vis - it

un - to you we bring. We come in faith and
and their seed en - fold. That an - cient prom - ise
us in grace to - day. These lit - tle ones you

hope and love; we dare your stead - fast word to prove.
stands se - cure and shall while heaven and earth en - dure.
did re - ceive; your pre - cious prom - ise we be - lieve.

4 They now the outward sign receive;
  your promised Holy Spirit give.
  O keep and help them by your power
  in every hard and trying hour.

5 Direct their feet in holy ways
  and shine on them through darkest days.
  Uphold them till their life is past
  and bring them all to heaven at last.

Chord symbols represent a simplifed harmony.

Words: E. Embree Hoss, 1905, alt., P.D.
Music (MELCOMBE 8.8.8.8): Samuel Webbe, 1783, P.D.

802 Wash, O God, Our Sons and Daughters

1 Wash, O God, our sons and daugh - ters, where your cleans-ing
2 We who bring them long for nur - ture; by your milk may
3 Oh, how deep your ho - ly wis - dom! Un - im - ag - ined,

wa - ters flow. Num-ber them a - mong your peo - ple; bless as
we be fed. Let us join your feast, par - tak - ing cup of
all your ways! To your name be glo - ry, hon - or! With our

Christ blessed long a - go. Weave them gar - ments bright and
bless - ing, liv - ing bread. God, re - new us, guide our
lives we wor - ship, praise! We your peo - ple stand be -

spark - ling; com - pass them with love and light. Fill, a -
foot - steps, free from sin and all its snares, one with
fore you, wa - ter - washed and Spir - it - born. By your

Words: Ruth Duck (b. 1947) © 1989 The United Methodist Publishing House, admin. The Copyright Company
Music (BEACH SPRING 8.7.8.7 D): *The Sacred Harp,* 1844; arr. *Selected Hymns,* 1985, © 1985 Augsburg Fortress

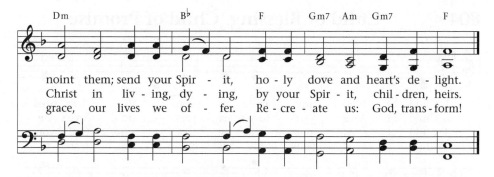

noint them; send your Spir - it, ho - ly dove and heart's de - light.
Christ in liv - ing, dy - ing, by your Spir - it, chil - dren, heirs.
grace, our lives we of - fer. Re - cre - ate us: God, trans - form!

Alternate text for Baptismal renewal

1 Wash, O God, your sons and daughters, where your cleansing waters flow.
Number us among your people; bless as Christ blessed long ago.
Weave us garments bright and sparkling; compass us with love and light.
Fill, anoint us; send your Spirit, holy dove and heart's delight.

2 We who gather long for nurture; by your milk may we be fed.
Let us join your feast, partaking cup of blessing, living bread.
God, renew us, guide our footsteps, free from sin and all its snares,
one with Christ in living, dying, by your Spirit, children, heirs.

3 Oh, how deep your holy wisdom! Unimagined, all your ways!
To your name be glory, honor! With our lives we worship, praise!
We your people stand before you, water-washed and Spirit born.
By your grace, our lives we offer. Recreate us: God, transform!

A New Heart and Spirit 803

EZEKIEL 36:25-28

I will sprinkle clean water on you, and you will be clean;
I will cleanse you from all your impurities and from all your idols.
I will give you a new heart and put a new spirit in you;
I will remove from you your heart of stone and give you a heart of flesh.
And I will put my Spirit in you and move you to follow my decrees
and be careful to keep my laws.

Then we will live in the land you gave our ancestors;
we will be your people, and you will be our God.

804   Child of Blessing, Child of Promise

1 Child of bless - ing, child of prom - ise, bap - tized with the Spir - it's sign, with this wa - ter God has sealed you un - to love and greace di - vine.

2 Child of love, our love's ex - pres - sion, love's cre - a - tion, loved in - deed! Fresh from God, re - fresh our spir - its, in - to joy and laugh - ter lead.

3 Child of joy, our dear - est trea - sure, God's you are; from God you came. Back to God we hum - bly give you: live as one who bears Christ's name.

4 Child of God, your lov - ing par - ent, learn to lis - ten for God's call. Grow to laugh and sing and wor - ship, trust and love God more than all.

Chord symbols represent a simplified harmony.

Words: Ronald S. Cole-Turner © 1981 Ronald S. Cole-Turner
Music (KINGDOM 8.7.8.7): V. Earle Copes, 1960, P.D.

Our Children, Lord, in Faith and Prayer 805

1 Our chil-dren, Lord, in faith and prayer, we
2 Such chil-dren you did once em - brace while
3 In all their days their hearts se - cure from

bap - tize in your name. Let them your cov - enant
dwell - ing here be - low; to us and ours, O
sin - ful snares, we pray. Through - out their lives let

mer - cies share as we our faith pro - claim.
Lord of grace, the same com - pas - sion show.
them en - dure in ev - ery right - eous way.

Optional prayer

Gracious God,
we thank you that you cleanse
and renew these your children
through grace alone.
Bless and strengthen them daily
with the gift of your Holy Spirit;
unfold to them the riches of your love,
deepening their faith,
keeping them from the power of evil,
and enabling them to live a holy
and blameless life until your kingdom comes.

Look with kindness upon these parents.
Let them ever rejoice in the gift
you have given them.

**Grant them the presence
of your Holy Spirit
that they may bring up these children
   to know you,
   to love you,
   and to serve you. Amen.**

Text: taken from the Order for the Sacrament of Baptism, *Worship the Lord, the Liturgy of the Reformed Church in America* © 2005 Reformed Church Press

Words: Thomas Haweis (1732-1820), alt., P.D.
Music (NAOMI 8.6.8.6): arr. Lowell Mason, 1836, P.D.

806   The Nicene Creed 2

We believe in one God,
the Father almighty,
maker of heaven and earth,
of all things visible and invisible.

Optional Refrain

And in one Lord Jesus Christ,
the only Son of God,
begotten from the Father before all ages,
God from God,
Light from Light,
true God from true God,
begotten, not made;
of the same essence as the Father.
Through him all things were made.
For us and for our salvation
he came down from heaven;
he became incarnate by the
Holy Spirit and the virgin Mary,
and was made human.
He was crucified for us under Pontius Pilate;
he suffered and was buried.
The third day he rose again,
according to the Scriptures.

He ascended to heaven
and is seated at the right hand of the Father.
He will come again with glory
to judge the living and the dead.
His kingdom will never end. *Optional*

Optional Refrain

And we believe in the Holy Spirit,
the Lord, the giver of life.
He proceeds from the Father and the Son,
and with the Father and the Son
is worshiped and glorified.
He spoke through the prophets.
We believe in one holy catholic
and apostolic church.
We affirm one baptism for the
forgiveness of sins.
We look forward to the
resurrection of the dead,
and to life in the world to come. Amen.

Optional Refrain

For an alternate version of the creed see 771

Words and Music (WE BELIEVE): Gregg DeMey © 2012 Re:Create Music, admin. Faith Alive Christian
Resources

All Who Are Thirsty

1 All who are thir - sty, come to the Lord;
2 Why spend your mon - ey on what's not bread?
3 Call on God's mer - cy while he is near;
4 Where once were bri - ers, flow - ers will grow.

all who are hun - gry, feed on his Word.
Why toil in la - bor and not be fed?
turn from your e - vil, come with-out fear;
Where lives were bar - ren, riv - ers will flow.

Buy with-out pay - ing, food with-out price,
God will pro - vide you rich - est of food.
ask him for par - don, grace will a - bound!
Praise to our Sav - ior, grace and re - nown.

eat with thanks-giv - ing God's sac - ri - fice.
Come to the wa - ters, drink what is good.
This is the mom - ent God can be found.
Ours is the bless - ing, his be the crown!

For an alternate arrangement see 744

Words: Michael Perry © 1993 The Jubilate Group, admin. Hope Publishing Company
Music (MALATE 9.9.9.9): Mutya Lopez Solis, Philippines © 1990, 2000 Christian Conference of Asia, admin. GIA Publications, Inc.; arr. Joel Navarro © 2012 Christian Conference of Asia, admin. GIA Publications, Inc.

808 Table of Plenty

1 O come and sit at my ta - ble where
2 O come and eat with - out mon - ey;
3 My bread will ev - er sus - tain you through
4 Your fields will flow - er in full - ness; your

saints and sin - ners are friends. I wait to
come to drink with - out price. My feast of
days of sor - row and woe. My wine will
homes will flour - ish in peace. For I, the

wel - come the lost and lone - ly to share the cup of my
glad - ness will feed your spir - it with faith and full - ness of
flow like a sea of glad - ness to flood the depths of your
giv - er of home and har - vest, will send my rain on the

To Refrain

love.
life.
soul.
soil.

809　Remembering with Love and Hope

1 Re - mem - ber - ing with love and hope, we
cel - e - brate the feast. Christ bids us come and
dine with him, our Host and great High Priest.

2 God's Word made known in flesh and blood, a
cov - e - nant of grace— in man - ger, cross, and
emp - ty tomb, we see God's lov - ing face.

3 Through all our lives, Lord, you are near— and
to the end of time. In bread and cup your-
self you give; our life in yours we find.

4 We break the bread and bless the cup;
your Spirit is outpoured.
Made one in you, we feast in love
until you come, O Lord.

5 We trust this pledge of your strong love
and pray your kingdom come,
when face to face we'll feast with you
in our eternal home.

Words: John Paarlberg (b. 1950) © 2000 John Paarlberg; © 2012 John Paarlberg
Music (LAND OF REST 8.6.8.6): American folk melody; harm. Annabel Morris Buchanan (1889-1983),
1938, P.D.

The Great Prayer of Thanksgiving 1   810

THE THANKSGIVING

Lift up your hearts.
We lift them up to the Lord.
Let us give thanks to the Lord our God.
It is right for us to give thanks and praise.

With joy we praise you, gracious God,
for you have created heaven and earth,
made us in your image,

and kept covenant with us—
even when we fell into sin.
We give you thanks for Jesus Christ, our Lord,
who by his life, death, and resurrection
opened to us the way of everlasting life.
Therefore we join our voices with all the
saints and angels and the whole creation
to proclaim the glory of your name.

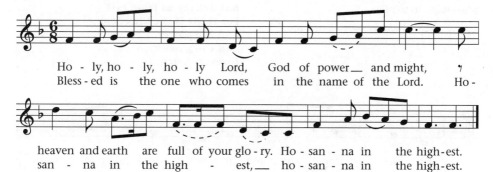

Ho - ly, ho - ly, ho - ly Lord, God of power___ and might,
Bless - ed is the one who comes in the name of the Lord. Ho -

heaven and earth are full of your glo - ry. Ho - san - na in the high-est.
san - na in the high - est,___ ho - san - na in the high-est.

THE INSTITUTION

We give thanks to God the Father
that our Savior, Jesus Christ, before he suffered,
gave us this memorial of his sacrifice,
until he comes again.
At his last supper, the Lord Jesus took bread,
and when he had given thanks,
he broke it *[here the minister breaks the bread]*
and said, "This is my body, which is for you;
do this in remembrance of me."

In the same way, he took the cup after supper
[here the minister pours the wine]
and said,
"This cup is the new covenant in my blood;
do this in remembrance of me."
For whenever we eat this bread
and drink this cup,
we proclaim the Lord's death
until he comes *(1 Cor. 11:23-26).*
Therefore we proclaim our faith
as signed and sealed in this sacrament:

Christ has died. Christ is ris - en. Christ will come a - gain.

(continues)

For accompaniment see 809

Text: taken from The Lord's Supper Liturgy of the Christian Reformed Church of North America, 1994
Music (LAND OF REST 8.6.8.6): American folk melody, P.D.

Prayer of Consecration

Lord, our God, send your Holy Spirit
so that this bread and cup may be for us
the body and blood of our Lord Jesus Christ.
May we and all your saints
be united with Christ
and remain faithful in hope and love.
Gather your whole church, O Lord,
into the glory of your kingdom.
We pray in the name of Jesus,
who taught us to pray:

(for sung versions of the Lord's Prayer see 911-917)

Our Father, who art in heaven
hallowed be thy name,
thy kingdom come,
thy will be done,
on earth as it is in heaven.
Give us this day our daily bread.
And forgive us our debts,
as we forgive our debtors.
And lead us not into temptation,
but deliver us from evil.
For thine is the kingdom,
and the power,
and the glory,
forever. Amen.

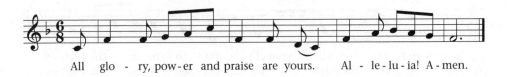

All glo - ry, pow-er and praise are yours. Al - le-lu-ia! A-men.

At this point the sacrament continues with the Preparation of the Elements, Invitation, and Communion.

Congregation in Christ, since the Lord has fed us at his table, let us praise his holy name with thanksgiving.

Read Psalm 103:1-5 or sing as follows:

Bless, the Lord, oh my soul; praise God's ho - ly name. Re -

mem - ber - ing God's ben - e - fits, God's mer - cies we pro-claim.

The Great Prayer of Thanksgiving 2   811

The Lord be with you.   And al - so with you.
Now lift up your hearts.   We lift them in praise.   O

let us give thanks to the Lord.   It is good and it is right, our

joy and our de - light to give God praise   at all

times and in all ways!

Vamp: may be played under reading

(continues)

Text: taken from *Worship the Lord, The Liturgy of the Reformed Church in America* © 2005 Reformed
  Church Press
Words: Ron Rienstra © 1999 Ron Rienstra
Music (DOMINUS VOBISCUM irregular): Ron Rienstra © 1999 Ron Rienstra; arr. Greg Scheer © 2008 Ron
  Rienstra

Holy and right it is,
and our joyful duty to give thanks to you
at all times and in all places,
O Lord our Creator,
almighty and everlasting God!
You created heaven with all its hosts
and the earth with all its plenty.
You have given us life and being,
and preserve us by your providence.

But you have shown us the fullness of your love
in sending into the world your Son,
Jesus Christ, the eternal Word,
made flesh for us and for our salvation.
For the precious gift of this mighty Savior
who has reconciled us to you
we praise and bless you, O God.
With your whole church on earth
and with all the company of heaven
we worship and adore your glorious name.

Most righteous God,
we remember in this Supper
the perfect sacrifice
offered once on the cross
by our Lord Jesus Christ
for the sin of the whole world.

In the joy of his resurrection
and in expectation of his coming again,
we offer ourselves to you
as holy and living sacrifices.
Together we proclaim the mystery of the faith:

For accompaniment see previous page

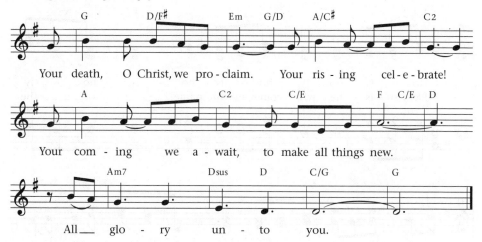

Your death, O Christ, we pro-claim. Your ris-ing cel-e-brate!

Your com-ing we a-wait, to make all things new.

All__ glo-ry un-to you.

Send your Holy Spirit upon us, we pray,
that the bread which we break
and the cup which we bless
may be to us the communion of the body
and blood of Christ.
Grant that, being joined together in him,
we may attain to the unity of the faith
and grow up in all things
into Christ, our Lord.

And as this grain has been gathered
from many fields into one loaf,
and these grapes from
many hills into one cup,
grant, O Lord, that your whole church
may soon be gathered
from the ends of the earth
into your kingdom.
Even so, come, Lord Jesus!

Al-le-lu-ia! Lord! A-men!

The Lord's Supper service continues with the Lord's Prayer, passing of peace, words of institution, and invitation to the table.

Memorial Acclamation   812

Each phrase is sung first by the leader, then repeated by all.

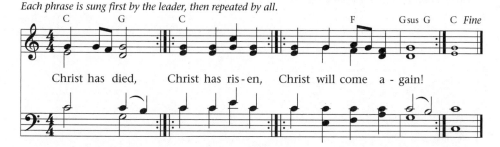

Christ has died, Christ has ris-en, Christ will come a-gain!

Words: from an ancient liturgy on the Lord's Supper, P.D.
Music (MEMORIAL ACCLAMATION): James A. Kriewold © 1995 The United Methodist Publishing House

813 Holy, Holy, Holy Lord

1 Ho - ly, ho - ly, ho - ly, ho - ly, ho - ly
2 Bless-ed is he who comes in the name___ of___ the

Lord, God of pow - er and might, heav - en and earth are
Lord, in the name of the Lord. Ho - san - na

full of your glo - ry. Ho - san - na in the high - est.
in___ the high - est, ho - san - na in the high - est.

Words: *Sanctus*, Isaiah 6:3, Psalm 118:26, P.D.
Music (HOLY, HOLY, HOLY LORD): Grayson Warren Brown (b. 1948); arr. Larry Adams © 1979 Grayson
  Warren Brown, admin. OCP Publications

Santo, Santo, Santo/Holy, Holy, Holy 814

Spanish "San-to, san-to, san - to," can-tan se - ra - fi - nes. "San-to, san-to,
English "Ho - ly, ho-ly, ho - ly," an - gel hosts are sing-ing. "Ho - ly, ho - ly

san-to, Dios es el Se - ñor. San-to, san-to, san-to, es fuer - te
ho - ly is the Lord our God. Ho-ly, ho-ly, ho - ly is God, the

nues-tro Dios. Tu glo-ria lle-na los cie - los, la tie - rra lle - na es -
Lord of might. Your glo-ry fills the heav - ens, your glo-ry fills the

tá." Ho-san-na en las al - tu-ras, ho - san-na la can-ción.
earth." Ho-san - na in the high-est, ho - san-na is our song.

Words: traditional Spanish from Isaiah 6:3; English para. Bert Polman, 1985, © 1987 Faith Alive Christian
Resources
Music (MERENGUE): Spanish; harm. AnnaMae Meyer Bush, 1985, © 1987 Faith Alive Christian Resources;
arr. Joel Navarro © 2012 Joel Navarro, admin. Faith Alive Christian Resources

815   Gift of Finest Wheat

Refrain C   Am   F   Am   Dm   Em   Csus C
Unison

You sat-is-fy the hun-gry heart with gift of fin-est wheat.

Am   Em7   Dm   G   Csus C

Come, give to us, O sav-ing Lord, the bread of life to eat.

Am   Cm   Csus C   F   G   Am

1 As when a shep - herd calls his sheep, they know and heed his voice;
2 With joy-ful lips we sing to you our praise and grat - i - tude,
3 Is not the cup we bless and share the blood of Christ out-poured?

Dm   G   Dm   F   Gsus G
To Refrain

so when you call your fam-ily, Lord, we fol - low and re-joice.
that you should count us wor-thy, Lord, to share this heaven-ly food.
Do not one cup, one loaf de-clare our one-ness in the Lord?

4 The mystery of your presence, Lord,
no mortal tongue can tell:
whom all the world cannot contain
comes in our hearts to dwell.

5 You give yourself to us, O Lord;
then selfless let us be
to serve each other in your name
in truth and charity.

*To use with Psalm 81: sing the Refrain, read Ps. 81:1-4, sing Refrain, read Ps. 81: 5-10, Refrain,
Ps. 81:11-16, Refrain.*

Words: Omer Westendorf, 1976, © 1977 Archdiocese of Philadelphia, published by International Liturgy Publications

Music (BICENTENNIAL 8.6.8.6 refrain 8.6.8.6): Robert E. Kreutz, 1976, © 1977 Archdiocese of Philadelphia, published by International Liturgy Publications

Father, We Give You Thanks

1 Fa - ther, we give you thanks, who plant - ed your ho - ly
2 Lord, you have made all for your plea - sure and given us
3 Watch o'er your church, O Lord, in mer - cy, save it from
4 As grain, once scat - tered on the hill - sides, was in the

name with - in our hearts; knowl - edge and faith and life im -
food for all our days, giv - ing in Christ the bread e -
e - vil, guard it still; per - fect it in your love, u -
bro - ken bread made one, so may your world - wide church be

Refrain

mor - tal Je - sus, your Son, to us im - parts.
ter - nal. Yours is the power; be yours the praise.
nite it, cleansed and con - formed un - to your will.   To you, O
gath - ered in - to your king - dom by your Son.

Lord, our hearts we raise; 'tis right to give our thanks and praise.

Chord symbols represent a simplified harmony.

Words: sts. based on the *Didache,* 2nd c.; F. Bland Tucker, 1941, alt; © 1943, 1961, 1981 The Church Pension
  Fund; ref. © 2012 Faith Alive Christian Resources
Music (NEUMARK/WER NUR DEN LIEBEN GOTT 9.8.9.8.8.8): Georg Neumark, 1657, P.D.

817

Taste and See

PSALM 34

For another setting of Ps. 34 see 406

Words: James E. Moore Jr © 1983 GIA Publications, Inc.
Music (TASTE AND SEE irregular): James E. Moore Jr © 1983 GIA Publications, Inc.

soul shall glo - ry___ in the Lord; for
called the Lord, who___ an - swered me; from
Taste and see that the Lord is good; in

God has been___ so good to me.
all my trou - bles I was set free.
God we need___ put all our trust.

Eat This Bread 818
JOHN 6:35

Refrain

Eat this bread, drink this cup; come to Christ and nev-er be hun-gry.

Eat this bread, drink this cup; trust in Christ, and you will not thirst.

819 I Love the Lord
PSALM 116

Refrain

I love the Lord; he is filled with com-pas-sion. He turned to
me on the day that I called. From the snares of the
dark, O Lord, save my life, be my strength.

1 Gra - cious is the Lord and just; our
2 How can I re - pay the Lord for
3 I shall live my vows to you be -

Words: based on Psalm 116 © 2003 Jesuit Communications Foundation, Inc.
Music (I LOVE THE LORD irregular): Arnel dC Aquino, SJ © 2003 Jesuit Communications Foundation, Inc.;
arr. Joel Navarro © 2011 Joel Navarro

820
Vengo a ti, Jesús amado/
Soul, Adorn Yourself with Gladness

Spanish 1 Ven-go_a ti, Je-sús a-ma-do: lí-bra-me de mi pe-

English 1 Soul, a-dorn your-self with glad-ness, leave the gloom-y haunts of
2 Now in faith I hum-bly pon-der o-ver this sur-pass-ing
3 Je-sus, source of last-ing pleas-ure, tru-est friend, and dear-est

ca-do. Cal-ma, Re-den-tor, mi llan-to; he pe-ca-do tan-to,
sad-ness; come in-to the day-light's splen-dor, there with joy your prais-es
won-der that the bread of life is bound-less, though the souls it feeds are
treas-ure, peace be-yond all un-der-stand-ing, joy in-to all life ex-

tan-to. Con la san-gre que ver-tis-te das con-
ren-der. Bless the one whose grace un-bound-ed this a-
count-less. With the choic-est wine of heav-en Christ's own
pand-ing: hum-bly now I bow be-fore you. Love in-

sue-lo_al al-ma tris-te; ham-bre tor-nas en har-
maz-ing ban-quet found-ed; he, though heaven-ly, high, and
blood to us is giv-en. Oh, most glo-rious con-so-
car-nate, I a-dore you. Wor-thi-ly let me re-

Words: sts. Johann Franck (1618-1677); ref. Esther Bertieaux; tr. composite © 1964, 1978, 1998 Augsburg
Fortress
Music (CANTO AL BORNQUEN 8.8.8.8 refrain 3.11.11): Evy Lucío Cordova © Peer International Corporation
of Puerto Rico

tu - ra, sal - va - ción me das se - gu - ra. ¡Oh
ho - ly, deigns to dwell with you most low - ly. Be
la - tion, pledge and seal of my sal - va - tion.
ceive you, and, so fa - vored, nev - er leave you.

Refrain

Cris - to! *¡Oh Cris - to!* ge - ne - ro - so! tú me_o - fre - ces la sa - lud,
thank - ful! *Be thank-ful!* Soul, a - dorn your - self with glad - ness and re - joice!

que_a los tu - yos siem - pre das con ple - ni - tud.
Bless the one whose grace un - bound - ed is our joy.

2 Vida_ofrece,_y paz preciosa
  tu palabra poderosa;
  por unirse_al elemento
  hace_el santo sacramento.
  Con el pan y vino_adquiero
  cuerpo_y sangre del Cordero.
  ¡Oh, misterio tan profundo!
  ¿Quién lo_entiende_en este mundo?
  Refrain

3 Ya mi alma tú libraste,
  y_el pecado tú quitaste,
  cual preludio de tu cielo,
  hoy me gozo_en tu consuelo.
  Cielos, tierra, noche_y día
  te den gracias a porfía:
  "Por tus multiples favores,
  ¡gracias mil y mil loores!"
  Refrain

821 Let All Mortal Flesh Keep Silence

1 Let all mor-tal flesh keep si-lence, and with fear and
2 King of kings, yet born of Mar-y, once up-on the
3 Rank on rank, the host of heav-en stream be-fore him
4 At his feet the six-winged ser-aph, cher-u-bim with

trem-bling stand; set your minds on things e-ter-nal,
earth he stood; Lord of lords we now per-ceive him
on the way, as the Light of Light, de-scend-ing
sleep-less eye veil their fac-es to his pres-ence,

for with bless-ing in his hand Christ our Lord to earth de-
in the bod-y and the blood. He has given to all the
from the realms of end-less day, comes, the powers of hell to
as with cease-less voice they cry: "Al-le-lu-ia, al-le-

scend-ed, came our hom-age to com-mand.
faith-ful his own self for heaven-ly food.
van-quish, clears the gloom of hell a-way.
lu-ia! Al-le-lu-ia, Lord Most High!"

Words: Liturgy of St. James; tr. Gerard Moultrie, 1864, P.D.
Music (PICARDY 8.7.8.7.8.7): French 17th c.

Lamb of God

Leader Cm ... Gm

1,2 Lamb of God, you take a-way the sin of the world;
3 Lamb of God, you take a-way the sin of the world;

All

(on us.) 1,2 Lamb of God, you take a-way the sin of the
3 Lamb of God, you take a-way the sin of the

Cm | 1,2 | 3 | Cm

have mer-cy on us.
grant us your peace. Grant us your

world; have mer-cy
world; grant us your peace.

peace. Grant us your peace.

Grant us your peace. Grant us your peace.

Optional prayer

Lord Jesus, **grant us your peace.**
Lamb of God, **grant us your peace.**
Bread of life, **grant us your peace.**
Light of the world, **grant us your peace.**
Word made flesh, **grant us your peace.**
Wisdom of God, **grant us your peace.**
Great shepherd of the sheep, **grant us your peace.**
Living water, **grant us your peace.**
Bright and morning star, **grant us your peace.**

[Add other names for Jesus as appropriate]

Amen.

Words: *Agnus Dei,* based on John 1:29, P.D.
Music (LAMB OF GOD IONA): The Iona Community © 1995 Wild Goose Resource Group, Iona Community, Scotland, GIA Publications, Inc., exclusive North American agent

823 O Jesus, Joy of Loving Hearts

1 O Jesus, joy of loving hearts, the fount of life, the light of all, from full-est bliss that earth im-parts we turn un-filled to hear your call.

2 Your truth un-changed has ev-er stood; you save all those who on you call. To those who seek you, you are good; to those who find you, all in all.

3 We taste you, ev-er-liv-ing Bread, and long to feast up-on you still; we drink of you, the foun-tain-head, our thirst to quench, our souls to fill.

4 Our restless spirits yearn for you
where'er our changeful lot is cast;
glad when you smile on us anew,
blest that our faith can hold you fast.

5 O Jesus, ever with us stay;
make all our moments calm and bright!
Chase the dark night of sin away;
shed o'er the world your holy light!

Words: Latin, 12th c.; tr. Ray Palmer, 1858, alt., P.D.
Music (QUEBEC 8.8.8.8): Henry Baker, 1854, P.D.

The King of Love My Shepherd Is

824

PSALM 23

1 The King of love my Shep - herd is, whose good - ness
2 Where streams of liv - ing wa - ter flow my ran - somed
3 Per - verse and fool - ish oft I strayed, but yet in
4 In death's dark vale I fear no ill with thee, dear

fail - eth nev - er; I noth - ing lack if
soul he lead - eth, and where the ver - dant
love he sought me, and on his shoul - der
Lord, be - side me; thy rod and staff my

I am his and he is mine for - ev - er.
pas - tures grow, with food ce - les - tial feed - eth.
gent - ly laid, and home, re - joic - ing, brought me.
com - fort still, thy cross be - fore to guide me.

5 Thou spreadst a table in my sight;
   thy unction grace bestoweth;
   and, oh, what transport of delight
   from thy pure chalice floweth!

6 And so through all the length of days
   thy goodness faileth never;
   Good Shepherd, may I sing thy praise
   within thy house forever.

For other settings of Ps. 23 see 368, 369, 456, 732

Chord symbols represent a simplified harmony.

Words: Henry Williams Baker, 1868, P.D.
Music (ST. COLUMBA 8.7.8.7): Ancient Irish melody, P.D.

825 **Beneath the Cross**

1 Be - neath the cross of Je - sus, I find a place to stand, and won - der at such mer - cy that calls me as I am. For hands that should dis - card me hold wounds which tell me, "Come."

2 Be - neath the cross of Je - sus, his fam - ily is my own. Once strang - ers chas - ing self - ish dreams, now one through grace a - lone. How could I now dis - hon - or the ones that you have loved?

3 Be - neath the cross of Je - sus, the path be - fore the crown, we fol - low in his foot - steps where prom - ised hope is found. How great the joy be - fore us to be his per - fect bride.

Words and Music (BENEATH THE CROSS 7.6.7.6 D): Keith Getty and Kristyn Getty © 2006 Thankyou Music (PRS), admin. worldwide at EMICMGPublishing.com except Europe which is admin. by Kingswaysongs

Be - neath the cross of Je - sus, my un -
Be - neath the cross of Je - sus, see the
Be - neath the cross of Je - sus, we will

wor - thy soul is won.
chil - dren called by God.
glad - ly live our lives.

Affirmation: What God Says Through the Supper

826

Our Lord commands all believers
to eat this broken bread and to drink this cup
in true faith and in the confident hope of his return in glory.

**In this supper God declares to us
that our sins have been completely forgiven
through the one sacrifice of Jesus Christ,
which he himself finished on the cross once for all.**

He also declares to us
that the Holy Spirit grafts us into Christ,
who with his very body
is now in heaven at the right hand of the Father,
where he wants us to worship him.
Alleluia! Amen.

Text: from Heidelberg Catechism Q&A 75, 80

827 Now the Feast and Celebration

Refrain

Now the feast and cel - e - bra-tion— all of cre - a - tion sings for joy to the God of life and love and free-dom; praise and glo - ry for - ev - er - more!

Stanza 1

1 Now is the feast of the Lamb once slain, whose blood has freed and u - nit - ed us to be

Words and Music (NOW THE FEAST irregular): Marty Haugen (b. 1950) © 1990 GIA Publications, Inc.

one great peo - ple of God.

Stanza 2

2 Pow - er and rich - es, wis - dom and might, all hon - or and

glo - ry to Christ for - ev - er.

Stanza 3

3 For God has come to dwell with us, to make us peo - ple of

God, to make all things new.

828 O Christ, Our Hope, Our Heart's Desire

1 O Christ, our hope, our heart's de - sire, re - demp-tion's on - ly spring,
2 How vast the mer - cy and the love which laid our sins on thee,
3 But now the bands of death are burst, the ran - som has been paid;

Cre - a - tor of the world art thou, its Sav - ior and its King.
and led thee to a cru - el death to set thy peo - ple free.
and thou art on thy Fa - ther's throne, in glo - rious robes ar - rayed.

4 O Christ, be thou our lasting joy,
our ever great reward;
our only glory may it be
to glory in the Lord!

5 All praise to you, ascended Lord;
all glory ever be
to Father, Son, and Spirit blest
through all eternity.

Words: Latin hymn, ca. 8th c.; tr. John Chandler (1806-1876), alt., P.D.
Music (MANOAH 8.6.8.6) H.W. Greatorex's *Collection*, 1851, P.D.

829 Affirmation: The Sacrament of Christ's Body and Blood

Our Savior Jesus Christ
has ordained and instituted this Holy Supper
to nourish and sustain those
who are born again and grafted into his family: his church.
Christ has instituted
an earthly and visible bread as the sacrament of his body
and wine as the sacrament of his blood.
Just as truly as we take and hold the sacraments in our hands
and eat and drink them in our mouths,
by which our life is then sustained,
so truly we receive into our souls, for our spiritual life,
the true body and true blood of Christ, our only Savior.
We receive these by faith, which is the hand and mouth of our souls.
This banquet is a spiritual table
at which Christ communicates himself to us with all his benefits.
By the use of this holy sacrament
we are moved to a fervent love of God and our neighbors.

Text: Belgic Confession Article 35

Let Us Talents and Tongues Employ

830

1 Let us tal - ents and tongues em - ploy, reach - ing out with a
2 Christ is a - ble to make us one. At the ta - ble he
3 Je - sus calls us in, sends us out bear - ing fruit in a

shout of joy. Bread is bro - ken, the wine is poured,
sets the tone, teach - ing peo - ple to live to bless,
world of doubt, gives us love to tell, bread to share.

Refrain (descant may be added on repeat)

Christ is spo - ken and seen and heard.
love in word and in deed ex - press. Je - sus lives a - gain,
God (Em - man - u - el) ev - ery - where!

earth can breathe a - gain; pass the Word a - round: loaves a - bound!

Words: Fred Kaan (b. 1919) © 1975 Hope Publishing Company
Music (LINSTEAD 8.8.8.8 refrain 5.5.5.3): Jamaican folk tune; adapt. Doreen Potter (1925-1980) © 1975 Hope
  Publishing Company

831 Alleluia! Sing to Jesus

1 Al - le - lu - ia! Sing to Je - sus! His the scep - ter, his the throne;
2 Al - le - lu - ia! Not as or - phans are we left in so - row now;
3 Al - le - lu - ia! Heaven - ly High Priest, here on earth our help, our stay;
4 Al - le - lu - ia! King e - ter - nal, you the Lord of lords we own:

Al - le - lu - ia! His the tri - umph, his the vic - to - ry a - lone.
Al - le - lu - ia! He is near us; faith be - lieves nor ques - tions how.
Al - le - lu - ia! Hear the sin - ful cry to you from day to day.
Al - le - lu - ia! born of Mar - y, earth your foot-stool, heaven your throne:

Hark! The songs of peace-ful Zi - on thun - der like a might - y flood.
Though the cloud from sight re-ceived him when the for - ty days were o'er,
In - ter - ces - sor, friend of sin - ners, earth's Re - deem - er, hear our plea,
you with - in the veil, have en - tered, robed in flesh our great High Priest:

Je - sus, out of ev - ery na - tion, has re-deemed us by his blood.
shall our hearts for-get his prom - ise, "I am with you ev - er-more"?
where the songs of all the sin - less sweep a-cross the crys-tal sea.
by your Spir - it, lift us heaven-ward, in the Eu - char-is - tic feast!

Words: William C. Dix, 1866, alt., P.D.
Music (HYFRYDOL 8.7.8.7 D): Rowland Hugh Prichard, 1831, P.D.

At the Lamb's High Feast We Sing 832

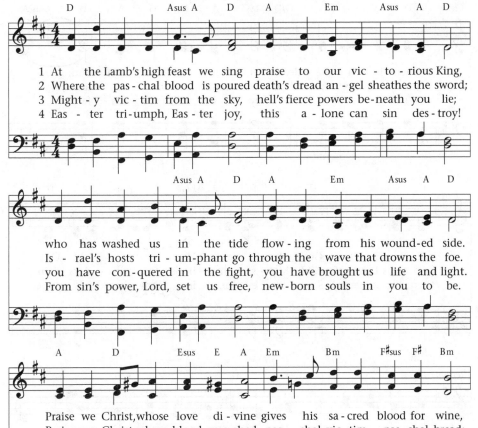

1 At   the Lamb's high feast we sing praise to our vic - to - rious King,
2 Where the pas - chal blood is poured death's dread an - gel sheathes the sword;
3 Might - y   vic - tim from the sky,   hell's fierce powers be-neath you   lie;
4 Eas - ter tri - umph, Eas - ter joy,   this   a - lone can   sin   des - troy!

who has washed us   in the tide flow - ing   from his wound-ed side.
Is - rael's hosts tri - um-phant go through the   wave that drowns the foe.
you have con - quered in   the fight, you have brought us   life and light.
From sin's power, Lord, set   us free, new - born souls   in   you   to be.

Praise we Christ, whose love   di - vine gives   his sa - cred blood for wine,
Praise we Christ, whose blood was shed, pas - chal vic - tim, pas - chal bread;
Now   no more can death ap - pall, now   no more the   grave en - thrall;
Fa - ther, who   the crown shall give; Sav - ior, by whose death we   live;

gives his bod - y   for the feast—Christ the   vic - tim, Christ the priest.
with sin - cer - i - ty and love   eat we man - na from a - bove.
you have o - pened par - a - dise,   and your saints in   you shall rise.
Spir - it, guide through all our days: Three in   One, your name we praise.

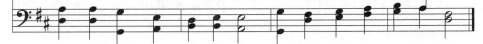

For an alternate arrangement see 546

Words: Latin hymn, 17th c.; tr. Robert Campbell (1814-1868), alt., P.D.
Music (SALZBURG 7.7.7.7 D): Jakob Hintze (1622-1702); harm. after Johann S. Bach (1685-1750), P.D.

833

There Is a Redeemer

1 There is a Re-deem-er, Je-sus, God's own Son;
2 Je-sus, my Re-deem-er, name a-bove all names,
3 When I stand in glo-ry I will see his face;

pre-cious Lamb of God, Mes-si-ah, Ho - ly One.
pre-cious Lamb of God, Mes-si-ah, hope for sin-ners slain.
there I'll serve my King for-ev-er, in that ho - ly place.

Refrain

Thank you O my Fa-ther, for giv-ing us your Son, and

leav - ing your Spir-it till the work on earth is done.

Words and Music (THERE IS A REDEEMER 6.5.8.3 refrain 6.6.7.6): Melody Green (b. 1946) © 1982 Birdwing
Music (ASCAP)/BMG Songs (ASCAP)/Ears to Hear Music (ASCAP), admin. EMICMGPublishing.com

Draw Us in the Spirit's Tether

834

1 Draw us in the Spir-it's teth - er, for when hum - bly
2 As dis - ci - ples used to gath - er in the name of
3 All our meals and all our liv - ing make as sac - ra -

in your name two or three are met to - geth - er,
Christ to sup, then with thanks to God the giv - er
ments of you, that by car - ing, help-ing, giv - ing,

you are in the midst of them. Al - le - lu - ia!
break the bread and bless the cup— Al - le - lu - ia!
we may be dis - ci - ples true. Al - le - lu - ia!

Al - le - lu - ia! Touch we now your gar - ment's hem.
Al - le - lu - ia! So now bind our friend - ship up.
Al - le - lu - ia! We will serve with faith a - new.

Chord symbols represent a simplified harmony.

Words: Percy Dearmer (1867-1936), from *Enlarged Songs of Praise* 1931, alt., reproduced by permission of Oxford University Press

Music (UNION SEMINARY 8.7.8.7.8.7): Harold Friedell (1905-1958) © 1957, 1985 The H.W. Gray Company, admin. Alfred Publishing Co., Inc.; arr. © 2012 The H.W. Gray Company, admin. Alfred Music Publishing Co., Inc.

835 One Bread, One Body

Words and Music (ONE BREAD, ONE BODY 4.4.6 refrain 9.8.9.9): John B. Foley, SJ © 1978 John B. Foley, SJ, admin. OCP Publications

wom - an   or   man,   no   more.
one   in   the   Lord   of   all.
gath -ered   to   one,   for   all.

Bless the Lord, My Soul   836

PSALM 103:1

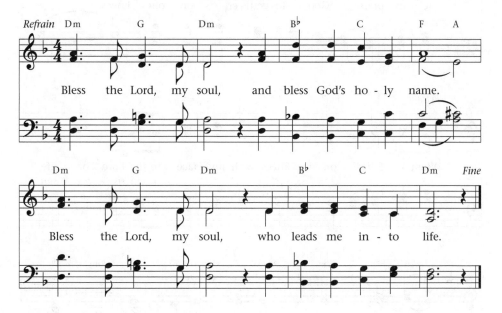

Bless   the Lord,   my soul,   and bless God's ho - ly name.

Bless   the Lord,   my soul,   who leads me in - to life.

For other settings of Ps. 103 see 516, 571, 671, 672

Words: Robert Batastini (b. 1942) and The Community of Taizé © 1991, 1998 Ateliers et Presses de Taizé, Taizé
Community, France, GIA Publications, Inc., exclusive North American agent
Music (BLESS THE LORD MY SOUL 5.6.5.6): Jacques Berthier (1923-1994) © 1991, 1998 Ateliers et Presses de
Taizé, Taizé Community, France, GIA Publications, Inc., exclusive North American agent

837   Let Us Break Bread Together

1 Let us break bread to-geth-er on our knees;
2 Let us drink wine to-geth-er on our knees;
3 Let us praise God to-geth-er on our knees;

let us break bread to-geth-er on our knees.
let us drink wine to-geth-er on our knees.
let us praise God to-geth-er on our knees.

Refrain

When I fall on my knees, with my face to the Lord of life,
(alt. text) ris - ing sun

O Lord, have mer-cy on me.

Words: African American spiritual, P.D.
Music (BREAK BREAD TOGETHER 10.10.14.7): African American spiritual; harm. Dale Grotenhuis
(1931-2012), 1984, © 1987 Faith Alive Christian Resources

Now Behold the Lamb 838

1 Now be-hold the Lamb, the pre-cious Lamb of God.
2 Ho-ly is the Lamb, the pre-cious Lamb of God.
3 Thank you for the Lamb, the pre-cious Lamb of God.

Bore all my sin that I may
Why you love me so, Lord, I shall
Be-cause of your grace I can fin -

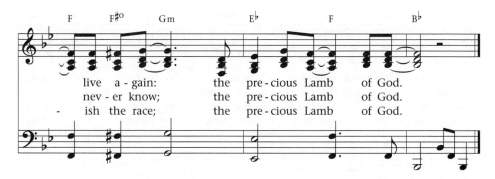

live a-gain: the pre-cious Lamb of God.
nev-er know; the pre-cious Lamb of God.
-ish the race; the pre-cious Lamb of God.

Words and Music (NOW BEHOLD THE LAMB 5.6.5.6.6): Kirk Franklin (b. 1970) © 2007 Lilly Mack Publishing (BMI), admin. EMI CMG Publishing

Worthy Is the Lamb 839

REVELATION 1:5-6, 5:12

To Jesus Christ, who loves us
and freed us from our sins by his blood,
and made us to be a kingdom,
priests serving his God and Father,
to him be glory and dominion forever and ever.
Worthy is the Lamb, who was slain,
to receive power and wealth and wisdom and strength
and honor and glory and praise!

Text: from Revelation 1:5-6, NRSV, and Revelation 5:12, NIV

840 — **Behold the Lamb**

Words and Music (COMMUNION HYMN 10.8.10.7.8.8.8.8): Keith Getty, Kristyn Getty and Stuart Townend
© 2006 Thankyou Music (PRS), admin. worldwide at EMICMGPublishing.com except Europe which is
admin. by Kingswaysongs

sac - ri - fice as a sign of our bonds of peace
sac - ri - fice as a sign of our bonds of love
sac - ri - fice as a sign of our bonds of grace
come a - gain! And we'll join in the feast of heaven

a - round the ta - ble of the King.
a - round the ta - ble of the King.
a - round the ta - ble of the King.
a - round the ta - ble of the King.

Lamb of God (Agnus Dei)   841

Lamb of God, who takes away the sin of the world, have mercy on us.
Lamb of God, who takes away the sin of the world, have mercy on us.
Lamb of God, who takes away the sin of the world, grant us your peace.
Amen.

This prayer is a traditional congregational response that may be spoken or sung
after the breaking of the bread. It is often called the Agnus Dei (Latin for "Lamb of God").

Text: *Agnus Dei*, traditional, P.D.

842 I Am the Bread of Life

JOHN 6:35, 44; 11:25

Words: Suzanne Toolan (b. 1927), based on John 6:35, 44; 11:25; © 1970 GIA Publications, Inc.
Music (I AM THE BREAD irregular): Suzanne Toolan; harm. Betty Pulkingham (b. 1928) © 1970
GIA Publications, Inc.

up,   and I will raise   them up   on the   last   day.

Be Present at Our Table, Lord 843

Be pres-ent at our ta - ble, Lord; be here and ev - ery - where a-dored;

thy crea-tures bless, and grant that we may feast in par-a - dise with thee.

Optional table blessing

Blessed are you, Lord, our God,
giver of every good and perfect gift.
As we receive this gift of food and fellowship,
we praise you for Jesus, our Lord—
the bread of life, that gives life to the world.
By your Spirit, help us to be nourished
in body and soul, in life and death,
through Christ, our Lord. Amen.

For an alternate arrangement see 1, 924, 965

Words: John Cennick, 1741, alt., P.D.
Music (GENEVAN 134/OLD HUNDREDTH 8.8.8.8): Louis Bourgeois, 1551, P.D.

844 Lift Up Your Hearts unto the Lord

4 Therefore we celebrate the feast . . .
5 Sing alleluia to the Lord . . .
Add additional stanzas as desired.

Words: st. 1-4 from early Christian liturgy; st. 5 Linda Stassen, 1974, © 1974 Linda Stassen
Music (SING ALLELUIA): Linda Stassen, 1974; harm. Dale Grotenhuis, 1986, © 1974, 1986 Linda Stassen

This Is the Feast of Victory

REVELATION 5:12-14

845

This is the feast of vic-to-ry for our God. Hal-le-lu - jah, hal-le-lu - jah, hal-le - lu - jah lu - jah!

1 ⸙ Wor - thy is Christ, the Lamb who was slain, whose blood set us free___ to be peo - ple of God.
2 Pow - er, rich - es, wis - dom, and strength and hon - or,___ bless - ing and glo - ry are his.
3 Sing with all the peo - ple of God, and > join in the hymn of all cre - a - tion.
4 Bless - ing, hon - or, glo - ry, and might be to God and the Lamb for - ev - er. A - men.
5 For the Lamb_____ who was slain, has be - gun his___ reign.___ Hal - le - lu - jah!

Words: from Revelation 5:12-14; para. John W. Arthur (1922-1980) © 1978 *Lutheran Book of Worship*, admin. Augsburg Fortress
Music (FESTIVAL CANTICLE 9.11 refrain 11.12): Richard Hillert (1923 - 2010) © 1975, 1988 Richard Hillert

846 **Baptized in Christ**

1 Bap - tized in Christ, we claim his cross, the vic - to -
2 Bap - tized in Christ we live his life: God's will in
3 Bap - tized in Christ, we fol - low him, and we with
4 Bap - tized in Christ we tes - ti - fy the king - dom

ry he won. And, dy - ing, we shall
us be done. May we by all we
him shall run un - til we match his
has be - gun. Christ sows and reaps through -

rise with him, for we with Christ are one.
do pro - claim the love that makes us one.
ev - ery step and so with Christ are one.
out the world and gath - ers us as one.

5 Baptized in Christ,
   we know his grace
that cannot be undone.
Its bounty spreads throughout the earth
and leavens us as one.

6 Baptized in Christ
   we praise our God:
the Father and the Son
who with the Spirit live and reign,
eternal Three in One.

Words: Harry Hagan, OSB, © 2008 Saint Meinrad Archabbey
Music (BALLERMA 8.6.8.6): from *Southern Harmony* by F.H. Bertémon; arr. Karl Cothern, OSB, © 2008, 2010
   Saint Meinrad Archabbey

This Holy Covenant Was Made

847

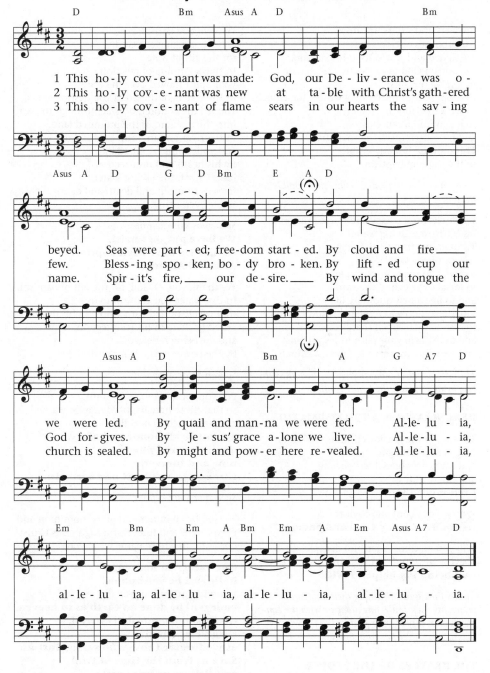

1 This ho-ly cov-e-nant was made: God, our De-liv-erance was o-
2 This ho-ly cov-e-nant was new at ta-ble with Christ's gath-ered
3 This ho-ly cov-e-nant of flame sears in our hearts the sav-ing

beyed. Seas were part-ed; free-dom start-ed. By cloud and fire____
few. Bless-ing spo-ken; bo-dy bro-ken. By lift-ed cup our
name. Spir-it's fire,____ our de-sire.____ By wind and tongue the

we were led. By quail and man-na we were fed. Al-le-lu - ia,
God for-gives. By Je-sus' grace a-lone we live. Al-le-lu - ia,
church is sealed. By might and pow-er here re-vealed. Al-le-lu - ia,

al-le-lu - ia, al-le-lu - ia, al-le-lu - ia, al-le-lu - ia.

Chord symbols represent a simplified harmony. For an alternate arrangement see 208, 317, 551

Words: Sylvia Dunstan (1955-1993) © 1991 GIA Publications, Inc.
Music (LASST UNS ERFREUEN 8.8.4.4.8.8 with alleluias): *Auserlesen Catholische Geistliche Kirchengesänge*,
  Cologne, 1623; adapt. and harm. Ralph Vaughan Williams, 1906, P.D.

848 Affirming Baptism and Professing Faith

Brothers and sisters in Christ,
the promises of God's grace
are signed and sealed to us in baptism.
In baptism God promises by grace alone
to forgive our sins;
to adopt us into the body of Christ, the church;
to send the Holy Spirit daily
to renew and cleanse us;
and to resurrect us to eternal life.
This promise is made visible
in the water of baptism.

*Here water may be poured visibly and audibly into
the font.*

Water cleanses, purifies, refreshes, sustains;
Jesus Christ is living water.
Through baptism Christ calls us
to new obedience:
to love and trust God completely,
to forsake the evil of the world,
and to live a new and holy life.
I invite you now to remember God's promise,
to turn away from all that is evil,
and to reaffirm your faith in Jesus Christ
and your commitment to Christ's church.

*The people may stand and encircle the font. When
people are in place, the leader continues.*

RENUNCIATIONS AND AFFIRMATION

Trusting in the gracious promises of God,
do you renounce sin
and the power of evil in your life
and the world?
I renounce them.

Who is your Lord and Savior?
Jesus Christ is my Lord and Savior.

Will you be Christ's faithful disciple,
obeying his Word and showing his love?
God being my helper, I will.

*At this time those affirming their baptism or
professing their faith may alone or with the congregation testify to their faith using the words of
the Apostles' Creed as found at xxx*

THE PRAYERS OF THE PEOPLE

The Lord be with you.
And also with you.

Let us give thanks to the Lord our God.
It is right to give our thanks and praise.

We give you thanks,
O holy and gracious God,
for the gift of water.
In the beginning of creation
your Spirit moved over the waters.
In the waters of the flood you destroyed evil.
You led the children of Israel through the sea
into the freedom of the promised land.
In the river Jordan, John baptized our Lord
and your Spirit anointed him.
By his death and resurrection
Jesus Christ, the Living Water,
frees us from sin and death and opens the way
to life everlasting.

Spoken or Sung Refrain:
We have put on Christ.
In him we have been baptized.
Alleluia! Alleluia!

We thank you, O God, for the gift of baptism.
In this water you confirm to us
that we are buried with Christ in his death,
raised to share in his resurrection,
and are being renewed
by the power of the Holy Spirit.

Spoken or Sung Refrain

Pour out on us your Holy Spirit,
so that those here baptized may be washed
clean and receive new life.
To you be all honor and glory,
dominion and power,
now and forever,
through Jesus Christ our Lord. Amen.

Spoken or Sung Refrain

To God be all honor and glory, dominion and
power, now and forever, through Jesus Christ
our Lord, in whose name we are bold to pray:

Our Father in heaven,
hallowed be your name,
your kingdom come,
your will be done on earth as in heaven.
Give us today our daily bread.
Forgive us our sins
as we forgive those who sin against us.
Save us from the time of trial
and deliver us from evil.
For the kingdom, the power, and the
glory are yours now and forever. Amen.

(continues)

Text: adapt. by John Paarlberg from the liturgy for the sacrament of baptism of the Reformed Church in
America, 2001

RENEWING PROMISES

For reception from another congregation, those making reaffirmation of their faith, or those making a profession who have been previously baptized:

(Name), remember that you are baptized; you are sealed by the Holy Spirit and marked as God's own forever.

CHARGE AND BLESSING

Lead a life worthy of the calling to which you have been called,

with humility and gentleness, with patience, bearing with one another in love, making every effort to maintain the unity of the Spirit in the bond of peace.
(Eph. 4:1-2)

May the God of peace make you holy in every way and may your whole being— spirit, soul, and body— be kept sound and blameless at the coming of our Lord Jesus Christ.
(1 Thess. 5:23)

We Have Put on Christ   849

We have put on Christ; in him we have been bap - tized.

Al - le - lu - ia! Al - le - lu - ia!

Accompaniment pattern, repeat as needed

Words: from Galatians 3:27 © 1969 International Committee on English in the Liturgy, Inc., ICEL
Music (BAPTIZED IN CHRIST): from *Music for the Rite of Funerals and Rite of Baptism for Children,* International Committee on English in the Liturgy, Inc., ICEL

850 Commit Your Way to God the Lord

PSALM 37

1 Com-mit your way to God the Lord— your cause will
2 Be still be-fore the Lord and wait, and do not
3 Sal-va-tion comes from God a-lone: the faith-ful
4 Com-mit your way to God the Lord, to peace and

shine as bright as fire; de-light to do God's ho-ly
fret when wrong suc-ceeds; re-frain from an-ger, turn from
know their help is sure; to heav-en all our needs are
truth and grace as-pire; then mer-cy shall be your re-

word, and you shall find what you de-sire.
hate, for God will pun-ish e-vil deeds.
known, and in God's strength we are se-cure.
ward, God's prom-is-es your heart's de-sire.

For an alternate arrangement see 871

For another setting of Ps. 37 see 480

Words: Michael Perry © 1989 The Jubilate Group, admin. Hope Publishing Company
Music (ROCKINGHAM 8.8.8.8): *Second Supplement to Psalmody in Miniature,* ca. 1780; adapt. Edward Miller
   (1731-1807), 1790, P.D.

I Am the Holy Vine

851

JOHN 15:1-5

1 I am the ho - ly vine which God my Fa - ther tends.
2 If you a - bide in me, I will in you a - bide.
3 I am the fruit - ful vine, and you my branch - es are.

Each branch that yields no fruit my Fa - ther cuts a -
Each branch to yield its fruit must with the vine be
If you a - bide in me, I will in you a -

way. Each fruit - ful branch he prunes with care
one. So you shall fail to yield your fruit
bide. So shall you yield much fruit, but none

to make it yield a - bun - dant fruit.
if you are not with me one vine.
if you re - main a - part from me.

Words: from John 15:1-5; vers. James Quinn, 1969, alt. © 1969 James Quinn, SJ, reprinted with permission from the Bloomsbury Publishing Group
Music (LOVE UNKNOWN 6.6.6.6.8.8): John Ireland, 1918, by permission of the John Ireland Charitable Trust

852 **Faith Begins by Letting Go**

1 Faith be-gins by let-ting go, giv-ing up what had seemed sure,
2 Faith en-dures by hold-ing on, keep-ing mem-ory's roots a - live
3 Faith ma-tures by reach-ing out, stretch-ing minds, en - larg-ing hearts,

tak - ing risks and press-ing on, though the way feels less se - cure:
so that hope may bear its fruit; prom - ise-fed, our souls will thrive,
shar-ing strug-gles, liv - ing prayer, bind-ing up the bro - ken parts;

pil - grim - age both right and odd, trust-ing all our life to God.
not through mer - it we pos - sess but by God's great faith-ful - ness.
till we find the com-mon-place ripe with wit - ness to God's grace.

Optional Prayer

God of grace and glory,
we pray for the gift of the Holy Spirit—
for us, for those whom we love…
for those unknown to us but known and loved by you…
By your Spirit, reveal to our minds and seal upon our hearts
a firm and certain knowledge of your lavish generosity toward us,
founded on the truth of all your promises
given and confirmed in Jesus Christ, our Lord.
**Truly, you are the fountain of all goodness,
the giver of every good and perfect gift. Amen.**

Text: based on John Calvin, *Institutes of the Christian Religion*, III.2.7, and James 1:17

Words: Carl P. Daw Jr (b. 1944) © 1996 Hope Publishing Company
Music (LUX PRIMA 7.7.7.7.7.7): Charles F. Gounod (1818-1893), 1872, P.D.

God of the Prophets

853

1 God of the proph - ets, bless the proph-ets' heirs! E - li-jah's
2 A - noint us proph - ets! Teach us your in - tent: to hu-man
3 A - noint us priests! Help us to in - ter - cede with all your

man - tle o'er E - li - sha cast: each age for your own sol - emn
need, our quick-ened hearts a - wake; fill us with power, our lips make
roy - al priest-hood born of grace; through us your church pre - sents in

task pre - pares; make each one strong-er, nob - ler than the last.
el - o - quent for right-eous - ness that shall all e - vil break.
word and deed a liv - ing sac - ri - fice with thanks and praise.

4 Anoint us kings! Help us do justice, Lord!
Anoint us with the Spirit of your Son:
ours not a monarch's crown or tyrant's sword;
ours by the love of Christ a kingdom won.

5 Make us disciples, heralds of your cross;
forth may we go to tell all realms your grace:
by you inspired, may we count all but loss,
and stand at last with joy before your face.

Words: st. 1-2, 4-5 Denis Wortman, 1884, alt; st. 3 Carl P. Daw Jr, 1981, alt. st. 3 © 1982 Hope Publishing Company
Music (TOULON 10.10.10.10): *Genevan Psalter*, 1551; adapt. from GENEVAN 124, P.D.

854   I'm Gonna Live So God Can Use Me

PSALM 15

Additional stanzas: work, pray, etc.

Refrain

Lord, who may dwell in your sacred tent?
Who may live on your holy mountain?
The one whose walk is blameless,
who does what is righteous,
who speaks the truth from their heart;
whose tongue utters no slander,
who does no wrong to a neighbor,
and casts no slur on others;

Refrain

who despises a vile person
but honors those who fear the Lord;
who keeps an oath even when it hurts,
and does not change their mind;
who lends money to the poor without
interest;
who does not accept a bribe against the
innocent.
Whoever does these things
will never be shaken.

Refrain

For another setting of Ps. 15 see 612

Words: African American spiritual, P.D.
Music (I'M GONNA LIVE): traditional; arr. Wendell Whalum (1932-1987) © the Estate of Wendell Whalum

A Commissioning Liturgy 855

Beloved in the Lord,
we have come to commission
[name of position and/or person(s)]
in Christ's holy church.
Christ alone is the source
of all Christian ministry,
through the ages calling
men and women to serve.
By the Holy Spirit, all who believe
and are baptized receive a ministry
to witness to Jesus as Savior and Lord,
and to love and serve those with
whom they live and work.
We are ambassadors for Christ,
who reconciles and makes whole.
We are the salt of the earth;
we are the light of the world.
Following Christ's resurrection and ascension,
God has given the church
apostles, prophets, and teachers,
deeds of power, gifts of healing,
forms of assistance and leadership.

Seeking the guidance of the Holy Spirit,
we affirm the calling of *[name]*.

To those being commissioned:
Our Lord, who came among us to serve,
calls us to faith and a life of gratitude.
[Name],
you stand among us to
render a particular service,
a gift from God to equip us
in the work of ministry.
For as in one body we have many members,
and not all the members
have the same function,
so we, who are many, are one body in Christ,
and individually we are
members one of another.

We have gifts that differ
according to the grace given to us:
prophecy, in proportion to faith;
ministry, in ministering;
the teacher, in teaching;
the exhorter, in exhortation;
the giver, in generosity;
the leader, in diligence;
the compassionate, in cheerfulness.
(Romans 12:4-8)

Do you accept this ministry of
[name of ministry] in confidence
that it comes from God?
Yes, truly, with all my heart.

Will you fulfill this ministry
in accordance with the teaching
and practice of this church?
I will, and I ask God to help me.

Will you be diligent in your study of Scripture,
faithful in your use of the means of grace,
and constant in prayer?
I will, and I ask God to help me.

Will you trust in God's care,
seek to grow in love for those you serve,
strive for excellence in your work,
uphold the unity, purity,
and peace of this church,
and adorn the gospel with a godly life?
I will, and I ask God to help me.

Addressing the congregation.
Beloved people of God,
will you receive this *sister/brother*
as a servant of the Lord?
Will you encourage *her/him* as *she/he*
accepts this responsibility
for our common life?
Will you provide such financial
and personal support
that *she/he* will serve with joy?
We will.

COMMISSIONING

[Name],
we commission you for this ministry in the
name of the Father and of the Son and of the
Holy Spirit. Amen.

Let us pray.

Gracious God,
as you call workers to varied tasks
in the world and in your church,
so you have called this your servant
to this ministry.
Grant *her/him* joy,
that *her/his* work may stir up
each of us to a life of faithful service.
[additional prayers related to the particular ministry].

We pray all of this,
through Jesus Christ, our Lord,
the head of the body, the church,
in the power of the Holy Spirit,
who equips us for service. **Amen.**

Text: adapt. from the RCA liturgy for commissioning

856 How Clear Is Our Vocation, Lord

Unison

1 How clear is our vo - ca - tion, Lord, when
2 But if, for - get - ful, we should find your
3 We mar - vel how your saints be - come in
4 In what you give us, Lord, to do, to -

once we heed your call: to live ac - cord - ing
yoke is hard to bear; if world - ly pres - sures
hin - dranc - es more sure; whose joy - ful vir - tues
geth - er or a - lone, in old rou - tines and

to your word, and dai - ly learn, re - freshed, re - stored, that
fray the mind, and love it - self can - not un - wind its
put to shame the cas - ual way we wear your name, and
ven - tures new may we not cease to look to you, the

you are Lord of all, and will not let us fall.
tan - gled skein of care: our in - ward life re - pair.
by our faults ob - scure your power to cleanse and cure.
cross you hung up - on— all you en - deav - ored done.

Chord symbols represent a simplified harmony.

Words: Fred Pratt Green, 1981, © 1982 Hope Publishing Company
Music (REPTON 8.6.8.8.6.6): C. Hubert H. Parry, 1888, P.D.

Your Mercy and Your Justice

PSALM 101

857

Your mer - cy and your jus - tice will be my song of praise;
with heart and voice and be - ing I'll praise you all my days.

Refrain

What is the aim of the ninth commandment?
That I never give false testimony
against anyone, twist no one's words,
not gossip or slander,
nor join in condemning anyone rashly
or without a hearing.

Refrain

I will sing of your love and justice;
to you, Lord, I will sing praise.
I will be careful to lead a blameless life —
when will you come to me?
I will conduct the affairs of my house
with a blameless heart.
I will not look with approval
on anything that is vile.
I hate what faithless people do;
I will have no part in it.
The perverse of heart shall be far from me;
I will have nothing to do with
what is evil.

Whoever slanders their neighbor in secret,
I will put to silence;
whoever has haughty eyes
and a proud heart,
I will not tolerate.
My eyes will be on the faithful in the land,
that they may dwell with me;
the one whose walk is blameless
will minister to me.
No one who practices deceit
will dwell in my house;
no one who speaks falsely
will stand in my presence.
Every morning I will put to silence
all the wicked in the land;
I will cut off every evildoer
from the city of the Lord.

Refrain

What is the aim of the ninth commandment?
That I should love the truth, speak it
candidly, and openly acknowledge it.
And I should do what I can to guard
and advance my neighbor's good name.

Refrain

Text: adapt from Heidelberg Catehicsm Q&A 112; Psalm 101
Words: Martin Tel © 2011 Martin Tel, admin. Faith Alive Christian Resources
Music (ST. THEODULPH fragment): Melchior Teschner, 1615, P.D.

858

God Be in My Head

Words: Grayson Warren Brown (b. 1948) © 1999 Grayson Warren Brown, admin. OCP Publications
Music (GOD BE IN MY HEAD 5.5.5.5.5.12.5.5): Grayson Warren Brown; arr. Val Parker and Grayson Warren
  Brown © 1999 Grayson Warren Brown, admin. OCP Publications

Be Thou My Vision

1 Be thou my vi - sion, O Lord of my heart;
2 Be thou my wis - dom, and thou my true word;
3 Rich - es I heed not, nor vain, emp - ty praise;
4 High King of heav - en, my vic - to - ry won,

naught be all else to me, save that thou art—
I ev - er with thee and thou with me, Lord.
thou mine in - her - i - tance, now and al - ways:
may I reach heav - en's joys, O bright heaven's sun!

thou my best thought,___ by day or by night;
Thou my great Fa - ther; thine own may I be,
thou and thou on - ly first in my heart,
Heart of my own heart, what - ev - er be - fall,

wak - ing or sleep - ing, thy pres - ence my light.
thou in me dwell - ing and I one with thee.
high King of heav - en, my treas - ure thou art.
still be my vi - sion, O Rul - er of all.

Words: Irish hymn, 8th c.; tr. Mary E. Byrne (1880-19331); vers. Eleanor H. Hull (1860-1935), P.D.
Music (SLANE 10.10.10.10): Irish melody; arr. Jack Schrader (b. 1942) © 1989 Hope Publishing Company

860   Prayer of St. Francis

Lord, make me an instrument of your peace.
Where there is hatred, **let me sow love.**
Where there is injury, **pardon.**
Where there is doubt, **faith.**
Where there is despair, **hope.**
Where there is darkness, **light.**
Where there is sadness, **joy.**

O divine Master,
grant that I may not so much seek to be consoled, **as to console;**
to be understood, **as to understand;**
to be loved, **as to love.**
For it is in giving that we receive.
It is in pardoning that we are pardoned,
and it is in dying that we are born to eternal life.
Amen.

Text: traditional text, P.D.

861   In Our Lives, Lord, Be Glorified

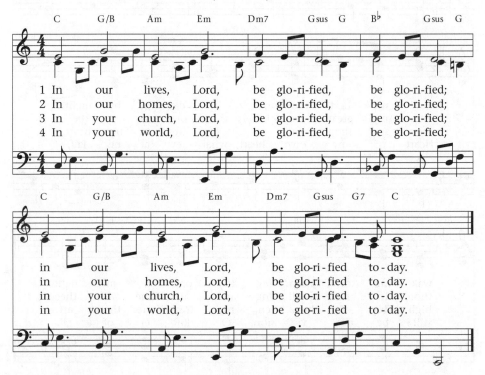

Words and Music (GLORIFIED): Bob Kilpatrick (b. 1952) © 1978 Bob Kilpatrick Music, admin. Lorenz
Publishing Company

Take Us as We Are, O God

862

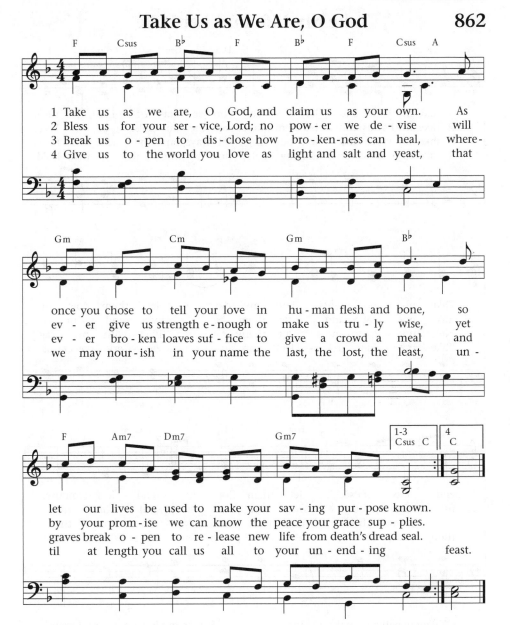

1 Take us as we are, O God, and claim us as your own. As
2 Bless us for your ser - vice, Lord; no pow - er we de - vise will
3 Break us o - pen to dis - close how bro - ken-ness can heal, where-
4 Give us to the world you love as light and salt and yeast, that

once you chose to tell your love in hu - man flesh and bone, so
ev - er give us strength e - nough or make us tru - ly wise, yet
ev - er bro - ken loaves suf - fice to give a crowd a meal and
we may nour - ish in your name the last, the lost, the least, un -

let our lives be used to make your sav - ing pur - pose known.
by your prom - ise we can know the peace your grace sup - plies.
graves break o - pen to re - lease new life from death's dread seal.
til at length you call us all to your un - end - ing feast.

Chord symbols represent a simplifed harmony.

Words: Carl P. Daw Jr (b. 1944) © 1995 Hope Publishing Company
Music (ENDLESS FEAST 7.6.8.6.8.6): Alfred V. Fedak (b. 1953) © 1995 Selah Publishing Company

863   Take My Life and Let It Be

1 Take my life and let it be con-se-crat-ed, Lord, to thee.
2 Take my hands and let them move at the im-pulse of thy love.
3 Take my voice and let me sing al-ways, on-ly, for my King.
4 Take my sil-ver and my gold; not a mite would I with-hold.

Take my mo-ments and my days; let them flow in
Take my feet and let them be swift and beau-ti-
Take my lips and let them be filled with mes-sag-
Take my in-tel-lect and use ev-ery power as

end-less praise, let them flow in end-less praise.
ful for thee, swift and beau-ti-ful for thee.
es from thee, filled with mes-sag-es from thee.
thou shalt choose, ev-ery power as thou shalt choose.

5 Take my will and make it thine;
  it shall be no longer mine.
  Take my heart—it is thine own;
  it shall be thy royal throne,
  it shall be thy royal throne.

6 Take my love; my Lord, I pour
  at thy feet its treasure store.
  Take myself, and I will be
  ever, only, all for thee,
  ever, only, all for thee.

Alternate tune: TEBBEN *(with no repeat) see 376, 864*

Words: Frances R. Havergal, 1874, P.D.
Music (HENDON 7.7.7.7 with repeat): H.A. Cesar Malan, 1827, P.D.

Holy Spirit, Truth Divine

864

1 Ho-ly Spir - it, truth di-vine, dawn up-on this soul of mine.
2 Ho-ly Spir - it, love di-vine, glow with-in this heart of mine.
3 Ho-ly Spir - it, power di-vine, fill and nerve this will of mine.
4 Ho-ly Spir - it, law di-vine, reign with-in this soul of mine.

Voice of God and in-ward light, wake my spir - it, clear my sight.
Kin-dle ev - ery high de - sire, pu - ri - fy me with your fire.
Bold-ly may I al-ways live, brave-ly serve, and glad-ly give.
Be my law, and I shall be firm-ly bound, for - ev - er free.

5 Holy Spirit, peace divine,
still this restless heart of mine.
Speak to calm this tossing sea,
grant me your tranquility.

6 Holy Spirit, joy divine,
gladden now this heart of mine.
In the desert ways I sing—
spring, O Living Water, spring!

For this music in a lower key see 376

Words: Samuel Longfellow, 1864, alt., P.D.
Music (TEBBEN 7.7.7.7): Timothy Hoekman, 1979, © 1985 Faith Alive Christian Resources

Affirmation: Sharing Gifts Within the Body 865

We affirm that "believers one and all,
as members of this community,
share in Christ and in all his treasures and
gifts."

**We affirm that "each member
should consider it a duty
to use these gifts readily and joyfully
for the service and enrichment
of the other members."**

By your Spirit, teach us to pray:

**Lord God, you call and equip persons
with so many different kinds
of gifts and abilities,
those society may consider
'abled' and 'disabled.'
Help us grow together as Christ' body,
so each gift may be used
to bless each other
and to share your peace
to the world that you so love.**

Text: Heidelberg Catechism Q&A 55

866 God, We Give to You Our Offerings

Words and Music (GRANDVILLE 8.7.8.7 refrain 7.7.7.7): Ken Medema © 2006 Ken Medema Music/Brier Patch Music; arr. Linda A. Missad © 2006 Ken Medema Music/Brier Patch Music

God, we give you grate-ful-ly all we are and hope to be.

For Such a Time as This 867

1 A hymn of joy to-day we raise for min-i-stries and gifts,
2 Your faith-ful life, O Christ, in-spires; your bro-ken-ness makes whole;
3 For all the saints whose lives shine forth as tem-plates of your grace,
4 Our world cries out to hear your name; the church in mis-sion risks

for all the ways you bid us join your cloud of wit-ness-es.
your res-ur-rec-tion calls us forth and o-pens long-closed doors.
we give you thanks and pledge our lives in gra-ti-tude to trace.
as men and wo-men join to serve for such a time as this.

Words: Carol M. Bechtel, 1998, © 2012 Carol Bechtel, admin. Faith Alive Christian Resources
Music (ST. ANNE 8.6.8.6): William Croft, 1708, P.D.

868 That's Why We Praise Him

869

Here I Am, Lord

1 I, the Lord of sea and sky, I have heard my peo-ple cry.
2 I, the Lord of snow and rain, I have borne my peo-ple's pain.
3 I, the Lord of wind and flame, I will tend the poor and lame.

All who dwell in dark and sin my hand will save.
I have wept for love of them. They turn a-way.
I will set a feast for them. My hand will save.

I, who made the stars of night, I will make their dark-ness bright.
I will break their hearts of stone, give them hearts for love a-lone.
Fin-est bread I will pro-vide till their hearts be sat-is-fied.

Who will bear my light to them? Whom shall I send?
I will speak my word to them. Whom shall I send?
I will give my life to them. Whom shall I send?

Words: Daniel L. Schutte (b. 1947) © 1981 OCP (New Dawn Music), admin. OCP Publications
Music (HERE I AM, LORD 7.7.7.4 D refrain 8.9.8.9): Daniel L. Schutte (b. 1947); arr. Michael Pope and John
Weissrock © 1981 OCP (New Dawn Music), admin. OCP Publications

Refrain

Here I am, Lord. Is it I, Lord?

I have heard you call-ing in the night.

I will go, Lord, if you lead me.

I will hold your peo-ple in my heart.

Optional prayer of blessing for commissioning

God of all grace,
we bless and thank you for the call
you have given to your servant(s) [names].
We bless and thank you for
prompting of your Spirit
which equips *them* to respond in faith.
Continue to pour out your Spirit upon *them*.
Bring forth in and through *them* the fruit of
love, joy, and peace; patience, kindness, and

goodness; faithfulness, gentleness,
and self-control.
May this harvest of righteousness
be multiplied
in every ministry,
every prayer,
every opportunity
for service to which you lead *them*.
In Jesus name, Amen.

870   Ahead of Us, a Race to Run

1 A - head of us, a race to run; we fix our eyes on God the Son—
2 He calls us now to run the race, the path we tread, the way of grace—

so look-ing at the past no more, for - get - ting what has gone be - fore,
dis-card-ing ev-ery weight and load to speed our way a - long the road;

with ea - ger dil - i - gence we train as for the prize a -
and though the jour - ney may be long, the grace of God will

head we strain, un - til at last our course is done.
keep us strong un - til we stand be - fore his face.

Words: based on Philippians 3:12-14, Martin E. Leckebusch © 1999 Kevin Mayhew, Ltd.
Music (SOLID ROCK 8.8.8.8.8.8.8.8): William B. Bradbury, 1863, P.D.

What Shall I Render to the Lord

871

PSALM 116:12-19

1 What shall I ren-der to the LORD for all his ben-e-fits to me? How shall my life, by grace re-stored, give wor-thy thanks, O LORD, to thee?

2 Sal-va-tion's cup of bless-ing now I take and call up-on God's name. Be-fore his saints I pay my vow and here my grat-i-tude pro-claim.

3 His saints the LORD de-lights to save; their death is pre-cious in his sight. He has re-deemed me from the grave, and in his ser-vice I de-light.

4 With thankful heart I offer now
my gift and call upon God's name.
Before his saints I pay my vow
and here my gratitude proclaim.

5 Within his house, the house of prayer,
I dedicate myself to God.
Let all his saints his grace declare
and join to sound his praise abroad.

For an alternate arrangement see 467, 850

Words: *Psalter,* 1912, P.D.

Music (ROCKINGHAM 8.8.8.8): *Second Supplement to Psalmody in Miniature,* ca. 1780; adapt. Edward Miller (1731-1807), 1790, P.D.

872 **Have We Any Gift Worth Giving**

1 Have we an-y gift worth giv-ing to the Giv-er of all
2 Christ by cost-ly in-car-na-tion dwelt in hu-man time and
3 Let us shun the self-ish mer-it world-ly wis-dom has de-

things? What would please the ev-er-liv-ing, one true
place to re-veal to all cre-a-tion God's re-
fined, but, re-newed by God's own Spir-it, be trans-

God from whom life springs? Not dead gold or mer-chan-dise,
deem-ing love and grace; so are we in flesh and bone
formed in heart and mind; by past mer-cies taught and led,

but a liv-ing sac-ri-fice: wor-ship both pro-found and
giv-en means of mak-ing known through the web of dai-ly
let us seek the path a-head, trust-ing that, like those be-

Words: based on Romans 12:1, Carl P. Daw Jr (b. 1944) © 1995 Hope Publishing Company
Music (COSTLY GIFTS 8.7.8.7.7.7.8.8): Alfred V. Fedak (b. 1953), 1995, © 1995 Selah Publishing Company, Inc.

free - ing, serv - ing God with all our be - ing.
liv - ing God's own pat - tern of self - giv - ing.
fore us, God will guide us and re - store us.

Praise and Thanksgiving 873

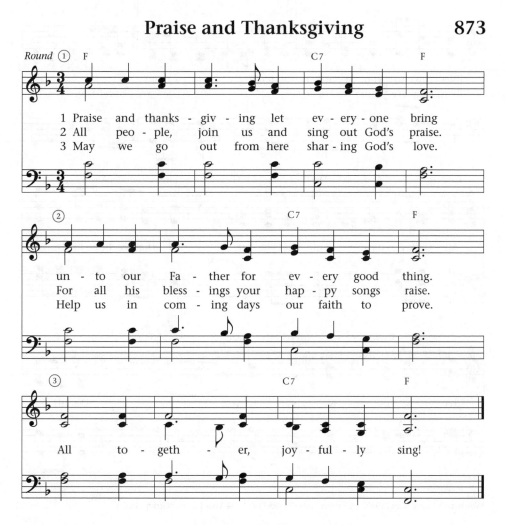

Round ① F

1 Praise and thanks - giv - ing let ev - ery - one bring
2 All peo - ple, join us and sing out God's praise.
3 May we go out from here shar - ing God's love.

②

un - to our Fa - ther for ev - ery good thing.
For all his bless - ings your hap - py songs raise.
Help us in com - ing days our faith to prove.

③

All to - geth - er, joy - ful - ly sing!

Words: st. 1, Alsatian; tr. Edith Lowell Thomas, 1950; st. 2-3, Marie Post, 1974, © 1987 Faith Alive Christian
Resources
Music (LOBET UND PRESIET 10.10.8): Alsatian round; harm. Dale Grotenhuis (1931-2012), 1985, © 1987
Faith Alive Christian Resources

874

We Are an Offering

Words and Music (OFFERING): Dwight Liles (b. 1957) © 1984 Word Music Group, LLC

voic - es, we lift our hands, we lift our lives up to you; we are an of - fer-ing, we are an of - fer-ing.

A Prayer: Almighty God, Father of all Mercies 875

Almighty God, Father of all mercies,
we, your unworthy servants, give you humble thanks
for all your goodness and loving-kindness
to us and to all whom you have made.

We bless you for our creation, preservation,
and all the blessings of this life,
but above all for your immeasurable love
in the redemption of the world by our Lord Jesus Christ,
for the means of grace, and for the hope of glory.

And, we pray, give us such an awareness of your mercies
that with truly thankful hearts we may show forth your praise,
not only with our lips, but in our lives,
by giving up our selves to your service,
and by walking before you
in holiness and righteousness all our days,
through Jesus Christ, our Lord,
to whom, with you and the Holy Spirit,
be honor and glory throughout all ages. Amen.

Text: *The Book of Common Prayer,* P.D.

876 God, Whose Giving Knows No Ending

1 God, whose giv-ing knows no end-ing, from your rich and
2 Skills and time are ours for press-ing toward the goals of
3 Trea-sure, too, you have en-trust-ed, gain through powers your

end-less store: na-ture's won-der, Je-sus' wis-dom, cost-ly
Christ, your Son: all at peace in health and free-dom, rac-es
grace con-ferred; ours to use for home and kin-dred, and to

cross, grave's shat-tered door; gift-ed by you, we turn
joined, the church made one. Now di-rect our dai-ly
spread the gos-pel word. O-pen wide our hands in

to you, of-fering up our-selves in praise; thank-ful
la-bor, lest we strive for self a-lone; born with
shar-ing, as we heed Christ's age-less call, heal-ing,

For an alternate arrangement see 802, 898

Words: Robert L. Edwards, 1961, © 1961, ren. 1989 The Hymn Society, admin. Hope Publishing Company
Music (BEACH SPRING 8.7.8.7 D): *The Sacred Harp*, 1844; alt. acc. © 2006 Augsburg Fortress

songs shall rise for - ev - er, gra - cious do - nor of our days.
tal - ents, make us ser - vants fit to an - swer at your throne.
teach - ing, and re - claim - ing, serv - ing you by lov - ing all.

We Give Thee but Thine Own 877

1 We give thee but thine own, what - e'er the gift may be;
2 May we thy boun - ties thus as stew - ards true re - ceive,
3 To com - fort and to bless, to find a balm for woe,

all that we have is thine a - lone, a trust, O Lord from thee.
and glad - ly, as thou bless - est us, to thee our first - fruits give.
to tend the lone - ly in dis - tress, is an - gels' work be - low.

4 The captive to release,
to God the lost to bring,
to teach the way of life and peace—
it is a Christlike thing.

5 And we believe thy Word,
though dim our faith may be;
whate'er for thine we do, O Lord,
we do it unto thee.

Words: William W. How, 1858, alt., P.D.
Music (SCHUMANN 6.6.8.6): Mason and Webb, *Cantica Laudis*, 1850, P.D.

878 God, We Honor You

Words and Music (ABUNDANT BLESSINGS irregular): James E. Clemens © 2008 James E. Clemens

Lord of All Good

1 Lord of all good, our gifts we bring to you; use them your
2 We give our minds to un - der-stand your ways; hands, voic - es,
3 Fa - ther, whose boun - ty all cre - a - tion shows; Christ, by whose

ho - ly pur - pose to ful - fill; to - kens of love and
eyes to serve your great de - sign; hearts with the flame of
will - ing sa - cri - fice we live; Spir - it, from whom all

pledg - es brought a - new, that our whole life is of - fered
your own love a - blaze: thus for your glo - ry all our
life in full - ness flows: to you with grate - ful hearts our -

Refrain

to your will.
powers com - bine. Lord of all good, our gifts we bring to you.
selves we give.

Chord symbols represent a simplified harmony.

Words: Albert F. Bayly (1901-1984), alt., © 1988 Oxford University Press, reproduced by permission
Music (GENEVAN 124/OLD 124TH 10.10.10.10.10): *Genevan Psalter*, 1551, P.D.

880 Take Our Silver and Our Gold

Optional Intro and Interlude

1 Giv - ing to you grate - ful - ly; learn-ing how to care for those you care for. Spend-ing for you lav - ish-ly; learn - ing how to love the ones you love. Set - ting ta-bles joy - ful-ly; learn-ing how to share with those who

2 Hold-ing noth-ing self - ish-ly; bask-ing in the joy of your pro - vi - sion. Liv - ing life ex - pan - sive-ly; trust - ing you to show us what is right. O - pen up our eyes to see. Help us to a - ban - don our re -

881 Use These Gifts

1 Use these gifts to
2 Use these gifts to

lift the low - ly. Use these gifts to raise the hum - ble.
show the na - tions what it means to find sal - va - tion.

Use these gifts to feed the hun - gry. Guide us on your
Use these gifts and those who give them. Make us yours, O

way.

God, we pray.

Words and Music (USE THESE GIFTS irregular): Ken Medema © 2007 Ken Medema Music/Brier Patch Music

Grant Now Your Blessing 882

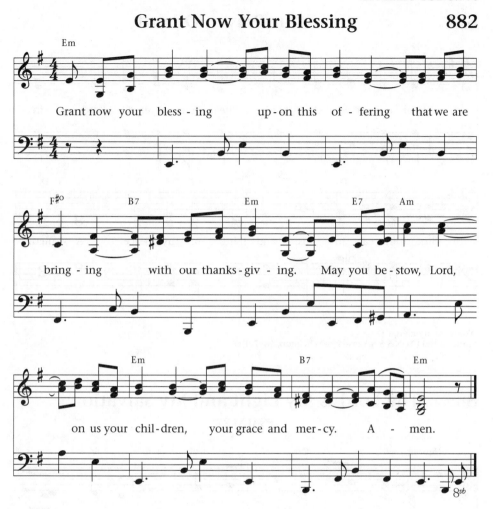

Words: Rolando S. Tinio
Music (HALAD 10.10.10.7): Elena G. Maquiso © 1962 Silliman University Music Foundation, Inc.; arr. Greg
  Scheer © 2007 Greg Scheer

A Prayer for the Offering 883

Blessed are you, O Lord our God, maker of all things.
Through your goodness you have blessed us with these gifts.
With them we offer ourselves to your service and dedicate our lives
to the care and redemption of all that you have made,
for the sake of him who gave himself for us—
Jesus Christ, our Lord. **Amen.**

Text: from *The Lutheran Book of Worship* © 1978 *Lutheran Book of Worship,* admin. Augsburg Fortress

884 Hear Our Prayer, O Lord

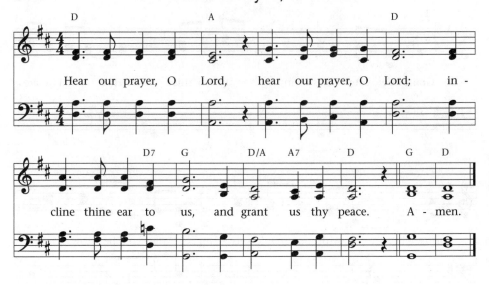

Hear our prayer, O Lord, hear our prayer, O Lord; in-cline thine ear to us, and grant us thy peace. A - men.

Words: anonymous, P.D.
Music (WHELPTON 5.5.6.5): George Whelpton, 1897, P.D.

885 The Lord Is My Light and My Salvation
PSALM 27

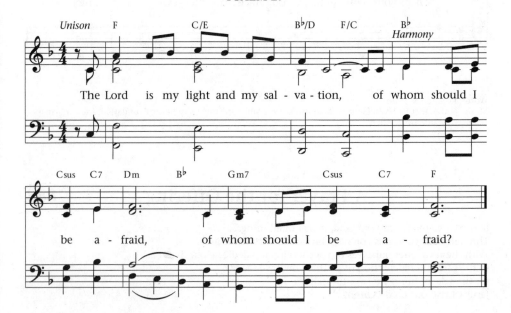

The Lord is my light and my sal - va - tion, of whom should I be a - fraid, of whom should I be a - fraid?

For other settings of Ps. 27 see 431, 773, 774

Words: Psalm 27:1 © 1983 GIA Publications, Inc.
Music (MY LIGHT AND MY SALVATION 9.7.7): David Haas (b. 1957) © 1983 GIA Publications, Inc.

Prayers of the People 1   886

Refrain see 884 or 885

O God, who is light in the darkness,
we pray for those among us
who in the night hours work their shifts,
 or those who labor in places
where light is dim.
Be for them and for us
protection in the dark.

O God, who is the bright Morning Star,
we pray for those among us
who grieve the loss of loved ones,
the tarnishing of innocence,
the failing of health,
the flight of security.
Be for them and for us a sure defense
and the promise of a new day.

Refrain

O God, who is sight to the blind,
we pray for those among us
whose eyes are clouded,
who are blind in soul, mind, or body.
Be for them and for us
both courage and sight.

O God, who is strength to the besieged,
we pray for those among us
who are beset by temptation,
those who are in danger,
those whose enemies are close
and whose help seems far away.
Be for them and for us a
present fortress against our foes.

Refrain

O God, who is salvation to the lost,
we pray for those among us
who have never found your way,
or who, having found it,
have strayed from your path.
Be for them and for us the beacon that
guides safely home.

Refrain

O God, who is comfort to the fearful,
we pray for those among us
who live in fear of threats real or imagined,
whose lives are torn by war,
whose thoughts are confused
by mental illness,
whose souls and bodies are ravaged by abuse.
Be for them and for us consolation and
surety against anxiety.

Refrain

Give us wisdom, O God, to turn to you
in times of stress, fear, and grief;
in times of blindness,
temptation, danger, and perdition.
Grant us patience to wait for you,
and courage to be strong in your might,
through Jesus Christ, our Lord. Amen.

Prayer: Kathleen Hart Brumm (b. 1958) © 2001 Brummhart Publishing

Let Us Pray to the Lord   887

Words and Music (LET US PRAY): Byzantine chant, P.D.

888   Lord, Listen to My Righteous Plea

PSALM 17

1 LORD, lis - ten to my right - eous plea; you will not find de -
2 LORD, as the ap - ple of your eye may I be kept in
3 For your own peo - ple you pro - vide; with gifts their chil - dren

ceit in me as my prayers rise. Ex - am - ine me and
safe - ty by your might - y hand. Be - neath the shad - ow
you sup - ply from your great store. At dawn I will be

probe my heart to see that I have kept a - part from ways of sin.
of your wings pro - tect me from all e - vil things sur - round - ing me.
sat - is - fied, when I in right-eous-ness a - bide be - fore your face.

Optional spoken introduction for 888 or 889 (from Ps. 70; 17)

Hasten, O God, to save me;
come quickly, LORD, to help me.
Keep me as the apple of your eye;
hide me in the shadow of your wings.
I call on you, my God, for you will answer me;
turn your ear to me and hear my prayer.

To use with all of Psalm 17: Sing st. 1; read Ps. 17:1-7; sing st. 2; read Ps. 17:8-15; sing st. 3.

Words: Helen Otte © 1987 Faith Alive Christian Resources
Music (ROSALIE MCMILLAN 8.8.4. D): James Ward, 1984, © 1987 Music A.D.

Lord, My Petition Heed

889

PSALM 86

1 LORD, my petition heed, now help me in my need,
or else I die. I am your servant, LORD; my trust is
in your word. Mercy to me accord; to you I cry.

2 Comfort your servant now, while at your throne I bow
and call to you. Your pardoning grace is free; sinners who
raise their plea your love and mercy see; they are made new.

3 LORD, hear me when I pray; in every troubled day
>I seek your face. O Lord, you far outshine the gods of
>our design; most bright your glories shine, O God of grace.

4 By nations you have made, your praise will be displayed
through earth abroad. Your name be glorified, your greatness
magnified; matchless your works abide, for you are God!

5 Lead me to do your will, in me your truth instill,
teach me your word. I will give thanks to you, your praise I
will pursue; all glory be to you, O Lord my God!

6 Great is your love to me;
from death you set me free
when foes alarm.
Your grace I surely know,
your anger, Lord, is slow;
your loving-kindness show,
save me from harm.

7 Show me your mercy true,
your servant's strength renew,
salvation send.
A sign of favor show,
your comfort, LORD, bestow;
let those who hate me know
you are my friend.

Chord symbols represent a simplifed harmony.

Words: *Psalter,* 1912; rev. Bert Polman, 1983, © 1987 Faith Alive Christian Resources
Music (MASON 6.6.4.6.6.6.4): William F. Sherwin (1826-1888); harm. Dale Grotenhuis (1931-2012), 1985,
© 1987 Faith Alive Christian Resources

890   O God, Defender of the Poor

PSALM 4

1 O God, de - fend - er of the poor, have
2 How long will peo - ple choose vain things, love
3 The saints, O LORD, you set a - part by
4 While man - y pray that you will bless and

mer - cy when I pray: you lis - tened to my prayer be -
emp - ty words and wrong? They scorn to serve the King of
grace to be your own: let sin - ners trem - ble, search their
bring them all they need, un - less they long for hol - i -

fore— LORD, hear my prayer to - day.
kings— O liv - ing God, how long?
hearts, and bow be - fore your throne.
ness, their prayers are vain in - deed.

5 Your light, O LORD, let us receive;
your face within us shine,
for richer is the joy you give
than all their grain and wine.

6 And even when I turn to sleep
your blessings still increase,
for you alone, O LORD, will keep
your child in perfect peace.

Words: Christopher Idle © 1986 The Jubilate Group, admin. Hope Publishing Company
Music (DUNFERMLINE 8.6.8.6): *Scottish Psalter*, 1615, P.D.

Gbemi, Jesu/Lift Me, Jesus 891

Optional stanzas
Yoruba Gbami, gbami, Jesu. Amen.
English Save me, save me, Jesus. Amen.

Words and Music (GBEMI, JESU): Yoruba, author and composer unknown

Be Still and Know 892

PSALM 46:10

For another setting of Ps. 46 see 432

Music (BE STILL AND KNOW BELL 8.8): John L. Bell (b. 1949) © 1989 and 1998 Wild Goose Resource Group, Iona Community, Scotland, GIA Publications, Inc., exclusive North American agent

893 Hear My Cry, O God, and Save Me

PSALM 77

1 Hear my cry, O God, and save me! Trou-bles and dis-
tress en-slave me. Day and night I seek your face,
yearn-ing for your light and grace. But these eyes—they can-not
see you; out-stretched arms—they can-not feel you.

2 You, O God, once walked be-side me. In the night your
songs re-vived me. Were your prom-is-es in vain?
Will you smile on me a-gain? Long a-go you brought re-
demp-tion; your right hand won our sal-va-tion.

3 All cre-a-tion bows be-fore you; saints in earth and
heaven a-dore you. Thun-der roars and tor-rents fall
at your word, O God of all! In our grief you stand be-
side us; there to lift us and to guide us;

Words: Michael Morgan © 2011 Michael Morgan, admin. Faith Alive Christian Resources
Music (GENEVAN 77 | 8.8.7.7 D): *Genevan Psalter,* 1551; arr. Alfred Fedak (b. 1953) © 2011 Faith Alive
  Christian Resources

My heart breaks in deep de-spair; my soul longs to hold you here.
I re-mem-ber deeds of old— now, re-mem-ber me, O Lord!
un-seen Sav-ior of our days, heir to end-less songs of praise!

May the Lord God Hear You Pray 894

PSALM 20

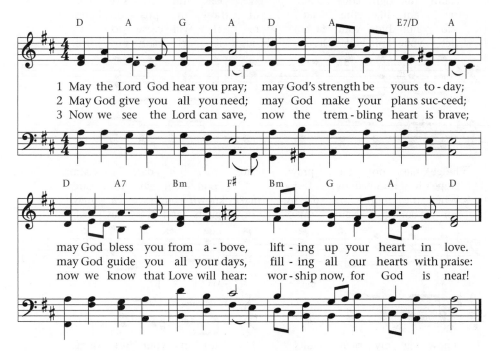

1 May the Lord God hear you pray; may God's strength be yours to-day;
2 May God give you all you need; may God make your plans suc-ceed;
3 Now we see the Lord can save, now the trem-bling heart is brave;

may God bless you from a-bove, lift-ing up your heart in love.
may God guide you all your days, fill-ing all our hearts with praise:
now we know that Love will hear: wor-ship now, for God is near!

For this music in a lower key see 376

Words: Michael Perry © 1990 The Jubilate Group, admin. Hope Publishing Company
Music (TEBBEN 7.7.7.7): Timothy Hoekman, 1979, © 1985 Faith Alive Christian Resources

895 Hear My Prayer, O God

PSALM 143

1 Hear my prayer, O God, and lis-ten to my plea;
2 Hound-ed by a foe who crushed me to the ground,
3 An-swer soon, O God; my spir-it faints in me;
4 Keep me safe, O God, and help me learn your will;

faith-ful, right-eous One, give ear and an-swer me.
I am like the dead or those in pris-on bound.
do not hide your face, or I will cease to be.
let your Spir-it lead through lev-el path-ways still.

Judge me not, I pray; no mer-it dare I claim;
Hope-less, numbed by fear, I pon-der all your care;
When the morn-ing dawns, make known your love a-new;
For your great Name's sake, my griefs and fears dis-pel;

know-ing my own faults, I trust in your just Name.
thirst-y as parched earth, I lift my hands in prayer.
show me how to walk, for I will trust in you.
free me from my foes, that I may serve you well.

Words: Carl P. Daw Jr (b. 1944) © 2005 Hope Publishing Company
Music (HYMN CHANT 5.6.5.6 D): Hal H. Hopson © 2006 Hope Publishing Company

Lord, Listen to Your Children Praying 896

Lord, lis-ten to your chil-dren pray - ing,

Lord, send your Spir-it in this place;

Lord, lis-ten to your chil-dren pray - ing,

send us love, send us power, send us grace!

Words and Music (CHILDREN PRAYING 9.8.9.9): Ken Medema © 1973 Hope Publishing Company

897   What a Friend We Have in Jesus

1 What a friend we have in Je - sus, all our sins and griefs to bear!
2 Have we tri - als and temp - ta - tions? Is there trou-ble an - y-where?
3 Are we weak and heav - y la - den, cum-bered with a load of care?

What a priv - i - lege to car - ry ev - ery-thing to God in prayer!
We should nev - er be dis - cour - aged— take it to the Lord in prayer.
Pre - cious Sav - ior, still our ref - uge— take it to the Lord in prayer.

Oh, what peace we of - ten for - feit; oh, what need-less pain we bear—
Can we find a friend so faith - ful who will all our sor-rows share?
Do your friends de - spise, for-sake you? Take it to the Lord in prayer.

all be - cause we do not car - ry ev - ery-thing to God in prayer.
Je - sus knows our ev - ery weak-ness—take it to the Lord in prayer.
In his arms he'll take and shield you; you will find a sol-ace there.

Alternate tune: BEACH SPRING see 898

Words: Joseph Scriven (1820-1866), P.D.
Music (CONVERSE/ERIE 8.7.8.7 D): Charles D. Converse, 1866, P.D.

What a Friend We Have in Jesus   898

1 What a friend we have in Je - sus, all our sins and griefs to bear!
2 Have we tri - als and temp - ta - tions? Is there trou - ble an - y - where?
3 Are we weak and heav - y la - den, cum - bered with a load of care?

What a priv - i - lege to car - ry ev - ery - thing to God in prayer!
We should nev - er be dis - cour - aged—take it to the Lord in prayer.
Pre - cious Sav - ior, still our ref - uge— take it to the Lord in prayer.

Oh, what peace we of - ten for - feit; oh, what need - less pain we bear—
Can we find a friend so faith - ful who will all our sor - rows share?
Do your friends de - spise, for - sake you? Take it to the Lord in prayer.

all be - cause we do not car - ry ev - ery - thing to God in prayer.
Je - sus knows our ev - ery weak - ness—take it to the Lord in prayer.
In his arms he'll take and shield you; you will find a sol - ace there.

Alternate tune: CONVERSE *see 897*

For an alternate arrangement see 802, 876

Words: Joseph M. Scriven, (1820-1866), P.D.
Music (BEACH SPRING 8.7.8.7 D): *The Sacred Harp*, 1844; harm. James H. Wood, 1958, © 1958, ren. 1986
  Broadman Press, admin. Music Services

899 **Seek Ye First**

1 Seek ye first the king-dom of God and his
2 Ask and it shall be giv-en un-to you; seek and
3 We do not live by bread a - lone, but by

right - eous - ness, and all these things shall be
you shall find; knock and the door shall be
ev - ery word that pro - ceeds from the

add - ed un - to you. Al - le - lu, al-le-lu - ia.
o - pened un - to you. Al - le - lu, al-le-lu - ia.
mouth of God. Al - le - lu, al-le-lu - ia.

Words: Matthew 6:33, 7:7, 4:4; para. Karen Lafferty, 1972, © 1972 Maranatha! Music, admin. Music Services
Music (LAFFERTY irregular): Karen Lafferty, 1972, © 1972 Maranatha! Music, admin. Music Services

O Holy Spirit, by Whose Breath

900

1 O Holy Spirit, by whose breath life rises
2 You are the seeker's only course, of burning
3 In you God's energy is shown, to us your
4 Flood our dull senses with your light; in mutual

vibrant out of death, come to create, renew,
love the living source, protector in the midst
varied gifts made known. Teach us to speak, teach us
love our hearts unite. Your power the whole creation

new, inspire; come, kindle in our hearts your fire.
midst of strife, the giver and the Lord of life.
us to hear; yours be the tongue and yours the ear.
ation fills; make strong our weak, uncertain wills.

5 From inner strife grant us release;
turn nations to the ways of peace.
To fuller life your people bring
that as one body we may sing:

6 Praise to the Father, Christ, his Word,
and to the Spirit: God the Lord,
to whom all honor, glory be
both now and for eternity.

For an alternate arrangement see 70, 374

Words: Latin hymn, *Veni Creator Spiritus,* 9th c.; tr. John W. Grant, 1968, alt. © 1968 John W. Grant
Music (PUER NOBIS 8.8.8.8): *Trier manuscript,* 15th c.; adapt. Michael Praetorius, 1609; harm. George Ratcliffe
Woodward, 1910; arr. Alfred V. Fedak © 2012 Alfred V. Fedak, admin. Faith Alive Christian Resources

901   Lord, I Pray

1 Lord, I pray, if to-day some should wrong or trou-ble me,
2 Should there be joy for me, help me thank you as I should.
3 If this day I should stray, show my heart the road to take.

make me kind; bring to mind, your for-give-ness makes me free.
Let me through all I do praise you, Lord, for all things good.
Should I fear, please be near, hear my prayer for Je-sus' sake. A-men.

Words: Jean C. Keegstra-De Boer, 1949, alt., P.D.
Music (KLOKJE KLINKT 3.3.7.3.3.7): Dutch melody, harm. AnnaMae Meyer Bush, 1985, © 1987 Faith Alive
  Christian Resources

902   Gathering Our Prayers

The following prompting questions can help expand the range of prayer topics suggested by members of the congregation. Leaders may choose to use a representative sample of these or similar questions each time requests are gathered.

PRAISE AND THANKSGIVING
- For which divine actions or attributes shall we bless God?
- For which blessings shall we thank God?
- For which aspects of biblical teaching shall we thank God?

PETITIONS
- For which country or region of the world shall we pray?
- For which ministry shall we pray?
- For which other congregations shall we pray?
- For which aspects of congregational life shall we pray?
- For which concerns in our town or city shall we pray?
- For which personal concerns shall we pray?
- For which voiceless and powerless persons shall we pray?
- For which spiritual gifts shall we pray?

O Lord, Hear My Prayer

903

1 O Lord, hear my prayer, O Lord, hear my prayer;
2 The Lord is my song, the Lord is my praise.

when I call an-swer me. O Lord, hear my prayer, O
All my hope comes from God. The Lord is my song, the

Lord, hear my prayer; come and lis-ten to me.
Lord is my praise. God, the well-spring of life.

Words: Psalm 102:1-2; adapt. The Community of Taizé © 1991 Ateliers et Presses de Taizé, Taizé Community, France, GIA Publications, Inc., exclusive North American agent
Music (HEAR MY PRAYER 5.5.6 D): Jacques Berthier (1923-1994) © 1991 Ateliers et Presses de Taizé, Taizé Community, France, GIA Publications, Inc., exclusive North American agent

904   Lord, Make Us Servants

4 May we not look for love's return
but seek to love unselfishly,
for in our giving we receive,
and in forgiving are forgiven.

5 Dying, we live, and are reborn
through death's dark night to endless day;
Lord, make us servants of your peace
to wake at last in heaven's light.

Words: James Quinn S.J. (b. 1919), based on a prayer attr. to Francis of Assisi (1182-1226) © James Quinn, S.J.,
admin. Selah Publishing Company, Inc.
Music (O WALY WALY 8.8.8.8): English folk melody; arr. and desc. Emily R. Brink (b. 1940) © 2001 Faith Alive
Christian Resources

오 소 서/Come Now, O Prince of Peace   905

Korean 1 오 소 서 오 소 서 평 화 의 임 금
English 1 Come now, O Prince of peace, make us one bod - y.
2 Come now, O God of love, make us one bod - y.
3 Come now and set us free, O God our Sav - ior.
4 Come, Hope of u - ni - ty, make us one bod - y.

우 리 가 한 몸 이 루 게 하 소 서
Come, O Lord Je - sus; re - con - cile all peo - ple.

Korean

2 오소서 오소서
사랑의 임금
우리가 한 몸
이루게 하소서

3 오소서 오소서
자유의 임금
우리가 한 몸
이루게 하소서

4 오소서 오소서
통일의 임금
우리가 한 몸
이루게 하소서

Optional prayer

God of righteousness and mercy,
grant us your peace.

When violence haunts our streets,
grant us your peace.

When anxieties haunt our minds and hearts,
grant us your peace.

For the people of [___] who face the violence and conflict, we pray:
Grant them your peace.

Turn our hearts toward the Prince of Peace, we pray:
Grant us your peace. Amen.

Words and Music (O-SO-SO 6.5.6.5): Geonyong Lee (b. 1947) © 1988 Geonyong Lee; English para. Marion Pope (b. 1928); Korean characters Eunae Chung © 2012 Geonyong Lee

906 Saranam, Saranam/Jesus, Savior, Lord

PSALM 61

Tamil Ye-su raa-ja-nin thi-ru-ve-di-ku.
English Je-sus, Sav-ior, Lord, now to you I come.

Sa-ra-nam, sa-ra-nam, sa-ra-nam. Aath-me naa-dhe-rin ma-le-
Sa-ra-nam, sa-ra-nam, sa-ra-nam. You're my Rock, my ref-uge, my

re - di-ku. Sa-ra-nam, sa-ra-nam, sa-ra-nam. 1 Paar
heaven-ly home. Sa-ra-nam, sa-ra-nam, sa-ra-nam.

pot - trum thuu -ye thuu-ye dhee-va-nee me-i raa-jaa-vee___
1 From the earth wher-ev-er I may be, out of des-per-a-tion
2 In your heart give me a hid-ing place, and be-neath your wings let
3 Then with joy to you my vows I'll pay, and give thanks for all your
4 Glo-ry to the Fa-ther and the Son, with the Ho-ly Spir-it

For another setting of Ps. 61 see 415

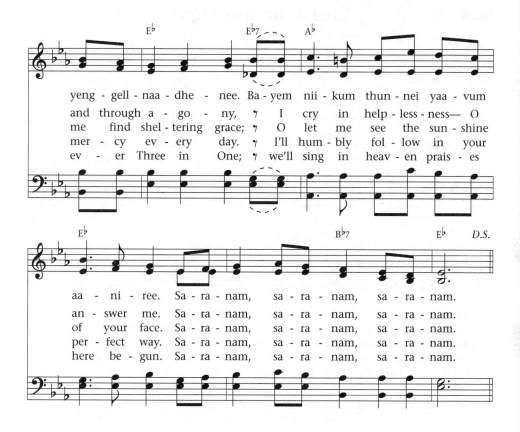

yeng - gell - naa - dhe - nee. Ba - yem nii - kum thun - nei yaa - vum
and through a - go - ny, I cry in help - less - ness— O
me find shel - tering grace; O let me see the sun - shine
mer - cy ev - ery day. I'll hum - bly fol - low in your
ev - er Three in One; we'll sing in heav - en prais - es

aa - ni - ree. Sa - ra - nam, sa - ra - nam, sa - ra - nam.
an - swer me. Sa - ra - nam, sa - ra - nam, sa - ra - nam.
of your face. Sa - ra - nam, sa - ra - nam, sa - ra - nam.
per - fect way. Sa - ra - nam, sa - ra - nam, sa - ra - nam.
here be - gun. Sa - ra - nam, sa - ra - nam, sa - ra - nam.

Be Still and Know 907

PSALM 46:10

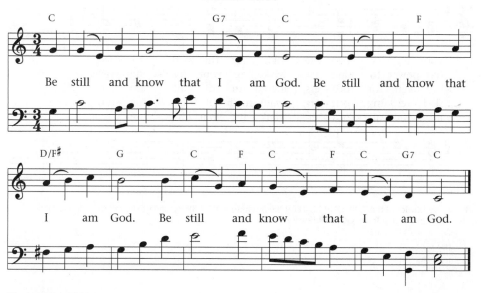

Be still and know that I am God. Be still and know that

I am God. Be still and know that I am God.

Words: Psalm 46:10
Music (BE STILL AND KNOW 8.8.8): anonymous; arr. Norma de Waal Malefyt, 1992, © 1994 Faith Alive
  Christian Resources

908 Christ, Be Our Light

1 Long - ing for light,___ we wait in dark - ness. Long-ing for
2 Long - ing for peace,___ our world is trou - bled. Long-ing for
3 Long - ing for food, ___ ma - ny are hun - gry. Long-ing for
4 Long - ing for shel - ter, ma - ny are home-less. Long-ing for
5 Ma - ny the gifts,___ ma - ny the peo - ple, ma - ny the

truth,_____ we turn to you. Make us your own,_____
hope,_____ man - y de - spair. Your Word a - lone_____
> wa - ter, man - y still thirst. Make us your bread,_____
warmth,_____ ma - ny are cold. Make us your build - ing,
hearts that yearn to be - long. Let us be ser - vants

your ho - ly peo - ple, light for the world to see.
has power to save us. Make us your liv - ing voice.
> bro - ken for oth - ers, shared un - til all are fed.
shel - ter - ing oth - ers, walls made of liv - ing stone.
to one an - oth - er, mak - ing your king - dom come.

Words and Music (CHRIST, BE OUR LIGHT 9.8.9.6 refrain 4.4.5.4.8): Bernadette Farrell (b. 1957) © 1993
Bernadette Farrell, admin. OCP Publications

Optional prayer litany

Let us pray in spoken and sung word.

Light of the World . . . *Sing stanzas 1-2*
We pray for all peacemakers . . . *Sing stanza 3*
We pray for all who provide food and water . . . *Sing stanza 4*
We pray for all who provide shelter . . . *Sing stanza 5*

Lord Jesus Christ, sun of righteousness,
in a world that so often seems cold and heartless,
your grace breaks in with warmth and light.

How grateful we are for the privilege of your call
to us to reflect this warmth and light as mirrors of your grace.
May we reflect this light so that many will see it
and bring praise to you, the true light of the world. Amen.

909 Mayenziwe/Your Will Be Done

Words: from the Lord's Prayer, Matthew 6:10
Music (MAYENZIWE 8.8.8.8.8.8): South African traditional, as taught by George Mxadana; arr. John L. Bell
(b. 1949) © 1990 Wild Goose Resource Group, Iona Community, Scotland, GIA Publications, Inc., exclusive
North American agent

Prayers of the People 2

Gracious God,
we pray for the faithful all over the world,
that all who love you may be united in your service.
We pray for the church . . .
Let us pray to the Lord.
Lord, hear our prayer.

We pray for the peoples and leaders of the nations,
that they may be reconciled one to another
in pursuit of your justice and peace.
We pray for the world . . .
Let us pray to the Lord.
Lord, hear our prayer.

We pray for all who suffer from prejudice, greed, or violence,
that the heart of humanity may warm with your tenderness.
We pray especially for all prisoners of politics or religion
and for all refugees.
We pray for all who are oppressed . . .
Let us pray to the Lord.
Lord, hear our prayer.

We pray for all in need
because of famine, flood, or earthquake,
that they may know the hope of your faithfulness
through the help of others.
We pray especially for the people of . . .
Let us pray to the Lord.
Lord, hear our prayer.

We pray for the land, the sea, the sky—
for your whole creation, which longs for its redemption.
We pray that we may live with respect for your creation
and use your gifts with reverence.
We pray for the creation . . .
Let us pray to the Lord.
Lord, hear our prayer.

We pray for all who suffer the pain of sickness,
loneliness, fear, or loss,
that those whose names are in our hearts,
in the hearts of others,
or known to you alone,
may receive strength and courage.
We pray for those in need . . .
Let us pray to the Lord.
Lord, hear our prayer.

God of compassion,
into your hands we commend all for whom we pray,
trusting in your mercy now and forever. **Amen.**

Following each "hear our prayer" *the congregation may sing 909, or "Let us pray to the Lord, hear our prayer" could be sung to 887.*

Text: from *Worship for All Seasons,* volume 1, Selections from *Gathering for Advent, Christmas, Epiphany,* United Church Publishing House, 1993

911 Abana alathi fi ssama/Abana in Heaven

MATTHEW 6:9-13

Words and Music (ABANA): Laila Constantine, Lebanon © 2002 *Songs of the Evangelical Presbyterian Church of Egypt*, Council of Pastoral Work and Evangelism, admin. Faith Alive Christian Resources; tr. and adapt. Anne Emile Zaki, Emily R. Brink (b. 1940), Greg Scheer and Maged Dakouk © 2008, 2012 Faith Alive Christian Resources; arr. Greg Scheer © 2008 Greg Scheer

Arabic

أبانــا الــذي في الســماء ليتقــدس اسمك
ليــأت ملكوتــك لتكــن مشــيئتك
كمــا في الســماء كـذلك على الأرض
وخبزنــا كفافنــا أعطنــا في أيامنــا
وأغفــر لنــا ذنوبنــا كما نحن لغيرنــا
لا تــدخلنا في تجربــة بل نجنا من الشــرير
لأن لك الملــك والقــوة والمجــد
من الأزل إلــى الأبــد ... آميــن

912 The Lord's Prayer

MATTHEW 6:9-13

Words: Matthew 6:9-13, traditional
Music (MALOTTE): Albert Hay Malotte, 1935, © 1976 (renewed) by G. Schirmer, Inc.

Prayers of the People 3

913

MATTHEW 6:9-13

Our Father in heaven, hallowed be your name. . . .
[prayers of adoration and thanksgiving]

Your kingdom come. Your will be done, on earth as it is in heaven. . . .
[prayers of longing for God's shalom]

Give us this day our daily bread. . . .
[prayers for the needs of the community]

Forgive us our debts, as we also have forgiven our debtors. . . .
[prayers for interpersonal reconciliation]

And do not bring us to the time of trial, but rescue us from the evil one. . . .
[prayers for the world and for personal struggles with temptation and evil]

For the kingdom and the power and the glory are yours forever. **Amen.**

Text: based on Matthew 6:9-13, NRSV

914

Our Father in Heaven

MATTHEW 6:9-13

Our Fa-ther in heav-en, hal-lowed be your name. Your king-dom come, your will be done on earth as in heaven. Give us to-day our dai-ly bread, and for-give us our sins as we for-give those who sin a - gainst us. Save us from the time of trial and de-liv-er us from e - vil, for the

Words: Matthew 6:9-13
Music (ASAS): Swee Hong Lim © 2010 Swee Hong Lim, admin. Faith Alive Christian Resources

king-dom, the power, and the glo-ry are yours now and for-

ev-er. A-men. For-ev-er. A-men.

Amen 915

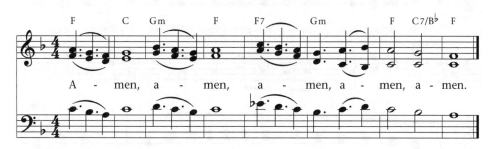

A-men, a-men, a-men, a-men, a-men.

Words: traditional
Music (AMEN THEMBA): South African traditional; transcr. John L. Bell (b. 1949) of the Sunrise Hospice, Themba © 2008 Wild Goose Resource Group, Iona Community, Scotland, GIA Publications, Inc., exclusive North American agent

Amen, Father 916

Amen, Father, on your planning.
Amen, for you'll see us through.
Amen, when the cross lies heavy,
Amen everything you do.

Text: Stanley Wiersma, used with permission

917 Our Father in Heaven

MATTHEW 6:9-13

Words: Matthew 6:9-13
Music (OUR FATHER RIMSKY-KORSAKOV): Nicholas Rimsky-Korsakov (1844-1908); arr. George Black
(b. 1931) © George Black

Litany: The Lord's Prayer 918

Our Father in heaven,
hallowed be your name.
Help us to really know you,
to bless, worship, and praise you
for all your works
and for all that shines
forth from them:
your almighty power, wisdom, kindness,
justice, mercy, and truth.
Help us to direct all our living—
what we think, say, and do—
so that your name will never
be blasphemed because of us
but always honored and praised.

Quiet

Your kingdom come.
Rule us by your Word
and Spirit in such a way
that more and more we submit to you.
Keep your church strong, and add to it.
Destroy the devil's work;
destroy every force that
revolts against you
and every conspiracy
against your Word.
Do this until your kingdom
is so complete and perfect
that in it you are all in all.

Quiet

Your will be done on earth as in heaven.
Help us and all people
to reject our own wills
and to obey your will
without any back talk.
Your will alone is good.
Help us one and all to carry out the
work we are called to,
as willingly and faithfully
as the angels in heaven.

Quiet

Give us today our daily bread.
Do take care of all our physical needs
so that we come to know
that you are the only source
of everything good,
and that neither our work and worry
nor your gifts
can do us any good
without your blessing.

And so help us to give up
our trust in creatures
and to put trust in you alone.

Quiet

Forgive us our debts,
as we also have forgiven our debtors.
Because of Christ's blood,
do not hold against us,
poor sinners that we are,
any of the sins we do
or the evil that constantly clings to us.
Forgive us, just as we are
fully determined,
as evidence of your grace in us,
to forgive our neighbors.

Quiet

And lead us not into temptation,
but deliver us from the evil one.
By ourselves we are too weak
to hold our own even for a moment.
And our sworn enemies—
the devil, the world,
and our own flesh—
never stop attacking us.
And so, Lord,
uphold us and make us strong
with the strength of your Holy Spirit,
so that we may not go down to defeat
in this spiritual struggle,
but may firmly resist our enemies
until we finally win the complete
victory.

Quiet

For yours is the kingdom and the power
and the glory forever.
We have made all these requests of you
because, as our all-powerful King,
you not only want to,
but are able to give us all that is good;
and because your holy name,
and not we ourselves,
should receive all the praise, forever.
It is even more sure
that you listen to our prayer,
than that we really desire
what we pray for. Amen.

Text: based on Heidelberg Catechism Q&A's 119, 122-129

919 Our Father, Lord of Heaven and Earth

MATTHEW 6:9-13

1 Our Father, Lord of heaven and earth, let praise and hon-or
2 For-give us, Lord, our sins and debts as we to debt-ors

clothe your name. Your king-dom come, your will be done;
show your grace. Re-move us from all tempt-ing paths,

through-out the world com-plete your reign. Teach us, O Lord,
and guard us from the dev-il's ways; for glo-ry, strength,

to trust in you for bread and breath each day a-new.
and heav-en's throne be-long to you, and you a-lone. A-men.

For an alternate arrangement see 573

Words: Matthew 6:9-13; vers. Henry J. de Jong, 1982, © 1987 Faith Alive Christian Resources
Music (VATER UNSER 8.8.8.8.8.8): V. Schumann's *Geistliche Lieder,* 1539; harm. Johann S. Bach, 1723, in the
St. John Passion, P.D.

A Concluding Prayer

920

Gracious God,
accept all these prayers offered in Jesus' name,
and give us now the strength to wait patiently for your answer,
and to live faithfully in response to your call.
Through Christ, our Lord. **Amen.**

Amen, siakudu misa/
Amen, We Praise Your Name, O God

921

Words and Music (MASITHI): S.C. Molefe (1921-1983), South African; tr. David Dargie (b. 1938) © 1991
Lumko Institute

922 All on Earth and All in Heaven

PSALM 29

1 All on earth and all in heav-en raise to God a
2 Trees shall bow in awe and won-der, bend their branch-es

song on high; strength un-mea-sured, love un-bound-ed,
to the ground; from God's lips one word in an-ger

God a-lone we glo-ri-fy. At God's voice the clouds as-
wreaks de-struc-tion all a-round. But the Word which sets in

sem-ble, thun-der roars, and tor-rents fall; earth shall quake be-
mo-tion such tra-vails can make them cease; that same voice which

For another setting of Ps. 29 see 114

Chord symbols represent a simplified harmony. This music in a higher key see 796

Words: Michael Morgan © 2011 Michael Morgan, admin. Faith Alive Christian Resources
Music (EBENEZER 8.7.8.7 D): Thomas J. Williams, (1869-1944), 1890, P.D.

fore God's pres - ence, moun - tains trem - ble at God's call.
tu - mult beck - ons in a gen - tler breath speaks peace.

Peace Before Us 923

Peace* be - fore us, peace be - hind us, peace un - der our

feet. Peace with - in us, peace

o - ver us, let all a - round us be peace.

Additional stanzas: 2 Love, 3 Light, 4 Christ

Words: based on a Navaho prayer; David Haas (b. 1957) © 1987 GIA Publications, Inc.
Music: David Haas (b. 1957) © 1987 GIA Publications, Inc.

924   Come, All You Servants of the Lord

PSALM 134

For an alternate arrangement see 1, 843, 965

Words: Arlo D. Duba, 1984, © 1986 Arlo D. Duba
Music (GENEVAN 134/OLD HUNDREDTH 8.8.8.8): Louis Bourgeois, 1551, P.D.; arr. Eelco Vos © 2011 Eelco
  Vos, admin. Faith Alive Christian Resources

Go to the World

1 Go to the world! Go in - to all the earth. Go preach the cross where Christ re - news life's worth, bap - tiz - ing as the sign of our re - birth. Al - le - lu - ia!

2 Go to the world! Go in - to ev - ery place. Go live the word of God's re - deem - ing grace. Go seek God's pres - ence in each time and space. Al - le - lu - ia!

3 Go to the world! Go strug - gle, bless, and pray; the nights of tears give way to joy - ous day. As ser - vant Church, you fol - low Christ's own way. Al - le - lu - ia!

4 Go to the world! Go as the ones I send, for I am with you till the age shall end, when all the hosts of glo - ry cry "A - men." Al - le - lu - ia!

Accompaniment for final stanza

Words: Sylvia Dunstan (1955-1993) © 1991 GIA Publications, Inc.
Music (ENGELBERG 10.10.10 with alleluia): Charles Villiers Stanford (1852-1924), P.D.

926 God of Grace and God of Glory

1 God of grace and God of glo-ry, on your peo-ple pour your power;
2 Lo! the hosts of e-vil round us scorn the Christ, as-sail his ways!
3 Cure your chil-dren's war-ring mad-ness; bend our pride to your con-trol;
4 Save us from weak res-ig-na-tion to the e-vils we de-plore;

crown your an-cient chur-ch's sto-ry, bring its bud to glo-rious flower.
From the fears that long have bound us free our hearts to faith and praise.
shame our wan-ton, self-ish glad-ness, rich in things and poor in soul.
let the gift of your sal-va-tion be our glo-ry ev-er-more.

Grant us wis-dom, grant us cour-age for the fac-ing of this
Grant us wis-dom, grant us cour-age for the liv-ing of these
Grant us wis-dom, grant us cour-age, lest we miss your king-dom's
Grant us wis-dom, grant us cour-age, serv-ing you whom we a-

hour, for the fac-ing of this hour.
days, for the liv-ing of these days.
goal, lest we miss your king-dom's goal.
dore, serv-ing you whom we a-dore.

For an alternate arrangement see 43

Words: Harry E. Fosdick (1930), alt., P.D.
Music (CWM RHONDDA 8.7.8.7.8.7.7): John Hughes, 1907; harm. Henry V. Gerike (b. 1948) © 1969
  Concordia Publishing House

God, the Father of Your People

927

1 God, the Fa-ther of your peo - ple, you have called us to be one;
2 May the grace of Christ, our Sav - ior, and the Fa-ther's bound-less love,

grant us grace to walk to - geth - er in the joy of Christ, your Son.
with the Ho - ly Spir - it's fav - or, rest up - on us from a - bove.

Chal-lenged by your Word and Spir - it, blest with gifts from heaven a - bove,
May we now re - main in u - nion with each oth - er and the Lord,

as one bod - y we will serve you and bear wit - ness to your love.
and pos - sess, in sweet com - mu - nion, joys that earth can - not af - ford.

For an alternate arrangement see 766

Words: st. 1 Alfred E. Mulder, 1978, © 1987 Faith Alive Christian Resources; st. 2 John Newton, 1779, P.D.
Music (HOLY MANNA 8.7.8.7 D): W. Moore, *Columbian Harmony*, 1825; harm. Norman E. Johnson, 1973,
© 1973 Covenant Publications

928 Lord, Whose Love in Humble Service

1 Lord, whose love in hum-ble ser-vice bore the weight of
2 Still your chil-dren wan-der home-less; still the hun-gry
3 As we wor-ship, grant us vi-sion till your love's re -
4 Called through wor-ship to your ser-vice, forth in your dear

hu-man need, who up - on the cross, for-sak-en,
cry for bread; still the cap-tives long for free-dom;
veal-ing light in its height and depth and great-ness
name we go, to the child, the youth, the a - ged,

worked your mer - cy's per - fect deed, we, your
still in grief we mourn our dead. As you,
dawns up - on our quick-ened sight, mak-ing
love in liv - ing deeds to show. Hope and

ser - vants, bring the wor - ship not of voice a -
Lord, in deep com - pas - sion healed the sick and
known the needs and bur - dens your com - pas - sion
health, good - will and com - fort, coun - sel, aid, and

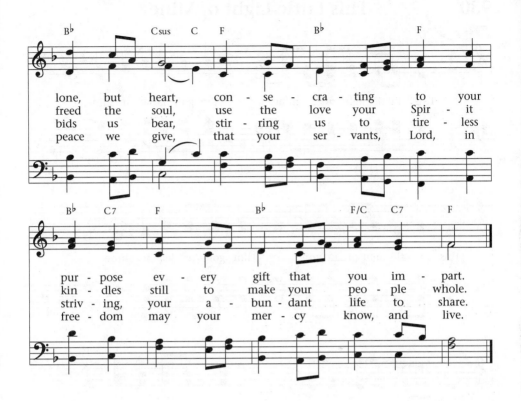

		Bb	Csus	C	F		Bb			F
lone,	but	heart,	con -	se -	cra -	ting		to		your
freed	the	soul,	use	the	love	your		Spir -		it
bids	us	bear,	stir -	ring	us	to		tire -		less
peace	we	give,	that	your	ser -	vants,		Lord,		in

	Bb	C7	F			Bb		F/C	C7	F
pur -	pose	ev -	ery	gift	that	you	im -	part.
kin -	dles	still	to	make	your	peo -	ple	whole.
striv -	ing,	your	a -	bun -	dant	life	to	share.
free -	dom	may	your	mer -	cy	know,	and	live.

See My Hands and Feet 929

1 Touch that soothes and heals the hurting,
hands that break a loaf of bread;
steps that walk beside the weary,
bearing burdens in their stead: *Refrain*

Refrain
See my hands and feet, said Jesus,
love arisen from the grave.
Be my hands and feet, said Jesus,
live as ones I died to save.

2 Feed the hungry, clothe the naked,
visit ones in need of care,
give the homeless warmth and shelter:
Christ will find a welcome there. *Refrain*

3 Love and serve without distinction
all earth's people, first and least.
Know within each act of kindness
hope and wholeness are increased. *Refrain*

4 Hands that beckon little children,
bind a wound, prepare a meal;
feet that rush to share good tidings,
Christ arisen, still reveal. *Refrain*

For music see 928

Words: Mary Louise Bringle (b. 1953) © 2002 GIA Publications, Inc.

930

This Little Light of Mine

2 Everywhere I go, I'm gonna let it shine . . .
3 Jesus gave it to me; I'm gonna let it shine . . .

Words: African American spiritual, P.D.
Music (LIGHT OF MINE 12.12.12.9): African American spiritual; arr. Nolan Williams Jr (b. 1969) © 2000 GIA
  Publications, Inc.

Sizohamba naye/We Will Walk with God   931

Words: Swaziland traditional hymn; tr. © 2002 Wild Goose Resource Group, Iona Community, Scotland,
GIA Publications, Inc., exclusive North American agent
Music (SIZOHAMBA NAYE): Swaziland traditional hymn, P.D.

932 Savior, Again to Your Dear Name We Raise

1 Savior, again to your dear name we raise
2 Grant us your peace upon our home-ward way;
3 Grant us your peace, Lord, through the com-ing night;
4 Grant us your peace through-out our earth-ly life:

with one ac-cord our part-ing hymn of praise.
with you be-gan, with you shall end the day.
turn all our dark-ness to your per-fect light.
com-fort in sor-row, cour-age in the strife.

We give you thanks be-fore our wor-ship cease,
Guard now the lips from sin, the hearts from shame,
Then, while we sleep, our hope and strength re-new,
Then when your voice shall make our con-flict cease,

and now de-part-ing, wait your word of peace.
that in this house have called up-on your name.
for dark and light are both a-like to you.
call us, O Lord, to your e-ter-nal peace.

Words: John Ellerton, 1866, alt., P.D.
Music (ELLERS 10.10.10.10): Edward J. Hopkins, 1869, P.D.

Lord, Dismiss Us with Your Blessing

933

1 Lord, dis-miss us with your bless-ing; fill our hearts with
2 Thanks we give and ad - o - ra - tion for your gos-pel's

joy and peace. Let us each, your love pos - sess - ing,
joy - ful sound. May the fruits of your sal - va - tion

tri - umph in re - deem-ing grace. O di - rect us
in our hearts and lives a - bound. Ev - er faith - ful,

and pro - tect us trav - el-ing through this wil - der - ness.
ev - er faith - ful to your truth may we be found.

Chord symbols represent a simplified harmony.

Words: attr. John Fawcett, 1773, alt., P.D.
Music (SICILIAN MARINERS 8.7.8.7.8.7): Sicilian, 18th c., P.D.

934 God of Mercy, God of Grace

PSALM 67

1 God of mer-cy, God of grace, show the bright-ness of your face.
2 Let the peo-ple praise you, Lord; be by all that live a-dored.
3 Let the peo-ple praise you, Lord; earth shall then its fruits af-ford.

Shine up-on us, Sav-ior, shine; fill your world with light di-vine;
Let the na-tions shout and sing glo-ry to their gra-cious King;
Un-to us your bless-ing give; we to you de-vot-ed live,

all your sav-ing health ex-tend un-to earth's re-mot-est end.
at your feet their trib-ute pay, and your ho-ly will o-bey.
all be-low and all a-bove, one in joy and light and love.

Optional blessing (Num. 6:24-26)

The LORD bless you and keep you;
the LORD make his face to shine upon you
and be gracious to you;
the LORD turn his face toward you
and give you peace.
Alleluia! Amen.

For a descant see 19

Words: Henry F. Lyte, 1834, alt., P.D.
Music (DIX 7.7.7.7.7.7): Conrad Kocher, 1838; adapt. William H. Monk, 1861, P.D.

Now May Your Servant, Lord

935

LUKE 2:29-32

1 Now may your ser - vant, Lord, ac - cord-ing to your word,
2 You did for all pre - pare this gift so great, so rare,

de - part in ex - ul - ta - tion. My peace shall be se - rene,
ful - fill - ing proph-ets's sto - ry— a light to show the way

for now my eyes have seen your won-der-ful sal - va - tion.
to Gen - tiles gone a - stray, and un - to Is-rael's glo - ry.

Optional Blessing (Is. 42:6-9)

"I, the LORD, have called you in righteousness;
I will take hold of your hand.
I will keep you and will make you
to be a covenant for the people
and a light for the Gentiles,
to open eyes that are blind,
to free captives from prison
and to release from the dungeon
those who sit in darkness.

"I am the LORD; that is my name!
I will not yield my glory to another
or my praise to idols.
See, the former things have taken place,
and new things I declare;
before they spring into being
I announce them to you."
To God alone be glory!

Words: Luke 2:29-32; vers. Dewey Westra, 1931, alt., P.D.
Music (NUNC DIMITTIS 6.6.7.6.6.7): Louis Bourgeois (ca. 1510-1561), 1551; harm. Claude Goudimel
(ca. 1505-1574), 1564, P.D.

936   Sent Forth by God's Blessing

1 Sent forth by God's bless-ing, our true faith con - fess-ing, the
2 With praise and thanks - giv-ing to God ev - er - liv-ing, the

peo - ple of God from this dwell-ing take leave. The sup-per is
tasks of our ev - ery - day life we will face— our faith ev - er

end - ed. Oh, now be ex - tend-ed the fruits of this ser - vice in
shar-ing, in love ev - er car-ing, em - brac-ing God's chil-dren, the

all who be - lieve. The seed of Christ's teach - ing, re -
whole hu - man race. With your feast you feed us, with

For a descant see 5

Words: Omer Westendorf (1916-1997), alt. © 1964 World Library Publications
Music (ASH GROVE 6.6.11.6.6.11 D): Welsh, P.D.

cep - tive souls reach-ing, shall blos - som in ac - tion for
your light now lead us; u - nite us as one in this

God and for all. Your grace shall in - cite us, your love shall u -
life that we share. Then may all the liv - ing with praise and thanks -

nite us to work for your king - dom and an - swer your call.
giv - ing give hon - or to Christ and his name that we bear.

Optional blessing (Eph. 3:20-21)

Now to him who by the power at work within us
is able to accomplish abundantly far more
than all we can ask or imagine,
to him be glory in the church and in Christ Jesus
to all generations, forever and ever. **Amen.**

937   Live a Life Worthy of the Calling
EPHESIANS 4:1b-6

I urge you to live a life worthy of the calling you have received.
Be completely humble and gentle;
be patient, bearing with one another in love.
Make every effort to keep the unity of the Spirit through the bond of peace.
There is one body and one Spirit,
just as you were called to one hope when you were called;
one Lord, one faith, one baptism;
one God and Father of all,
who is over all and through all and in all.

938   My Friends, May You Grow in Grace
2 PETER 3:18

Words and Music (BENEDICTION 7.11.7.9.6.5.7.6.5.7): 2 Peter 3:18; Timothy James Meaney (b. 1965) and
Sean Diamond (b. 1968); rev. Gregg DeMey (b. 1972) and Gregory Kett (b. 1970) © 1991, 2001 Wiseman
Music

939   May the Love of the Lord/ 惟 愿 神 的 爱

May the Lord, Mighty God

940

* = finger cymbals

Words: based on Numbers 6:24-26
Music (WEI YUAN SHEN): Chinese folk tune; attr. to Pao-chen Li (1907-1979)

941 Canto de esperanza/Song of Hope

Words: st. 1 Spanish traditional; English tr. Alvin Schutmaat (1921-1988); st. 2 Tom Mitchell (b. 1947) © 1993 Choristers Guild; Sp. tr. Frank W. Roman (b. 20th c.)
Music (ARGENTINA 11.11.11.11 refrain 7.7.7.7): Argentine folk melody; arr. Tom Mitchell (b. 1947) © 1993 Choristers Guild

942

God Be with You

God Be with You Till We Meet Again 943

1 God be with you till we meet a-gain; by his coun - sels
2 God be with you till we meet a-gain; 'neath his wings pro-
3 God be with you till we meet a-gain; when life's per - ils
4 God be with you till we meet a-gain; keep love's ban - ner

guide, up - hold you, with his sheep se - cure - ly fold you:
tect - ing hide you, dai - ly man - na still pro - vide you:
thick con - found you, put his arms un - fail - ing round you:
float - ing over you, smite death's threat-ening wave be - fore you:

God be with you till we meet a - gain.
God be with you till we meet a - gain.
God be with you till we meet a - gain.
God be with you till we meet a - gain.

Words: Jeremiah E. Rankin, 1880, P.D.
Music (RANDOLPH 9.8.8.9): Ralph Vaughan Williams, 1906, P.D.

944   God Be with You Till We Meet Again

1 God be with you till we meet a-gain; by his coun-sels guide, up-
2 God be with you till we meet a-gain; 'neath his wings pro-tect-ing
3 God be with you till we meet a-gain; when life's per-ils thick con-
4 God be with you till we meet a-gain; keep love's ban-ner float-ing

hold you, with his sheep se-cure-ly fold you:
hide you, dai - ly man - na still pro - vide you:
found you, put his arms un - fail - ing round you:
over you, smite death's threat-ening wave be - fore you:

*Refrain

God be with you till we meet a-gain. Till we meet, till we meet,

till we meet at Je - sus' feet. Till we meet,

*Refrain may be sung last time only.

till we meet,

Words: Jeremiah E. Rankin, 1880, P.D.
Music (GOD BE WITH YOU 9.8.9.8 refrain 6.7.6.9): William G. Tomer (1833-1896), P.D.

till we meet, God be with you till we meet a - gain.

Thuma mina/Send Me, Lord 945

Leader Send me, Lord. *All*

Zulu 1 Thu - ma mi - na, thu - ma mi - na, thu-ma
English 1 Send me, Je - sus, send me, Je - sus, send me,

mi - na, som - and - la.
Je - sus, send me, Lord.

2 Lead me, Lord.

2 Lead me,
Lord.

Possible additional stanzas
2 Lead me, Jesus . . .
3 Fill me, Jesus . . .

946 Go, My Children, with My Blessing

Words: Jaroslav J. Vajda (b. 1919) © 1983 Concordia Publishing House
Music (AR HYD Y NOS 8.4.8.4.8.8.8.4): Welsh melody (ca. 1794); desc. Hal Hopson (b. 1933) © 1992 GIA
Publications, Inc.

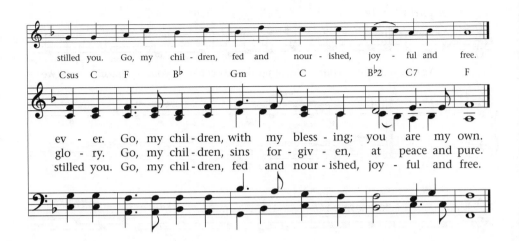

stilled you. Go, my chil-dren, fed and nour-ished, joy - ful and free.

Csus C F B♭ Gm C B♭2 C7 F

ev - er. Go, my chil-dren, with my bless - ing; you are my own.
glo - ry. Go, my chil-dren, sins for - giv - en, at peace and pure.
stilled you. Go, my chil-dren, fed and nour-ished, joy - ful and free.

Optional blessing

May God go before you to lead you;
May God go behind you to guard you;
May God go beneath you to support you;
May God go beside you to befriend you.
Do not be afraid.
Let the blessing of God come upon you today.
Do not be afraid.
Go in peace to love and serve the Lord.

Text: unknown

947

We Receive Your Blessing

Celtic feel

We re-ceive your bless-ing; we re-ceive your grace, as we walk in the light shin-ing from your face. May the peace that you give change the way that we live. We re-ceive your bless-ing as we leave this place. Praise

Words and Music (WE RECEIVE YOUR BLESSING): Grace and Natasha Moes © 2003 Unity Music Ministries

948
The Lord Bless You

The Lord bless you, the Lord keep you; may his
love ev - er, al - ways sur - round you, pro -
tect you, and guide you in all that you do: our
prayer for you. A - men.

Words and Music (THE LORD BLESS YOU): E. Fred Morris arr. Tim TenClay © E. Fred Morris

キリストの平和が /
May the Peace of Christ Be with You

Japanese キ リ ス ト の 平 和 が わ た
English May the peace of Christ be with you._____ May the

し た ち の 心 の す み ず み に ま
love of Christ dwell deep in your heart. May the Spir - it en-light-en your

で ゆ き わ た り ま す よ う に。
way. May you walk in the com-fort of God's care.

Words: Japanese blessing; English tr. Lori True © 2008, 2010 GIA Publications, Inc.
Music (KI RI SU TO NO): Japanese folk melody; arr. Lori True and acc. Mary Howarth © 2008, 2010
GIA Publications, Inc.

950

Go Now in Peace

Optional blessing (from Phil. 4:7)

The peace of God,
which passes all understanding,
keep your hearts and minds
in the knowledge and love of God,
and of God's Son, Jesus Christ, our Lord;
and the blessing of God Almighty,
the Father, the Son, and the Holy Spirit,
remain with you always.
Amen.

Now Go in Peace

Words: Michael Mair (b. 1942) © Church of Scotland Panel on Worship
Music (JUNKANOO): Caribbean folk melody, arr. Albert Chung © 2012 Albert Chung, admin. Faith Alive
  Christian Resources

952 Praise God! Earth and Heaven Rejoice

PSALM 150

1 Praise God! Earth and heaven re-joice! All cre-a-tion, with one voice,
2 Trum-pets, raise the joy-ful song; strings and pipes, now play a-long!

God's great maj-es-ty de-clare to all peo-ple, ev-ery-where:
Cym-bals crash, as never be-fore; danc-ing feet, be still no more!

Sing, shout, "Glo-ry, hal-le-lu-jah!" God, who won-drous deeds has done;
Sing, shout, "Glo-ry, hal-le-lu-jah!" May our breath through-out our days

who for us sal-va-tion won: Al-le-lu-ia, al-le-lu-ia!
fill the earth with songs of praise: Al-le-lu-ia, al-le-lu-ia!

Chord symbols represent a simplified harmony.

For other settings of Ps. 150 see 7, 563

Words: Michael Morgan © 2011 Michael Morgan, admin. Faith Alive Christian Resources
Music (GENEVAN 150 | 7.7.7.7.8.7.7.8): *Genevan Psalter,* 1562, P.D.; harm. Dale Grotenhuis (1931-2012), 1985,
© 1987 Faith Alive Christian Resources

Now Blessed Be the Lord Our God 953

PSALM 72:18-19

1 Now bless-ed be the Lord our God, the God of Is - ra - el,
2 And bless-ed be his glo - rious name through all e - ter - ni - ty;

for he a - lone does won - drous works: his glo-rious deeds ex - cel;
the whole earth let his glo - ry fill: A - men! so shall it be;

for he a - lone does won - drous works: his glo-rious deeds ex - cel.
the whole earth let his glo - ry fill: A - men! so shall it be.

For other settings of Ps. 72 see 109, 219

Chord symbols represent a simplified harmony.

Words: Psalm 72:18-19; Scottish Psalter, 1650, alt., P.D.
Music (CORONATION 8.6.8.6.8.6): Oliver Holden, 1793, P.D.

Blessing: The Same Voice Speaks 954

The same voice that speaks over the waters and shakes the wilderness,
The same voice that says "I am your God, you are my people,"
The same voice that said "this is my beloved son."
Now blesses the people with peace:
   "So do not fear, for I am with you;
   do not be dismayed, for I am your God.
   I will strengthen you and help you;
   I will uphold you with my righteous right hand."

Text: based on Psalm 29:2, 9; Ex. 20:9; Matt. 3:17; Is. 41:10

955 Mungu ni mwema/Know that God Is Good

PSALM 73

French
C'est vrai: Dieu est bon! C'est vrai: Dieu est bon!
C'est vrai: Dieu est bon! Dieu est bon! Dieu est bon!

Luganda
Katonda mulungi, katonda mulungi,
katonda mulungi, mulungi, mulungi.

Swahili phonetics: Moon-goo nee mway-mah

Words: Anonymous
Music (MUNGU NI MWEMA): Anonymous; arr. John L. Bell (b. 1949) © 1990, 2008 Wild Goose Resource Group, Iona Community, Scotland, admin. GIA Publications, Inc., exclusive North American agent

To God Be the Glory

Words and Music (MY TRIBUTE 6.6.12.7.7.12): Andraé Crouch © 1971 Bud John Songs (ASCAP), admin. at EMICMGPublishing.com

957 Haleluya! Pelo tsa rona/ Hallelujah! We Sing Your Praises

Words and Music (HALELUYA! PELO TSO RONA): South African © 1984 Utryck, admin. Walton Music Corporation

bread; I am wine, I am bread. Give to all who thirst and hun-

ger. Now he sends us all out, strong in faith, a-mid

To Refrain

doubt, strong in faith, a-mid doubt. Tell to all the joy-ful gos-pel.

Alleluia, Alleluia 958

Al-le-lu - ia, al-le-lu - ia, al-le-lu - ia, al-le-lu - ia.

Al-le-lu - ia, al-le-lu - ia, al-le-lu - ia, al-le-lu - ia.

959 Glory Be to the Father

Glo-ry be to the Fa-ther and to the Son and to the Ho-ly Ghost, as it was in the be-gin-ning is now, and ev-er shall be, world with-out end. A-men, a-men.

Words: Goria Patri, *The Lesser Doxology,* 2nd c., P.D.
Music (MEINEKE): Charles Meineke, 1844, P.D.

960 Alle, Alle, Alleluia

Al - le, al - le, al - le-lu - ia!

Al - le, al - le, al - le-lu, al - le, al - le-lu - ia!

Words: traditional
Music (ALLELUIA URUGUAY): traditional melody, Uruguay; arr. *More Voices,* 2007, © 2007 The United Church of Canada

Glory Be to the Father

961

Glory be to the Father and to the Son and to the Holy Ghost, as it was in the beginning is now, and ever shall be, world without end. A-men, a-men.

Words: Anonymous, 2nd c., P.D.
Music (GLORIA PATRI): from Henry W. Greatorex' *Collection*, 1851, P.D.

Alleluia

962

Alleluia, alleluia, alleluia.

Words: traditional
Music (ALLELUIA MONTEIRO): Simei Monteiro © 1999 Choristers Guild

963 Heleluyan/Hallelujah, We Are Singing

Refrain E♭

He - le - lu-yan, yah - hay-kahth-leez, Hel - le, He - le - u - yan!
Hal - le - lu - jah, we are sing - ing, hal - le, hal - le - lu - jah!

Fine

He - le - lu-yan, yah - hay-kahth - leez, Hel - le, He - le - u - yan!
Hal - le - lu - jah, we are sing - ing, hal - le, hal - le - lu - jah!

1 Chris - tians ev - ery-where shall sing now and al - way
2 Town and coun - try peo - ple sing to___ Je - sus
3 Peo - ple far and near will join in the cho - rus:

He - le, He - le - lu - yan.

Chris - tians ev - ery-where shall sing now and al - way
Town and coun - try peo - ple sing to___ Je - sus
Peo - ple far and near will join in the cho - rus:

To Refrain

He - le, He - le - lu - yan.

Muscogee

1 Mekosahpahlket may mahn ahpokeez
   Helle, Heleluyan
2 Elthkeenahkahkee . . .
3 Pohahlhahlket . . .
4 Pochosahlket . . .

5 Powahntahket . . .
6 Hopoetahket . . .
7 Uhkuhsahmulket . . .
8 Emestuhlket . . .

May be accompanied by a hum on a low E♭ or other low drone-like instrument.

Words: traditional Muscogee (Creek) hymn from *Muskoke Hymns of Faith;* English vers. Brian Wren © 2008 admin. The General Board of Global Ministries
Music (HELELUYAN): traditional (Muscogee Creek); transcr. Carlton R. Young from *Yvhiketv Vhecicvlke* © 2008 admin. The General Board of Global Ministries

Praise God, from Whom All Blessings Flow 964

Words: Thomas Ken (1637-1711), P.D.
Music (NEW DOXOLOGY 8.8.8.8): traditional Black Gospel

965   Praise God, from Whom All Blessings Flow

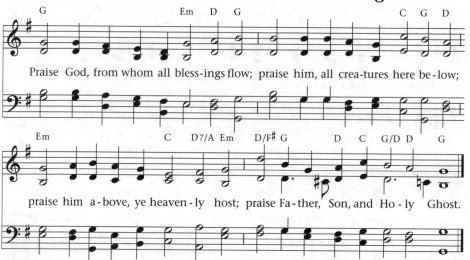

Praise God, from whom all bless-ings flow; praise him, all crea-tures here be-low;

praise him a-bove, ye heaven-ly host; praise Fa-ther, Son, and Ho-ly Ghost.

Cherokee
Oo ne la nuh hiIikidodah,
Oo ne la nuh hi Oo weji,
Oo ne la nuh
    hi̲ahdahnuhdo,
Kehdiluhgwodah hnagwase.

Mohawk
Ron wa sen naiens ne Niio
ron wa sen naiens
    ne non kwe,
ron we sen naiens
    neh ne ken
ron wa sen naiens ro ni ha.

Navajo
Bóhólníihii baa dahohniih,
'Éí baa 'ahééh danohsinii,
Nihookáá' diné nohlíinii
Chánahgo bich'i'
    dahohtaal.

German
Gott Vater, dem sei
    ewig Herr,
Gott Sohn, der ist der
    einig Herr,
und dem Tröster,
    Heiligen Geist,
von nun an bis in Ewigkeit.

French
Gloire à Dieu,
    notre Créateur;
gloire à Christ,
    notre Rédempteur;
gloire à l'Esprit Consolateur!
Louange et gloire
    à Dieu, Sauveur.

Portuguese
A Deus, supremo benfeitor.
Ao FilhoIeterno,
    Deus deIamor.
Ao Santo Deus consolador,
Ó anjos e̲homens,
    dai louvor.

Spanish
A Dios, el Padre celestial,
al Hijo, nuestro Redentor,
al eternal Consolador
unidos todos alabad.

Dutch
Aan God de Vader zij de eer,
aan God de Zoon
    voor immermeer,
aan God do Geest
    die troost en leidt
zij lof ne en to allen tijd.

Korean
만복의 근원 하나님
만물아 찬양하여라
알렐루야 알렐루야
복 주시는 주 하나님
힘 주시는 주 예수님
주의 성령 찬양하라
알렐루야 알렐루야 알렐루야

Japanese
たたえよ主の民
御使いとともに
恵みにあふれる
父・子・聖霊を

Mandarin
颂赞上主万福之源；
颂赞基督救赎恩洪；
颂赞圣灵，我保惠师；
崇敬至尊三一真神。
阿们，阿们。

For an alternate arrangement see 843, 924

Words: Thomas Ken, 1709, P.D.; Portugese adapt. Sarah Poulton Kalley, 1861, © *Imprensa Metodista*;
    Korean The United Methodist Hymnal Committee © 2001 The United Methodist Publishing House,
    admin. The Copyright Company; Cherokee tr. traditional; Mohawk tr. traditional; Dutch Ambrose (340-397)
    tr. J. W. Nordholt, P.D.; German Martin Luther, 1543 P.D.
Music (GENEVAN 134/OLD HUNDREDTH 8.8.8.8): Louis Bourgeois, 1551, P.D.

Indices

Index of Copyright Holders

This is a partial list of copyright holders represented in this hymnal and contains the major companies who have given their permission to print their copyrighted materials. For a complete list of copyright holders, go to www.liftupyourheartshymnal.org .

Augsburg Fortress Publishers
100 South Fifth St., PO Box 1209
Minneapolis, MN 55440-1209
Phone: 800-421-0239
Fax: 800-722-7766
copyright@augsburgfortress.org

Church Pension Group/
Church Publishing, Inc.
445 Fifth Ave.
New York, NY 10016
copyrights@cpg.org

Concordia Publishing House
3558 S. Jefferson Ave.
St. Louis, MO 63118
copyrights@cph.org

Conexion Media Group, Inc.
2400 Crestmoor Rd., Ste. 321
Nashville, TN 37215

Copyright Company, The
PO Box 128139
Nashville, TN 37212-8139
Phone: 615-244-9848
Fax: 615-244-9850
Lynda.pearson@thecopyrightco.com

Eerdman's Publishing Company
2140 Oak Industrial Dr. NE
Grand Rapids, MI 49505
Phone: 616-234-0551
Fax: 616-742-6111

EMI CMG Publishing
PO Box 5085
Brentwood, TN 37024
Emicmgpublishing.com

Faith Alive Christian Resources
2850 Kalamazoo Ave., SE
Grand Rapids, MI 49560
Phone: 866-823-0008
Fax: 616-726-1164
permissions@crcna.org

G. Schirmer, Inc.
The Music Sales Group
257 Park Ave. South, 20th Floor
New York, NY 10010
Phone: 212-254-2100
Fax: 212-254-2013
schirmer@schirmer.com

Gaither Copyright Management
1703 South Park Ave.
Alexandria, IN 46001
Phone: 765-724-833

General Board of Global Ministries
t/a GBG Musik
475 Riverside Dr.
New York, NY 10115
kdonato@gbgm-umc.org
Lorengo@gbgm-umc.org

GIA Publications, Inc.
7404 S. Mason Ave.
Chicago, IL 60638
Phone: 708-496-3858
Fax: 708-496-3828
kylec@giamusic.com

Hal Leonard Corporation
Attn: Copyright Department
7777 West Bluemound Rd.
PO Box 13819
Milwaukee, WI 53213
Fax: 414-774-3259
hlcopyright@halleonard.com

Hope Publishing Company
380 South Main Place
Carol Stream, IL 60188
Phone: 800-323-1049
Fax: 630-665-2552
www.hopepublishing.com

International Liturgy Publications
PO Box 50476
Nashville, TN 37205
Phone: 888-898-SONG
www.ILPmusic.org

Kevin Mayhew Ltd.
Buxhall Stowmarket
Suffolk IP14 3BW
United Kingdom
Phone: 011-44-845-388-1634
info@kevinmayhewltd.com

Licensing Associates
Kathleen Karcher
935 Broad St. #31
Bloomfield, NJ 07003
Phone: 973-743-6444
KathleenKarcher@hotmail.com

Liturgical Press
Saint John's Abbey
PO Box 7500
Collegeville, MN 56321-7500
Phone: 800-858-5458
Fax: 320-363-3278
www.litpress.org

MorningStar Music Publishers
1727 Larkin Williams Rd.
Fenton, MO 63026-2024
Fax: 636-305-0121
copyrights@morningstarmusic.com
www.morningstarmusic.com

Music Services, Inc.
5409 Maryland Way, Ste. 200
Brentwood, TN 37027
Phone: 615-371-1320
Fax: 615-371-1351
www.musicservices.org

OCP Publications
5536 NE Hassalo
Portland, OR 97213
Phone: 800-LITURGY
Fax: 503-535-8120
www.ocp.org

Oxford University Press
Music Department
Great Clarendon St.
Oxford OX2 6DP
United Kingdom
Phone: 800-445-9714
Fax: 919-677-1303
www.oup.com

Pilgrim Press, The
700 Prospect Ave.
Cleveland, OH 44115-1100
Frencht@ucc.org

Selah Publishing Company, Inc.
4055 Cloverleaf St., PO Box 98066
Pittsburgh, PA 15227
licensing@selahpub.com
Phone: 412-886-1020
Fax: 412-886-1022

Stainer & Bell Ltd.
PO Box 110
Victoria House, 23 Gruneisen Rd.
London N3 1DZ
United Kingdom
post@stainer.co.uk

Wayne Leupold Editions, Inc.
8510 Triad Dr.
Colfax, NC 27235
Phone: 1-800-765-3196
www.wayneleupold.com

Westminster John Knox Press
Presbyterian Publishing Corporation
100 Witherspoon St.
Louisville, KY 40202-1396
Fax: 502-569-5113
www.wjkbooks.com

Word Music Group, Inc.
20 Music Square East
Nashville, TN 37203
Phone: 615-733-1885
Fax: 615-733-1880
www.wordmusic.com

World Library Publications
3708 River Rd., Ste. 400
Franklin Park, IL 60131-2158
www.wlp.jspaluch.com

Yamuger Indonesian Institute
for Sacred Music
Mr. Sony Widyanto Utomo
Jalan Wisma Jaya 11
13220 Jakarta Timur
Indonesia
yamuger@bit.net.id

Acknowledgments

Scripture Versions
Unless otherwise indicated, Scripture quotations are from The Holy Bible, New International Version®, NIV®, copyright © 1973, 1978, 1984, 2011 by Biblica, Inc.™ Used by permission. All rights reserved worldwide.

Other Scriptures from the New Revised Standard Version Bible (NRSV), copyright © 1989 by the National Council of the Churches of Christ in the United States of America. Used by permission. All rights reserved.

Other Scriptures from the Holy Bible, New International Reader's Version® (NirV), copyright © 1996, 1998 by Biblica, Inc.™ All rights reserved throughout the world. Used by permission of Biblica.

Confessions and Statements of Faith
Apostles' Creed, translated from the fourth-century Latin text. © 1988, Faith Alive Christian Resources, Grand Rapids, Mich.; or RCA approved translation, © Reformed Church Press.

Nicene Creed, translated from the Greek text approved at the Council of Chalcedon in 451, revised in 589. © 1988, Faith Alive Christian Resources, Grand Rapids, Mich.

Belgic Confession (1561), translated from the French text of 1619 adopted at Synod of Dort (1618-1619). © 2011, Faith Alive Christian Resources, Grand Rapids, Mich. This translation approved by Synod 2011 of the Christian Reformed Church in North America and by General Synod 2011 of the Reformed Church in America. All rights reserved.

Heidelberg Catechism (1563), translated from the first edition of the German text. © 2011, Faith Alive Christian Resources, Grand Rapids, Mich. This translation approved by Synod of 2011 of the Christian Reformed Church in North America and by General Synod 2011 of the Reformed Church in America. All rights reserved.

Belhar Confession, a translation of the original Afrikaans text adopted by the synod of the Dutch Reformed Mission Church in South Africa in 1986, which united with the Dutch Reformed Church in Africa in 1994 to form the Uniting Reformed Church in Southern Africa (URCSA). Inclusive language text prepared by the Office of Theology and Worship, Presbyterian Church (U.S.A.). In 2009 the General Synod of the Reformed Church in America (RCA) adopted the Belhar Confession, and in 2010 the RCA ratified and incorporated it as a doctrinal standard. Synod 2012 of the Christian Reformed Church in North America adopted the Belhar Confession as an Ecumenical Faith Declaration.

Our Song of Hope, approved in 1978 by the General Synod of the Reformed Church in America as a statement of the church's faith for use in its ministry of witness, teaching, and worship. © 1975, Wm. B. Eerdmans Publishing Co., Grand Rapids, Mich.

Our World Belongs to God: A Contemporary Testimony, Second Edition, adopted by the Christian Reformed Church in North America in 2008. © 2008, Faith Alive Christian Resources, Grand Rapids, Mich.

Creative Commons sources
Creative Commons— written prayers, litanies, and readings not credited with a copyright © symbol are considered to be covered under a Creative Commons license, which means you may reprint and use it for worship, review, and educational purposes without obtaining further permission. Please credit the use of such texts as follows:

—Faith Alive Christian Resources, 2013, © Creative Commons Attribution-NonCommercial-ShareAlike

For other uses contact permissions@faithaliveresources.org.

Grateful acknowledgment

We are grateful for the contributions of everyone who helped with the development and production of this important volume for worship, noting especially the following:

The initial team who laid the foundation for this project in meetings that occured back in 2006, Ken Bradsell, Kent Hendricks, Clay Libolt, Gary Mulder, Tim TenClay, and John Witvliet.

Production and Evaluation: Linda Missad, typesetting; Paul Detterman, indexing; Dean Heetderks, design; Sandy Huttenga, design and page assembly; Dorothy Kuperus, purchasing; Paul Faber, editing; Norma deWaal Malefyt, tune committee, music review; Emily Brink, music review; Yudha Thianto and John Hulst, text evaluation; Calvin Institute of Christian Worship staff; Faith Alive Christian Resources staff

Language advisors—Arabic: Maged Dakouk and Anne Zaki; Bengali: Jeff Bos; Dutch and German: Herman DeVries; Filipino: Joel Navarro; French: Ginette Galipeau; Hebrew: Arie Leder; Hungarian: Frank Sawyer; Indonesian: Philip Djung; Japanese: Reita Yazawa; Korean: Eunae Chung; Latin: Kenneth Bratt; Mandarin: Phoebe H'fe, Kurt Selles, and various people from Back to God Ministries International; Yoruba: Bernard Ayoola; Spanish: Marcie Pyper and Claudia Cortes; Portuguese: Carl Bosma

Various hymnal consultants: David Eicher (PCUSA), Martin Seltz (Augsburg Fortress), Alan Hommerding WLP), Bob Batistini (GIA), Scott Shorney (Hope), David Schaap (Selah)

Behind the scenes: Many, many people worked behind the scenes, including: Judy Hibelink, Karen Vanden Akker, Michelle Scripps, Jeanie Kammeraad, Rick Vanderwal, Jan Zuidema, Heather Sukkau, Audrey VanderSchans, Lynda Westervelt, Susan Van Kley, Julia Bailey, David Banga, Rachel Katje, and Lynn Setsma.

Copyright advice and assistance from our colleagues in various publishing companies, especially from Kyle Cothern (GIA) and Susan Gilbert (Hope Publishing)

Project managers and contributors to collections that fed into this hymnal: Greg Scheer, (*Global Songs for Worship*, 2010), Paul Ryan (*Contemporary Songs for Worship*, 2008), Bert Polman (*Hymns for Worship*, 2010), and Martin Tel (*Psalms for All Seasons*, 2012).

Index of Authors, Composers, and Sources

Index of Genre and Musical Styles

The following index highlights the diversity of many of the major musical and textual traditions represented in this hymnal. Its aim is to help congregations and worship leaders identify those settings that are most accessible in their context, as well as particular settings that might stretch or challenge them. Whenever possible, this guide functions as an "index of the index," referring to an entry (name or publication) in the Index of Authors, Composers, and Sources (see pp. 1044-1050) rather than to specific instances. Any attempt to distinguish unique traditions or genres is complicated by the fact that many individual composers or poets contribute to more than one tradition or genre, and some musical examples reflect multiple stylistic influences. Nevertheless, this guide offers a preliminary sketch of some of the primary traditions and styles included in this volume.

Genres and Traditions of Musical Settings

1. *Settings from various Eastern Orthodox Chant traditions*
   See 112, 631, 635, 887, 917 (see also texts at 112, 634, 821)

2. *Gregorian Chant and other Medieval and Renaissance Traditions*
   See 38, 54, 61, 71, 78, 231, and contributions by G. Gastoldi, G. P. Palestrina, and Thomas Tallis.

3. *16th-Century Genevan Psalter*
   See Genevan Psalter 1539, 1542, 1543, 1547, 1551, 1562, and contributions from Louis Bourgeois and Claude Goudimel

4. *Lutheran Chorale Tradition*
   See contributions from Johann S. Bach, Tobias Clausnitzer, Johann Crüger, *Enchirida* (1524), Freylinghausen's *Geistreiches Gesangbuch* (1704), various *Gesangbuch (1666, 1667, 1784)* Hans Leo Hassler, Johann Heerman, Nikolaus Herman, Jakob Hintze, Martin Luther, Joachim Neander, Philipp Nicolai, Georg Neumark, Michael Praetorius, and Melchoir Vulpius.

5. *17th-19th Century American Tunes*
   See William Billings, William B. Bradbury, A. Catherine Hankey, William H. Doane, Funk's *A Compilation of Genuine Church Music, New England Psalm Singer, Supplement to Kentucky Harmony*, William J. Kirkpatrick, Robert Lowry, Lowell Mason, *The Sacred Harp*, Walkers's *Southern Harmony*, Wyeth's *Repository of Sacred Music*.

6. *African American Spirituals*
   See African American spirituals, and contributions by Harry T. Burleigh, Wendell Whalum, and John W. Work.

7. *Traditional Hymn Tunes from England and Continental Europe*
   See contributions by George N. Allen, Ludwig van Beethoven, William U. Butcher, William Croft, Henry S. Cutler, John Darwall, John B. Dykes, John D. Edwards, George J. Elvey, Charles H. Gabriel, Charles Gounod, John Hatton, G. F. Handel, Franz Joseph Haydn, Johann Michael Haydn, Jessie Seymour Irvine, George Kirbye, Conrad Kocher, James Langran, William Lloyd, Frederick Charles Maker, Felix Mendelssohn, William H. Monk, Joseph Parry, Charles H. Purday, Richard Redhead, Lewis H. Redner, Jean Sibelius, Robert A. Schumann, Arthur Sullivan, James Walch, Thomas J. Williams.

8. *English and North American Cathedral Traditions*
   See contributions by Joseph Barnby, Richard Dirksen, John Goss, Charles F. Gounod, Gustav Holst, Sydney Nicholson, C. Hubert H. Parry, Henry Purcell, Charles Villiers Stanford, Arthur S. Sullivan, Thomas Tallis, Samuel S. Wesley, Ralph Vaughan Williams, Healey Willan

9. *Recently Written Responsorial Psalmody and other Folk Liturgical Music*
   See contributions by Mary Kay Beall, James Hart Brumm, AnnaMae Meyer Bush, Rory Cooney, Gregg DeMey, Andrew Donaldson, Bernadette Farrell, Alfred V. Fedak, John Foley, David Haas, Marty Haugen, Hal H. Hopson, J. Michael Joncas, David Lee, James E. Moore

Jr., Betty Pulkingham, Daniel L. Schutte, K. Lee Scott, James Seddon, Martin Tel, Suzanne Toolan, Christopher Walker, Steven C. Warner, Norman Warren

10. *Recently Written Hymn Tunes*
See contributions by John Barnard, John L. Bell, Herbert Brokering, Paul Bunjes, Anna Mae Meyer Bush, Kathleen Hart Brumm, James E. Clemens, Alfred V. Fedak, Harold Friedell, John Ferguson, Henry Bryan Hays O. S. B., Timothy Hoekman, Roy Hopp, David Hurd, Hal Hopson, John Horman, David N. Johnson, Ken Medema, William Rowan, Carl Schalk, Christian Strover, Larry Visser, David Ashley White, James Ward, Norman L. Warren.

11. *Settings from Contemporary or Popular Worship Music from the 1970s and 1980s*
See contributions by Dave Doherty, David Evans, Rick Founds, Graham Kendrick, Gloria Gaither, William Gaither, Melody Green, Frank Herdandez, Bob Kilpatrick, Karen Lafferty, Michael Ledner, Edith McNeill, Rich Mullins, Martin Nystrom, Henry Smith, David Strasser, Wes Sutton, Donn Thomas, James Ward, Charles Williams.

12. *Settings from Contemporary or Popular Worship Music from the 1990s and 2000s*
See contributions by Paul Baloche, Bruce Benedict, Margaret Becker, Marc Byrd, Barbara Boertje, Daniel Chua, Vicki Cook, Gregg DeMey, Lynn De Shazo, Brian Doerksen, Louie Giglio, Ben Fielding, Billy Foote, Keith Getty, Kristyn Getty, Charlie Hall, Steve Hindalong, Israel Houghton, Tim Hughes, Marc Imboden, Darwin Jordan, Bob Kauflin, Kevin Keil, Aaron Keyes, Matt Maher, Ken Medema, Steve Merkel, Boyd McCann, Christopher Miner, Reuben Morgan, Craig Musseau, Betty Carr Pulkingham, Matt Redman, Jesse Reeves, Ron Rienstra, Tammy Rhoton, Douglas Romanow, Greg Scheer, Paul Thé, Chris Tomlin, Stuart Townend, Eelco Vos, James Ward, Matt Westerholm, Tommy Walker, Darlene Zschech, see also 277.

13. *Settings from the Spectrum of African American Gospel Music*
See contributions by Jimmie Abbington, Doris Akers, Horace Clarence Boyer, Grayson Warren Brown, Lillian Bouknight, Glenn Burleigh, Melva Costen, Andre Crouch, Kurt Carr, J. Jefferson Cleveland, Andraé Crouch, Thomas Dorsey, Margaret J. Douroux, Kirk Franklin, Albert Goodson, John D. Horman, Walter Hawkins, J. Rosamond Johnson, Jeffrey LaValley, V. Michael McKay, Leon C. Roberts, Richard Smallwood; Charles Tindley, Wyatt Tee Walker, Nolan Williams, Jr. see also 99, 100, 964.

14. *Settings from North American Indigenous peoples*
See 27, 692, 752, 873, 923, 963 and additional texts in 965.

15. *Settings from the Spectrum of Latino and/or Hispanic American Traditions*
See contributions by Rubén Ruiz Avila, Osvaldo Cartena, Miguel Cassina, Jorge Lockward, Raquel M. Martinez, Fernando Rodriguez, Juan Salinas, Ricardo Villarreal and also 106,192, 241, 255, 275, 279, as well as settings from Latin American Countries (see below) and music in Spanish (see below)

16. *Settings from Contemporary Communities of Prayer and Renewal*
See contributions from The Iona Community, The Community of Taizé, John L. Bell, Jacques Berthier, Graham Maule, see also 107.

17. *Settings from Latin America and Southern North American Countries, States, and Regions*
Argentina: 244, 260, 941
Brazil: 493, 663
Caribbean: 768, 951
Ecuador: 37
El Salvador: 293, 596
Honduras: 183
Jamaica: 830
Mexico: 452, 504, 522
Nicaragua: 141
Puerto Rico: 106, 192, 820
Uruguay: 960

See also contributions by Guillermo Cuellar, Maria Simeone, Orlando Juarez, Simei Monteiro, Carlos Rosas, Pablo Sosa, Horatio Vivares, as well as contributions by Alberto Taulé (Spain), and 116.

Note: several of the Spanish-language contributions derive from one or more Central or South American country.

18. *Settings from the Middle and Near East*
Israeli, Hasidic, and other Jewish melodies: 50, 144, 312, 751
Pakistan and/or India: 125, 906
India: 514

19. *Settings from Eastern Europe and Russia*
Hungary: *684*
Latvia (melody): 349, 664, 651
Russia: 635

20. *Settings from Africa*
Cameroon: 445
Congo: 600
Egypt: 298, 911
Ghana: 242, 299, 637
Kenya: 576, 708
Malawi: 390, 773
South Africa: 129 (Zulu), 564, 909, 915, 921, 945, 957
Sudan: 609
Swaziland: 931
Tanzania: 320, 753
Yoruba people (Nigeria): 891
Zimbabwe: 496, 520

See also contributions by Abel Nkuinji, and Patrick Matsikenyiri

21. *Settings from Asia and the Pacific Islands*
China: 939, 940
Indonesia: 233, 550
Japan: 319, 767, 949
Korea: 905 (see also several Korean language hymns)
New Zealand (Maori): 619
Philippines: 94, 285, 391, 442, 744, 807, 819
Taiwan: 588
Thailand/Philippines: 285

See also contributions by Francisco F. Feliciano, Swee Hong Lim, Joel Navarro, I-to Loh.

Genres and Traditions of Texts

1. For Biblical texts, see the scriptural index, and especially entries for the Psalms, the Ten Commandments, and the Songs of Mary, Zechariah, and Simeon

2. *Texts from the early church*
See 381, 392, 393, 540, 541, 542, 630, 635, 637, 811, 812, 816, 821, 822, 841, 844, 900 and contributions by Ambrose of Milan, Fortunatus, Prudentius, and texts from the Didache.

3. *Texts from the medieval period*
See 71, 79, 98, 111,168, 208, 231, 232, 250, 354, 386, 478, 523, 823, 828 859, 900, and contributions by Bede, Bernard of Cluny, Francis of Assisi, John of Damascus, Rhabanus Maurus, Julian of Norwich, Theodulph of Orleans, Bianco de Siena, and translations by John Mason Neale.

4. *For texts from the Reformation period*
See Lutheran Chorales and Genevan Psalms (above), and entries in the index for Heidelberg Catechism, Caspar Olivianus, Zacharius Ursinus,

5. *16th- to Early 20th-Century Metrical Psalmody and Hymnody*
See contributions by Cecil Alexander, Henry Alford, Henry Williams Baker, Albert F. Bayly, Horatius Bonar, Margaret Clarkson, William Cowper, Fanny Crosby, Katherine K. Davis, William Dix, Philip Doddridge, John Dryden, Timothy Dwight, Charlotte Elliott, Frederick William Faber, Harry E. Fosdick, Thomas Hastings, Edwin Hatch, Frances Havergal, Reginald Heber, William W. How, Robert Grant, William Kethe, Thomas Ken, Henry F. Lyte, James Montgomery, John Newton, Francis Pierpoint, Horatio Spafford, Augustus Toplady, Henry Van Dyke, Isaac Watts, Charles Wesley, Nicholas von Zinzendorf, entries from *Psalter* (1887), *Psalter* (1912), *Scottish Psalter* (1615), *Scottish Psalter* (1650).

6. *Metrical Psalms and Hymns Written Since 1960, a period often described as the "hymn renaissance"*
See contributions by Carol Bechtel, John L. Bell, Emily R. Brink, Herbert Brokering, Mary Louise Bringle, James Hart Brumm, Susan Palo Cherwien, Carl P. Daw Jr., Marva Dawn, David J. Diephouse, Andrew Donaldson, Edith Sinclair Downing, Arlo D. Duba, Ruth C. Duck, Timothy Dudley-Smith, Dolores Dufner, Sylvia Dunstan, Rusty Edwards, Bernadette Farrell, Doug Gay, Keith Getty, Norman Goreham, Gracia Grindal, Bev Herrema, Christopher Idle, Willard F. Jabusch, Fred Kaan, Mary Nelson Keitahn, David Landegent, Richard Leach, Martin Leckebusch, Swee Hong Lim, Madeline Forell Marshall, Daniel Meeter, Michael Morgan, Shirley Erena Murray, Craig Musseau, Helen Otte, John Paarlberg, Joy F. Patterson, Ian Pitt-Watson, Michael Perry, Bert Polman, Marie J. Post, Fred Pratt Green, James Quinn, Ada Roeper-Boulogne, Michael Saward, Greg Scheer, James E. Seddon, Calvin Seerveld, Herman Stuempfle, Henrietta Ten Harmsel, John Thornburg, Adam M. L. Tice, Stuart Townend, Thomas Troeger, Jaroslva Vajda, Clarence P. Walhout, Christopher L. Webber, Dewey Westra, Stanley Wiersma, Brian Wren, William W. Reid, and Henry Zylstra.

Texts in Languages Other than English

Arabic: 268, 609, 634, 911
Bengali: 629
Cherokee: 965
Chinese: see Mandarin
Dutch: 84, 268, 595, 634, 965
Filipino: 391
French: 82, 268, 584, 590, 595, 634, 955, 965
German: 268, 634, 965
Greek: 633, 634, 635, 637
Hebrew: 288, 751
Hungarian: 417,
Indonesian: 233, 550
Japanese: 590, 634, 767, 949, 965
Korean: 136, 268, 417, 590, 600, 905, 965
Latin: 154, 591, 592
Lugandan: 777, 955
Mandarin: 417, 590, 939, 965
Maori: 619
Mohawk: 965
Muscogee: 963
Navajo: 692, 965
Ngala: 600
Pawltay (Kiowa): 752
Portuguese: 357, 493, 663, 777, 965
Shona: 496, 957

Metrical Index of Tunes

Tune Names Index

Index of Non-Musical Texts

OTHER TEXTS

Scripture Index

Topical Index

First Lines and Common Titles